Test Bank
to accompany
Organic Chemistry
Fifth Edition

Kay Brummond

W. H. Freeman and Company
New York

ISBN: 0-7167-2565-7
EAN: 97807167-2565-7

First printing

W. H. Freeman and Company
41 Madison Avenue
New York, NY 10010
Houndmills, Basingstoke RG21 6XS England
www.whfreeman.com

Contents

Chapter 1: Structure and Bonding in Organic Molecules

1. What is the molecular formula of limonene, the major volatile compound in orange peel oil?

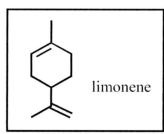

A) $C_{10}H_{18}$ B) $C_{10}H_{20}$ C) $C_{10}H_{16}$ D) $C_{11}H_{14}$ E) $C_{11}H_{18}$
Ans: C

2. Of those indicated, which would be the shortest carbon-carbon bond in α-selinene?

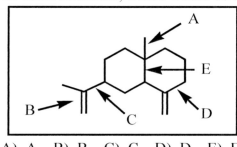

A) A   B) B   C) C   D) D   E) E
Ans: B

3. What would be the ideal value for the indicated bond angle?

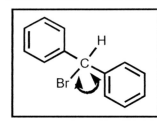

A) 120°   B) 90°   C) 104°   D) 180°   E) 109°
Ans: E

4. What would be the "polygon" form of the following condensed structure?

$$CH_3CH_2CH(CN)CH=CH_2$$

A)

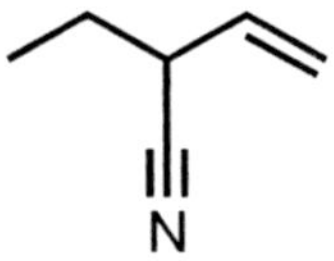

B)

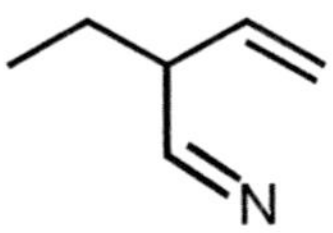

C)

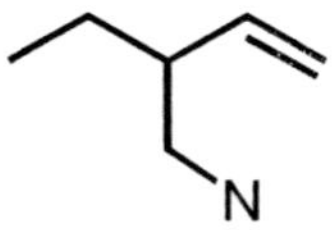

D)

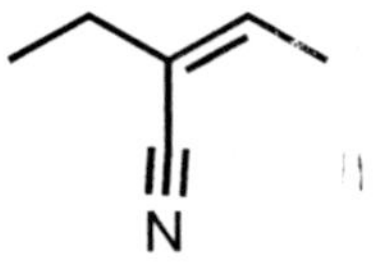

E)

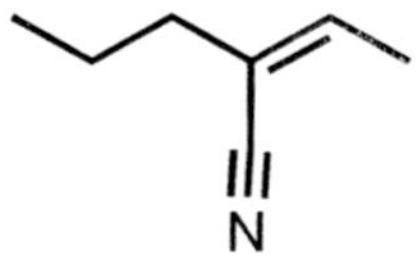

Ans: A

5. Which one of the following structures must be incorrect?

A)

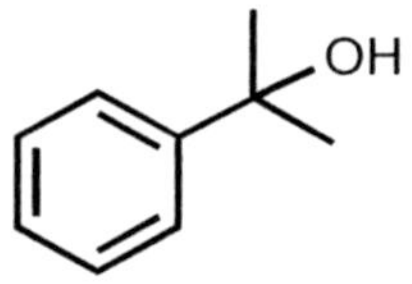

B)

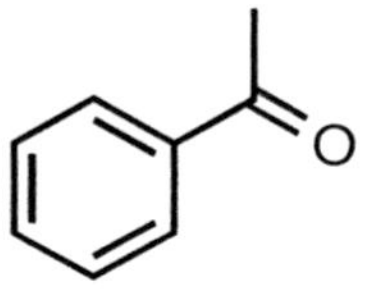

C)

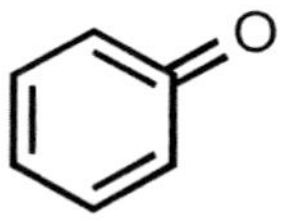

D)

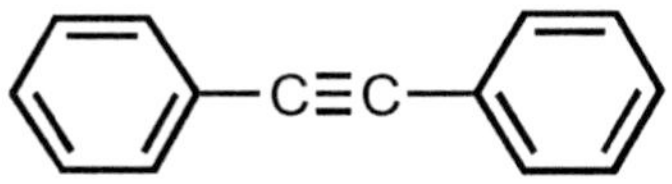

E)

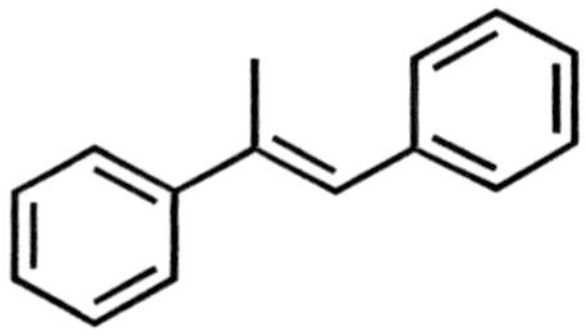

Ans: C

6. Which of the following is **not** a resonance structure of the others?

A)

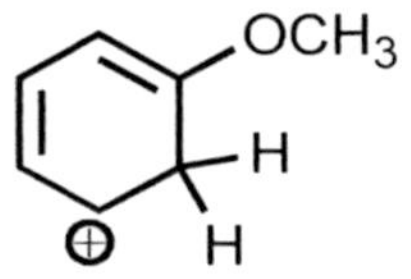

B)

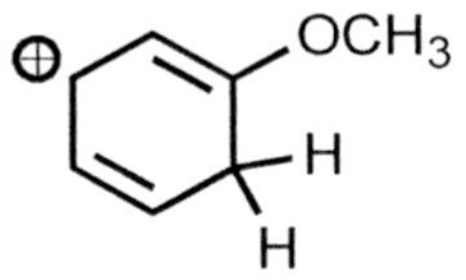

C)

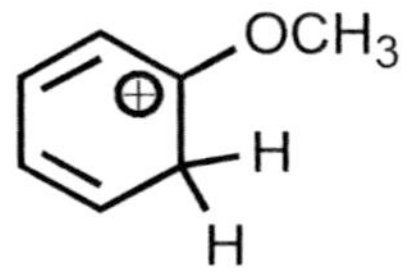

D)

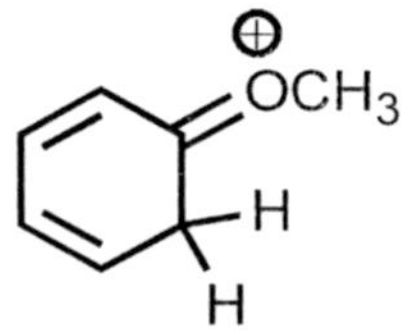

E)

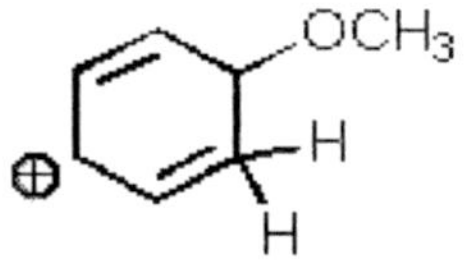

Ans: E

7. Which one of the resonance structures below would be the most important (i.e., most stable)?

A)

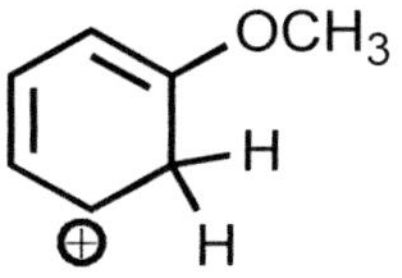

B)

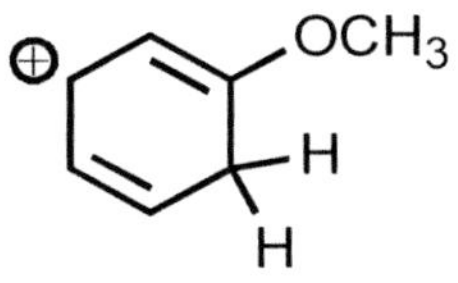

C)

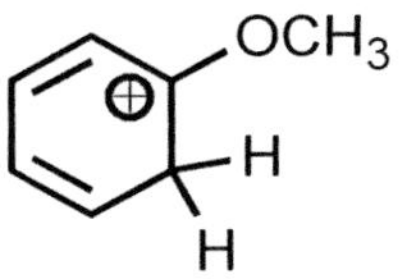

D)

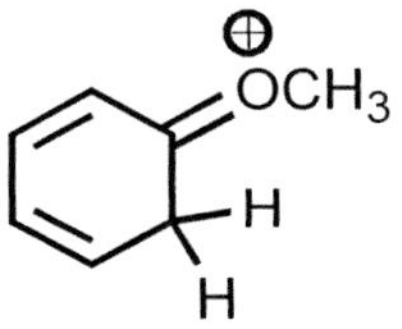

E)

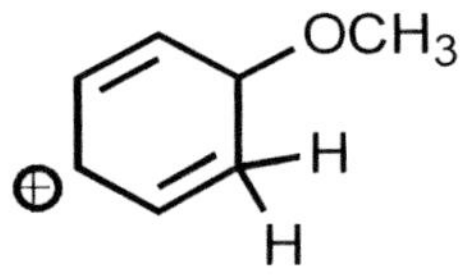

Ans: D

8. How many atoms in ethene are required by sp^2 bonding to lie in the same plane?

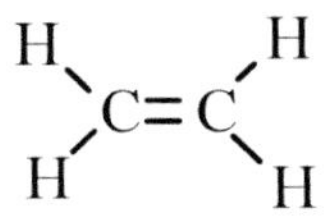

ethene

A) 2 B) 3 C) 4 D) 5 E) 6

Ans: E

9. Which one of the following structures is not chemically identical to the others?

A)

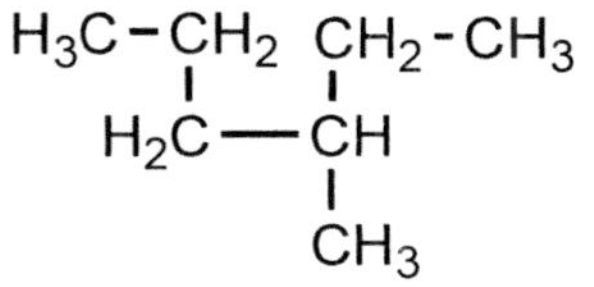

$$H_3C-CH_2 \quad CH_2-CH_3$$
$$H_2C - CH$$
$$CH_3$$

B)

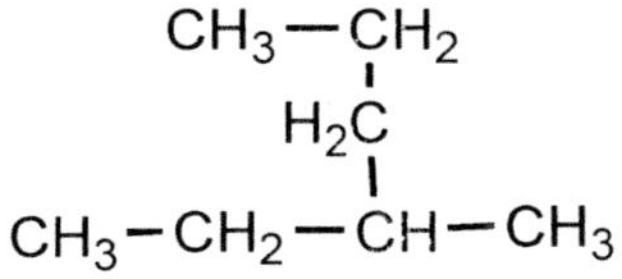

$$CH_3-CH_2$$
$$H_2C$$
$$CH_3-CH_2-CH-CH_3$$

C)

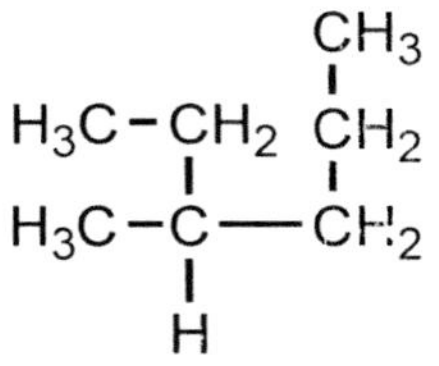

$$CH_3$$
$$H_3C-CH_2 \quad CH_2$$
$$H_3C-C - CH_2$$
$$H$$

D)

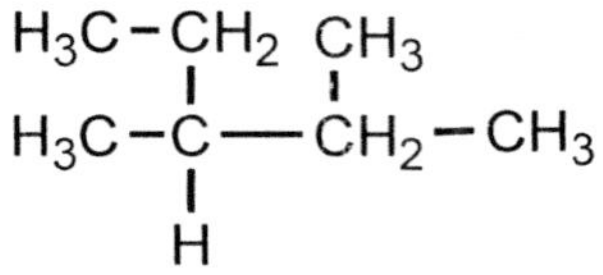

$$H_3C-CH_2 \quad CH_3$$
$$H_3C-C - CH_2-CH_3$$
$$H$$

E)

$$CH_2-CH_3$$
$$HC-CH_3$$
$$CH_3-CH_2-CH_2$$

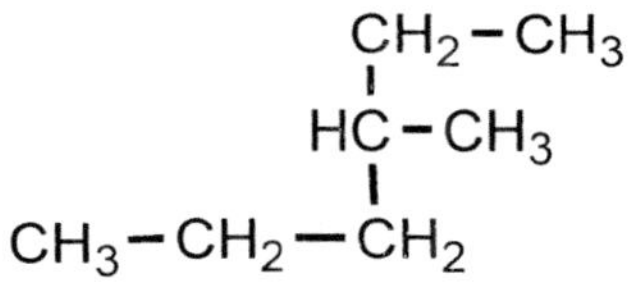

Ans: D

10. Which of the following pairs are **not** resonance structures of each other?

A)

$H_2\overset{\ominus}{C}-C\equiv C-H$ and $H_2C=C=\overset{\ominus}{C}H$

B)

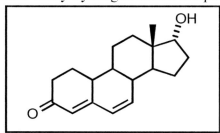

and

C)

and

D)

and

E)   All are pairs of resonance structures

Ans: E

11. How many hydrogen atoms are part of the following steroid?

A) 18   B) 20   C) 21   D) 22   E) 24

Ans: E

12. In the following molecule, how many carbon atoms are in the sp^3 hybridization state?

A) 2   B) 4   C) 5   D) 6   E) 11

Ans: D

13. In the following molecule, how many carbon atoms are in the sp^2 hybridization state?

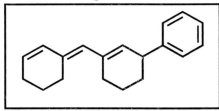

A) 0   B) 1   C) 2   D) 4   E) 6
Ans: D

14. In the following molecule, how many carbon atoms are in the sp hybridization state?

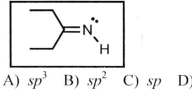

A) 2   B) 4   C) 6   D) 12   E) none of the above
Ans: E

15. The lone-pair of electrons on nitrogen in the following molecule reside in what type of orbital?

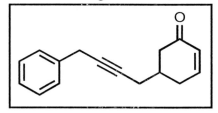

A) sp^3 B) sp^2 C) sp D) $2p$ E) $2s$
Ans: B

16. In the following molecule, how many carbon atoms are in the sp^2 hybridization state?

A) 1   B) 3   C) 7   D) 8   E) 9
Ans: E

17. The boxed item most likely represents what?

A)   *s* orbital
B)   *sp*³ orbital
C)   *p* orbital

D)   could be any of A–C
E)   none of the above

Ans: B

18. The following molecule contains how many carbon atoms in the *sp* hybridization state?

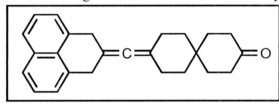

A) 1   B) 3   C) 8   D) 13   E) 16
Ans: A

19. The nitrogen of trimethylamine [$(CH_3)_3N$] contains how many lone pairs of electrons?
A) none   B) one   C) two   D) three   E) there is no nitrogen in this molecule
Ans: B

20. A positive charge on oxygen generally occurs when:
A)   oxygen has too many electrons.
B)   oxygen has too few electrons.
C)   oxygen is sharing one of its non-bonding electron pairs.
D)   oxygen has too many non-bonding electron pairs.
E)   oxygen is borrowing electrons from another atom.
Ans: C

21. The carbon atom in CH_2Cl_2 has what hybridization?
A) *sp*   B) *sp²*   C) *sp³*   D) *sp⁴*   E) they are not hybridized
Ans: C

22. The molecular formula for piperitone is

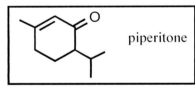

piperitone

A) $C_9H_{16}O$ B) $C_{10}H_{18}O$ C) $C_9H_{18}O$ D) $C_{10}H_{14}O$ E) $C_{10}H_{16}O$
Ans: E

23. Which structure is different from the others?

A)

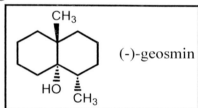

B) $CH_3CHClCH(CH_3)_2$

C)

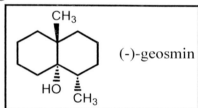

D)

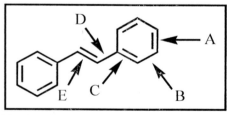

E)   all are identical

Ans: E

24. A fairly common algal metabolite is the compound (-)-geosmin, which imparts a musty odor to water even at concentrations in the ppb range. What is the molecular formula of geosmin?

(-)-geosmin

A) $C_{11}H_{20}O$ B) $C_{12}H_{22}O$ C) $C_{11}H_{21}O$ D) $C_{12}H_{20}O$ E) $C_{12}H_{21}O$

Ans: B

25. Which of the carbon-carbon bonds indicated would you expect to be the **longest** in stilbene?

A) A   B) B   C) C   D) D   E) E

Ans: D

26. Which of the following pairs are **not** resonance structures of each other?

A)

B)

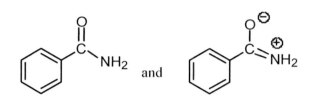

and

C)

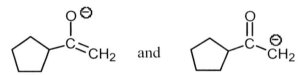

and

D)

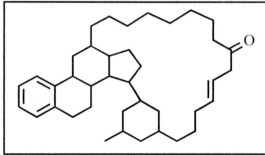

and

E)   All are pairs of resonance structures

Ans: A

27. The following molecule has what molecular formula?

A) $C_{39}H_{58}O$ B) $C_{40}H_{58}O$ C) $C_{39}H_{60}O$ D) $C_{44}H_{44}O$ E) none of the above

Ans: A

28. What is the molecular formula of carvone, the major volatile compound in caraway oil?

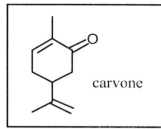

carvone

A) $C_{10}H_{18}O$ B) $C_{10}H_{17}O$ C) $C_{10}H_{16}O$ D) $C_{10}H_{14}O$ E) $C_{10}H_{15}O$
Ans: D

29. Of those indicated, which would be the shortest carbon-carbon bond in β-cadinene?

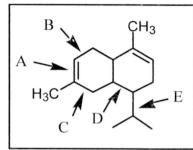

A) A   B) B   C) C   D) D   E) E
Ans: A

30. What would be the ideal value for the indicated bond angle?

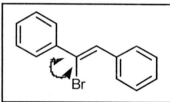

A) 120°   B) 90°   C) 104°   D) 180°   E) 109°
Ans: A

31. What would be the "polygon" form of the following condensed structure?

$ClCH_2CH(CH_3)CH_2CH_3$

A)

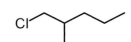

B)

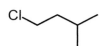

C)

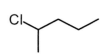

D)

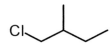

E)

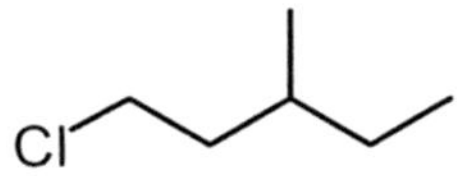

Ans: D

32. Which one of the following structures must be incorrect?

A)

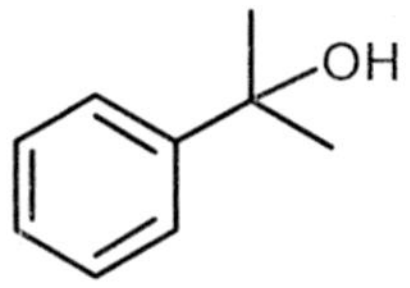

B)

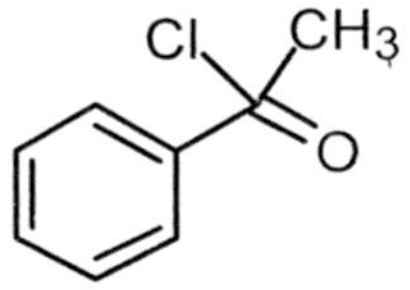

C)

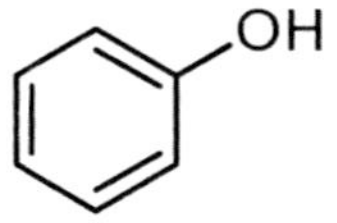

D)

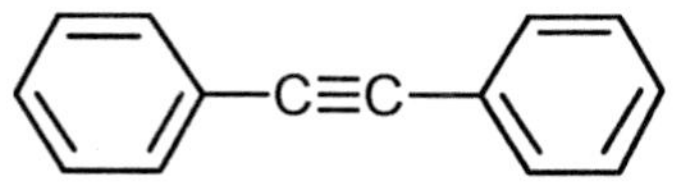

E)

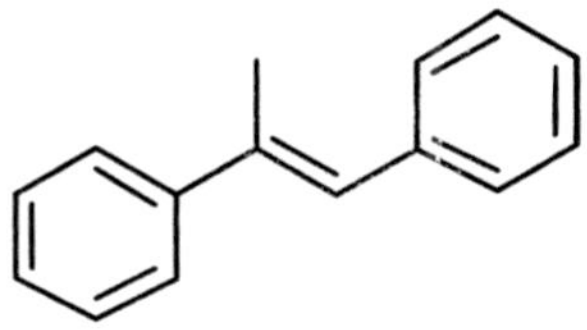

Ans: B

33. How many sp^2 hybridized carbon atoms are in the potent anticancer compound hydroxymethylacylfulvene?

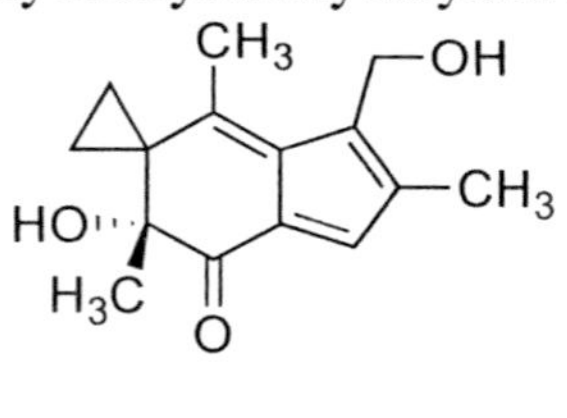

hydroxymethylacylfulvene

A) 2   B) 4   C) 6   D) 8   E) none of the above
Ans: E

34. In the following molecule, how many carbon atoms are in the sp^3 hybridization state?

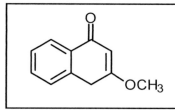

A) 2   B) 4   C) 5   D) 6   E) 9
Ans: A

35. Which of the following statements are true of sp orbitals?
    A)   Orbitals of the *sp* type are 50% *s* and 50% *p* character.
    B)   They are hybrid orbitals.
    C)   They are linear.
    D)   They result when one *s* orbital and one *p* orbital are mixed.
    E)   all are correct
    Ans: E

36. Which of the following molecules are most likely to be held together by a purely covalent bond?
    A) NaCl   B) H_2 C) HF   D) BH_3 E) KI
    Ans: B

37. What is the molecular formula of camphor?

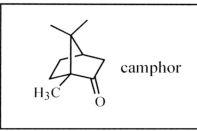

A) $C_{10}H_{15}O$ B) $C_{10}H_{16}O$ C) $C_{10}H_{17}O$ D) $C_{11}H_{18}O$ E) $C_{11}H_{16}O$
Ans: B

38. Camptothecin is an important anticancer compound; how many carbons are in the *sp* hybridization state?

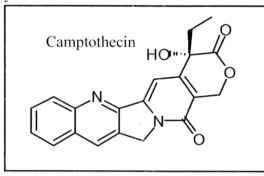

A) 0   B) 1   C) 2   D) 3   E) 4
Ans: A

39. How many *sp³* carbons are in the following molecule?

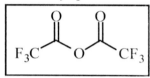

A) 0   B) 1   C) 2   D) 3   E) 4
Ans: C

40. The process of adding electrons one by one to atomic orbitals beginning with the lowest energy is described by:
A)   the Aufbau Principle.
B)   Hund's Rule.
C)   the de Broglie Relation.
D)   the Pauli Exclusion Principle.
E)   Coulomb's Law.
Ans: A

41. Which of the following cannot be a correct Lewis structure?

    A)

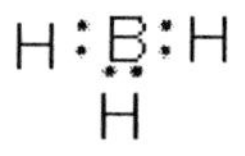

    H:B̤:H
       H

    B)

    :F̈:
    :F̈:C̈:F̈:
    :F̈:

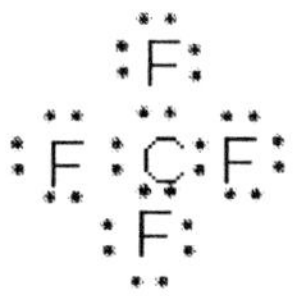

    C)

    :Ö::N̤::Ö:
        H

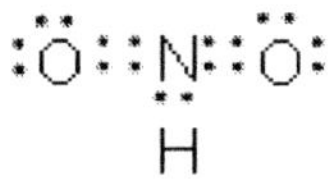

    D)

         H
    H:C̤::C̤:H

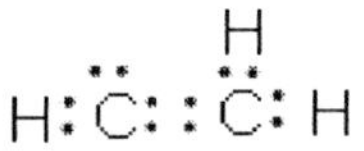

    E)   all are correct

    Ans: C

42. How many different resonance structures can be drawn for the benzyl cation (shown below) which place the plus charge on a carbon atom in the ring?

    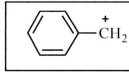

    A) 1   B) 2   C) 3   D) 5   E) 6

    Ans: C

43. Which of the following represent resonance contributing Lewis structures for CH_2N_2?

    A)

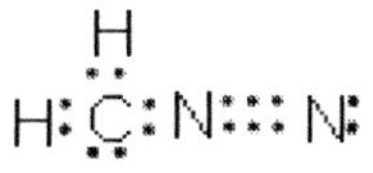

         H
    H:C̤:N:::N̤:

    B)

         H
    H:C::N̈::N̤:

    C)

         H
    H:C̈::N:N̈:

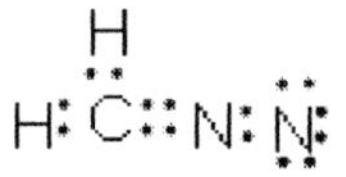

    D)

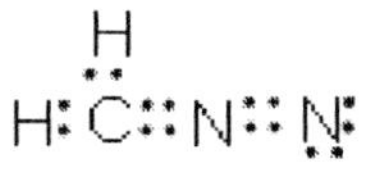

    H:C̈::N::N̈:H

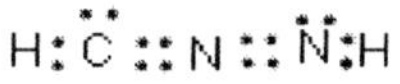

    E)   both A and B are correct

    Ans: E

44. The following molecule belongs to a class of compounds known as allenes. Based on your knowledge of bonding, predict the hybridization of the carbon atom indicated by the arrow.

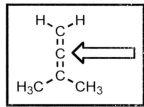

A) sp B) sp^2 C) sp^3 D) p-p pi   E) a hypervalent carbon
Ans: A

45. How many isomers of C_4H_9Br are possible?
A) two   B) three   C) four   D) five   E) six
Ans: C

46. How many isomers of C_5H_{12} are possible?
A) two   B) three   C) four   D) five   E) six
Ans: B

47. Which of the following most correctly defines "structural isomers"?
A)   molecules with different molecular formulas but the same connectivity
B)   compounds that are not constitutional isomers
C)   molecules with the same molecular formula but different connectivity
D)   *Anti* and *gauche* conformers
E)   both B and C
Ans: C

48. How many structural isomers exist for the formula C_6H_{14}?
A) 3   B) 4   C) 5   D) 6   E) 7
Ans: C

49. A hydrocarbon with a double bond and a ring will have the general formula?
A) C_nH_{2n+2} B) C_nH_{2n} C) C_nH_{2n-2} D) C_nH_{2n-4} E) $C_{2n}H_{2n}$
Ans: C

50. What is the hybridization of the each of the labeled atoms for the potent neurotoxin (-)-gephyrotoxin?

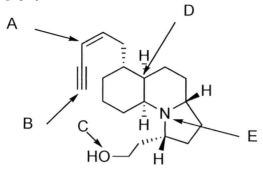

(-)-gephyrotoxin
source: poison frog
acitivty: neurotoxin

A) A = sp^2, B = sp, C = sp^2, D = sp^3, E = sp^3
B) A = sp^2, B = sp, C = sp^3, D = sp^3, E = sp^2
C) A = sp^2, B = sp, C = sp^2, D = sp^3, E = sp^2
D) A = sp^2, B = sp, C = sp^3, D = sp^3, E = sp^3
E) A = sp, B = sp, C = sp^3, D = sp^3, E = sp^3
Ans: D

Chapter 2: Structure and Reactivity: Acids and Bases, Polar and Nonpolar Molecules

1. The correct name of the following molecule would be:

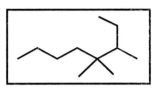

   A)   2-ethyl-3,3-dimethylheptane   D)   2-butyl-3-methylpentane
   B)   6-ethyl-5,5-dimethylheptane   E)   2-sec-butyl-2-methylhexane
   C)   3,4,4-trimethyloctane
   Ans: C

2. What is the name given to the Newman projection of the butane conformation shown here?

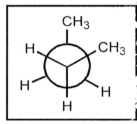

A) anti   B) gauche   C) staggered   D) eclipsed   E) skewed
Ans: B

3. At room temperature, the various conformations of butane
   A)   do not interconvert with only the *anti* form present.
   B)   do not interconvert, but all forms are present.
   C)   interconvert slowly.
   D)   interconvert rapidly.
   E)   There is no way to determine if interconversion occurs.
   Ans: D

4. What statement is true of the following energy diagram?

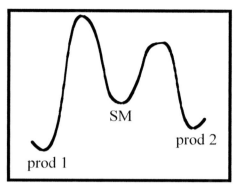

A)   For irreversible reactions, product 1 will dominate.
B)   For reversible reactions, product 2 will dominate at equilibrium.
C)   For reversible reactions, equal amounts of 1 and 2 will be formed.
D)   For irreversible reactions, equal amounts of 1 and 2 will be formed.
E)   None of the above are true.
Ans: E

5. What would be the correct name of the following?

$$CH_3-CH_2-CH_2-CH-CH_3$$
$$CH_3-CH_2-CH-CH_2-CH_3$$

A)   3-(sec-pentyl)pentane   D)   3-ethyl-4-methylheptane
B)   5-ethyl-4-methylheptane   E)   3-ethyl-4-propylpentane
C)   3-(sec-butyl)hexane
Ans: D

6. The following Newman projection corresponds to which molecule?

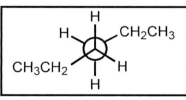

A) pentane   B) butane   C) 3-ethylbutane   D) hexane   E) 3-methylpentane
Ans: D

7. Rotation around the carbon-carbon bond of the molecule depicted by the following Newman projection requires how much energy?

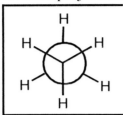

A) 0 kcal/mol   B) 3 kcal/mol   C) 6 kcal/mol   D) 9 kcal/mol   E) 15 kcal/mol
Ans: B

8. What is the correct IUPAC name for the following molecule?

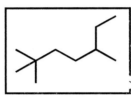

A) 1,1,1,4-tetramethylhexane   D) 3,6,6,6-tetramethylhexane
B) 4-ethyl-1,1,1-trimethylpentane   E) 2,2,5-trimethylheptane
C) 5-ethyl-2,2-dimethylhexane
Ans: E

9. The following represents what functional group?

A) ester   B) ether   C) alcohol   D) thiol   E) ketone
Ans: B

10. The following represents what functional group?

A) alcohol   B) aldehyde   C) carboxylic acid   D) amide   E) ketone
Ans: B

11. The following represents what functional group?

A) amide   B) thiol   C) ketone   D) nitrile   E) amine
Ans: D

12. What is the correct structure for tertbutyl bromide?
   A)

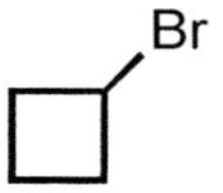

   B)

   C)

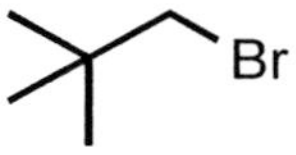

   D)

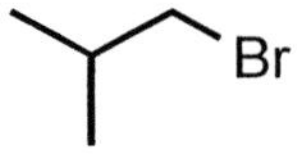

   E)

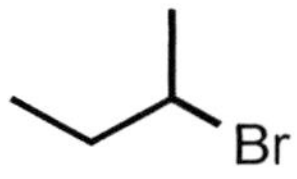

   Ans: B

13. The following Newman projection represents which molecule?

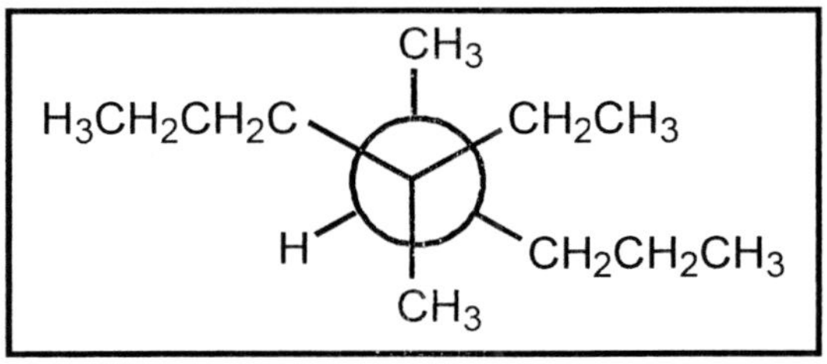

CH$_3$

H$_3$CH$_2$CH$_2$C　　　CH$_2$CH$_3$

H　　CH$_2$CH$_2$CH$_3$

CH$_3$

A)

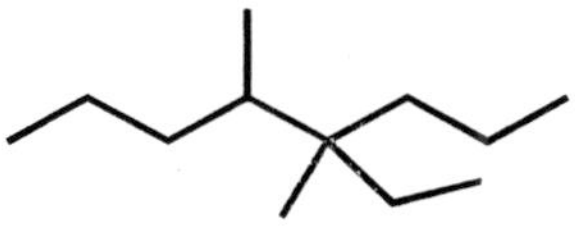

B)

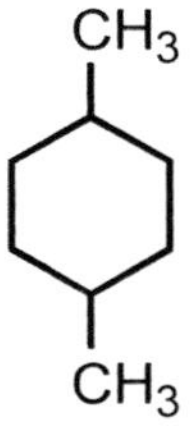

CH$_3$

CH$_3$

C)

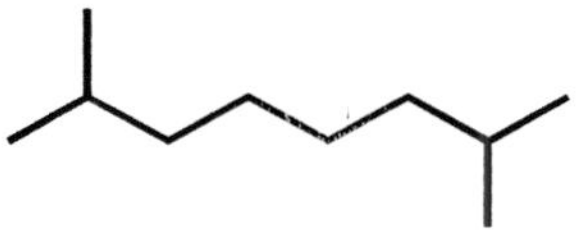

D)

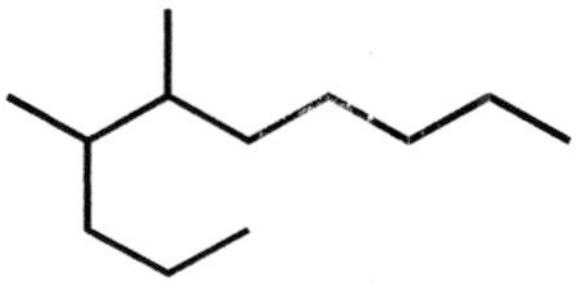

E)

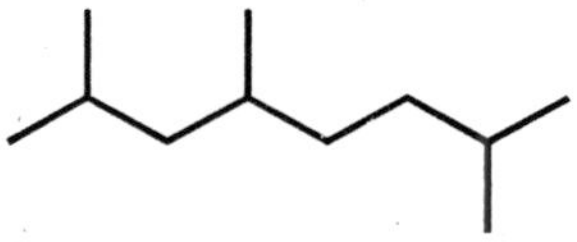

Ans: A

14. Name the following functional group:

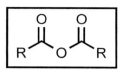

A) ester   B) ketone   C) alcohol   D) carboxylic acid   E) anhydride
Ans: E

15. Which isomer of C_7H_{16} shown would have the highest boiling point?
A)

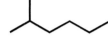

B)

C)

D)

E)

Ans: A

16. Which of the following contains the isobutyl group?
A) $(CH_3)_2CHCH_2Cl$ D) $CH_3CH_2CH_2CH_2Cl$
B) $(CH_3)_3CCl$ E)   none of the above
C) $CH_3CH_2CH(CH_3)Cl$
Ans: A

17. Which of the following contains the *sec*-butyl group?
A) $(CH_3)_2CHCH_2Cl$ D) $CH_3CH_2CH_2CH_2Cl$
B) $(CH_3)_3CCl$ E)   None of the above
C) $CH_3CH_2CH(CH_3)Cl$
Ans: C

18. How would the following molecule be properly named?

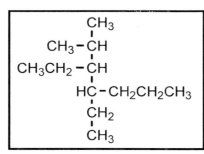

A)   3-ethyl-2-methyl-4-propylhexane   D)   3-isopropyl-4-propylhexane
B)   3,4-diethyl-2-methylheptane   E)   none of the above
C)   4-ethyl-3-isopropylheptane
Ans: B

19. The IUPAC name for $[(CH_3)_3C]_2CHCH_3$ is:
A)   1,1-di-*tert*-butylethane   D)   2,4,4-trimethylheptane
B)   3-*tert*-butyl-2,2-dimethylbutane   E)   none of the above
C)   2,2,3,4,4-pentamethylpentane
Ans: C

20. What is the smallest alkane that is liquid at room temperature?
A) propane   B) butane   C) pentane   D) hexane   E) all are liquids
Ans: C

21. All steroids are derivatives of the ring system shown. How many **tertiary hydrogens** are in this ring system?

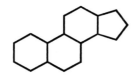

A) none   B) 2   C) 4   D) 5   E) 6
Ans: E

22. What is the correct IUPAC name for the following molecule:

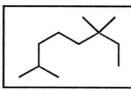

A)   2-ethyl-2,6-dimethylheptane   D)   2,6,6-trimethyloctane
B)   1,1,5,5-tetramethylhexane   E)   4,4-dimethyl-1-isopropylhexane
C)   1,1,5,5-tetramethylheptane
Ans: D

23. What is the name given to the Newman projection of the butane conformation shown here?

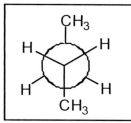

A) eclipsed   B) gauche   C) staggered   D) anti   E) skewed
Ans: D

24. Calculate ΔG° for the following reaction at 25 °C and $\Delta S = 0$

Bond	Ave Strength
C-C	83 (kcal/mol)
C-H	99 (kcal/mol)
C-Br	68 (kcal/mol)
H-Br	87 (kcal/mol)
Br-Br	46 (kcal/mol)

A)   −10 kcal/mol   D)   −34 kcal/mol
B)   10 kcal/mol   E)   none of the above
C)   34 kcal/mol
Ans: A

25. Which of the following has the highest pKa?
A) HI   B) NH_3 C) HNO_3 D) CH_3COOH E) H_2SO_4
Ans: B

26. The common name for 1-methylpropyl is:
A) Isopropyl   B) Isobutyl   C) *sec*-Butyl   D) *tert*-Butyl   E) none of the above
Ans: C

27. What is the correct Newman projection for the following molecule?

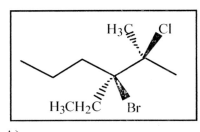

A)

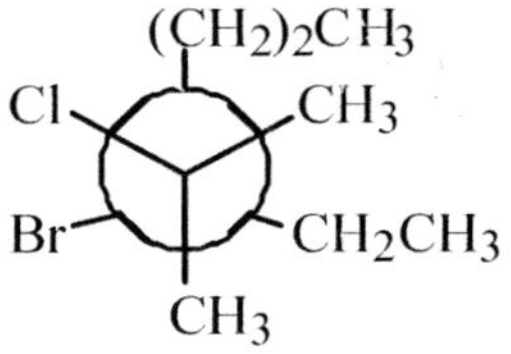

(CH$_2$)$_2$CH$_3$
Cl   CH$_3$
Br   CH$_2$CH$_3$
CH$_3$

B)

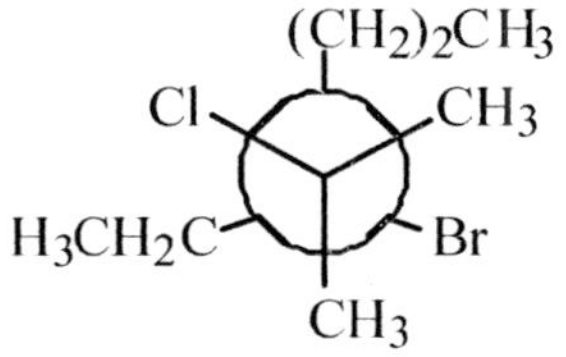

(CH$_2$)$_2$CH$_3$
Cl   CH$_3$
H$_3$CH$_2$C   Br
CH$_3$

C)

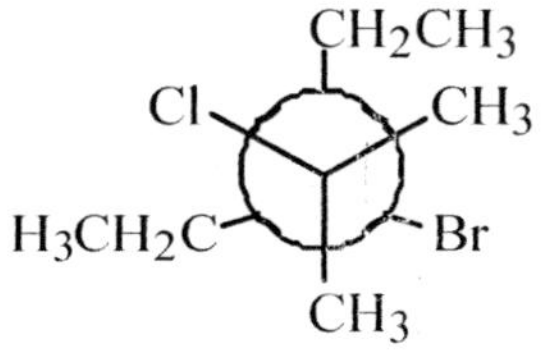

CH$_2$CH$_3$
Cl   CH$_3$
H$_3$CH$_2$C   Br
CH$_3$

D)

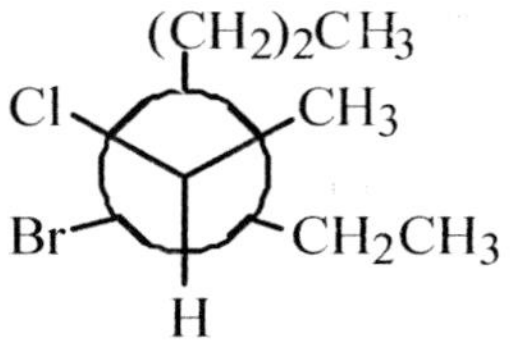

(CH$_2$)$_2$CH$_3$
Cl   CH$_3$
Br   CH$_2$CH$_3$
H

E)   none of the above

Ans: A

28. Which of the following molecules contain both an alcohol and an aldehyde functional group?

A)

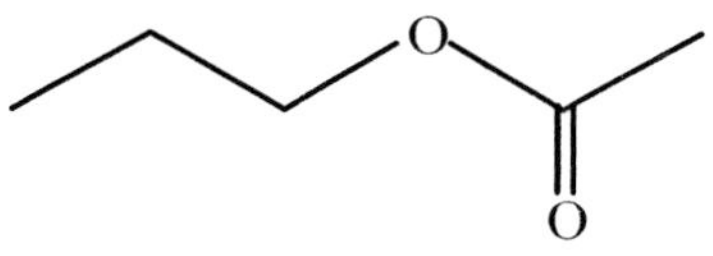

B)

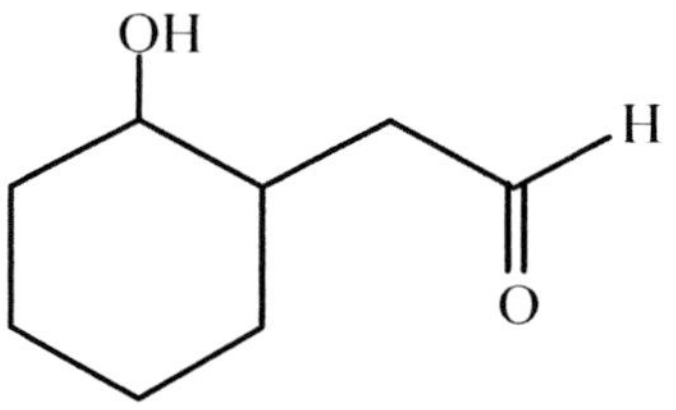

C)

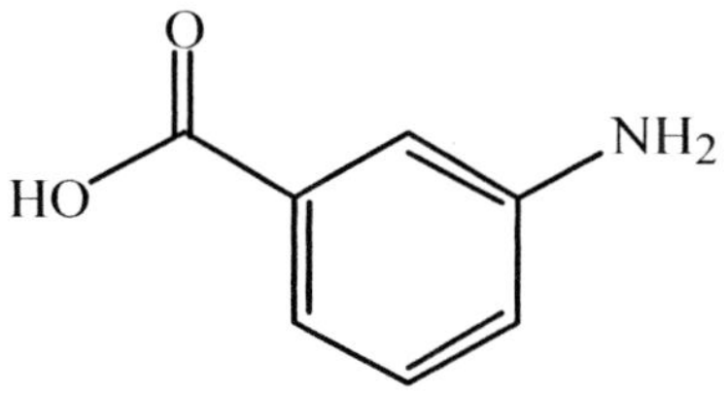

D)

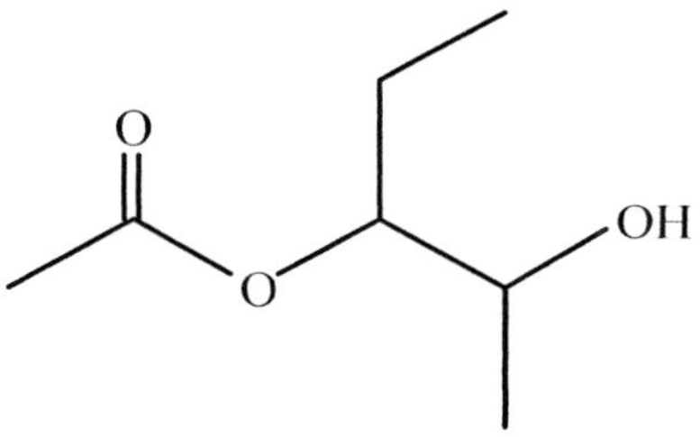

E)

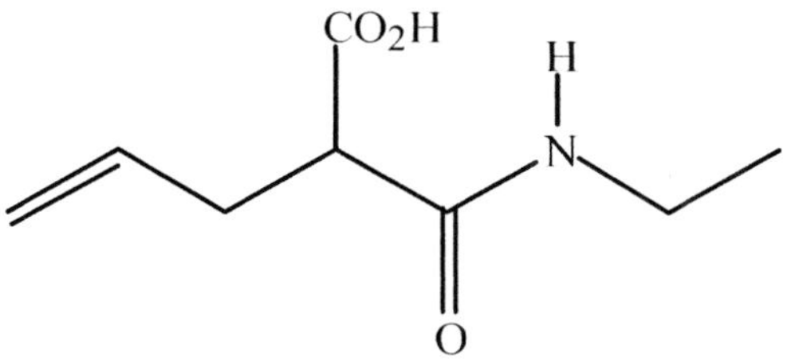

Ans: B

29. Consider the potential energy diagram for rotation about the C2–C3 bond in pentane. The position marked "A" most likely corresponds to which of the following Newman projections?

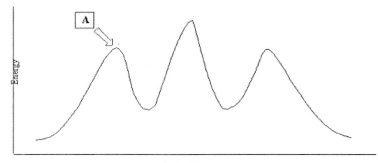

Angle of Rotation

A)

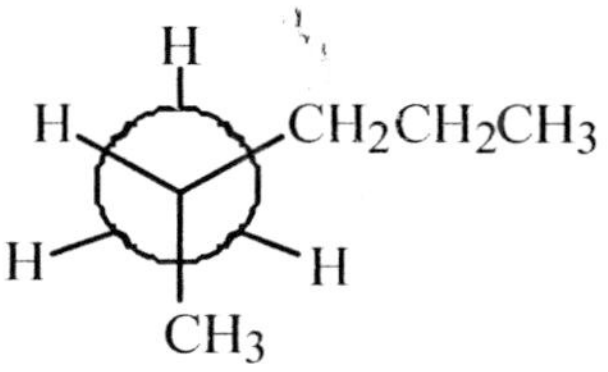

H
H. CH₂CH₂CH₃
H H
CH₃

B)

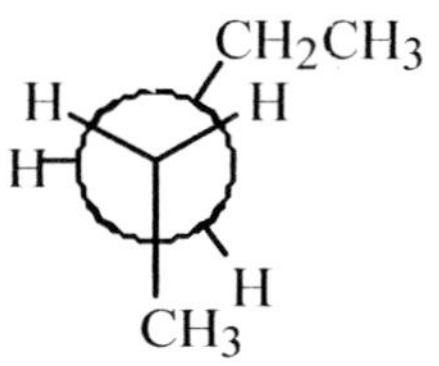

CH₂CH₃
H. H
H
H
CH₃

C)

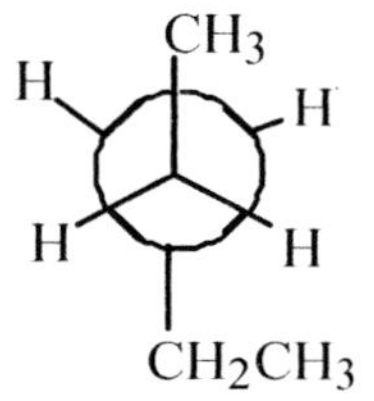

CH₃
H. H
H H
CH₂CH₃

D)

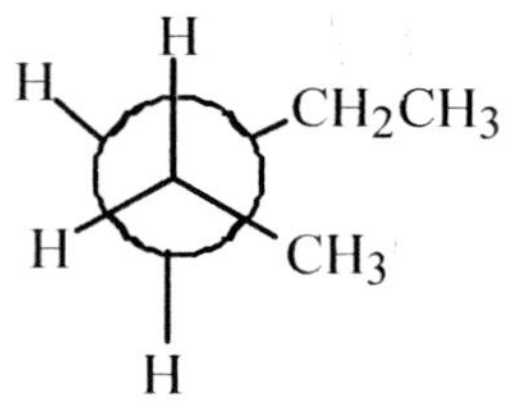

H
H. CH₂CH₃
H CH₃
H

E)

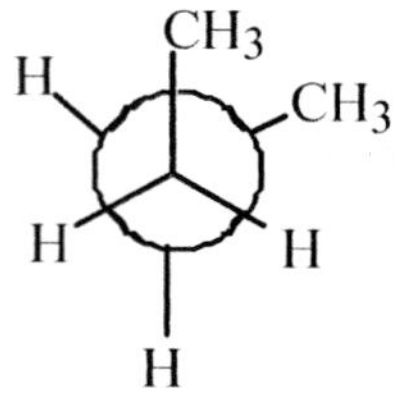

CH₃
H. CH₃
H H
H

Ans: B

30. What is the correct IUPAC name for the following molecule?

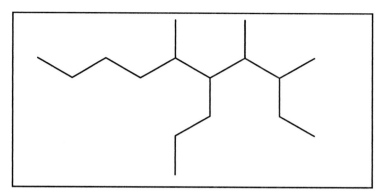

A) 6-propyl-5,7,8-trimethyldecane   D) 5-propyl-3,4,6-trimethyldecane
B) 5,7,8-trimethyl-6-propyldecane   E) none of the above
C) 3,4,6-trimethyl-5-propyldecane

Ans: C

31. Which of the following is not considered a Lewis acid?
A)   H⊕

B) CH_3OH
C) $AlCl_3$
D)

$$H_3C-\overset{\displaystyle CH_3}{\underset{\displaystyle CH_3}{\overset{|}{\underset{|}{C}}}}{}^{\oplus}$$

E) BF_3

Ans: B

32. Which of the following is considered to be a nucleophile?
A) CH_3Cl
B) CH_3CH_2I
C) :NH_3
D)   H⊕

E)

Ans: C

33. Which of the following reactions has a ΔS = 0?
    A)

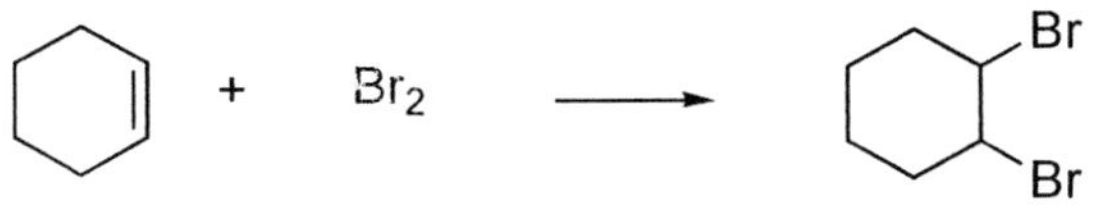

    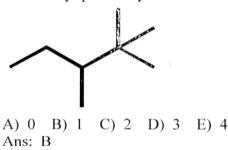

    B) $CH_3CH_2Cl + NaOH \rightarrow CH_2{=}CH_2 + H_2O + NaCl$
    C)

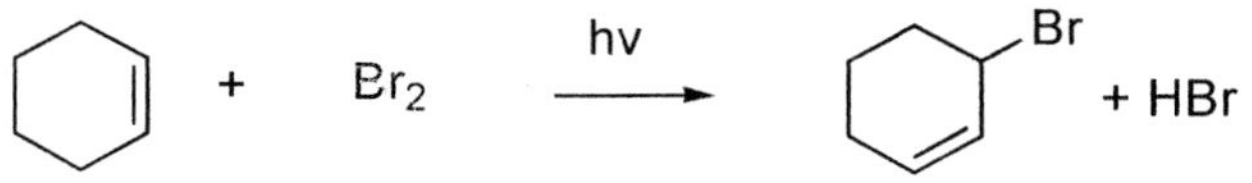

    D)

    E)   none of the above
    Ans: C

34. How many quaternary carbons are in the following molecule?

    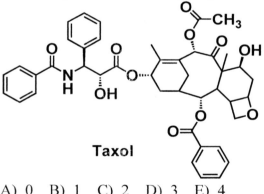

    A) 0   B) 1   C) 2   D) 3   E) 4
    Ans: B

35. How many ester functional groups are in the potent anticancer compound Taxol?

    Taxol

    A) 0   B) 1   C) 2   D) 3   E) 4
    Ans: D

36. Arrange these acids in the order of increasing acidity.
    HCl   HBr   HI   HF
    A) HBr, HI, HF, HCl   D) HI, HCl, HBr, HF
    B) HF, HCl, HBr, HI   E) HI, HBr, HCl, HF
    C) HF, HBr, HCl, HI
    Ans: B

37. Arrange these acids in the order of increasing acidity

    A) CH_4, H_2O, HF, NH_3 D) CH_4, NH_3, H_2O, HF,
    B) HF, H_2O, CH_4, NH_3 E) NH_3, CH_4, H_2O, HF,
    C) HF, H_2O, NH_3, CH_4,
    Ans: D

38. What is the correct IUPAC name for the following molecule?

    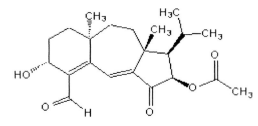

    A) 1-ethyl-2-methylhexane   D) 1-ethyl-2-methylcyclohexane
    B) 2-ethyl-1-methylcycloheptane   E) 1-methyloctane
    C) 4-ethyl-5-methylcyclohexane
    Ans: D

39. Guanacastepene is a natural product that was recently isolated and shown to be a potent antibiotic. How many **different** functional groups does this structure possess?

    Guanacastepene
    A) 1   B) 2   C) 3   D) 4   E) 5
    Ans: E

Chapter 3: Reactions of Alkanes: Bond-Dissociation Energies, Radical Halogenation, and Relative Reactivity

1. Given the relative reactivities of various kinds of hydrogens, the **major** product expected from mono-bromination of 2-methylbutane would be what?

$$H_3C-\underset{\underset{CH_3}{|}}{\overset{\overset{H}{|}}{C}}-CH_2-CH_3 \quad + \quad Br_2 \quad \xrightarrow{h\nu} \quad ?$$

type	relative reactivity
1°	1
2°	80
3°	1700

A)

$$H_3C-\underset{\underset{CH_3}{|}}{\overset{\overset{H}{|}}{C}}-CH_2-CH_2Br$$

B)

$$H_3C-\underset{\underset{CH_3}{|}}{\overset{\overset{H}{|}}{C}}-CHBr-CH_3$$

C)

$$H_3C-\underset{\underset{CH_2Br}{|}}{\overset{\overset{H}{|}}{C}}-CH_2-CH_3$$

D)

$$BrCH_2-\underset{\underset{CH_3}{|}}{\overset{\overset{H}{|}}{C}}-CH_2-CH_3$$

E)

$$H_3C-\underset{\underset{CH_3}{|}}{\overset{\overset{Br}{|}}{C}}-CH_2-CH_3$$

Ans: E

2. Which of the following is a **propagation** step in the free-radical bromination of methane?

A) $CH_3\cdot + Br\cdot \longrightarrow CH_3Br$

B) $Br_2 \xrightarrow{h\nu} 2\ Br\cdot$

C) $CH_3\cdot + Br_2 \longrightarrow CH_3Br + Br\cdot$

D) $CH_3\cdot + CH_3\cdot \longrightarrow CH_3CH_3$

E) $Br\cdot + Br\cdot \longrightarrow Br_2$

Ans: C

3. Which of the reactions below would you expect to have the largest positive Δ?

A) $CH_3\cdot + Br\cdot \longrightarrow CH_3Br$

B) $Br_2 \xrightarrow{h\nu} 2\ Br\cdot$

C) $CH_3\cdot + Br_2 \longrightarrow CH_3Br + Br\cdot$

D) $CH_3\cdot + CH_3\cdot \longrightarrow CH_3CH_3$

E) $Br\cdot + Br\cdot \longrightarrow Br_2$

Ans: B

4. What reactant is needed to complete and balance the following reaction?

$$? \quad + \quad 3\ O_2 \quad \xrightarrow{spark} \quad 3\ CO \quad + \quad 3\ H_2O$$

A) C_3H_8 B) C_2H_6 C) C_3H_4 D) C_3H_6 E) C_6H_{12}

Ans: D

5. Which one of the reactions below will **not** proceed and accounts for why iodine added to a free-radical chlorination or bromination will greatly slow or even stop the reaction?

A) $CH_3\cdot + I\cdot \longrightarrow CH_3I$

B) $I_2 \xrightarrow{h\nu} 2\ I\cdot$

C) $CH_3\cdot + I_2 \longrightarrow CH_3I + I\cdot$

D) $CH_4 + I\cdot \longrightarrow CH_3\cdot + HI$

E) $I\cdot + I\cdot \longrightarrow I_2$

Ans: D

6. Which of the following is **not** true of free-radical halogenation reactions?
    A)   Fluorine is more reactive than chlorine in these reactions.
    B)   Bromine is more selective than chlorine.
    C)   The reactions require either light or high temperatures to proceed.
    D)   Brominations are faster than chlorinations.
    E)   These reactions are irreversible.
    Ans: D

7. Which of the following reaction types are typical of alkanes?
    A)   addition   D)   reduction
    B)   elimination   E)   more than one of these is correct
    C)   radical substitution
    Ans: C

8. Alkanes are noted for their (choose one)
    A)   high reactivity with acids.   D)   lack of reactivity.
    B)   toxicity.   E)   water-solubility.
    C)   intense odor.
    Ans: D

9. What is the major product of the following reaction?

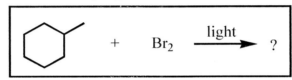

    A)

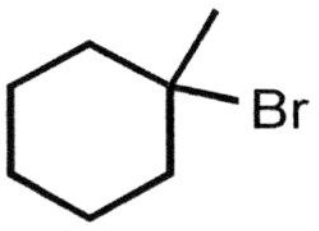

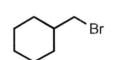

    B)

C)

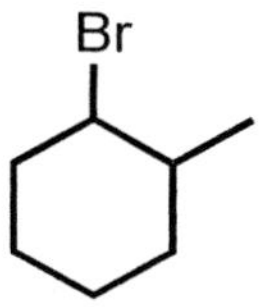

D)

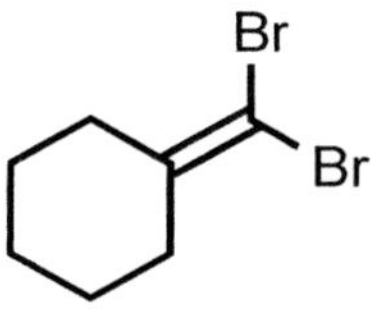

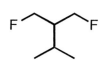

E)   no reaction occurs

Ans: A

10. Predict the **major** monofluorination product from the following reaction:

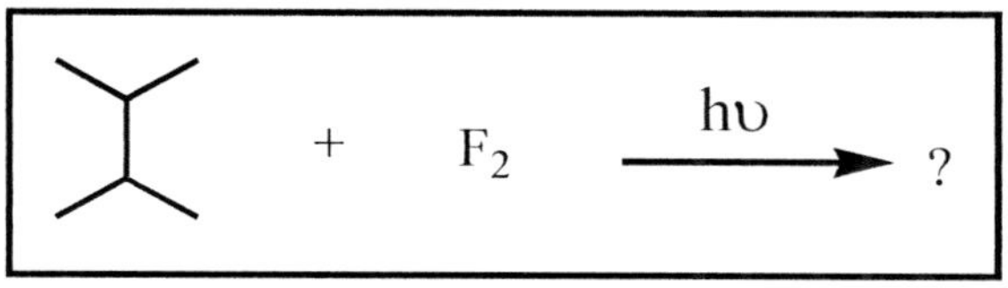

$$\text{(structure)} \quad + \quad F_2 \quad \xrightarrow{h\upsilon} \quad ?$$

A)

B)

C)

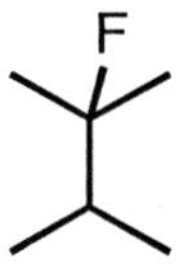

D)

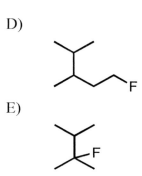

E)

Ans: A

11. In a carbon radical, the single unpaired electron resides in:
    A) sp^2 orbital   B) sp^3 orbital   C) s orbital   D) p orbital   E) none of the above
    Ans: D

12. The order of radical stability is:
    A) $3° > 2° > 1° > Me$
    B) $3° < 2° < 1° < Me$
    C)   all are about equal in stability
    D) $Me > primary$
    E)   tertiary and methyl are equal in stability
    Ans: A

13. Which of the following is true for an early transition state?
    A)   The starting materials resemble the products.
    B)   The reaction proceeds very slowly.
    C)   The transition state resembles the reactants.
    D)   The transition state resembles the products.
    E)   both B and C
    Ans: C

14. Hyperconjugation is most useful for stabilizing which of the following?
    A)   neopentyl radical   D)   ethyl radical
    B)   *tert*-butyl radical   E)   methyl radical
    C)   isopropyl radical
    Ans: B

15. In a carbon radical, the carbon possesses how many valence electrons?
    A) 4   B) 5   C) 6   D) 7   E) 8
    Ans: D

16. Which, if any, of the following would you choose to accomplish the reaction shown below in the best yield?

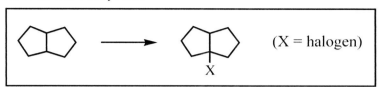 (X = halogen)

A) F₂, light   B) Cl₂, light   C) Br₂, light   D) I₂, light   E) none of the above
Ans: C

17. Predict the **major** product of the following reaction:

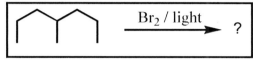 Br₂ / light ?

A)

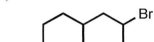
Br

B)

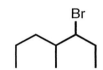
Br

C)

Br
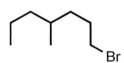

D)

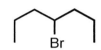
Br

E)

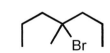
Br

Ans: E

18. Predict the **major** product of the following reaction:

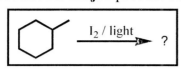

A)

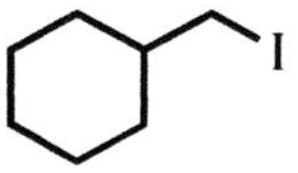

B)

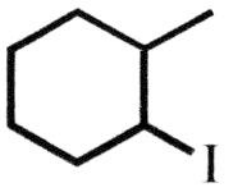

C)

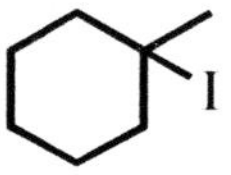

D)

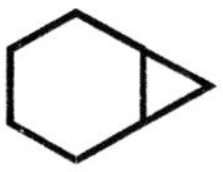

E)   no reaction

Ans: E

19. Free-radical fluorination demonstrates little regio-selectivity because
    A)   fluorine is too small to have steric hinderance.
    B)   free-radical reactions are never regio-selective.
    C)   a late transition state is involved.
    D)   an early transition state is involved.
    E)   fluorine is too unreactive.

    Ans: D

20. Which of the carbon-carbon bonds indicated would be the weakest?

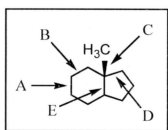

A) A   B) B   C) C   D) D   E) E

Ans: E

21. Which alkane below would you expect to have the **lowest** heat of combustion?

    A)

    B)

    C)

    D)

    E)   All would be the same.

    Ans: C

22. Which of the following would you **not** expect to be formed in even small amounts during the free-radical chlorination of methane?

    A) CH_2Cl_2

    B) CH_3CH_3

    C) $CHCl_3$

    D) CCl_4

    E)   Some of all of these would be formed.

    Ans: E

23. Given the relative reactivities of various kinds of hydrogens, the **major** product expected from mono-chlorination of 2-methylbutane would be what?

type	relative reactivity
1°	1
2°	4
3°	5

$$H_3C-\overset{\displaystyle H}{\underset{\displaystyle CH_3}{C}}-CH_2-CH_3 \quad + \quad Cl_2 \quad \xrightarrow{h\nu} \quad ?$$

    A)

$$H_3C-\overset{\displaystyle H}{\underset{\displaystyle CH_3}{C}}-CH_2-CH_2Cl$$

    B)

$$H_3C-\overset{\displaystyle H}{\underset{\displaystyle CH_3}{C}}-CHCl-CH_3$$

C)

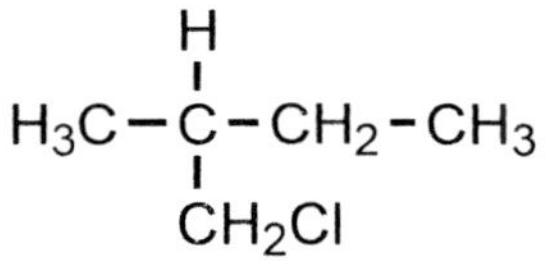

$$H_3C-\overset{\overset{\displaystyle H}{|}}{\underset{\underset{\displaystyle CH_2Cl}{|}}{C}}-CH_2-CH_3$$

D)

$$CH_3-\overset{\overset{\displaystyle Cl}{|}}{\underset{\underset{\displaystyle CH_3}{|}}{C}}-CH_2-CH_3$$

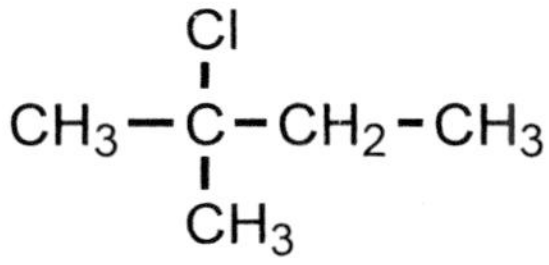

E)   There is no way to predict this.

Ans: B

24. Which of the following hydrocarbons would yield only a single mono-chloro derivative under free radical chlorination conditions? ($Cl_2/h\nu$)

A)

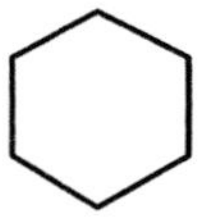

B)

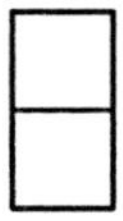

C)

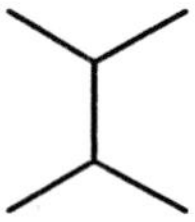

D)

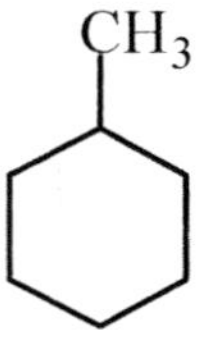

CH$_3$

E)

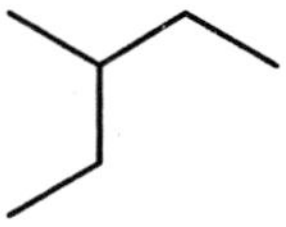

Ans: A

25. Give the relative reactivity in decreasing order for free radical halogenation of
    (CH₃)₃CH.
    A)   F > Cl > Br   D)   Br > Cl > F
    B)   Cl > Br > F   E)   I > F > Cl
    C)   Br > F > Cl
    Ans: A

26. Which is **most** true about the function of a catalyst?
    A)   Catalysts speed up the reaction by lowering the transition state of a reaction.
    B)   Catalysts usually need higher temperatures to promote reactions.
    C)   Catalysts lower the energies of the reactants.
    D)   Catalysts lower the energies of the products.
    E)   Catalysts increase the yield of the reaction.
    Ans: A

27. In a free radical termination step:
    A)   an initiator starts a chain reaction.
    B)   free radicals recombine with one another.
    C)   a radical reacts to form another radical.
    D)   the activation energy is high.
    E)   a reactive intermediate is formed.
    Ans: B

28. Rank the following radicals in decreasing order of stability.

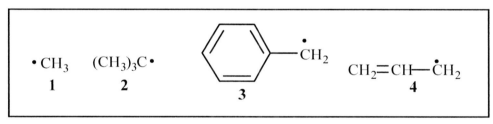

    A)   3 > 4 > 2 > 1   D)   2 > 4 > 3 > 1
    B)   3 > 2 > 4 > 1   E)   1 > 2 > 3 > 4
    C)   2 > 3 > 4 > 1
    Ans: A

29. Carbon dioxide is an essential greenhouse gas that insulates the planet and maintains a surface temperature that allows life to flourish. Human activities have resulted in a dramatic increase in the greenhouse gases in the atmosphere. Which of the following reactions produce the most carbon dioxide per mole of carbon-containing starting material? (Note that these equations are not balanced.)

    A)

    $$C_8H_{18} + O_2 \longrightarrow CO_2 + H_2O$$
    major component
    of gasoline

    B)

    $$CH_4 + O_2 \longrightarrow CO_2 + H_2O$$
    major component
    of natural gas

    C)

    $$C_{12}H_{22}O_{11} + O_2 \longrightarrow CO_2 + H_2O$$
    sugar

    D)   All produce the same amount of carbon dioxide.
    E)   None of these reactions produce carbon dioxide.

    Ans: C

30. Chemists have determined that chlorofluorocarbons are contributing to destruction of the protective ozone layer. Upon irradiation of chlorofluorcarbons, chlorine radicals are produced and react with the ozone via the chemical process shown below. Which of the following statement(s) are true based upon these equations?

    $$\overset{\bullet}{Cl} + O_3 \longrightarrow \overset{\bullet}{Cl}O + O_2$$

    $$\overset{\bullet}{Cl}O + O \longrightarrow \overset{\bullet}{Cl} + O_2$$

    A)   Termination steps in the equations above are contributing to ozone depletion.
    B)   A single chlorine radical is capable of destroying many molecules of ozone since it is regenerated.
    C)   Chlorine radicals are the result of a heterolytic cleavage of the C-Cl bond of the chlorofluorocarbon.
    D)   A, B and C are correct.
    E)   B and C are correct.

    Ans: B

31. What reactant is needed to complete and balance the following reaction?

    $$? + 5\,O_2 \xrightarrow{\text{spark}} 3\,CO_2 + 4\,H_2O + \Delta$$

    A) C_3H_8 B) C_2H_6 C) C_3H_4 D) C_3H_6 E) C_6H_{12}

    Ans: A

32. Which of the following compounds has the **highest** heat of combustion per CH_2 group?

    A) cyclopropane
    B) cyclobutane
    C) cyclopentane
    D) cyclohexane
    E) All have equal heats of combustion.

    Ans: A

33. How many constitutional isomers can be formed from the monochlorination of the hydrocarbon shown below?

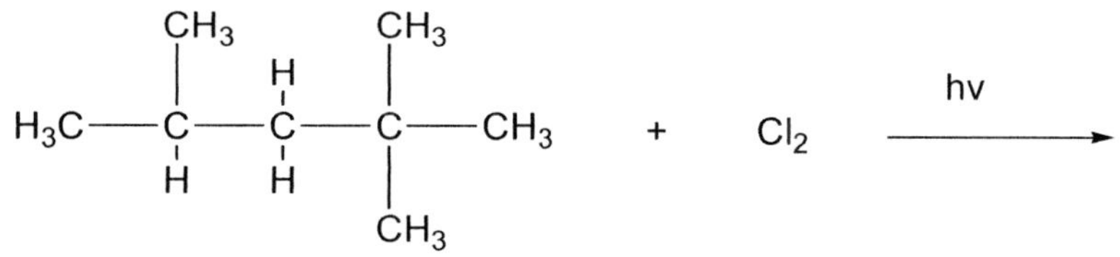

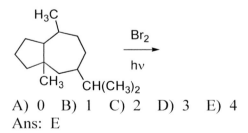

    A) 1 B) 2 C) 3 D) 4 E) 5
    Ans: D

34. The following reaction represents what type of process?

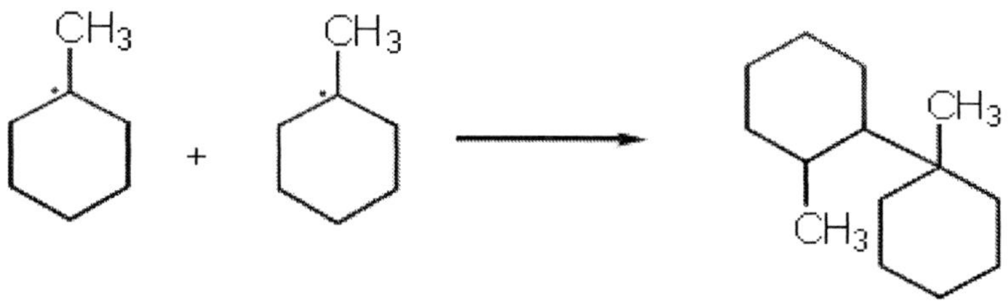

    A) Propagation
    B) Termination
    C) Initiation
    D) Nucleophilic addition
    E) None of the above

    Ans: B

35. How many different products will result if radical **monobromination** of the following compound only occurs at 3° carbons.

    A) 0 B) 1 C) 2 D) 3 E) 4
    Ans: E

Chapter 4: Cycloalkanes

1. What would be the name of the following?

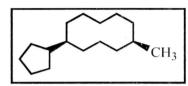

   A)   5-cyclopentyl-1-methylcyclononane
   B)   *cis*-1-cyclopentyl-5-methylcyclodecane
   C)   *cis*-5-methyl-1-cyclopentylcyclododecane
   D)   *trans*-cyclopentyl-5-methylcyclodecane
   E)   (5-methylcyclodecyl)cyclopentane
   Ans: B

2. Which of the following isomers would you expect to have the **lowest** heat of combustion? (i.e., be most stable)
   A)   *cis*-1,2-dimethylcyclohexane
   B)   *trans*-1,3-dimethylcyclohexane
   C)   *cis*-1,4-dimethylcyclohexane
   D)   *cis*-1,3-dimethylcyclohexane
   E)   All should have the same heat of combustion.
   Ans: D

3. Terpenes can be considered to be built up from what units?
   A)

   B)

   C)

   D)

   E)

   Ans: E

4. Which of the following compounds has the **highest** heat of combustion **per CH$_2$ group**?
   A) cyclopropane
   B) cyclobutane
   C) cyclopentane
   D) cyclohexane
   E) All have equal $\Delta H_{combustion}$.
   Ans: A

5. What is the correct IUPAC name for the following molecule:

   A) 1-ethyl-2-methylhexane
   B) 2-ethyl-1-methylcycloheptane
   C) 4-ethyl-5-methylcyclohexane
   D) 1-ethyl-2-methylcyclohexane
   E) 1-methyloctane
   Ans: D

6. Which would be the **most stable** conformation of *trans*-1-methyl-3-isopropylcyclohexane?
   A)

   B)

   C)

D)

CH(CH₃)₂

H┤

CH₃

E)

CH₃ H

CH(CH₃)₂

H

Ans: E

7. Which one of the following cyclic alkanes has the greatest tendency to have a planar ring?
   A) cyclopropane
   B) cyclobutane
   C) cyclopentane
   D) cyclohexane
   E) none of the above are planar
   Ans: A

8. What would be the proper name of the following:

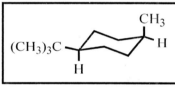

   A) *cis*-1-tert-butyl-4-methylcyclohexane
   B) *trans*-1-tert-butyl-4-methylcyclohexane
   C) axial,equatorial-1-tert-butyl-4-methylcyclohexane
   D) *cis*-1-isopropyl-4-methylcyclohexane
   E) *trans*-1-isopropyl-4-methylcyclohexane
   Ans: A

9. The most stable conformation of *cis* 1,3-dimethylcyclohexane has **how many** hydrogen atoms in axial positions?
   A) 4   B) 5   C) 6   D) 8   E) none of the above
   Ans: C

10. Which of the following disubstituted cyclohexanes could exist in a conformation that has both groups equatorial?
    A)   *cis*-1,3-dimethylcyclohexane
    B)   *cis*-1,4-dimethylcyclohexane
    C)   *trans*-1,3-dimethylcyclohexane
    D)   *cis*-1,2-dimethylcyclohexane
    E)   All or none can have both groups equatorial.
    Ans: A

11. Which of the following correctly represents cyclopropylcyclohexane?
    A)

    B)

    C)

    D)

    E)   none of the above
    Ans: D

12. Which of the following ring systems belongs to the class of compounds called steroids?
    A)

B)

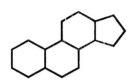

C)

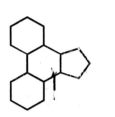

D)

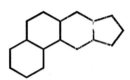

E)

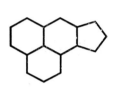

Ans: B

13. Which of the following could be classified as a **terpene**?
    A)

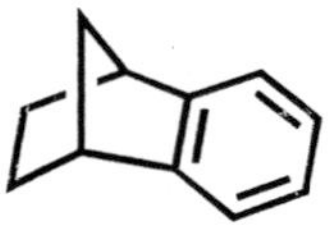

    B)

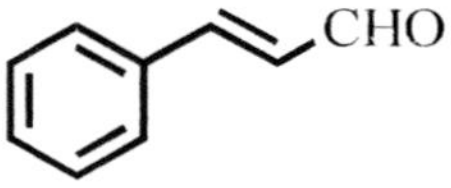

    CHO

C)

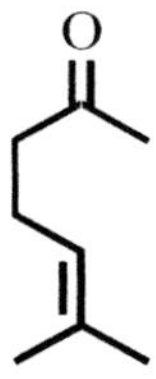

D)

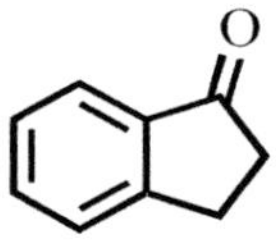

E)

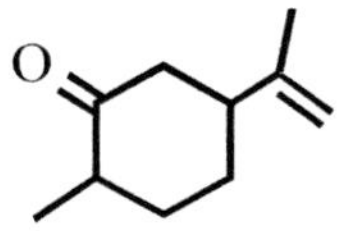

Ans: E

14. Which of the following could have **both** methyl groups in an **equatorial** orientation?
    A)

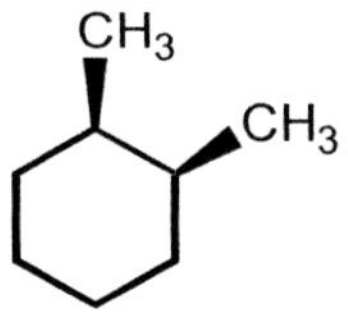

    B)

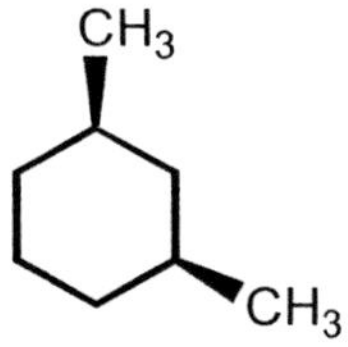

C)

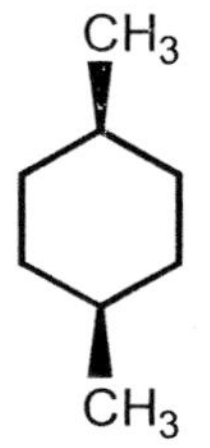

D)

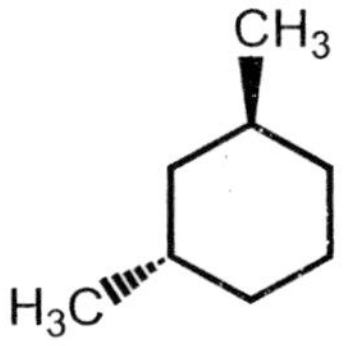

E)

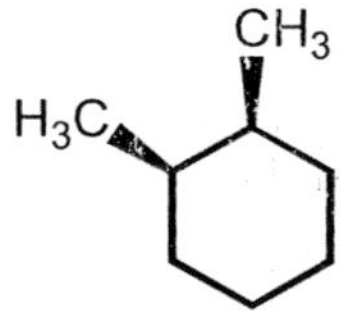

Ans: B

15. Which of the following compounds has the **lowest** heat of combustion **per CH$_2$ group**?
    A) cyclopropane
    B) cyclobutane
    C) cyclopentane
    D) cyclohexane
    E) All have equal $\Delta H_{combustion}$.
    Ans: D

16. Which, if either, of the two isomers of the compound shown below would be more stable?

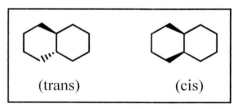

(trans)   (cis)

A) *Cis* is more stable.
B) *Trans* is more stable.
C) Both are equally stable.
D) Neither is stable.
E) There is no way to predict this.
Ans: B

17. Although five- and six-membered rings are generally the most stable, why is cyclopentane less stable than cyclohexane?
    A)   The angles in cyclopentane deviate significantly from the tetrahedral angle.
    B)   Five-membered rings have trans annular interactions.
    C)   Five-membered rings have eclipsing hydrogens.
    D)   Planar cyclohexane has bond angles closer to 109°.
    E)   Larger rings are always more stable than smaller rings.
    Ans: C

18. Which of the following correctly shows the Newman projection along a C-C bond in cyclohexane? (the squiggles indicate where the rest of the ring is attached)

    A) A   B) B   C) C   D) D   E) E
    Ans: D

19. Which of the following cyclic alkanes can be ring-opened under hydrogenation conditions?

    A)   cyclopropane   D)   cyclohexane
    B)   cyclobutane   E)   more than one of these
    C)   cyclopentane
    Ans: E

20. Which of the following statements about conformations of methylcyclohexane is true?

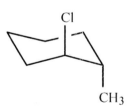

A)   The energy barrier to interconvert these is too high to be achieved at room temperature.
B)   The two forms are in equilibrium and are present in equal amounts at room temperature.
C)   The two forms are not in equilibrium but **are** present in equal amounts at room temperature.
D)   The two forms are in equilibrium but are **not** present in equal amounts at room temperature.
E)   The two forms are not in equilibrium and are **not** present in equal amounts at room temperature.
Ans: D

21. Cyclohexanes exhibit a higher_____than their straight-chain analogs. (Choose the correct answer)
    A)   boiling point   D)   All of these are correct.
    B)   melting point   E)   Two of these are correct.
    C)   density
    Ans: D

22. Which conformation of cyclohexane experiences the most transannular strain?
    A) Chair B) Planar C) Boat D) Twist boat E) All of these are stable.
    Ans: C

23. Which of the following is **not** in its most stable conformation?
    A)

B)

C)

D)

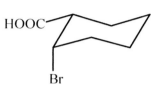

E)   All of these are in their most stable conformation.

Ans: A

24. What is the potential energy change to convert from a twist-boat to boat conformation?
    A)   −14 Kcal/mol
    B)   0 Kcal/mol
    C)   1.4 Kcal/mol
    D)   14 Kcal/mol
    E)   45 Kcal/mol

    Ans: C

25. Which of the following structures represent *cis*-1,4-dimethylcyclohexane?

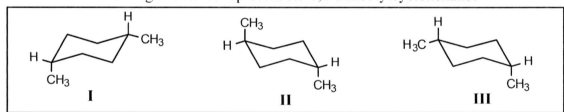

    A) I & II   B) I & III   C) II & III   D) all of the above   E) none of the above

    Ans: B

26. What is the correct structure of 2-methyl-1,3-butadiene?
    A)

    B)

    C)

    D)

    E)   none of the above
    Ans: B

27. Steroids frequently function as _____, which are regulators of biochemical activity.
    A) proteins   B) nucleic acids   C) hormones   D) fatty acids   E) triglycerides
    Ans: C

28. What is the most stable conformation of *trans*-1-fluoro-4-methylcyclohexane?
    A)

    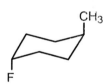

    B)

    C)

    D)

    CH₃

    E)

    F   CH₃

    Ans: E

29. What is the correct name for the following molecule?

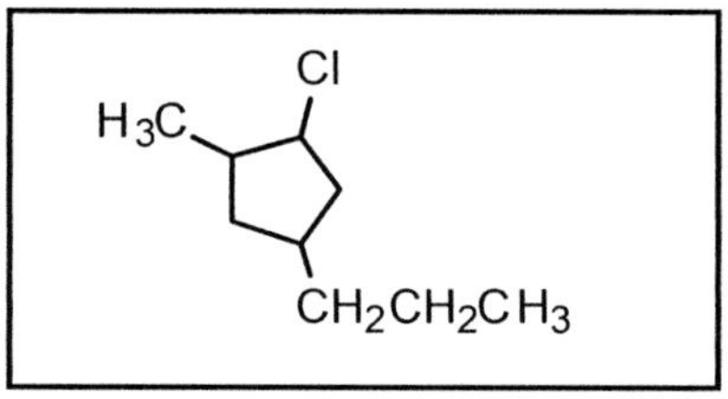

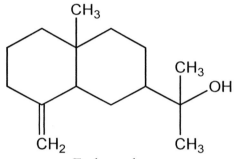

A)   1-chloro-2-methyl-4-propylcyclopentane
B)   2-chloro-1-methyl-4-propylcyclopentane
C)   1-chloro-5-methyl-3-propylcyclopentane
D)   5-methyl-1-chloro-3-propylcylopentane
E)   1-chloro-3-propyl-5-methylcyclopentane
Ans: A

30. How many isoprene units are in eudesmal?

CH₃

CH₃
OH
CH₂   CH₃
Eudesmol

A) 0   B) 1   C) 2   D) 3   E) Unable to determine
Ans: A

Chapter 5: Stereoisomers

1. How many chiral centers are present in β-cadinene?

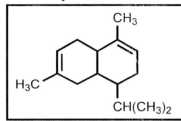

   A) none   B) 1   C) 2   D) 3   E) 4
   Ans: D

2. Counting **all** stereoisomers, how many monochlorinated products of the free-radical chlorination of (R)-2-bromobutane are possible? (Note that the starting compound is one enantiomer only.)

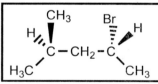

   A) 3   B) 4   C) 5   D) 6   E) 8
   Ans: D

3. Optically pure (S)-monosodium glutamate has a specific rotation of + 24°. What specific rotation would (R)-monosodium glutamate of 50% optical purity have?
   A) + 24°   B) - 24°   C) - 18°   D) - 12°   E) + 18°
   Ans: D

4. What would be the complete name of the following?

   A)   (2R,4S)-2-bromopentane   D)   (2R,4R)-2-bromo-4-methylpentane
   B)   (R)-2-bromo-4-methylpentane   E)   (S)-2-bromo-4-methylpentane
   C)   (S)-4-bromo-2-methylpentane
   Ans: B

5. How many total stereoisomers of the following are possible?

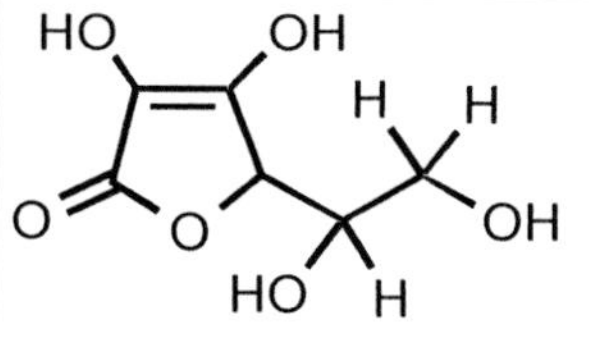

A) 1 B) 2 C) 3 D) 4 E) 6

Ans: D

6. How many total stereoisomers of the following are possible?

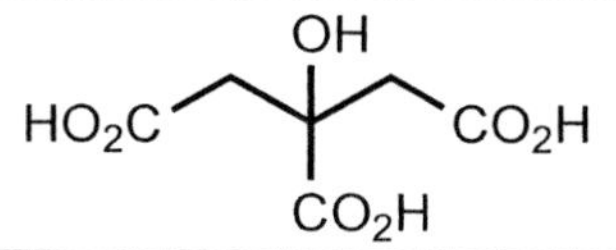

A) 1 B) 2 C) 3 D) 4 E) 6

Ans: A

7. How many total stereoisomers of the following are possible?

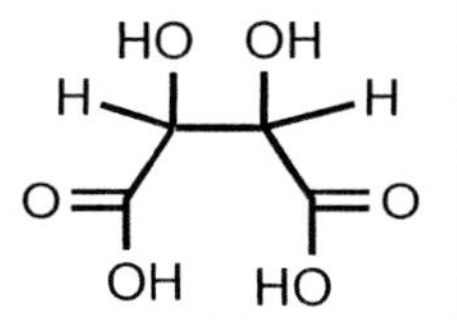

A) 1 B) 2 C) 3 D) 4 E) 6

Ans: C

8. Which of the amines below **might** be appropriate for the resolution of racemic Ibuprofen?

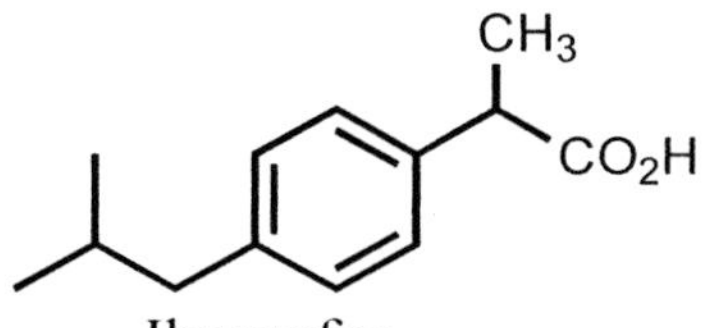

A)

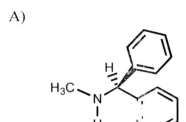

B)

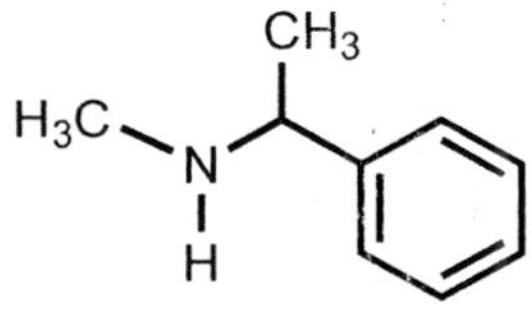

H_3C—N—CH(CH_3)—Ph

(racemic)

C)

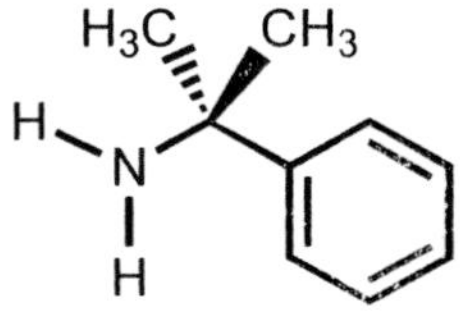

H_3C, CH_3

H—N—C—Ph

H

D)

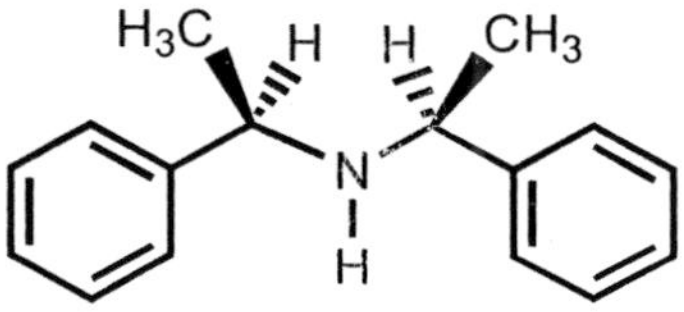

H_3C—H   H—CH_3

Ph—C—N—C—Ph

H

E)

H_3C—N—CH(CH_3)—Ph

H

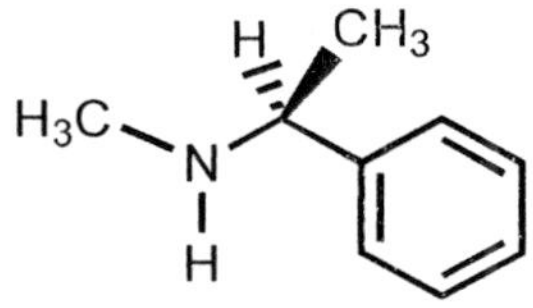

Ans: E

9. Which of the following Fischer projections represents (2*R*,3*R*)-tartaric acid?
    A)

    ```
         CO₂H
    H ───┬─── OH
    H ───┼─── OH
         CO₂H
    ```

    B)

    ```
          CO₂H
     H ───┬─── OH
    HO ───┼─── H
          CO₂H
    ```

    C)

    ```
           CO₂H
    HO ───┬─── H
    HO ───┼─── H
           CO₂H
    ```

    D)

    ```
           CO₂H
    HO ───┬─── H
     H ───┼─── OH
           CO₂H
    ```

    E)   none of the above
    Ans: B

10. Which of the following statements is **not** true?
    A)   Enantiomers have identical properties except in chiral environments or with
          plane-polarized light.
    B)   Reactions involving only achiral or racemic materials must produce achiral or
          racemic products.
    C)   Diastereomers have identical properties in all environments.
    D)   Enantiomers exhibit equal and opposite optical rotations.
    E)   All of the above are true.
    Ans: C

11. How many stereogenic (chiral) centers are found in Rhizoxin?

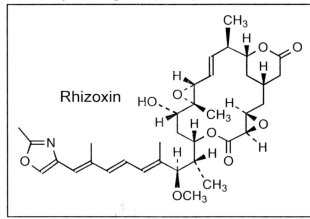

A) 5   B) 7   C) 9   D) 11   E) 14
Ans: D

12. The meso isomer of 3,4-dibromohexane has what stereochemical configuration?
A) 3R, 4S   B) 3R, 4R   C) 3S, 4S   D) 3S, 4R   E) both A and D
Ans: E

13. The following two molecules may be described as:

A)   constitutional isomers   D)   structural isomers
B)   diastereomers   E)   none of the above
C)   enantiomers
Ans: B

14. The following molecule has how many possible stereoisomers?

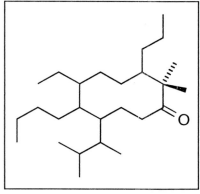

A) 1   B) 4   C) 8   D) 16   E) 32
Ans: E

15. The correct structure for (*R*)-bromofluoroiodomethane is:

A)

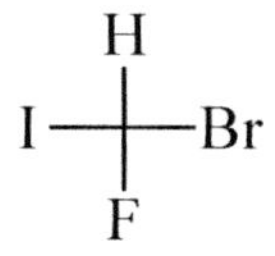

B)

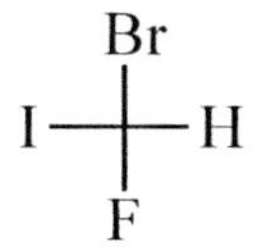

C)

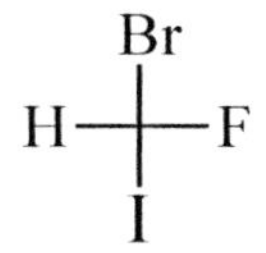

D)

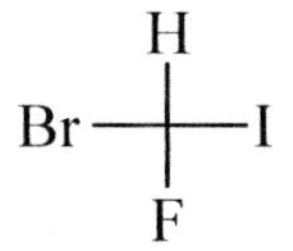

E)

Ans: A

16. The relationship between the following two compounds is:

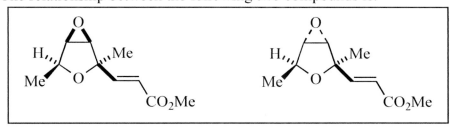

A)   same molecule   D)   mesos
B)   enantiomers   E)   conformers
C)   diastereomers
Ans: C

17. A particular reaction produces the following two alcohols in a ratio of 95:5.

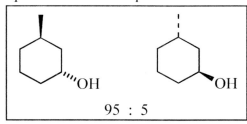

95 : 5

The enantiomeric excess (% ee) is:
A) 100   B) 95   C) 90   D) 85   E) none of the above
Ans: C

18. (*S*)-Naproxen, $[\alpha]_D = +66°$, is an analgesic (pain reliever), while its enantiomer is toxic. Say that you were given a solution that contains 1 g of Naproxen in 20 mL of liquid, but the optical purity is not specified. You place it in a polarimeter tube (10 cm) and get a reading of + 3.3° from the polarimeter. What is the percent optical purity of the sample?
A) 50   B) 100   C) 0   D) 10   E) 75
Ans: B

19. Which of the following molecules have the *S* configuration?

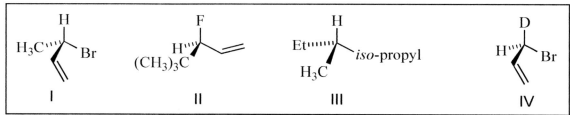

I   II   III   IV

A) I, II   B) I, III   C) III, IV   D) I, II, IV   E) all of the above
Ans: A

20. What (*R*) or (*S*) stereochemistry is proper for the following molecule?

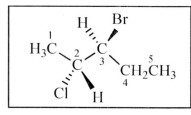

A) (2*R*,3*R*)   B) (2*R*,3*S*)   C) (2*S*,3*S*)   D) (2*S*,3*R*)   E) none of the above
Ans: B

21. The **best** (most reliable) test for the presence of chirality in a molecule is
    A)   carbon attached to four different groups.
    B)   existance of a mirror image.
    C)   non-superimposability on mirror image.
    D)   two or more isomers possible.
    E)   observation of optical rotation in a sample.
    Ans: C

22. Which of the following molecules is **not** chiral?
    A)

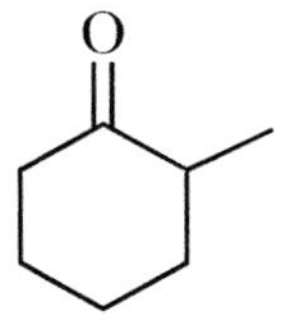

    B)

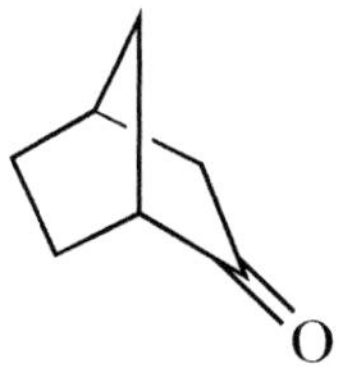

    C)

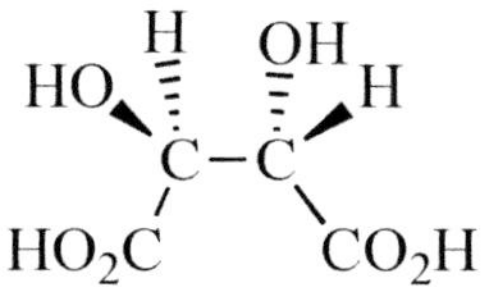

    D)

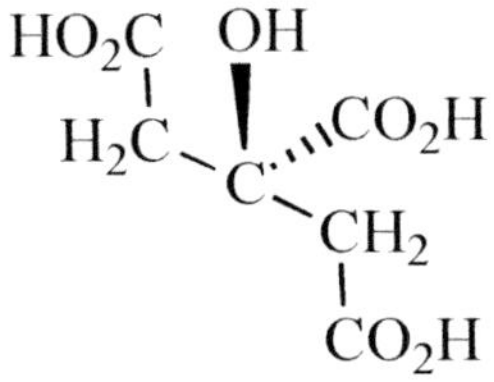

    E)

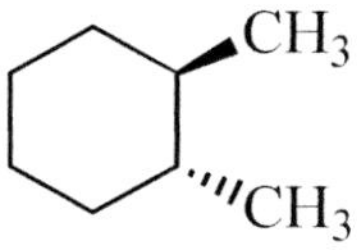

    Ans: D

23. What would be the proper name of the following?

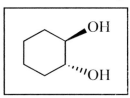

- A) (1R,2R)-trans-1,2-cyclohexanediol
- B) (1R,2S)-trans-1,2-cyclohexanediol
- C) (1S,2R)-trans-1,2-cyclohexanediol
- D) (1S,2S)-trans-1,2-cyclohexanediol
- E) (1S,2R)-cis-1,2-cyclohexanediol

Ans: A

24. An unknown compound has been isolated in pure form and found to exhibit $[\alpha]_D = +15°$ (c = 4, CH$_2$Cl$_2$). Which of the following **might** be the structure of the compound?

A)

B)

C)

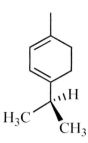

D)

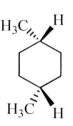

E)

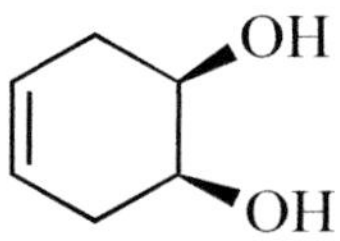

Ans: A

25. How would you most accurately describe the relationship between the following two molecules?

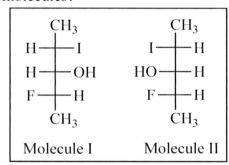

	CH₃	CH₃
	H——I	I——H
	H——OH	HO——H
	F——H	F——H
	CH₃	CH₃
	Molecule I	Molecule II

A)   enantiomers
B)   diastereomers
C)   meso compounds
D)   same compound
E)   Both C and D

Ans: B

26. Which of the following molecules represents a meso compound?

A)

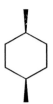

B)

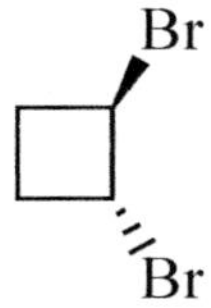

Br

Br

C)

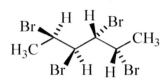

D)

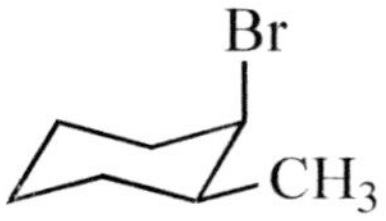

Br

CH₃

E)

CO₂H
H——OH
HO——H
CO₂H

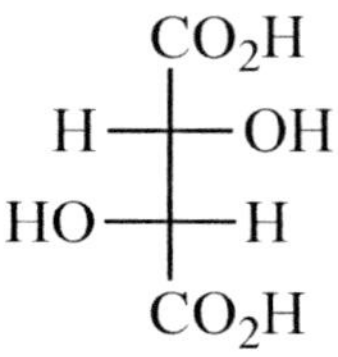

Ans: C

27. Sharpless epoxidation of geraniol gave two products, epoxide I (85%) and epoxide II (15%). This mixture of epoxides represents what percent optical purity (or percent enantiomeric excess, % ee)?

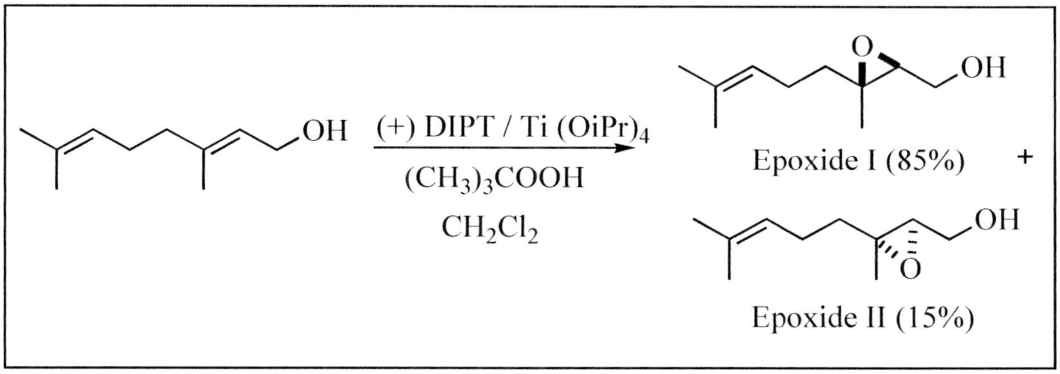

A) 0%   B) 15%   C) 70%   D) 85%   E) 100%
Ans: C

28. What is the correct structure for (R)- 4-methyl-2-heptanone?

A)

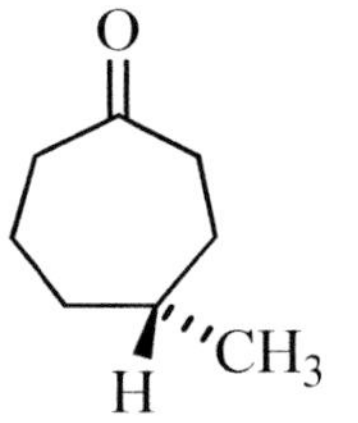

B)

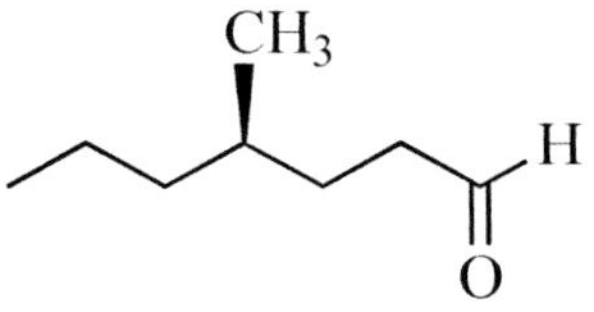

C)

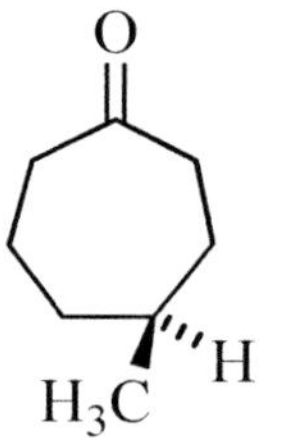

D)

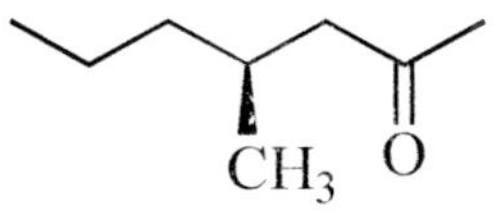

E)

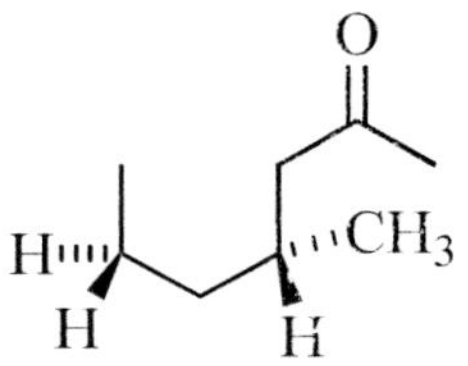

Ans: E

29. Which of the following is **not** true for a meso compound:
    A)   It is achiral.   D)   It is a stereoisomer.
    B)   It will rotate plane polarized light.   E)   It has a mirror plane.
    C)   It may be cyclic or acyclic.
    Ans: B

30. How many stereogenic (chiral) centers are present in the following molecule:

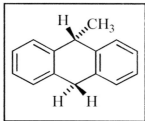

    A) none   B) one   C) two   D) three   E) four
    Ans: A

31. Which of the structures below are pairs of enantiomers?

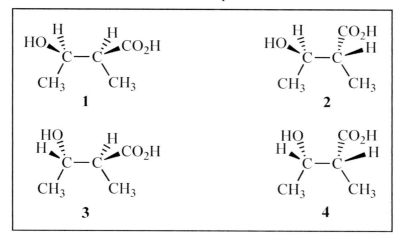

A) (1+2) and (3+4)   D) all of the above
B) (1+4) and (2+3)   E) none of the above
C) (1+3) and (2+4)

Ans: B

32. Which of the structures below are pairs of diastereomers?

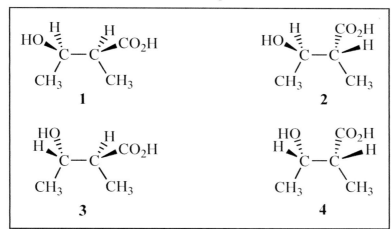

A) (1+4) and (2+3)   D) both A and B
B) (1+3) and (2+4)   E) both B and C
C) (1+2) and (3+4)

Ans: E

33. The structure of (-)-geosmin is shown below. Which structure would be that of its enantiomer, (+)-geosmin?

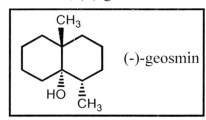

(-)-geosmin

A)

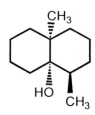

B)

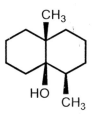

C)

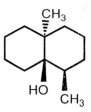

D)

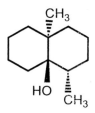

E)   none of the above

Ans: C

34. What is the *R* and *S* configuration for each stereogenic center of the following sugar from top to bottom?

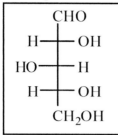

   A) *R, S, R*   B) *S, S, R*   C) *R, R, S*   D) *R, R, R*   E) *S, S, S*
   Ans: A

35. What technique(s) can be used to obtain non-racemic compounds from racemic material?
   A)   resolution
   B)   distillation
   C)   extraction
   D)   column chromatography
   E)   both B and C
   Ans: A

36. Penicillin V was discovered in the late 1920s by Sir Alexander Fleming in which he won the Nobel Prize for the development of this wonder drug. How many sterogenic centers does penicillin V contain?

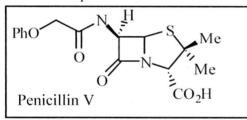

   A) 1   B) 2   C) 3   D) 4   E) 5
   Ans: C

37. A graduate student wishes to separate a racemic mixture of acids prepared in the laboratory as shown below. The best way(s) to accomplish this task is:

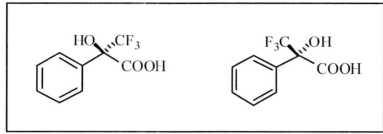

A) distillation
B) water solubility
C) reaction with a chiral amine to form diastereomers, then crystallization
D) column chromatography
E) both A and B
Ans: C

38. How are the following compounds related?

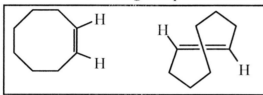

A) diastereomers   D) same compound
B) enantiomers   E) not related
C) meso compounds
Ans: A

39. How are the following compounds related?

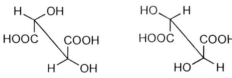

A) diastereomers   D) same compound
B) enantiomers   E) not related
C) meso compounds
Ans: B

40. How are the following compounds related?

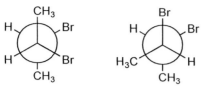

A)   Diastereomers
B)   Enantiomers
C)   Meso compounds

D)   Same compound
E)   Not related

Ans: C

41. How are the following compounds related?

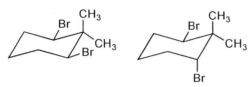

A)   diastereomers
B)   enantiomers
C)   meso compounds

D)   same compound
E)   not related

Ans: A

42. How are the following compounds related?

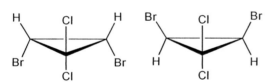

A)   diastereomers
B)   enantiomers
C)   meso compounds

D)   same compound
E)   not related

Ans: C

43. Label the following carbons as either (R) or (S).

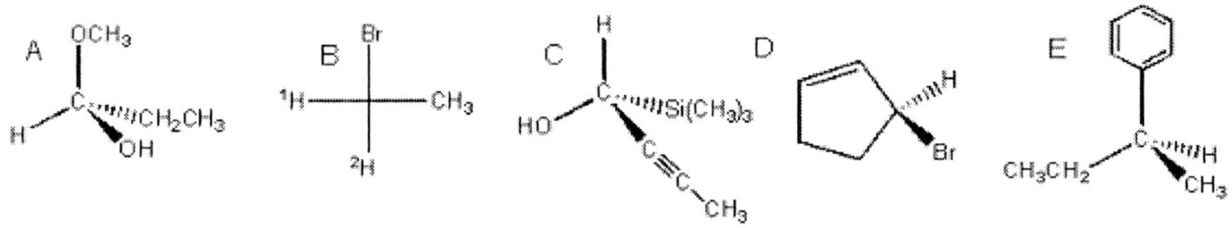

A)   A = R, B = R, C = R, D = R, E = R   D)   A = S, B = S, C = R, D = S, E = S
B)   A = S, B = S, C = S, D = S, E = S   E)   A = S, B = S, C = S, D = R, E = S
C)   A = S, B = R, C = S, D = S, E = S
Ans: D

44. A racemic mixture will rotate light?
    A)   0 degrees
    B)   180 degrees
    C)   need more information
    D)   There is no such thing as a racemic mixture of enantiomers.
    E)   none of the above
    Ans: A

Chapter 6: Properties and Reactions of Haloalkanes: Bimolecular Nucleophilic Substitution

1. Which of the following would you expect to have the highest boiling point?
   A) $CH_3CH_2CH_2Br$
   B) $CH_3CH_2CH_2I$
   C) $CH_3CH_2CH_2Cl$
   D) $CH_3CH_2CH_2F$
   E) $CH_3CH_2CH_3$

   Ans: B

2. What would be the name of the following?

   $CH_3CH_2CHBrCHBrCH(CH_3)_2$

   A)   3,4-dibromo-2-methylhexane
   B)   1,2-dibromo-1-isopropylbutane
   C)   2,3-dibromohexane
   D)   3,4-dibromo-5-methylhexane
   E)   3,4-dibromo-3-methylhexane

   Ans: A

3. What would be the major product of the following reaction?

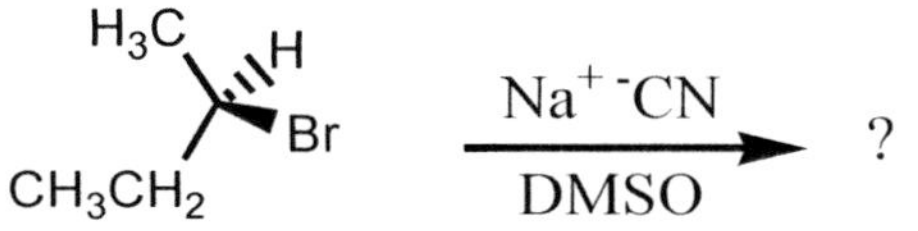

   A)

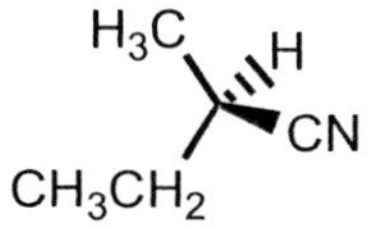

   B)

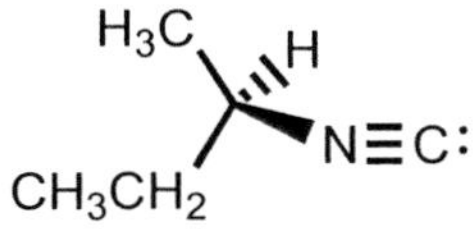

   C)

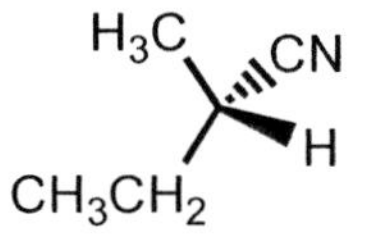

   D)

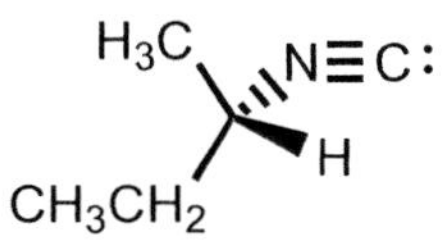

   E)

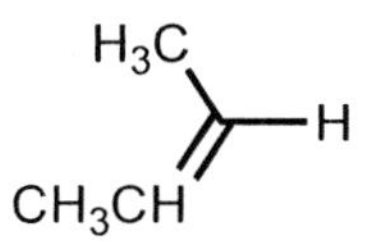

   Ans: C

4. Which of the following would you expect to react fastest with the nucleophile I⁻ (iodide)?

A) $CH_3CH_2CH_2Br$
B) $CH_3CH_2CH_2Cl$
C) $(CH_3)_2CHCH_2Br$
D) $(CH_3)_2CHCH_2Cl$
E) $(CH_3)_3CCH_2Br$

Ans: A

5. Complete the following reaction:

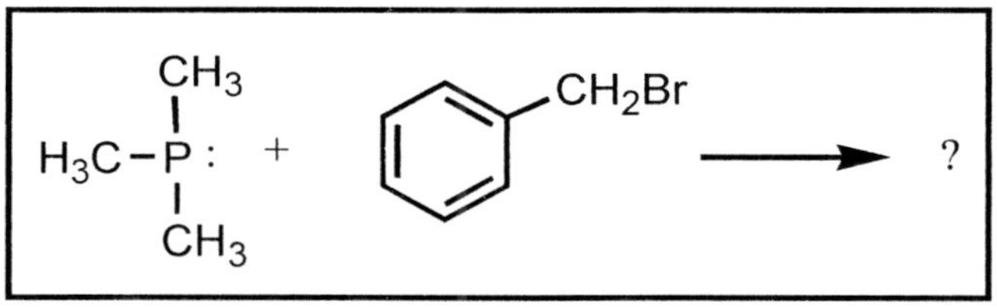

A)

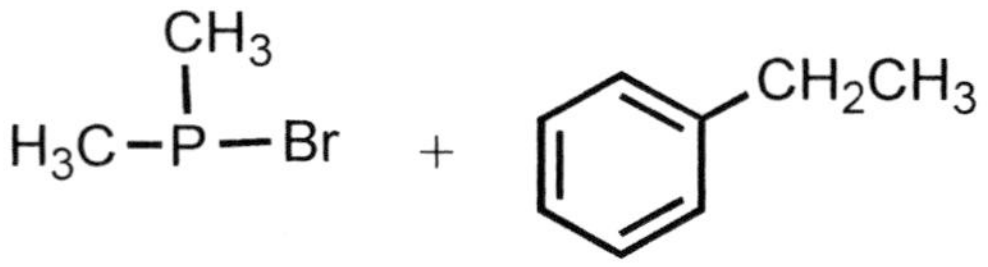

B)

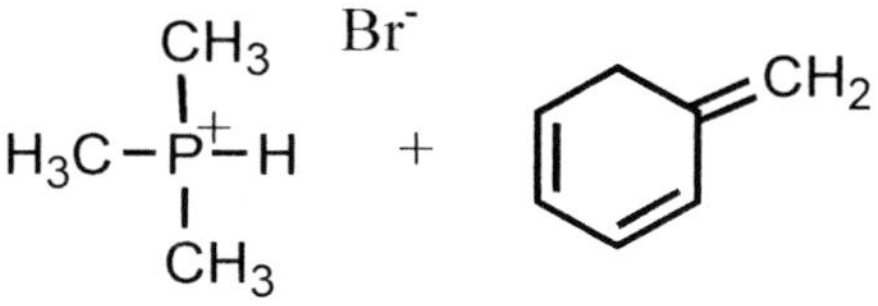

C)

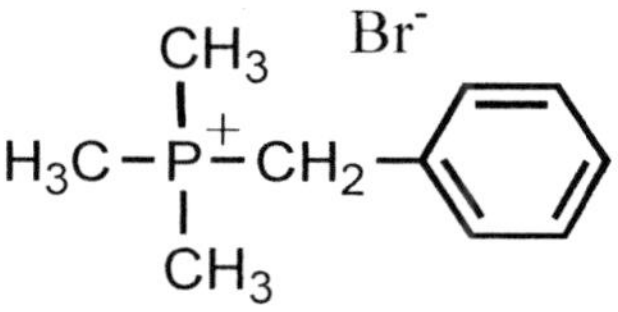

D)

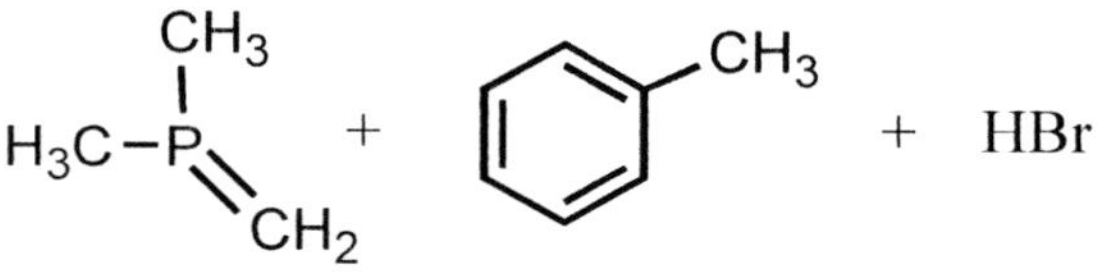

E)   no reaction will occur

Ans: C

6. Which of the following would you expect to have the weakest C-X bond?
A) CH_3Cl B) CH_3CH_2Br C) CH_3F D) CH_3CH_2I E) $(CH_3)_2CHBr$
Ans: D

7. Which of the following haloalkanes would **not** undergo the reaction below?

$$R\text{-}X \ + \ CH_3S^- \ \longrightarrow \ CH_3SR \ + \ X^-$$

A) $(CH_3)_2CHI$ B) CH_3Cl C) $(CH_3)_3CBr$ D) CH_3CH_2Br E) $CH_3CH_2CH_2I$

Ans: C

8. Predict the major product of the following reaction:

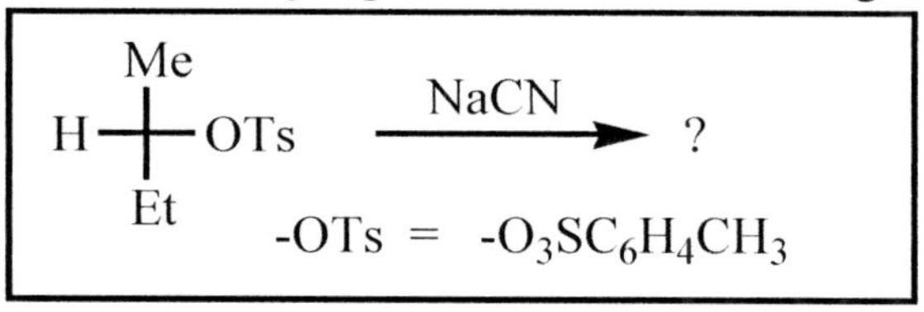

-OTs = -O_3SC_6H_4CH_3

A)

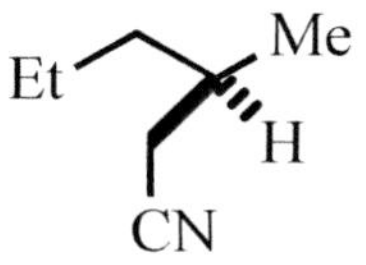

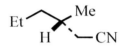

B)

C)

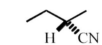

D)

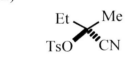

E)

Et   Me
TsO   CN

Ans: C

9. Predict the major product of the following reaction:

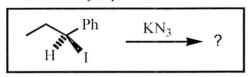

A)

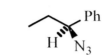

B)

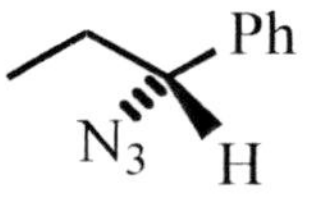

C)

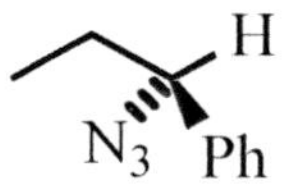

D)

E)   no reaction occurs
Ans: B

10. What is the **major** product of the following two-step reaction?

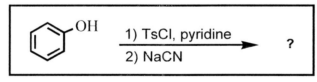

A)

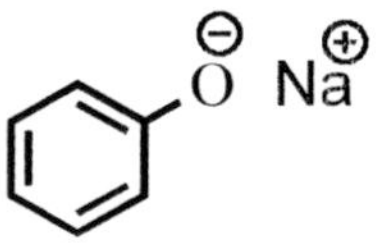

B)

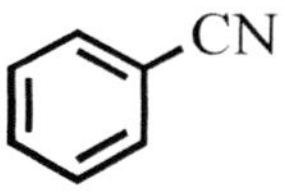

C)

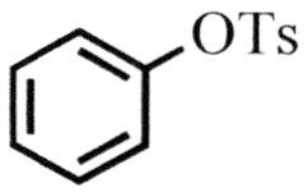

D)

E)   no reaction occurs
Ans: C

11. What is the **major** product of the following reaction:

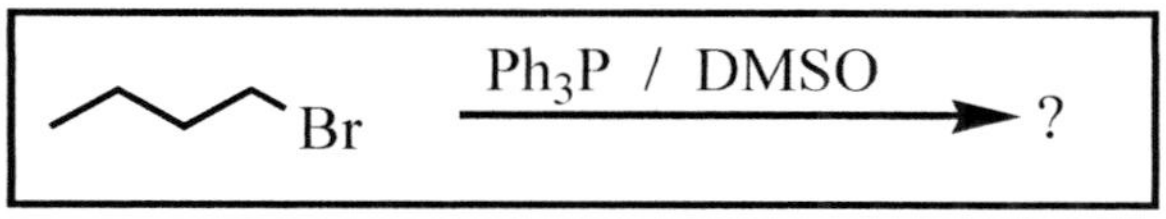

A)

B)

C)

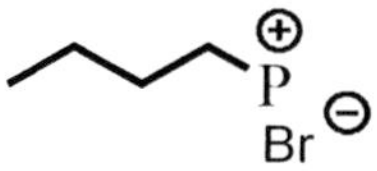

D)

E)   no reaction occurs
Ans: A

12. Indicate the reagents required to achieve the following transformation:

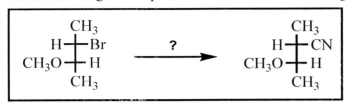

A)

NaCN

B)

1) NaF

2) KCN

C)

1) NaI

2) NaCN

D)

1) NaOMe

2) HCN / light

E)   none of the above

Ans: C

13. What reactants are required to achieve the following transformation?

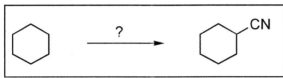

A)

1. PBr$_3$

2. NaCN

B)

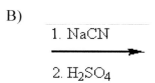

1. NaCN

2. H₂SO₄

C)

1. Br₂, hv

2. HCN

D)

1. SOCl₂

2. KCN

E)

1. Br₂, hv

2. KCN

Ans: E

14. What reactants are required to achieve the following transformation?

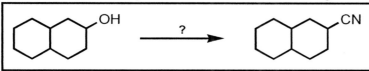

A)

NaCN

B)

1) NaOH

2) KCN

C)

1. 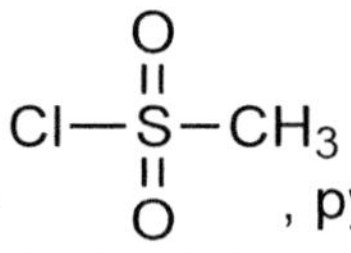 Cl—S—CH₃ , pyridine (with O double-bonded above and below S)

2. KCN

D)

1) Br₂ / light

2) NaCN

E)   none of the above

Ans: C

15. To which side (if any) would the following equilibrium lie?

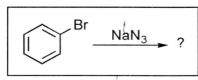

$CH_3CH_2S^-\ K^+\ +\quad HOH\ \rightleftharpoons\quad CH_3CH_2SH\ +\quad KOH$

   A)   to the left
   B)   to the right
   C)   equally to the right and left
   D)   there is no way to tell
   E)   only S_N2, S_N1 and E2 reactions are possible
   Ans: A

16. Several alkyl halides, including iodomethane, are known carcinogens or cancer-suspect materials. To destroy these materials by conversion to non-electrophilic species, you can react them with nucleophiles. Which of the following would be the best for rapidly destroying methyl iodide (iodomethane)?
   A) CH_3OH B) NH_3 C) H_2O D) NaI   E) CH_3CO_2H
   Ans: B

17. Which of the following is **not** normally a good leaving group on carbon?
   A) Br   B) OCH_3 C) Cl   D) OSO_2R E) I
   Ans: B

18. Predict the major product of the following reaction:

A)

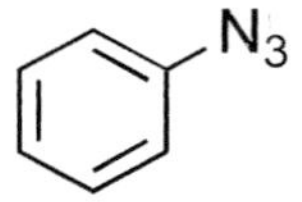

B)

C)

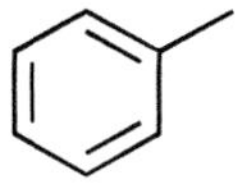

D)

E)   no reaction occurs
Ans: E

19. Which of the following reagents would best accomplish a typical S_N2 reaction?
A) CH_3OH B) H_2O C) HCN   D) KCN   E) KO^tBu
Ans: D

20. What would be the organic product of the following reaction?

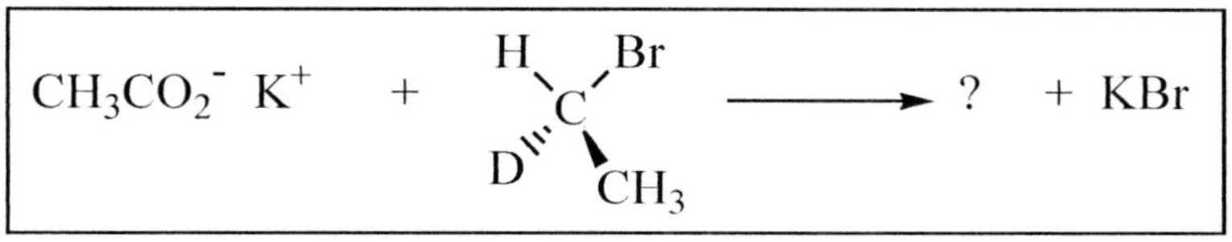

$$CH_3CO_2^- \ K^+ \quad + \quad \underset{D}{\overset{H}{\underset{\diagdown}{C}}}\overset{Br}{\diagup}CH_3 \quad \longrightarrow \quad ? \quad + \ KBr$$

A)

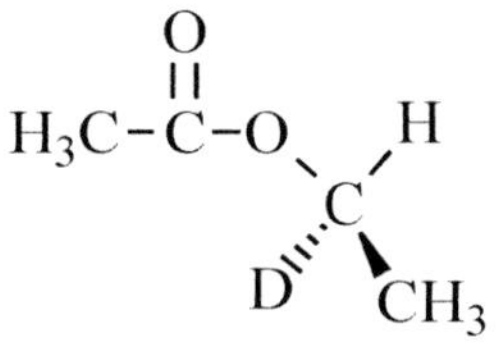

$$\underset{D}{\overset{O}{\underset{\diagup}{H_3C-\overset{\|}{C}-O}}}\overset{H}{\underset{CH_3}{\diagdown C \diagup}}$$

B)

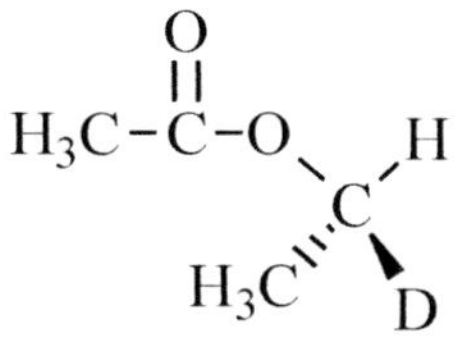

$$H_3C-\overset{O}{\overset{\|}{C}}-O\overset{H}{\underset{H_3C}{\diagdown C \diagup}}D$$

C)

$$\underset{(racemic)}{H_3C-\overset{O}{\overset{\|}{C}}-O}\underset{D}{\overset{H}{\diagup C \diagdown}}CH_3$$

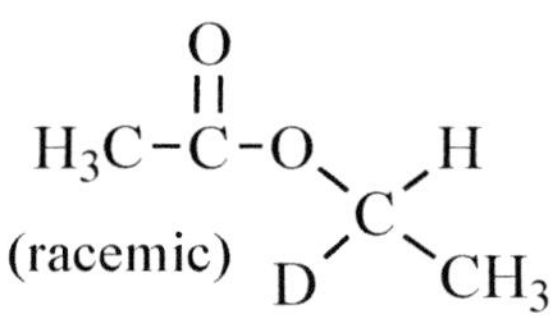

D)   all of the above
E)   none of the above
Ans: A

21. S_N2 substitution at secondary halides and sulfonates is often complicated by competing E2 elimination. Which of the nucleophiles below would you choose to obtain the highest yield in an S_N2 reaction with menthyl bromide?

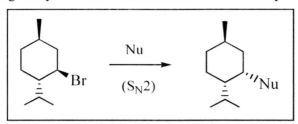

A) CH_3ONa B) CH_3CO_2Na C) $(CH_3)_3N$ D) $(CH_3)_3COK$ E) C_6H_5SNa
Ans: E

22. Arrange the following in order of increasing nucleophilicity.
$^{\ominus}NH_2$ NH_3 $^{\ominus}OH$ H_2O $^{\oplus}NH_4$

A) $^{\oplus}NH_4$ H_2O $^{\ominus}OH$ NH_3 $^{\ominus}NH_2$
B) $^{\oplus}NH_4$ $^{\ominus}OH$ $^{\ominus}NH_2$ H_2O NH_3
C) $^{\ominus}NH_2$ $^{\ominus}OH$ NH_3 H_2O $^{\oplus}NH_4$
D) $^{\oplus}NH_4$ NH_3 H_2O $^{\ominus}NH_2$ $^{\ominus}OH$
E) $^{\oplus}NH_4$ H_2O NH_3 $^{\ominus}OH$ $^{\ominus}NH_2$
Ans: E

23. Which of the haloalkanes shown below would react most rapidly with cyanide ion?

A **B** **C** **D** **E.** none would react with cyanide ion.

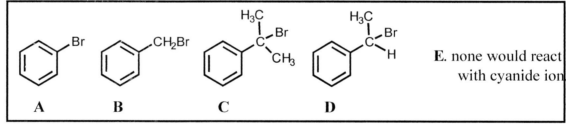

A) A B) B C) C D) D E) E
Ans: B

24. The Walden Inversion (inversion of configuration) is associated with which of the following?
A) E1 reaction
B) free-radical halogenation
C) S_N1 reaction
D) S_N2 reaction
E) none of the above
Ans: D

25. Predict the major product of the following reaction:

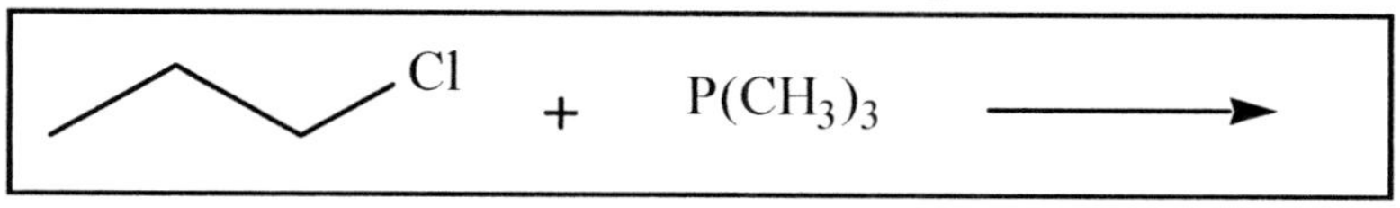

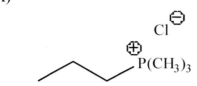

A)

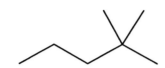

B)

C)

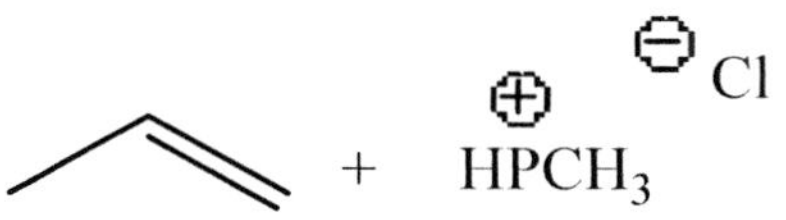

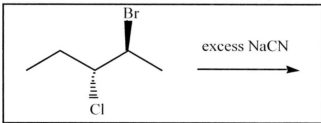

D)

E)   none of the above
Ans: A

26. Which of the following can be used to synthesize (R)-2-cyanopentane from (R)-2-bromopentane?
A)   NaBr   D)   NaCN followed by HI
B)   NaCN   E)   this reaction cannot occur
C)   NaI followed by KCN
Ans: C

27. What is the correct stereochemistry of the product of the following reaction:

A) 3R,4S   B) 2S,3R   C) 2R,3S   D) 2R,3R   E) 3R,4R
Ans: C

28. Which of the following is the best leaving group?

A) $I^{\ominus}$ B) $^{\ominus}NH_2$ C) $HO^{\ominus}$ D) $F^{\ominus}$ E) $CH_3O^{\ominus}$

Ans: A

29. Predict the major product of the following reaction:

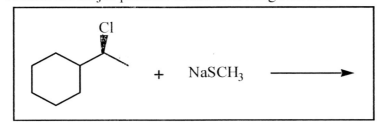

A)

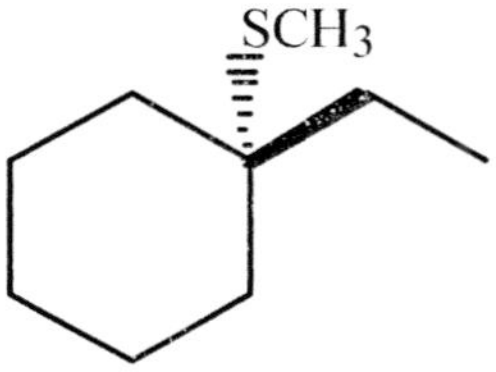

![structure]

B)

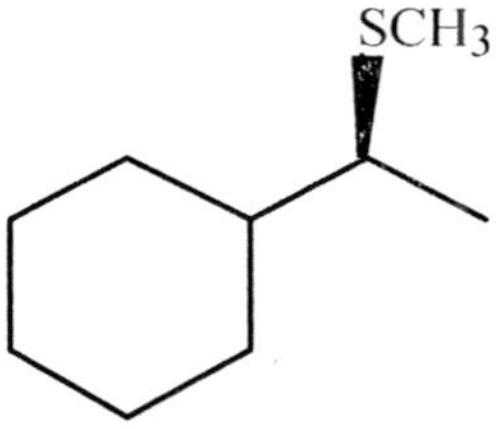

![structure]

C)

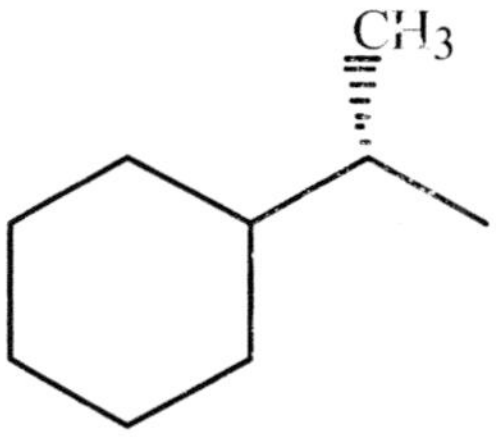

![structure]

D)

![structure]

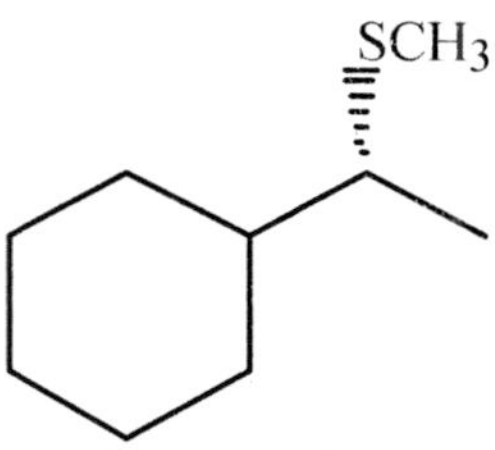

E)   no reaction will occur

Ans: D

30. If the reaction rate of the following reaction is x, doubling the concentration of KCN would give what rate?

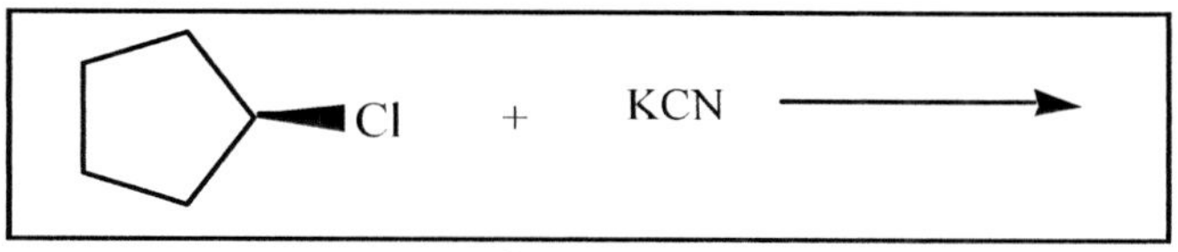

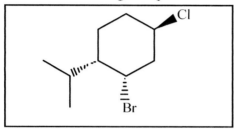

A) $2x$ B) $x/2$ C) x^2 D) $x^2/2$ E) no change in reaction rate

Ans: A

31. Name the following compound:

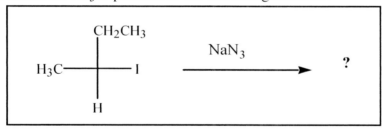

A)   (1S, 2S, 5R)-1-bromo-2-isopropyl-5-chlorocyclohexane
B)   (1R, 2R, 5R)-1-bromo-2-isopropyl-5-chlorocyclohexane
C)   (1S, 3S, 4R)-1-chloro-3-bromo-4-isopropylcyclohexane
D)   (1S, 2S, 4R)-2-bromo-4-chloro-1-isopropylcyclohexane
E)   (1R, 2S, 4R)-2-bromo-4-chloro-1-isopropylcyclohexane

Ans: D

32. Predict the major product of the following reaction:

$$\underset{\text{H}}{\overset{\text{CH}_2\text{CH}_3}{\text{H}_3\text{C}-\overset{|}{\underset{|}{\text{C}}}-\text{I}}} \xrightarrow{\text{NaN}_3} \quad ?$$

A)

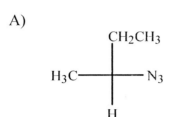

B)

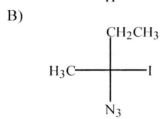

C)

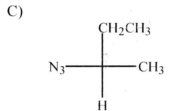

D)

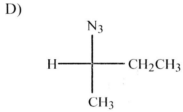

E)   none of the above

Ans: C

33. Which of the following statements best describes why I⁻ is a better nucleophile than F⁻ in solution?
    A)   F⁻ is a stronger base than I⁻.
    B)   Solvation of F⁻ impedes its nucleophilicity compared to I⁻.
    C)   I⁻ is a stronger base than F⁻.
    D)   Solvation of I⁻ increases its nucleophilicty compared to that of F⁻.
    E)   A and B both offer explanations as to why I⁻ is a better nucleophile than F⁻ in solution.

Ans: B

34. The curved arrows below represent what type of reaction mechanism?

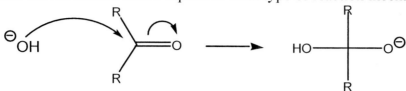

A)   nucleophilic substitution
B)   dissociation
C)   nucleophilic addition

D)   electrophilic addition
E)   none of the above

Ans: C

35. For the following reaction what is the most likely product?

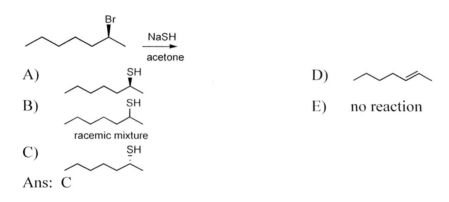

A)

B)

racemic mixture

C)

D)

E)   no reaction

Ans: C

36. Which of the following statements are **true** of an S_N2 reaction.
A)   follow a first order rate law
B)   typically are stereoselective
C)   the fastest step is the rate-determining step
D)   the carbocation intermediate adopts a trigonal planar geometry
E)   all of the above
Ans: B

37. Which set of reagents will best accomplish the following reaction?

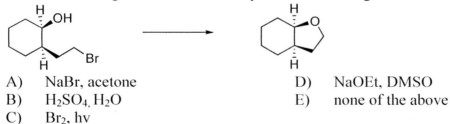

A)   NaBr, acetone
B) H_2SO_4, H_2O
C) Br_2, hv

D)   NaOEt, DMSO
E)   none of the above

Ans: D

38. What is the best way to prepare the compound below?

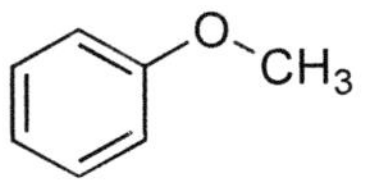

A)

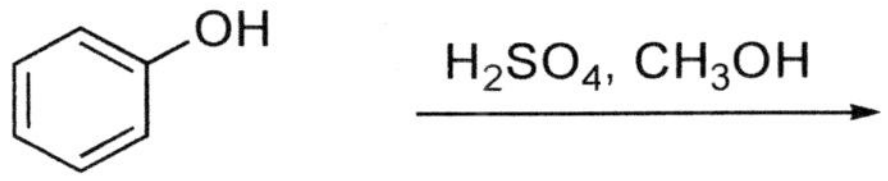

H$_2$SO$_4$, CH$_3$OH →

B)

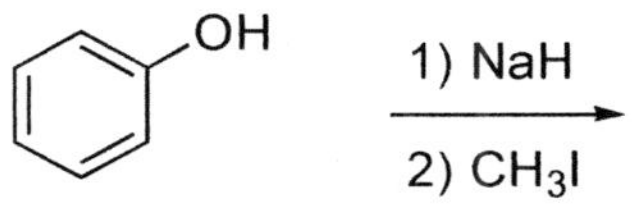

1) NaH
                        2) CH$_3$I

C)

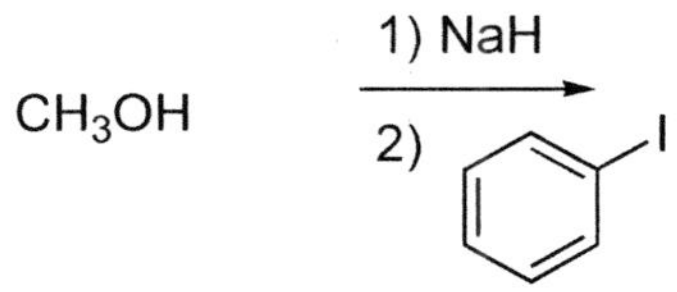

CH$_3$OH   1) NaH
            2)

D)

CH$_3$OH   H$_2$SO$_4$ →

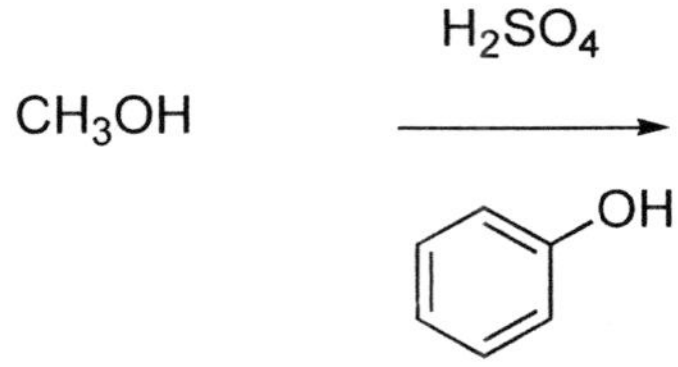

E)   none of the above

Ans: B

Chapter 7: Further Reactions of Haloalkanes: Unimolecular Substitution and Pathways of Elimination

1. Indicate the expected **major** product of the following reaction:

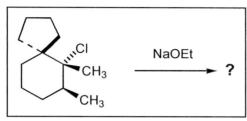

A)

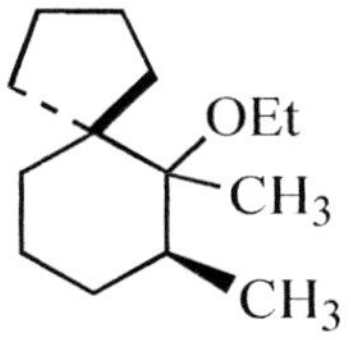

B)

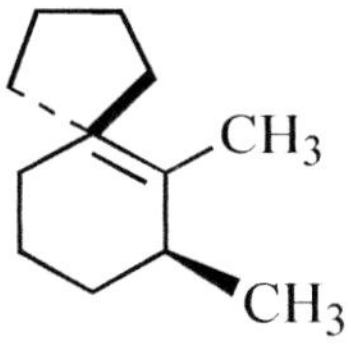

C)

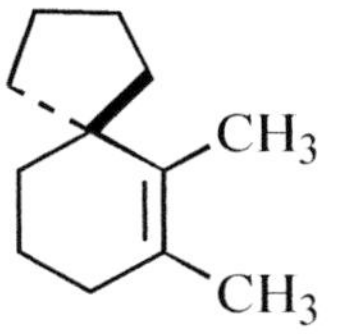

D)

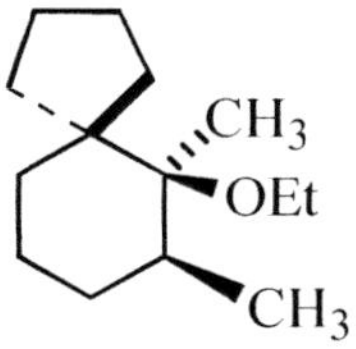

E)

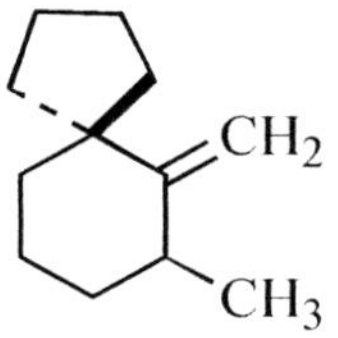

Ans: E

2. Predict the **major** product **if** the following reaction went by the S_N1 pathway:

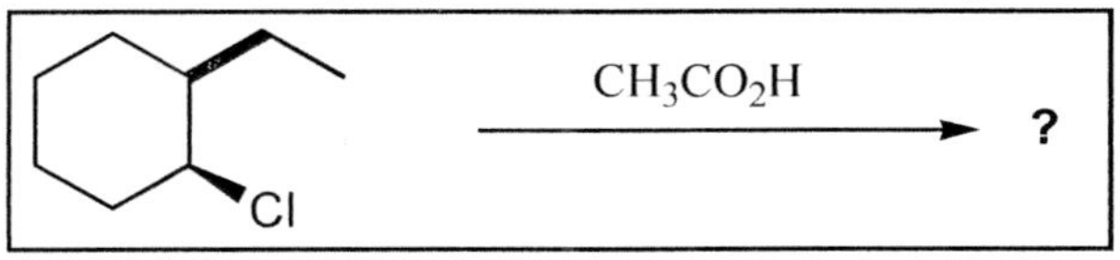

CH$_3$CO$_2$H

?

A)

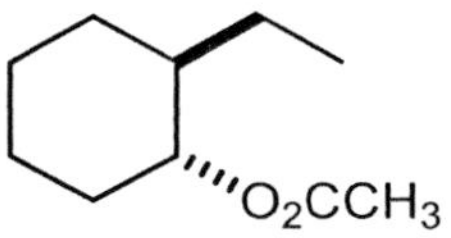

"O$_2$CCH$_3$

B)

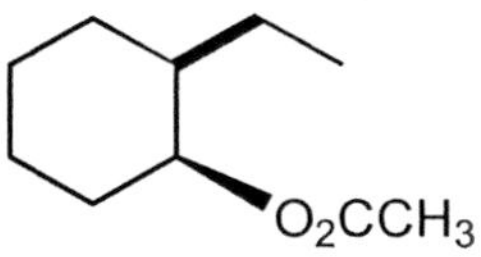

O$_2$CCH$_3$

C)

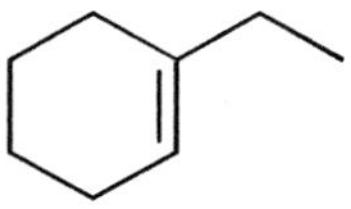

D)

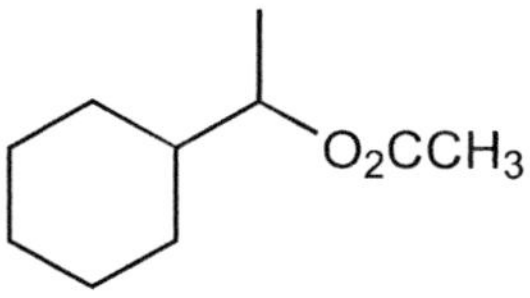

O$_2$CCH$_3$

E)

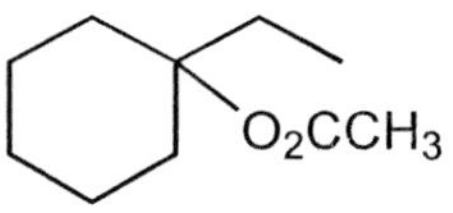

O$_2$CCH$_3$

Ans: E

3. If the concentration of NaOH is doubled in the following reaction, what will happen to the reaction rate?

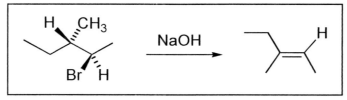

NaOH

A) no change   B) double   C) quadruple   D) cut in half   E) none of the above

Ans: B

4. The **major** product of the following reaction conditions will result from:

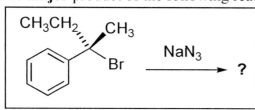

NaN₃ → ?

A) S_N2   B) S_N1   C) E2   D) E1   E) there is no way to know
Ans: C

5. Which of the following is the **least** nucleophilic base?
A)   (CH₃CH₂)₃N
B)

C)

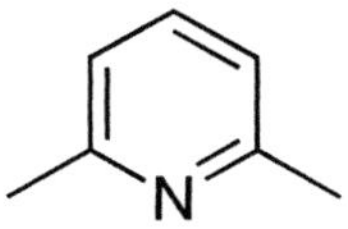

D)

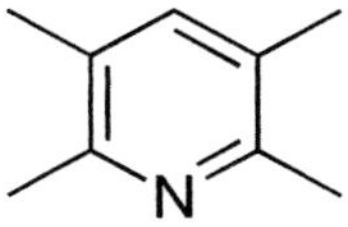

E)

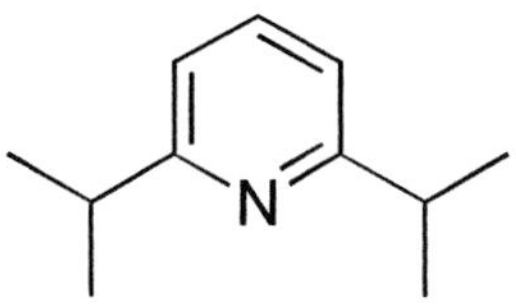

Ans: E

6. To which side, if any, would the following equilibrium lie? (Do **not** consider any further reactions here.)

A)   to the left   D)   there is no way to tell
B)   to the right   E)   this reaction cannot occur at all
C)   equally to the right and left
Ans: A

7. What would be the **major** organic product of the following reaction?

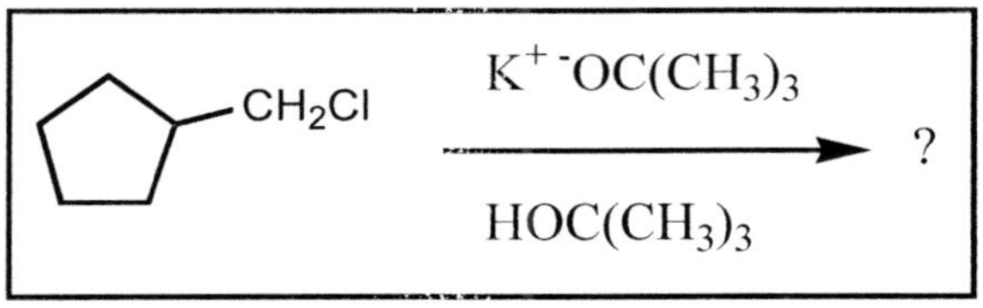

$$K^+ \, ^-OC(CH_3)_3$$

$CH_2Cl \xrightarrow{\hspace{3cm}} \; ?$

$$HOC(CH_3)_3$$

A)

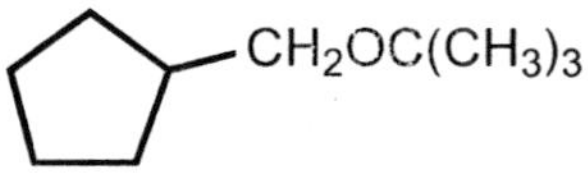

$CH_2OC(CH_3)_3$

B)

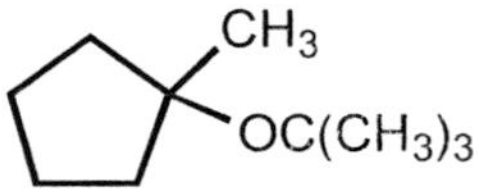

CH_3

$OC(CH_3)_3$

C)

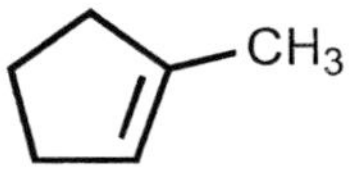

CH_3

D)

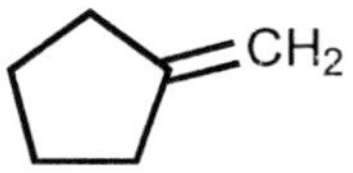

CH_2

E)

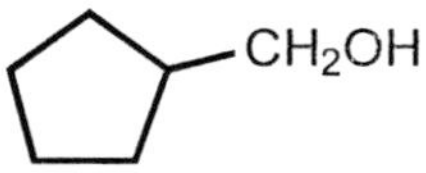

CH_2OH

Ans: D

8. What would be the **major** organic product of the following reaction?

CH_3

CD_3

C

Br

$\xrightarrow{CH_3O^- \, Na^+} \; ?$

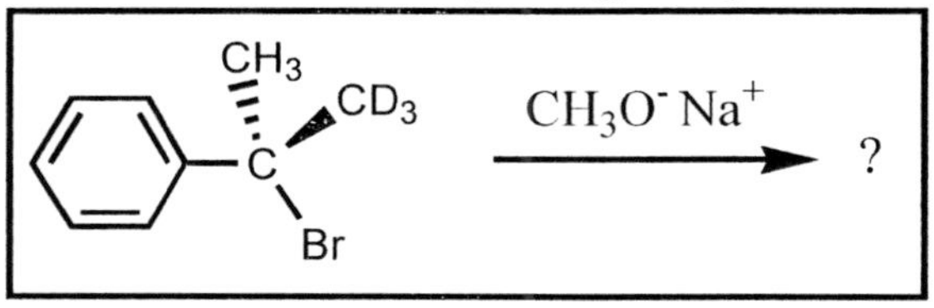

A)

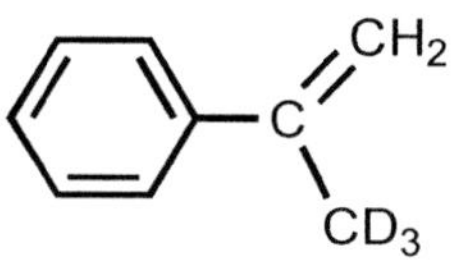

B)

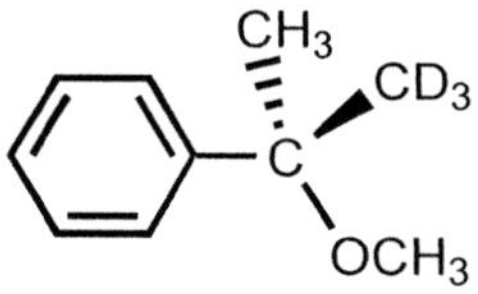

C)

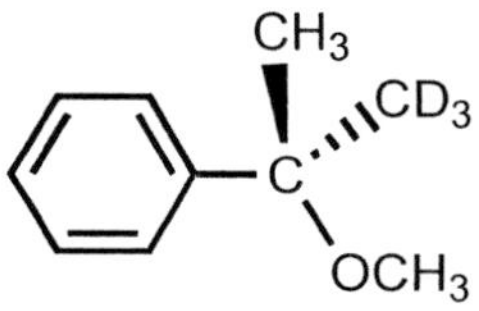

D)

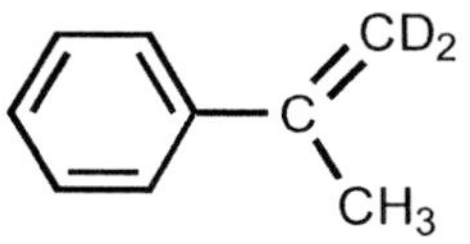

E)

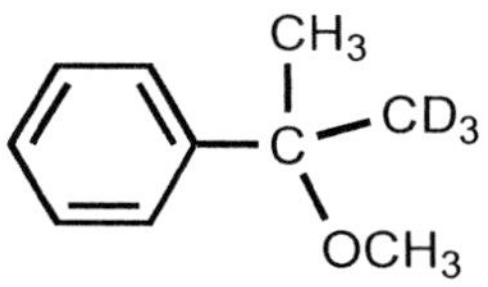

(racemic)

Ans: A

9. Which would be true of the following reactions?

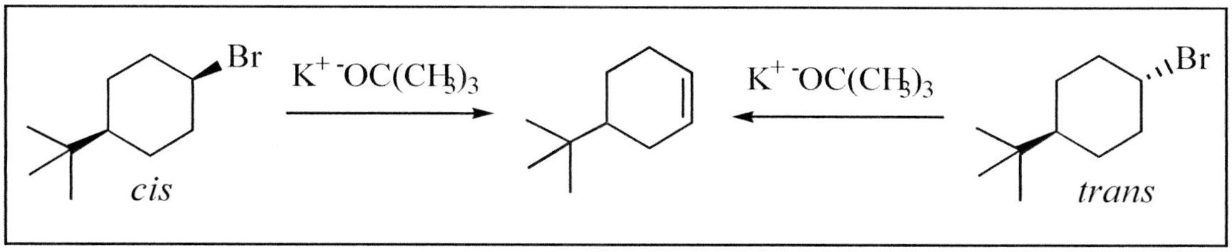

A)   *cis* would react faster
B)   *trans* would react faster
C)   *cis* and *trans* would react at the same rates
D)   no reaction is expected under these conditions
E)   the product shown would not be formed
Ans: A

10. What **major** product would result for the following reaction?

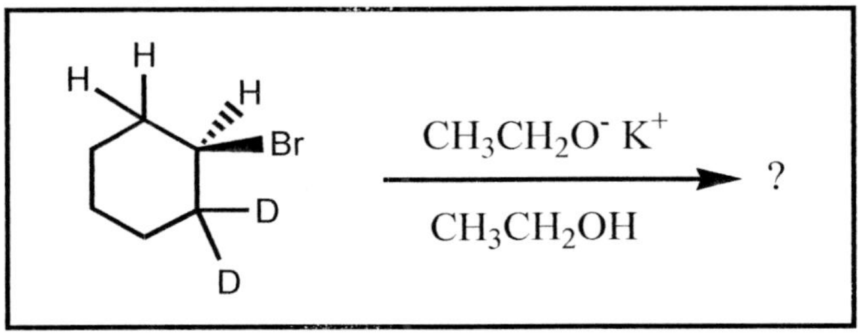

A)

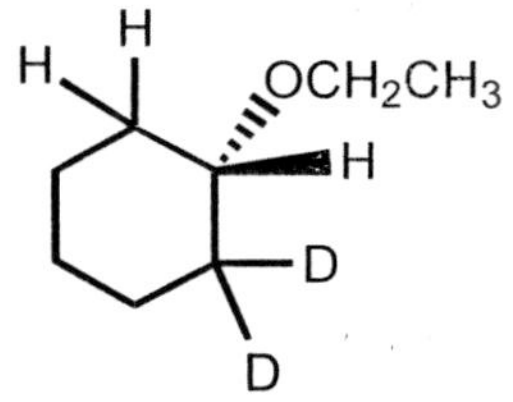

B)

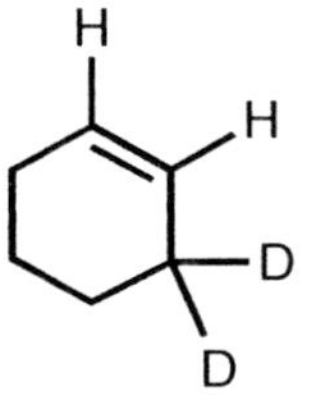

C)

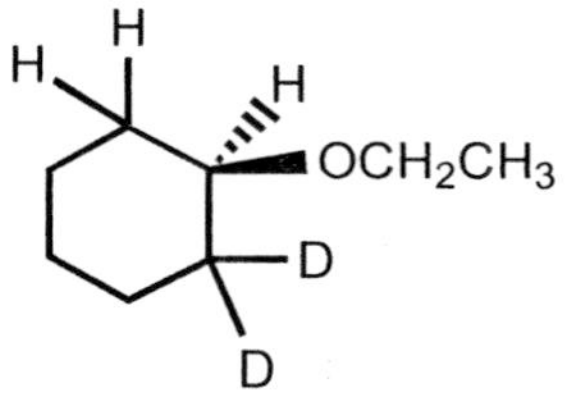

D)

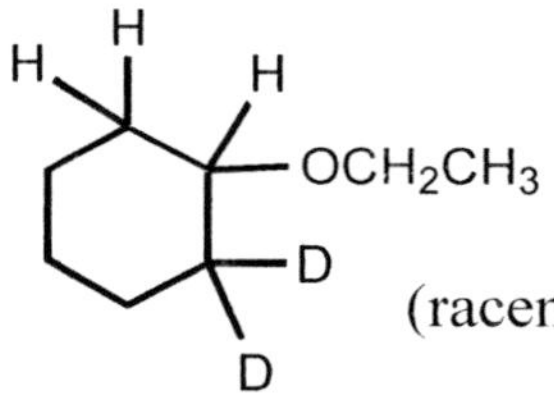

(racemic)

E)

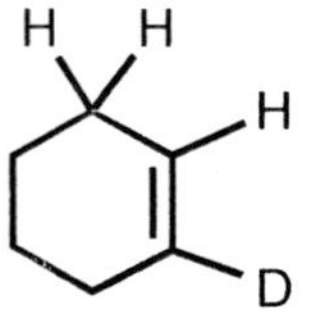

Ans: B

11. Which of the haloalkanes below would you expect to most rapidly undergo the reaction shown?

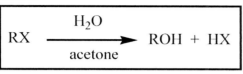

A) CH_3CH_2Br
B) CH_3Br
C) $(CH_3)_3CBr$
D) $CH_3CHBrCH_3$
E)

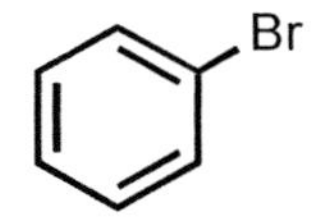

Ans: C

12. Which of the bases below would be best to accomplish the following reaction?

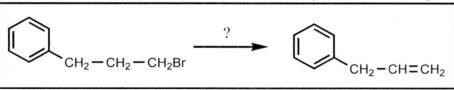

A) $CH_3O^- Na^+$ D) $(CH_3)_3CO^- Na^+$
B) $CH_3CH_2O^- Na^+$ E) $Na^+ {}^-OH$
C) $(CH_3)_2CHO^- Na^+$

Ans: D

13. What would be the major product of the following reaction?

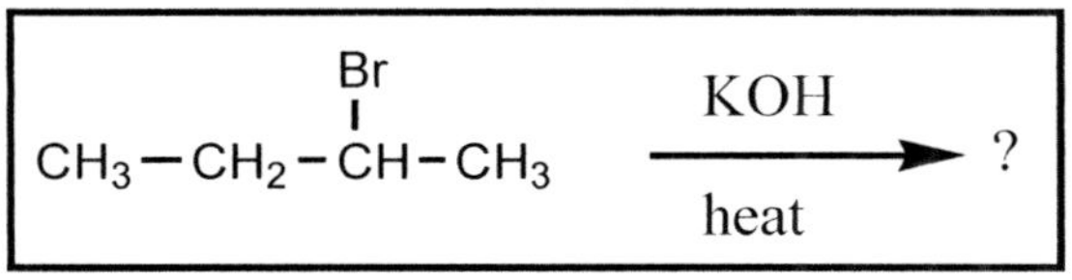

Br
|
$CH_3-CH_2-CH-CH_3$ →KOH, heat→ ?

A)

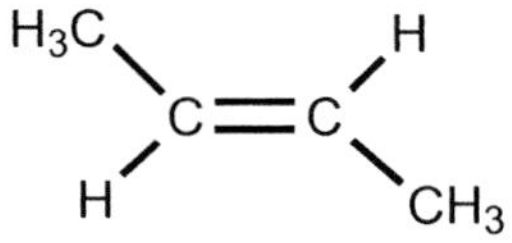

H3C   H
  \   /
   C == C
  /   \
 H   CH3

B)

$$\underset{\displaystyle CH_3-CH_2-\underset{\displaystyle OH}{\overset{\displaystyle |}{CH}}-CH_3}{}$$

C)

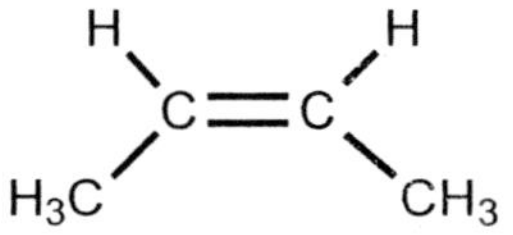

D) $CH_3-CH_2-CH\!\equiv\!CH_2$

E)

$$\underset{\displaystyle CH_3-CH_2-\overset{\displaystyle O}{\overset{\displaystyle \|}{C}}-CH_3}{}$$

Ans: A

14. Which of the following molecules will readily undergo an elimination reaction when treated with NaOCH$_3$?

A)

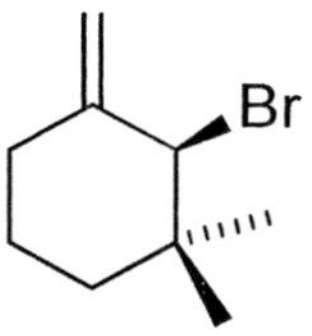

B)

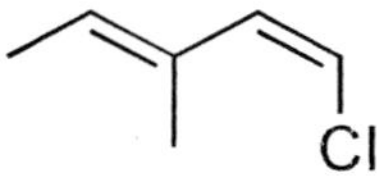

C)

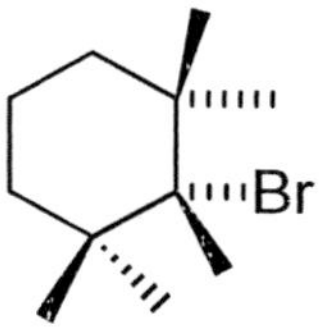

D)

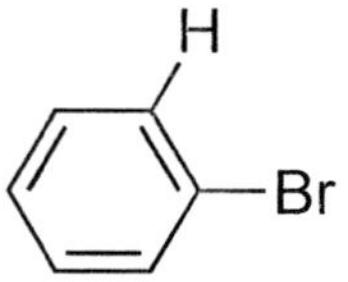

E)   none of the above

Ans: C

15. Which mechanism proceeds with inversion of configuration?
    A)   bimolecular elimination (E2)   D)   bimolecular substitution (S$_N$2)
    B)   unimolecular elimination (E1)   E)   free-radical halogenation
    C)   unimolecular substitution (S$_N$1)
    Ans: D

16. Which of the cyclohexyl bromides would you expect to react the **fastest** in the following reaction?

    alkyl bromide $\xrightarrow[\text{CH}_3\text{OH}]{\text{CH}_3\text{O}^-\ \text{Na}^+}$?

    A)
    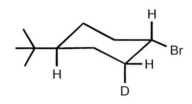

    B)
    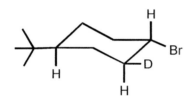

    C)
    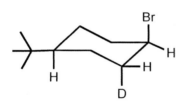

    D)
    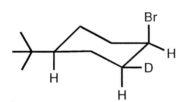

    E)   all would react at the same rate
    Ans: D

17. Predict the **major** product of the following S_N1 reaction:

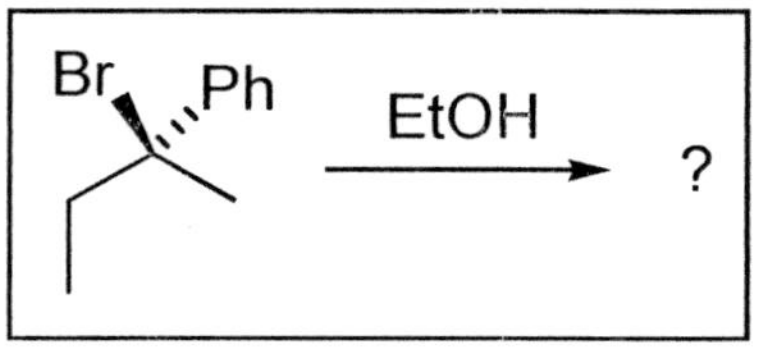

Br,,,Ph

EtOH ⟶ ?

A)

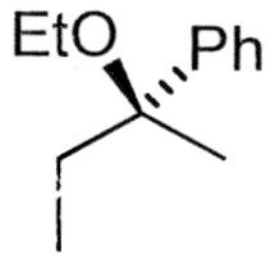

EtO ,,,Ph

B)

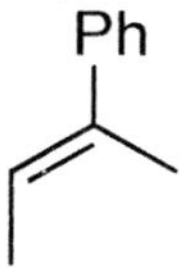

Ph

C)

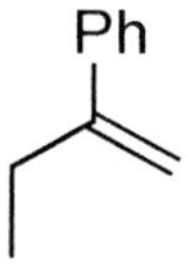

Ph

D)

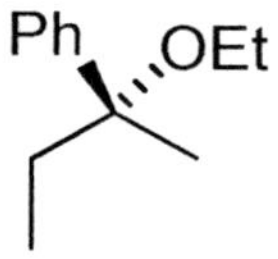

Ph ,,,OEt

E)

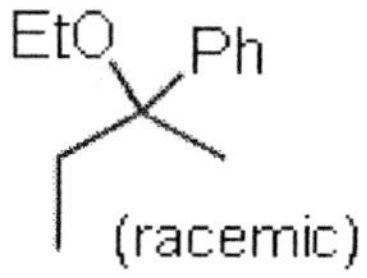

EtO Ph

(racemic)

Ans: E

18. Which of the following deuterated isomers of 3-bromo-2,2-dimethylpentane would undergo E2 elimination most slowly?

A)

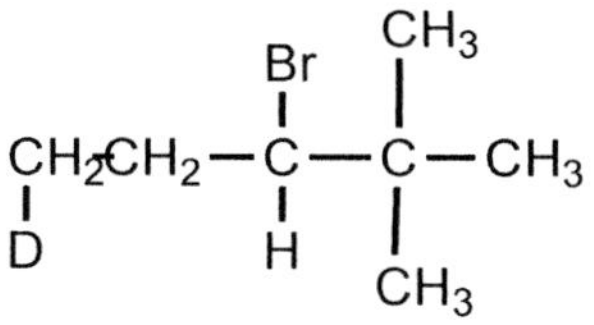

B)

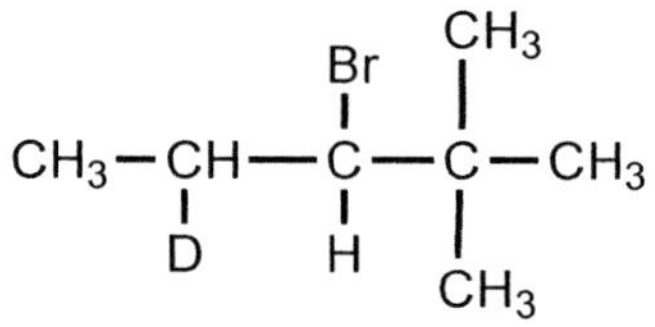

C)

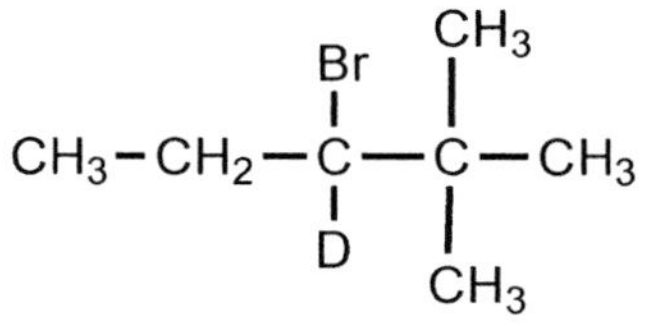

D)

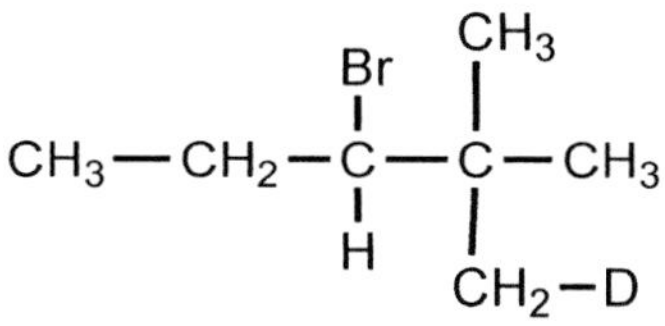

E)   all react at same rate

Ans: B

19. Which one of the following would undergo E2 elimination most rapidly?

A)

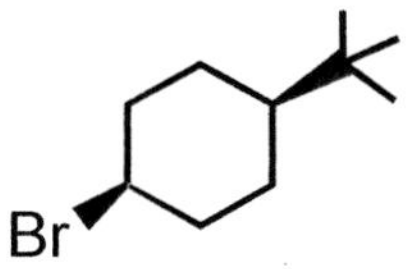

B)

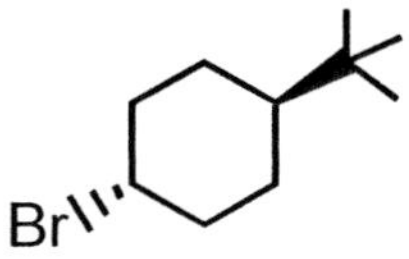

C)

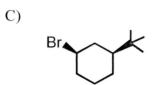

D)

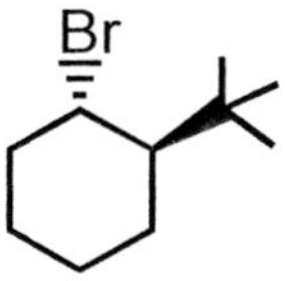

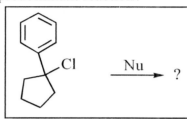

E)   All would react at the same rate

Ans: A

20. Which of the nucleophiles shown below would **not** cause an E2 elimination as the predominant reaction?

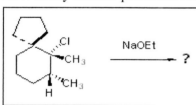

A) N_3^- B) CH_3CH_2OH C) ^-CN D) ^-OH E) CH_3O^-

Ans: B

21. How many alkene products are possible in the following reaction?

A) None; cannot eliminate   B) One   C) Two   D) Three   E) Four

Ans: C

22. Predict the product of the following reaction.

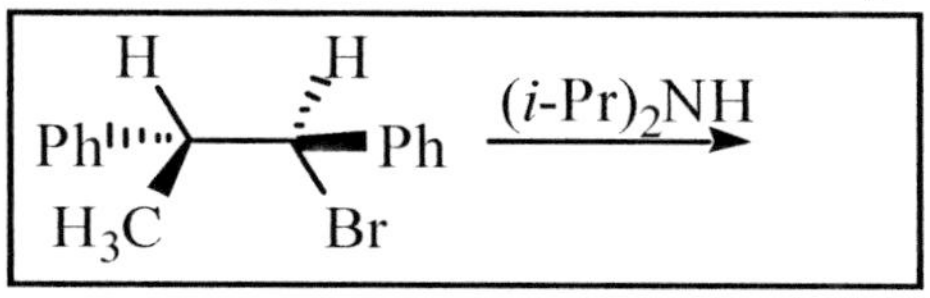

A)

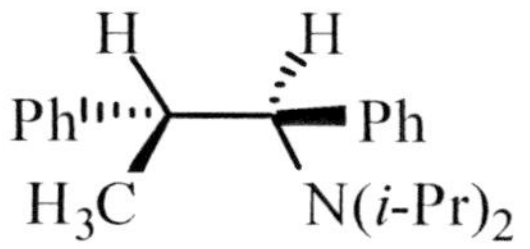

B)

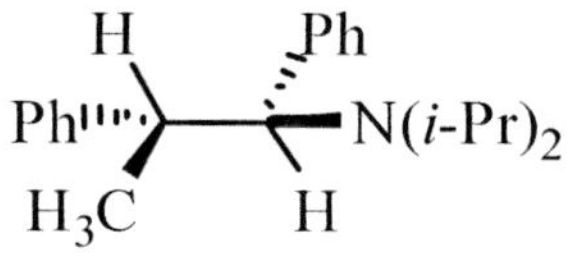

C)

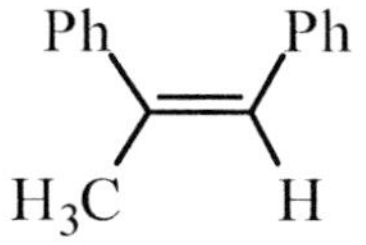

D)

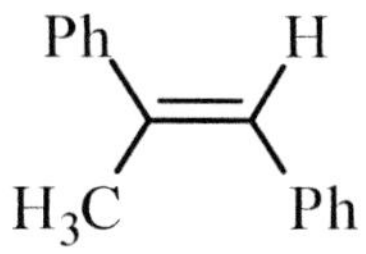

E)   no reaction

Ans: D

23. Solvolysis of 2-bromo-2-methylpropane occurs through what mechanism?
    A) S_N2 B) E1   C) E2   D) S_N1 E) A and C
    Ans: D

24. Predict the **major** product of the following reaction:

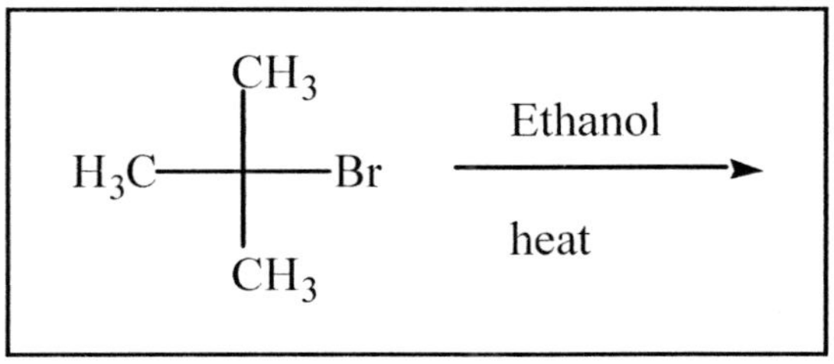

CH$_3$

H$_3$C———Br   Ethanol

CH$_3$ heat ⟶

A)

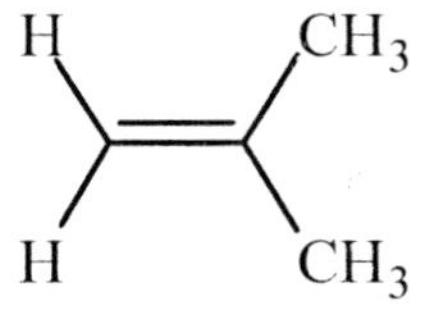

H   CH$_3$

H   CH$_3$

B)

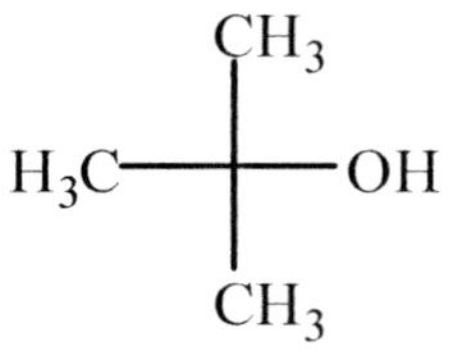

CH$_3$

H$_3$C———OH

CH$_3$

C)

CH$_3$

H$_3$C———OEt

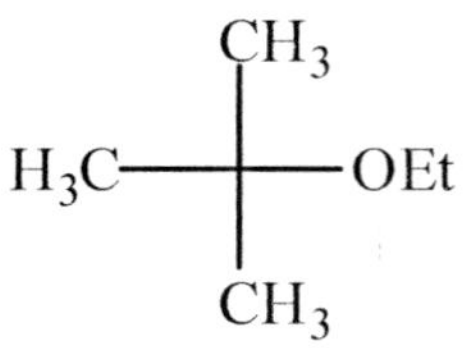

CH$_3$

D)

H$_3$C—CH=CH—CH$_3$

E)

CH$_3$

H$_3$C———H

CH$_2$OEt

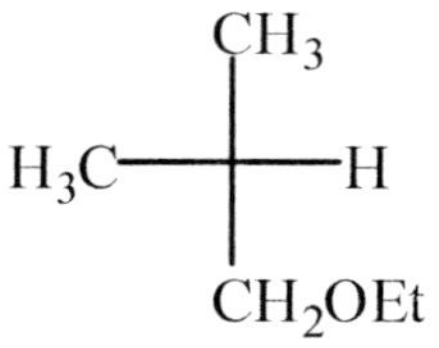

Ans: C

25. (S)-1-bromo-1-fluoroethane reacts with NaOMe to give:

$$H_3C\text{—}CHBrF \xrightarrow{\text{1 Eq. NaOMe}}$$

A)

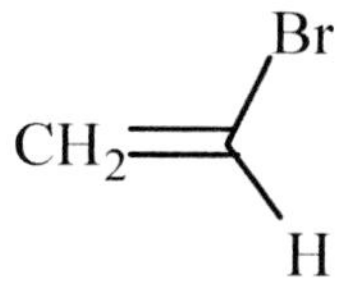

B)

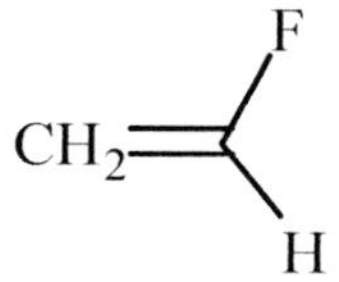

C)   CH₃CHFOCH₃
D)   CH₃CHBrOCH₃
E)   CH₃CH(OCH₃)₂
Ans: C

26. Predict the product of reaction of the following deuterated compound.

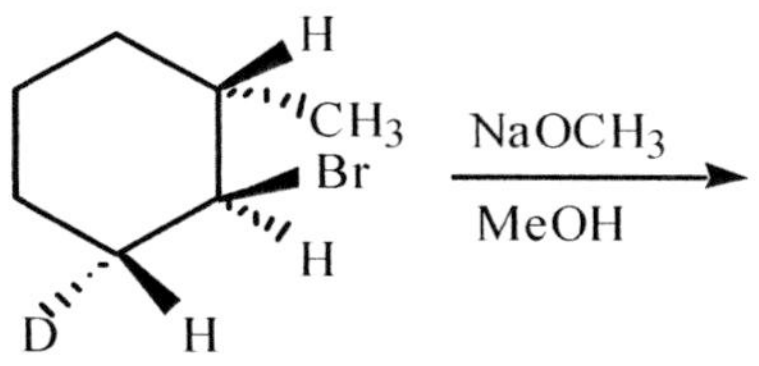

A)

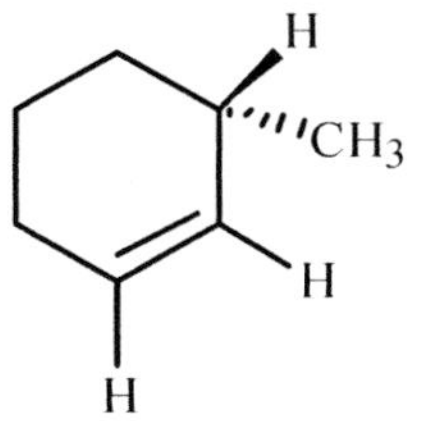

B)

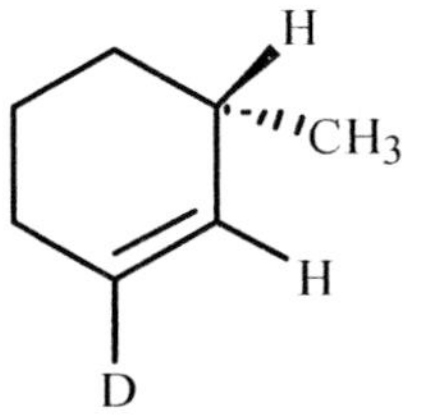

C)

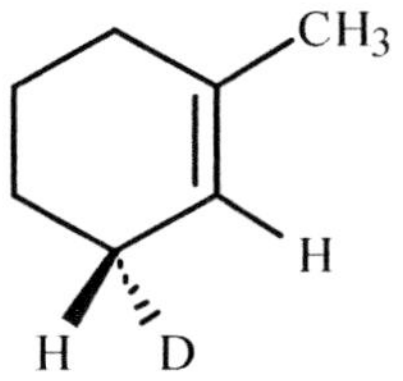

D)

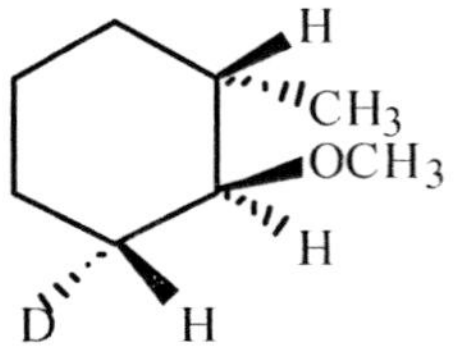

E)

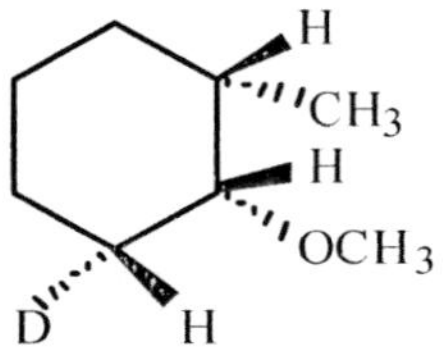

Ans: A

27. Rank the following carbocations according to their increasing stability.

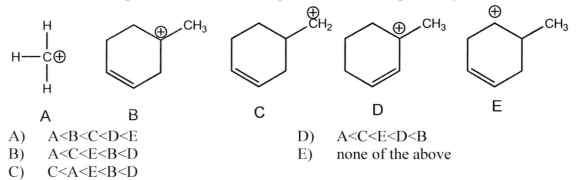

A B C D E

A) A<B<C<D<E
B) A<C<E<B<D
C) C<A<E<B<D
Ans: B

D) A<C<E<D<B
E) none of the above

28. Rank the following according to their increasing reactivity with water.
    CH_3CH_2Br CH_3Br $(CH_3)_3CBr$ $(CH_3)_2CHBr$

    A) $CH_3Br < CH_3CH_2Br < (CH_3)_3CBr < (CH_3)_2CHBr$
    B) $CH_3Br < CH_3CH_2Br < (CH_3)_2CHBr < (CH_3)_3CBr$
    C) $(CH_3)_3CBr < (CH_3)_2CHBr < CH_3CH_2Br < CH_3Br$
    D)   All of these will react with water at the same rate.
    E)   None of the above will react with water.

    Ans: B

29. For the transformation below, give the structure of the starting material.

    A)

    B)

    C)

    D)

    E)

    Ans: D

30. For the transformation below, give the structure of the starting material.

$$? \xrightarrow[\text{HOCH}_3]{\text{NaOCH}_3} \quad$$

A)

Br

B)

Br

C)

Br

D)

Br
Br

E)   Both B and C will provide the product shown
Ans: E

31. For the transformation of norepinephrine to epinephrine (adrenaline), what is the likely mechanism?

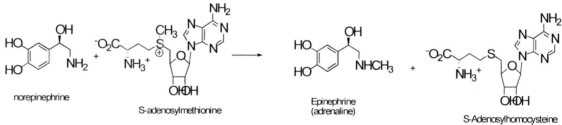

norepinephrine   S-adenosylmethionine   →   Epinephrine (adrenaline)   +   S-Adenosylhomocysteine

A) S_N1 B) S_N2 C) E1   D) E2   E) both A and B are likely
Ans: B

Chapter 8: Hydroxy Functional Group: Alcohols: Properties, Preparation, and Strategy of Synthesis

1. To which side, if any, would the following equilibrium lie?

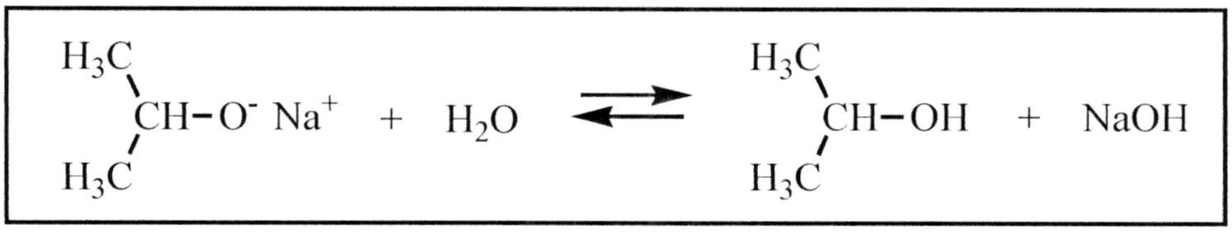

$$\underset{H_3C}{\overset{H_3C}{>}}CH-O^-\ Na^+ \ + \ H_2O \ \rightleftharpoons \ \underset{H_3C}{\overset{H_3C}{>}}CH-OH \ + \ NaOH$$

A)   to the left
B)   to the right
C)   equally to the right and left

D)   there is no way to tell
E)   this reaction cannot occur at all

Ans: B

2. What would be the name of the following compound?

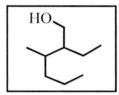

A)   3-hydroxymethyl-4-methylheptane
B)   2-*sec*-butyl-1-butanol
C)   2-ethyl-3-methyl-1-hexanol

D)   2-ethyl-3-propyl-1-butanol
E)   2-(*sec*-pentyl)-1-butanol

Ans: C

3. What would be the expected product(s) of the following reactions?

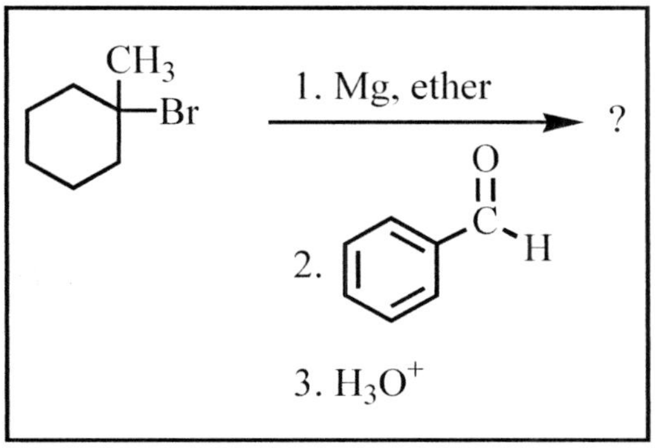

$$
\begin{array}{c}
\text{cyclohexane with } CH_3 \text{ and } Br \\
\xrightarrow[\substack{2.\ \text{benzaldehyde} \\ 3.\ H_3O^+}]{1.\ \text{Mg, ether}} \ ?
\end{array}
$$

A)

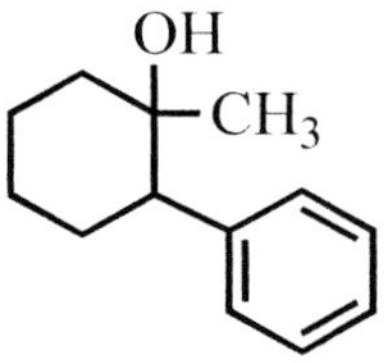

cyclohexane with OH and CH₃ and phenyl substituents

B)

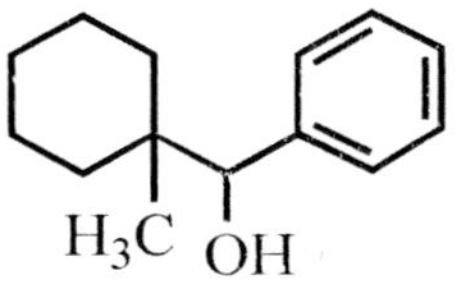

C)

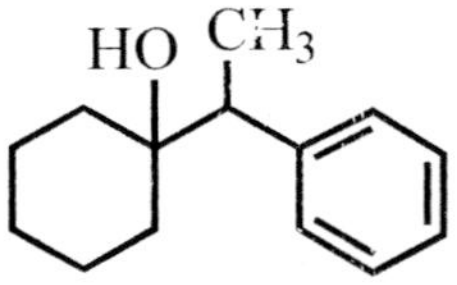

D)

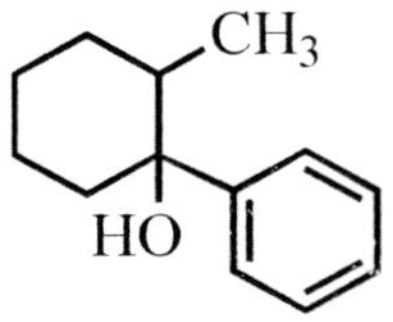

E)

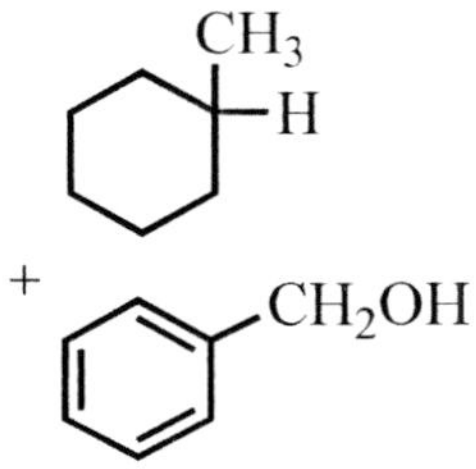

Ans: B

4. What would be the major organic product of the following reaction?

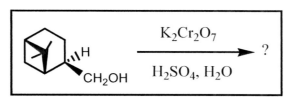

A)

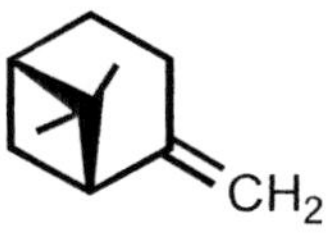

B)

C)

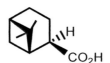

D)

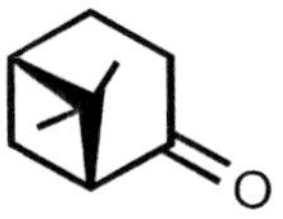

E)

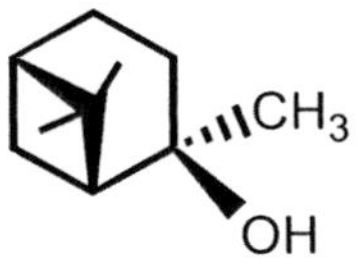

Ans: C

5. What would be the expected product(s) of the following reactions?

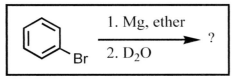

A) C_6H_5OH B) C_6H_5D C) C_6H_5OD D) C_6H_6 E) both A and C
Ans: B

6. Which of the following reactions would produce the alcohol shown?

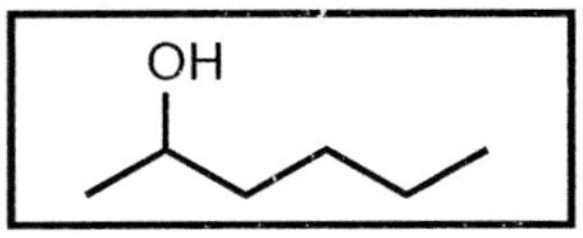

OH

A)

$$CH_3I \xrightarrow{\begin{array}{l}1.\ Mg,\ ether\\ 2.\ CH_3CH_2CH_2CH_2CHO\\ 3.\ H_3O^+\end{array}} ?$$

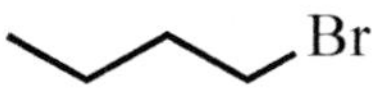

B)

Br $\xrightarrow{\begin{array}{l}1.\ Mg,\ ether\\ 2.\ CH_3CHO\\ 3.\ H_3O^+\end{array}}$?

C)

$$CH_3CH_2CH_2CH_2-\overset{\overset{\displaystyle O}{\|}}{C}-CH_3 \xrightarrow[CH_3OH]{NaBH_4} ?$$

D)   all of these
E)   none of these
Ans: D

7. Which of the following would be the **least** miscible with (= least soluble in) water?
   A) $H_3C-CH_2-CH_2-CH_2-OH$
   B)

$H_3C-CH_2-\underset{\underset{\displaystyle CH_3}{|}}{CH}-OH$

   C)

$H_3C-\underset{\underset{\displaystyle |}{|}}{\overset{\overset{\displaystyle CH_3}{|}}{CH}}-CH_2-OH$

   D)

$H_3C-\underset{\underset{\displaystyle CH_3}{|}}{\overset{\overset{\displaystyle CH_3}{|}}{C}}-OH$

   E)   all have equal water solubility
   Ans: A

8. Which of the following reagents would accomplish the reaction shown?

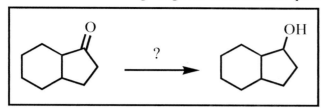

A) H_2SO_4, H_2O D) HO^-, H_2O
B) H_2CrO_4 E)   none of the above
C) O_2 (slow)

Ans: E

9. Which of the sequences below would accomplish the following transformation?

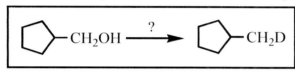

A)

      1. HBr

      2. $NaBD_4$, CH_3OH

B)

      1. PBr_3

      2. Mg, ether
      3. D_2O

C)

      D_2SO_4

D)

      1. $LiAlD_4$

      2. H_3O^+

E)

      1. H_2SO_4

      2. D_2, catalyst

Ans: B

10. Which of the following five-carbon alcohols would you expect to be the **most** soluble in water?

A) $CH_3-CH_2-CH_2-CH_2-CH_2OH$

B)

$$\underset{\displaystyle CH_3-CH_2-CH_2-\overset{\textstyle OH}{\overset{|}{C}H}-CH_3}{}$$

C)

$$CH_3-CH_2-\overset{\textstyle OH}{\overset{|}{C}H}-CH_2-CH_3$$

D)

$$CH_3-CH_2-\underset{\underset{\textstyle CH_3}{|}}{C}H-CH_2OH$$

E)

$$CH_3-\underset{\underset{\textstyle CH_3}{|}}{\overset{\overset{\textstyle CH_3}{|}}{C}}-CH_2OH$$

Ans: E

11. What reagent(s) would accomplish the following transformation?

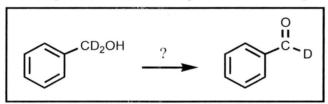

A)   Pyridinium chlorochromate   D)   Potassium dichromate
B)   LiAlD$_4$ then H$_3$O$^+$ E)   H$_2$SO$_4$
C)   H$_2$CrO$_4$
Ans: A

12. Which statement about the preparation of Grignard reagents is **not** true?

$$RX + Mg \longrightarrow RMgX$$

A)   The reaction must be done in an ether solvent.
B)   The reagent should be protected from air.
C)   Methyl, primary, secondary, tertiary and aryl halides may be used.
D)   Rearrangement may accompany Grignard formation.
E)   The halogen may be chloride, bromide, or iodide.
Ans: D

13. Predict the product of the following reaction:

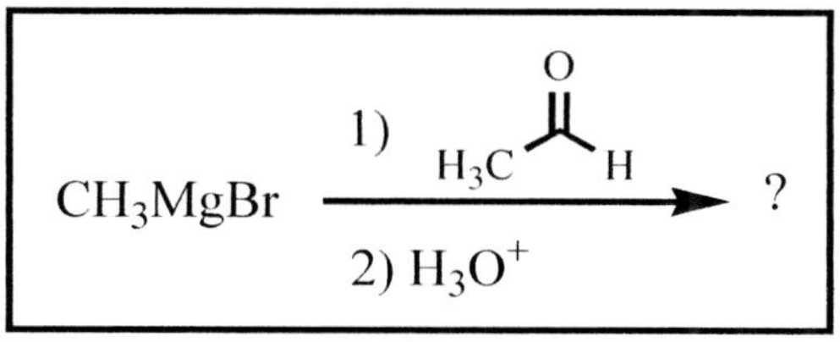

$$CH_3MgBr \xrightarrow[\text{2) } H_3O^+]{\text{1) } H_3C \overset{O}{\overset{\|}{C}} H} \quad ?$$

A)

B)

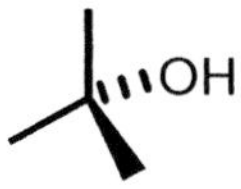

C)

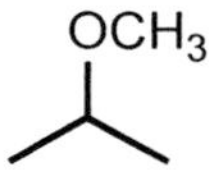

D)

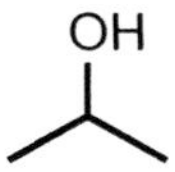

E)

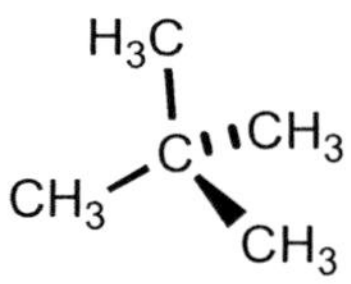

Ans: D

14. Grignard reagents are prepared in ether solvents because:
    A)   THF and diethyl ether will dissolve the Mg metal.
    B)   Ether solvents stabilize the Grignard reagent by coordination to the organomagnesium.
    C)   Ether solvents stabilize magnesium metal by forming a covalent bond.
    D)   Ethers have many acidic protons.
    E)   Ether solvents keep water away from the reaction.
    Ans: B

15. Which is the correct structure for the following IUPAC name?

(2S) - 2-(hydroxymethyl)-4,4-dimethylcyclohexanone

A)

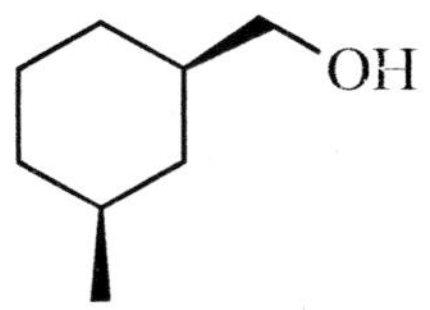

B)

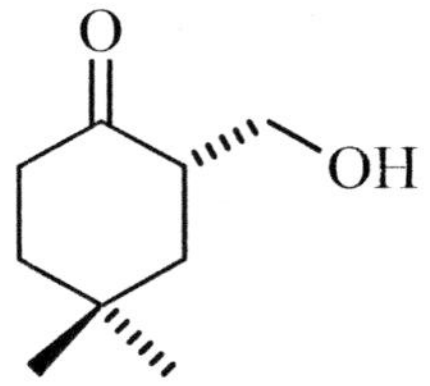

C)

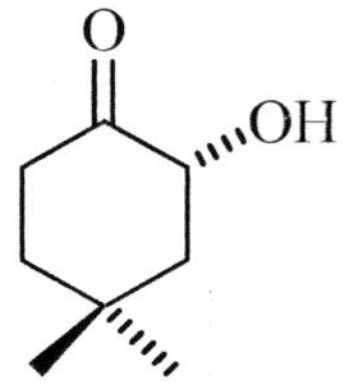

D)

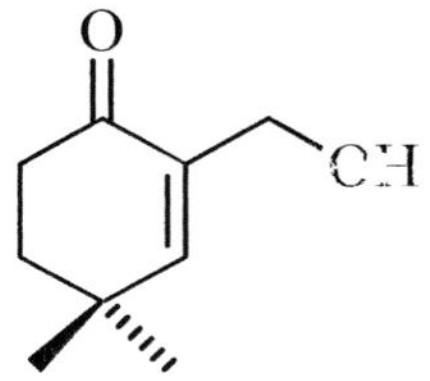

E)

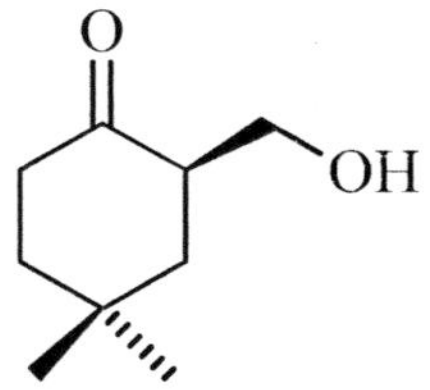

Ans: B

16. What is the **major** product of the following reaction?

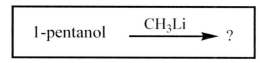

A)

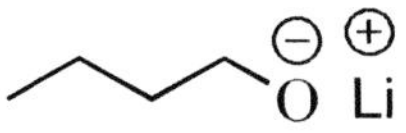

B)

C)

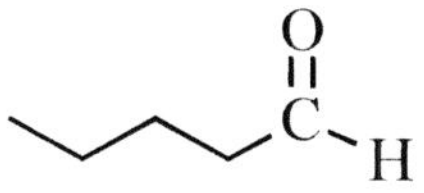

D)

E)

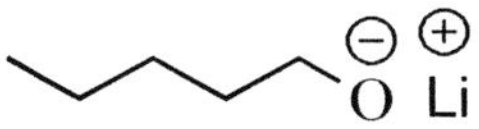

Ans: E

17. What is the expected product of the following reaction?

$CH_3CH_2CH_2CH_2Cl$ ———→ ?

1. HO^- , H_2O
2. PCC, CH_2Cl_2
3. 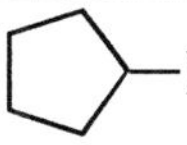 ⬠—Li^- , Et_2O
4. H_3O^+

A)

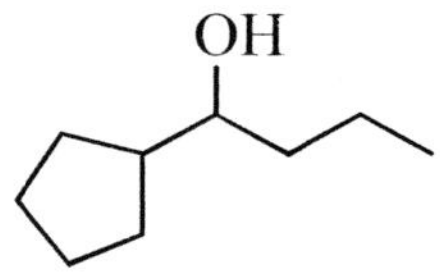

B)

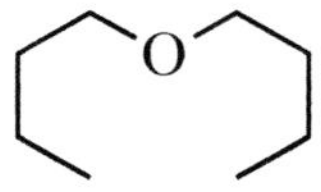

C)

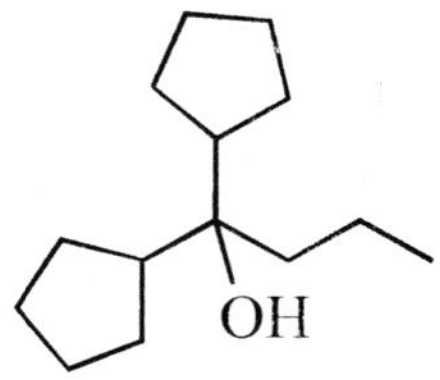

D)

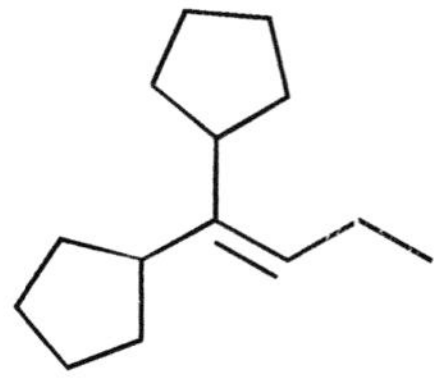

E)

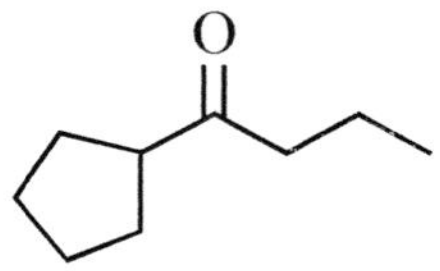

Ans: A

18. What is the **major** product of the following reaction?

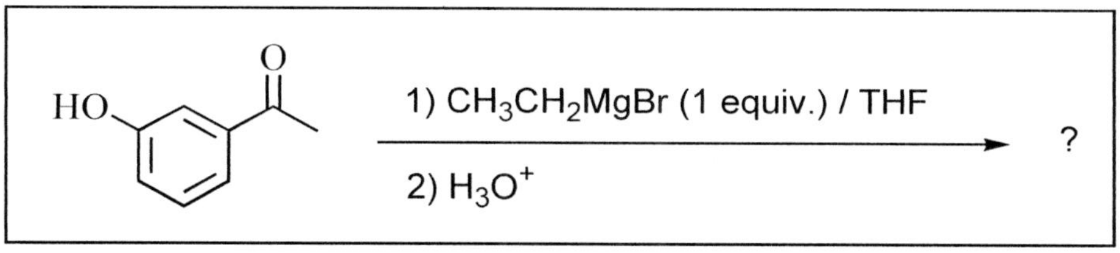
HO
O
1) CH3CH2MgBr (1 equiv.) / THF
2) H3O+
?

A)

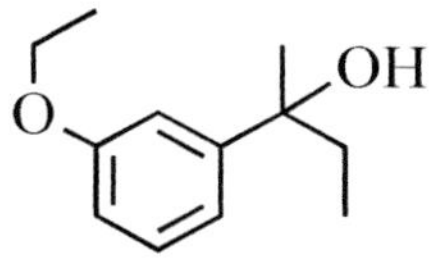
O
OH

B)

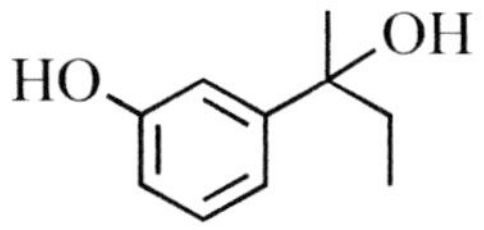
HO
OH

C)

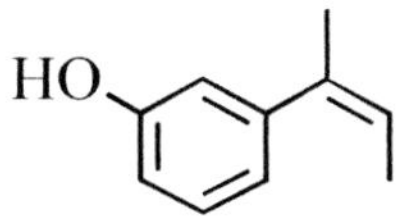
HO

D)

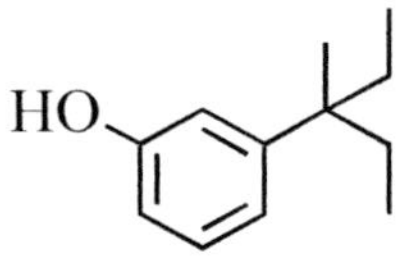
HO

E) no net reaction occurs
Ans: E

19. What is the major product of the following reaction?

$CH_3CH_2CH_3$ → ?

1) Br_2 / light
2) Mg / THF
3) acetone
4) H_3O^+

A)

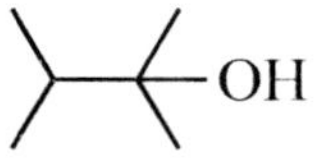

B)

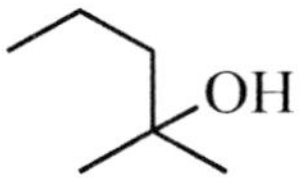

C)

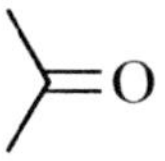

D)

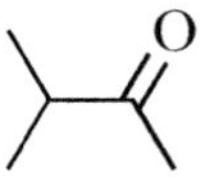

E)

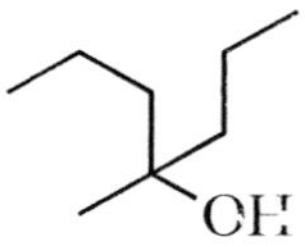

Ans: A

20. What is the **major** product of the following reaction?

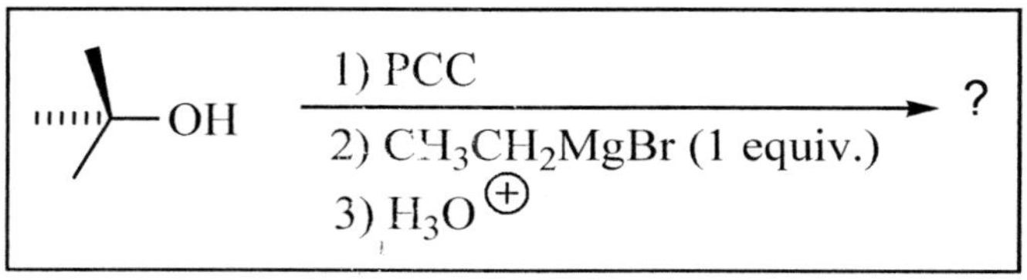

1) PCC

2) CH₃CH₂MgBr (1 equiv.)

3) H₃O⊕

?

A)

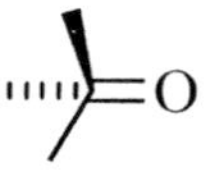

B)

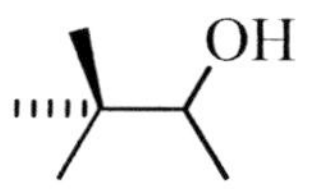

C)

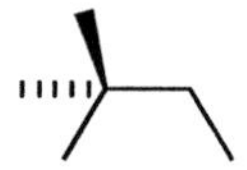

D)

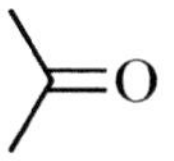

E) no net reaction occurs

Ans: E

21. What is the **major** product of the following reaction?

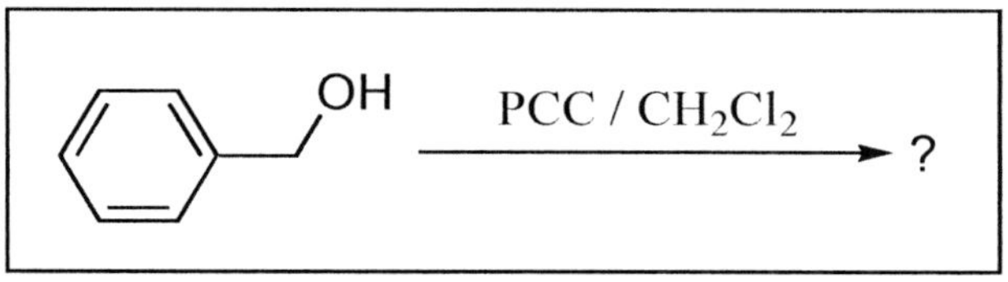

A)

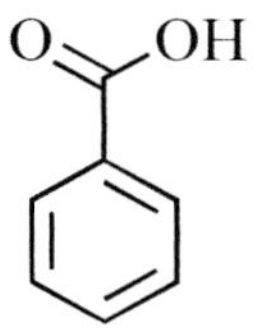

B)

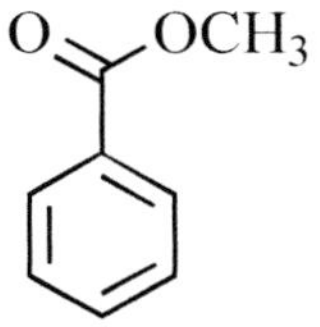

C)

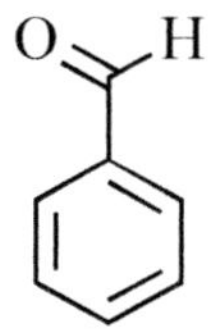

D)

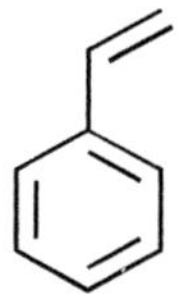

E)   no reaction occurs

Ans: C

22. Ingestion of which of the following toxic alcohols can cause blindness?
    A) CH_3OH D) C_6H_5OH
    B) CH_3CH_2OH E) $HOCH_2CH_2OH$
    C) $(CH_3)_2CHOH$

    Ans: A

23. Which reagents would accomplish the following reaction?

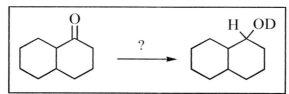

    A)   1. $LiAlD_4$
          2. D_2O
    B)   1. $LiAlD_4$
          2. H_2O
    C)   1. $LiAlH_4$
          2. H_2O
    D)   1. $LiAlH_4$
          2. D_2O
    E)   1. $NaBD_4$, CH_3OH
          2. D_2O

    Ans: D

24. Which of the following reactions would produce the alcohol shown below?

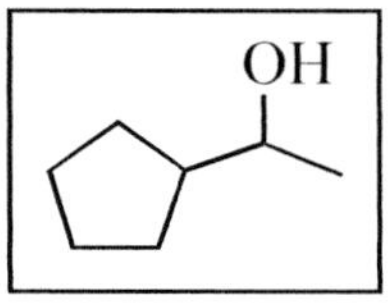

A)

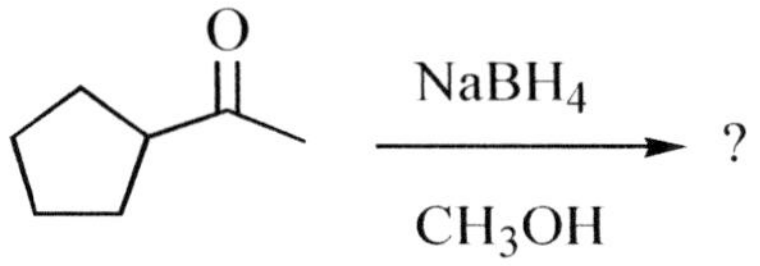

$$\text{NaBH}_4$$
$$\xrightarrow{\hspace{1cm}} \ ?$$
$$\text{CH}_3\text{OH}$$

B)

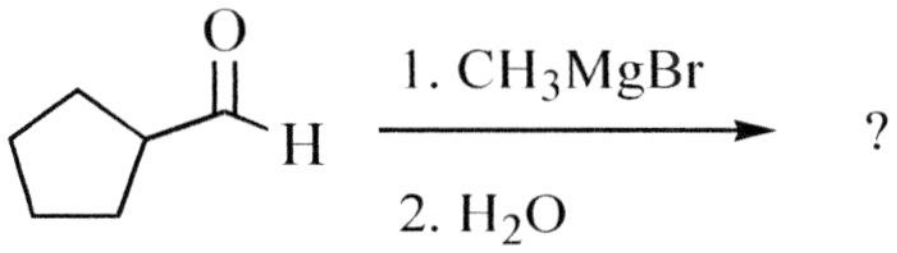

1. CH_3MgBr
$\xrightarrow{\hspace{1cm}} \ ?$
2. H_2O

C)

MgBr   1. CH_3CHO
$\xrightarrow{\hspace{1cm}} \ ?$
2. H_2O

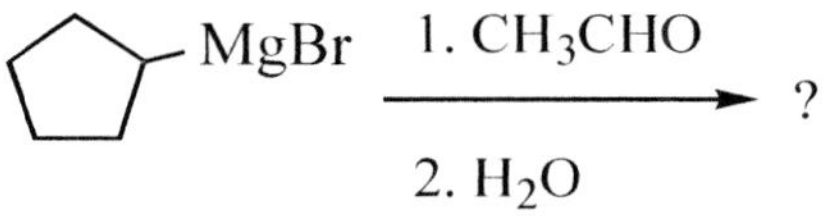

D)   all of the above
E)   two of the above
Ans: D

25. What is the **major** product of the following reaction?

1) PhMgCl (1 equiv.)
$\xrightarrow{\hspace{1cm}} \ ?$
2) H_2O

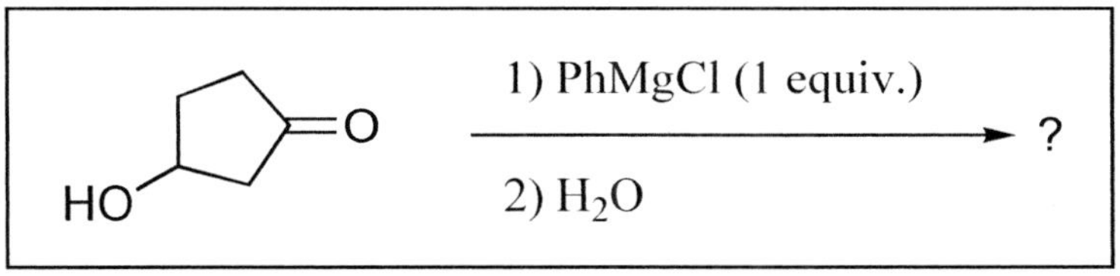

A)

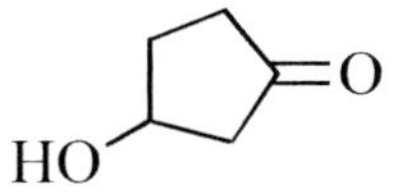

B)

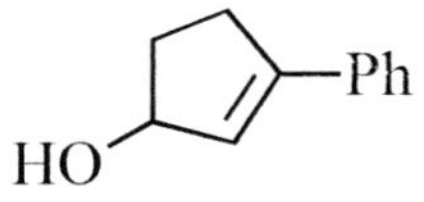

C)

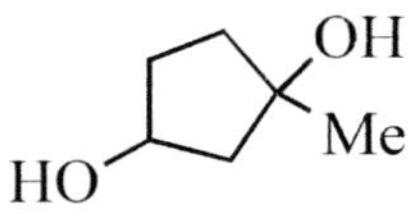

D)

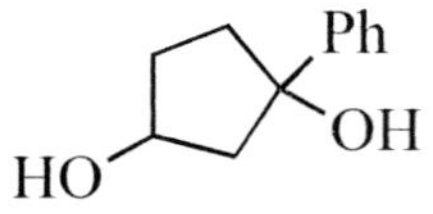

E)

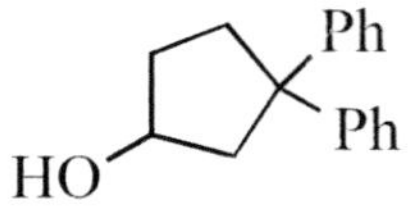

Ans: A

26. What would be the expected organic product of the following reaction?

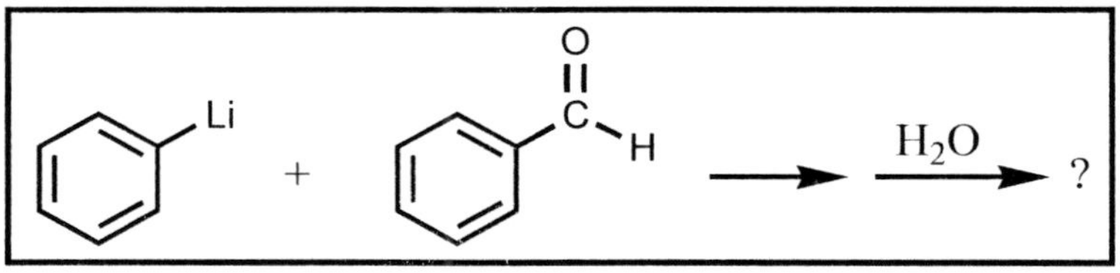

A)

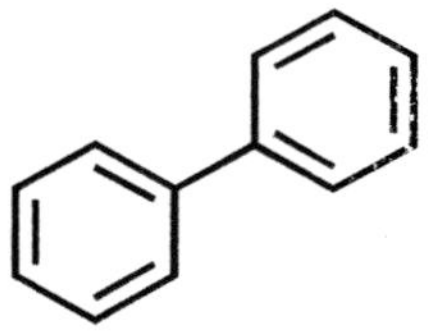

B)

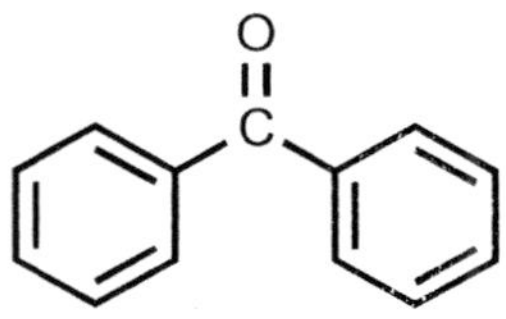

C)

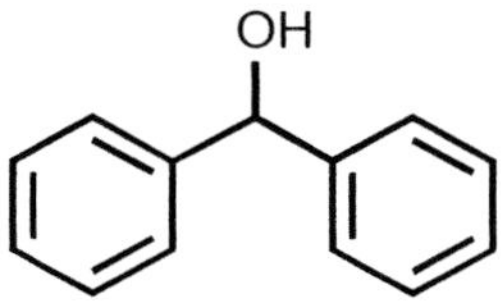

D)

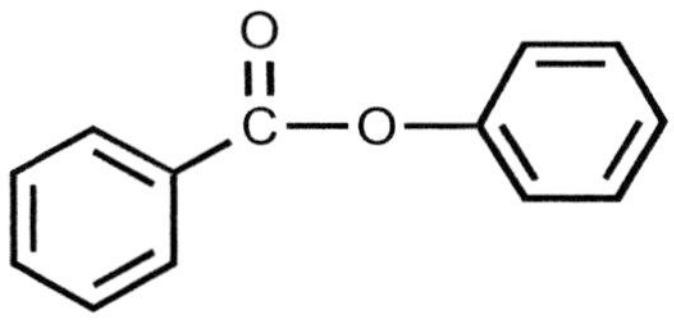

E)

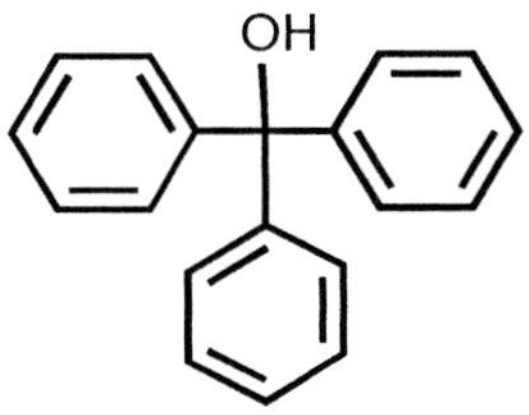

Ans: C

27. Predict the **major** product of the following reaction:

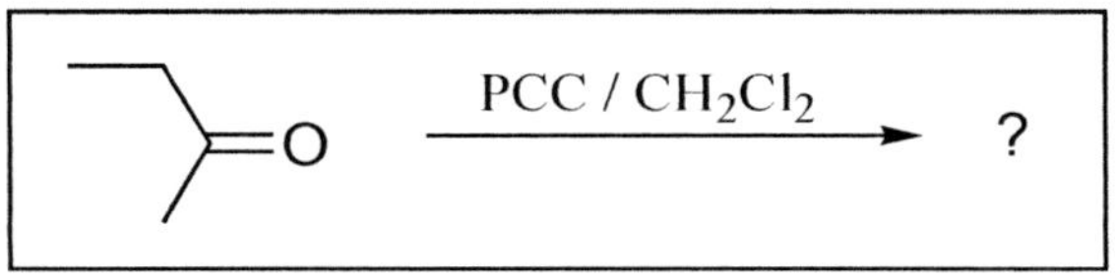

A)

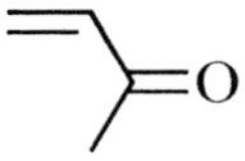

B)

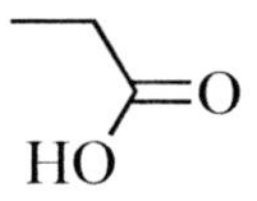

C)

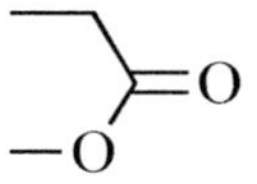

D)

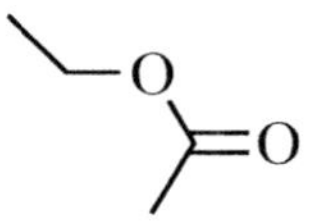

E)   no reaction occurs
Ans: E

28. Which alcohol could be prepared by the greatest number of **different** combinations of Grignard reagents and carbonyl compounds (aldehydes, ketones, and/or esters)? (No multi-step reactions are intended here.)

A)

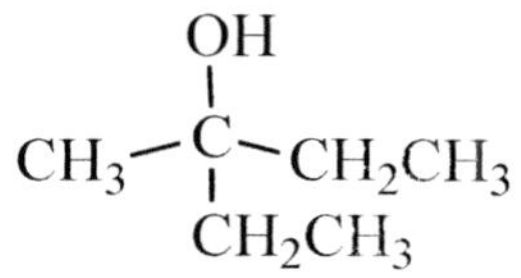

$$CH_3-\underset{\underset{CH_2CH_3}{|}}{\overset{\overset{OH}{|}}{C}}-CH_2CH_3$$

B)

OH

C)

$$H_3C-\underset{\underset{H}{|}}{\overset{\overset{OH}{|}}{C}}-CH_3$$

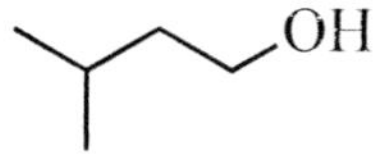

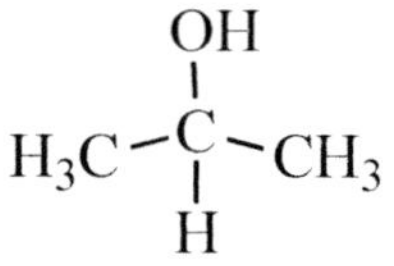

D)

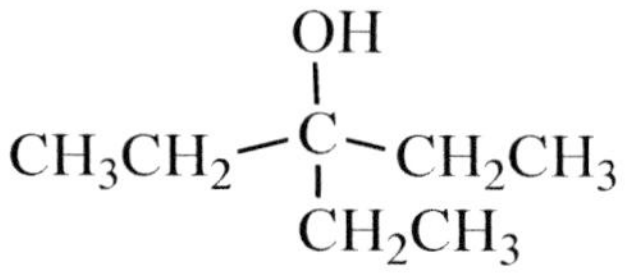

$$CH_3CH_2\underset{\underset{\displaystyle CH_2CH_3}{|}}{\overset{\overset{\displaystyle OH}{|}}{C}}CH_2CH_3$$

E)

$$H_3C\underset{\underset{\displaystyle H}{|}}{\overset{\overset{\displaystyle OH}{|}}{C}}\underset{\underset{\displaystyle CH_3}{|}}{CH}CH_3$$

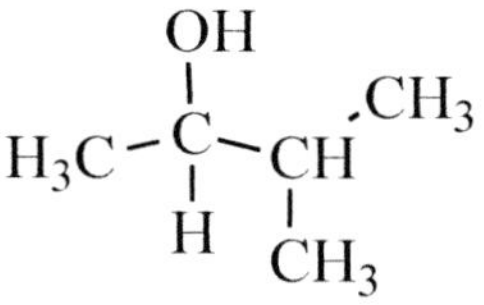

Ans: A

29. What would be the expected product for the following reaction?

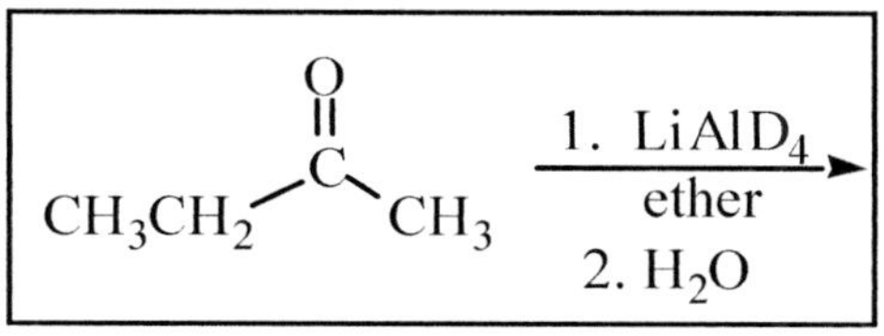

$$CH_3CH_2\overset{\overset{\displaystyle O}{\|}}{C}CH_3 \xrightarrow[\text{2. } H_2O]{\substack{\text{1. } LiAlD_4 \\ \text{ether}}}$$

A)

$$CH_3CH_2\underset{CH_3}{\overset{\overset{\displaystyle OD}{|}}{C}}{-}D$$

B)

$$CH_3CH_2\underset{CH_3}{\overset{\overset{\displaystyle OH}{|}}{C}}{-}D$$

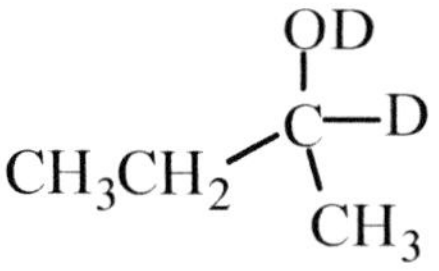

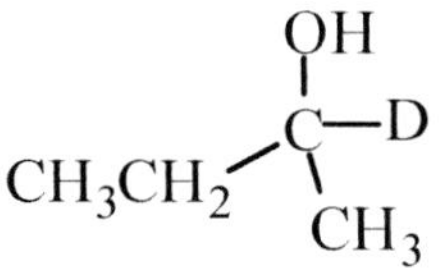

C)

$$CH_3CH_2\underset{CH_3}{\overset{\overset{\displaystyle OD}{|}}{C}}{-}H$$

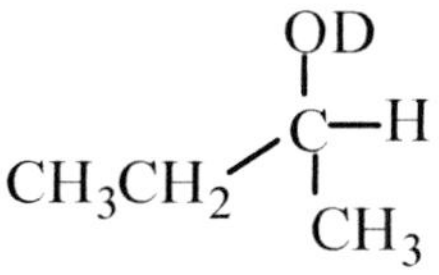

D) $CH_3CH_2CD_2CH_3$

E)

$$CH_3CH_2\underset{CH_3}{\overset{\overset{\displaystyle OH}{|}}{C}}{-}H$$

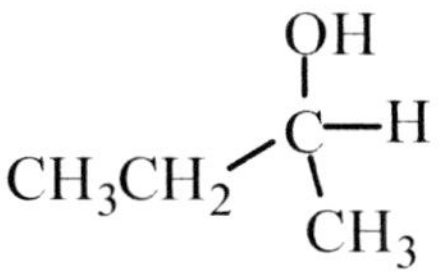

Ans: B

30. Rank the following alcohols in order of decreasing acidity in solution.

CH_3OH	CH_3CH_2OH	$(CH_3)_2CHOH$	$(CH_3)_3COH$
1	**2**	**3**	**4**

A) $1 > 2 > 3 > 4$
B) $2 > 1 > 3 > 4$
C) $4 > 3 > 2 > 1$

D) $4 > 3 > 1 > 2$
E) $1 > 3 > 2 > 4$

Ans: A

31. Rank the following organic compounds in order of increasing acidity.

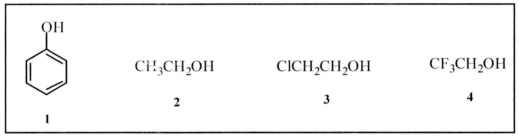

A) $1 < 4 < 3 < 2$
B) $1 < 3 < 4 < 2$
C) $2 < 1 < 3 < 4$

D) $2 < 3 < 4 < 1$
E) $1 < 4 < 2 < 3$

Ans: D

32. Which of these reagents will best accomplish the transformation below?

A) $NaOH, H_2O$
B)
$$\xrightarrow[HOC(CH_3)_3]{KOC(CH_3)_3}$$
C)

$$\xrightarrow{\substack{1) H_3C\text{-}C(=O)\text{-}ONa \\ DMF,\ 80\ °C}}$$

2) $NaOH, H_2O$

D)
1) $LiAlH_4, (CH_3CH_2)_2O$

2) H_3O+, H_2O

E)   none of the above
Ans: C

33. For this series of alcohols, which one will have an equilibria that lies the furthest to the right in a basic solution?

CH_3OH FCH_2OH $ClCH_2OH$ $BrCH_2OH$

A) CH_3OH D) $BrCH_2OH$
B) FCH_2OH E)   All equilibria will be the same
C) $ClCH_2OH$

Ans: B

34. For the transformations below, what is the structure of the starting material?

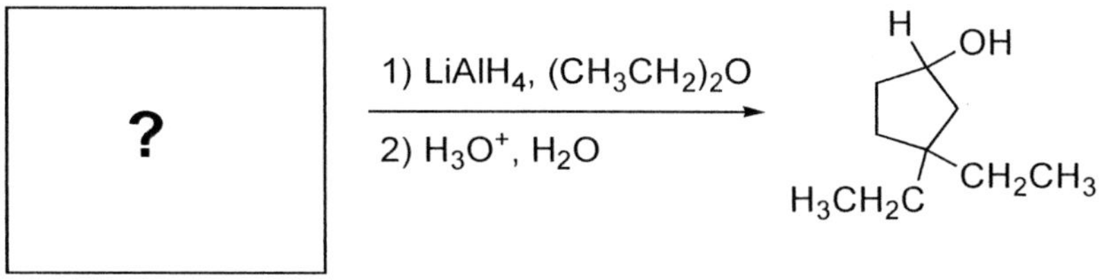

1) $LiAlH_4$, $(CH_3CH_2)_2O$

2) H_3O^+, H_2O

A)

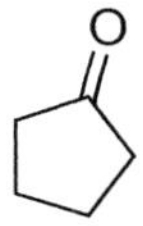

B)

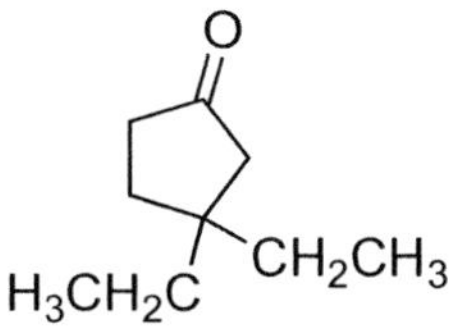

C)

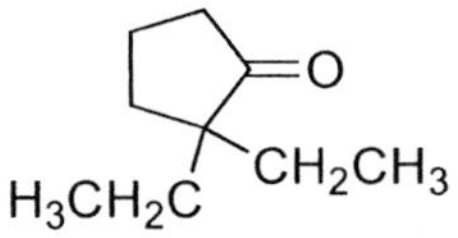

D)

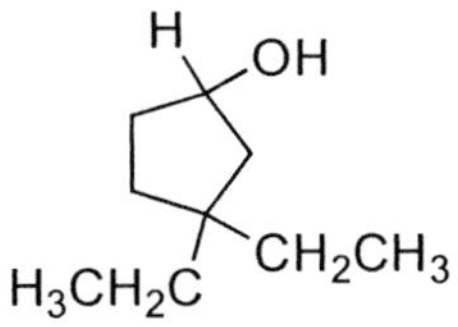

E)

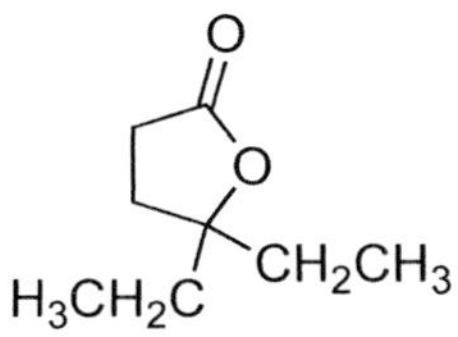

Ans: B

35. Choose the reagents to make the conversion from I to II.

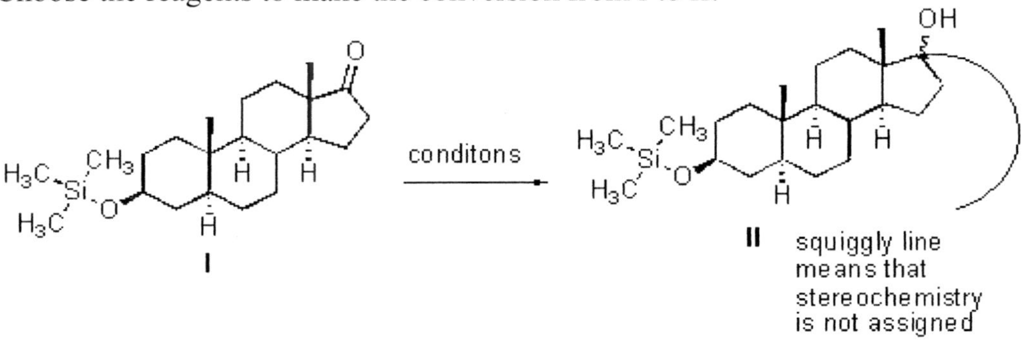
H3C
CH3
Si
O
H
H
H
O
I
conditons
H3C
CH3
Si
O
H3C
H
H
H
OH
II
squiggly line
means that
stereochemistry
is not assigned

A) NaH B) $LiAlD_4$ C) $NaBH_4$ D) H_3O^+ E) all of the above
Ans: C

36. What is the product of the following reaction?

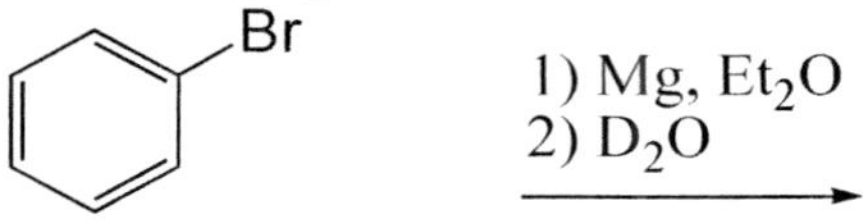
Br
1) Mg, Et2O
2) D2O

A)

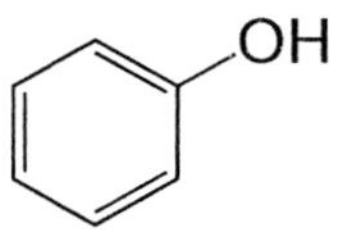
OH

B)

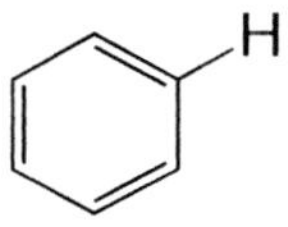
H

C)

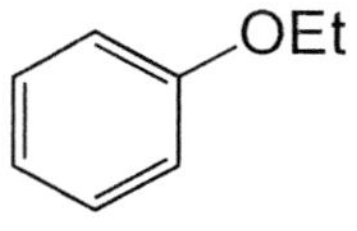
OEt

D)

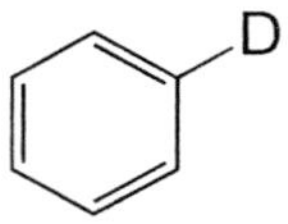
D

E) none of the above
Ans: D

37. What is the product of the following reaction?

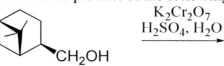

A)

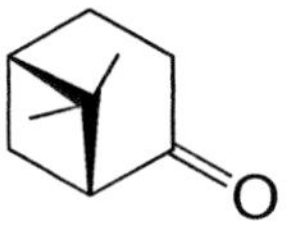

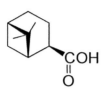

B)

C)

D)

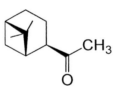

E)

Ans: B

38. What is the product of the following reaction?

1) PhMgCl (1 equiv)
2) H₃O+

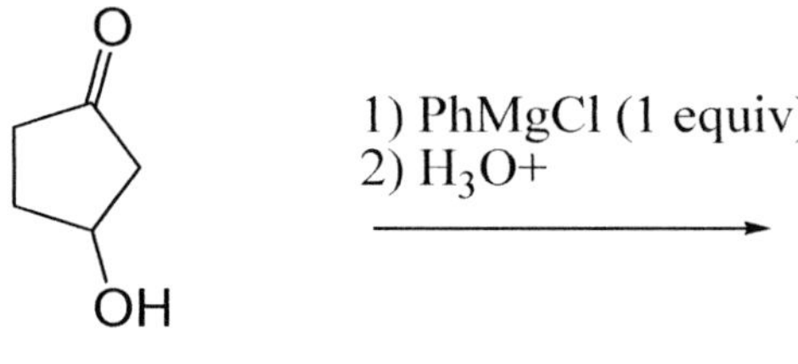

A)

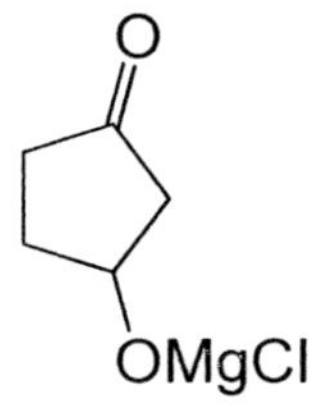

B)

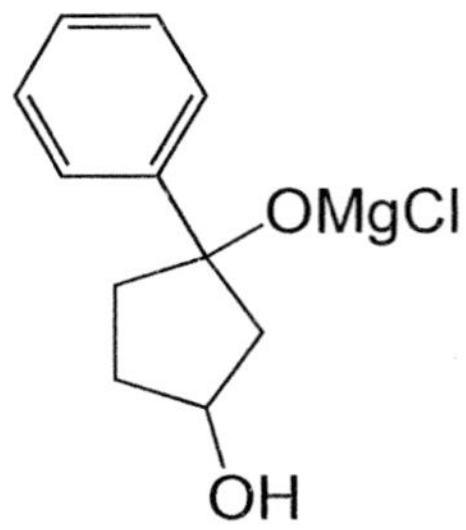

C)

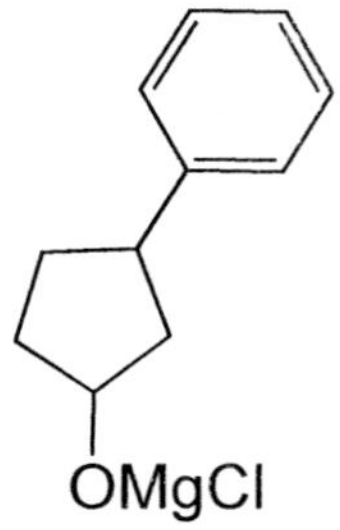

D)

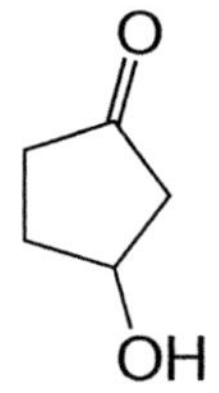

E)   All of the above are the end products of this reaction.

Ans: D

39. What would be the major organic product expected from the following reaction?

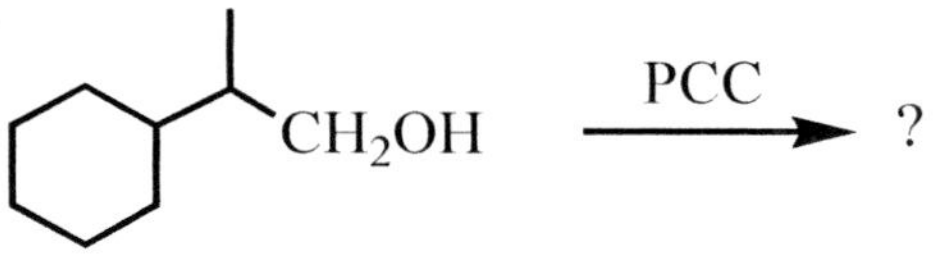

PCC

?

CH$_2$OH

(PCC = CrClO$_3^-$ R$_3$NH$^+$)

A)

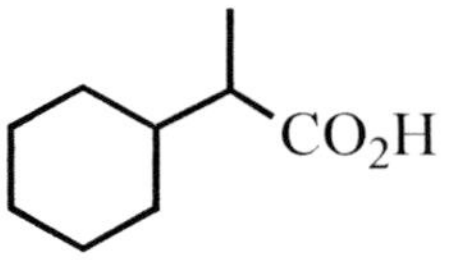

CO$_2$H

B)

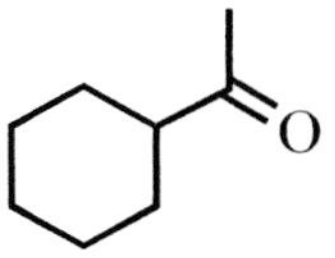

O

C)

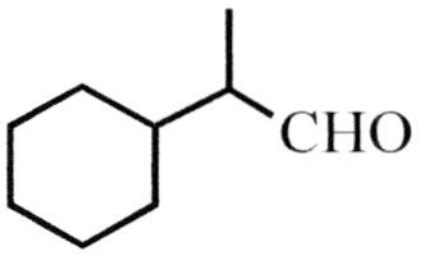

CHO

D)

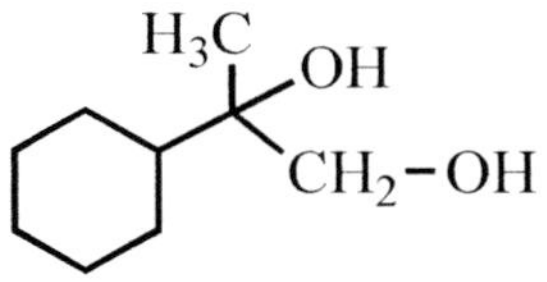

H$_3$C OH

CH$_2$—OH

E)

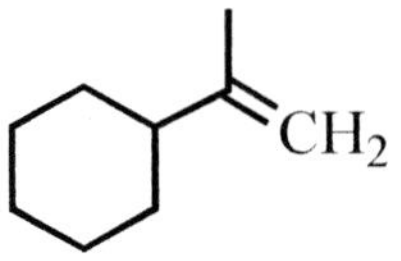

CH$_2$

Ans: C

40. Which of these reactions will give the product shown?

A)

1) [cyclohexyl-MgBr] + [propanone structure]

2) H$^+$, H$_2$O

B)

1) [cyclohexyl acetyl structure] + CH$_3$CH$_2$MgBr

2) H$^+$, H$_2$O

C)

1) [cyclohexyl propanoyl structure] + CH$_3$MgBr

2) H$^+$, H$_2$O

D)   A and B are correct.
E)   All of the above will give the product.
Ans: C

41. Identify the reagent that you would use to go from PGE$_1$ to PGE$_{1\alpha}$?

PGE$_1$ PGE$_{1a}$

A) CrO$_3$-2pyridine   B) NaH   C) NaBH$_4$ D) H$_2$O   E) H$_2$SO$_4$
Ans: C

Chapter 9: Further Reactions of Alcohols and the Chemistry of Ethers

1. What would be the product of the following reaction?

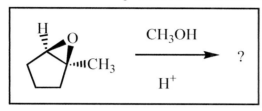

A)

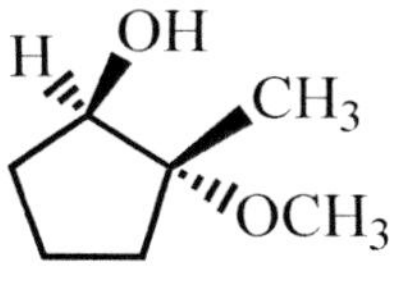

CH₃OH

B)

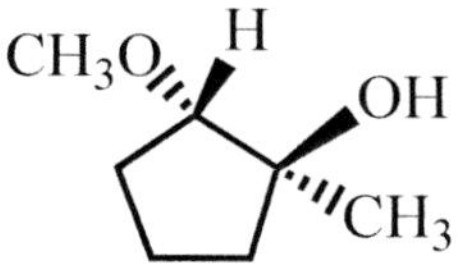

C)

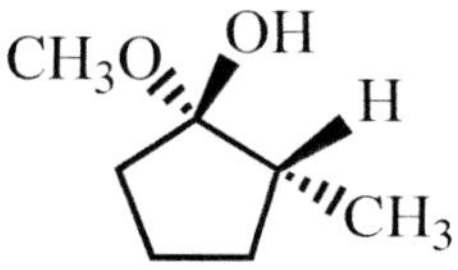

D)

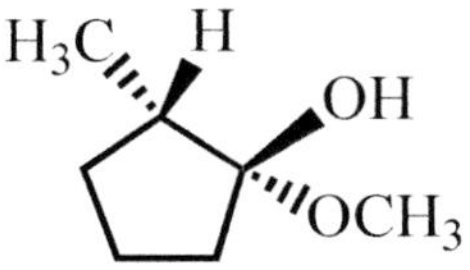

E)

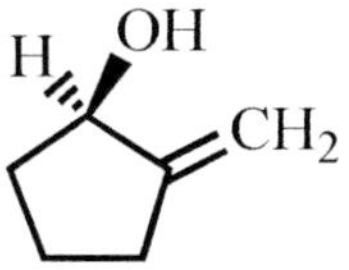

Ans: A

2. What would be the product of the following reaction?

$$CH_3CH_2OCH_2CH_3 \quad + \quad O_2 \quad \xrightarrow[\text{(slow)}]{25\,°C} \quad ?$$

A) $CO_2 + H_2O$

B)

$$CH_3-CH-O-CH_2-CH_3$$
$$|$$
$$OOH$$

C) $CH_3-CH_2-O-CH_2-CH_2-OOH$

D) $CH_3-CH_2-O-O-CH_2-CH_3$

E) $CH_3-CH_2-O-CH_2-CH_2OH$

Ans: B

3. Which of the following would you expect to have the **lowest** boiling point?

A) CH_3CH_2OH D) CH_3SCH_3

B) CH_3CH_2SH E) boiling points would be the same.

C) CH_3OCH_3

Ans: C

4. What reagent would best accomplish the following reaction?

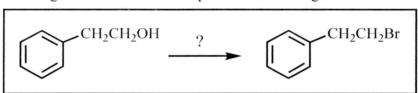

A) Br_2 B) NaBr   C) CH_3Br D) $NH_4^+ Br^-$ E) PBr_3

Ans: E

5. What would be the expected product of the following reaction?

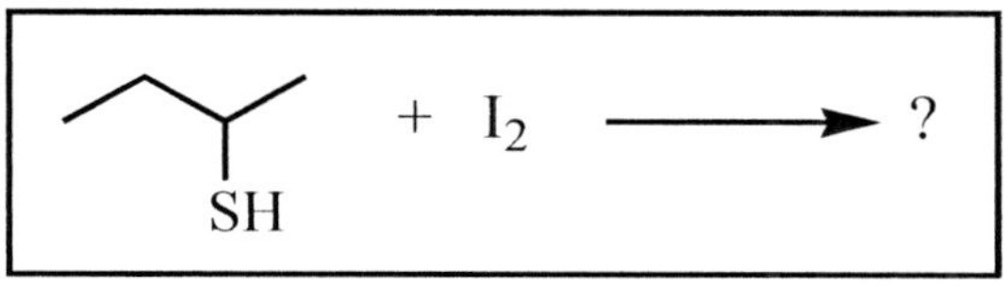

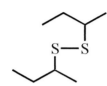 + I$_2$ ⟶ ?

A)

B)

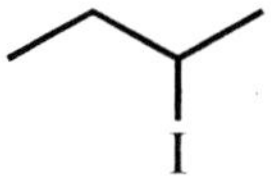

(structure with I)

C)

(trans)

D)

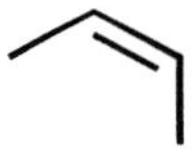

(cis)

E)

(structure with O=S=O, OH)

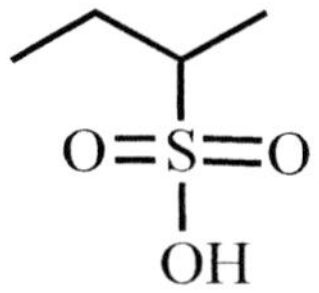

Ans: A

6. What would be the expected product(s) of the following reaction?

$$CH_3CH_2CH_2CH_2-O-CH_2CH_2CH_2CH_3 \xrightarrow[\text{heat}]{\text{HI (excess)}} ?$$

A) $CH_3CH_2CH_2CH_2OH + CH_3CH_2CH_2CH_2I$
B) $CH_3CH_2CH_2CHI-O-CH_2CH_2CH_2CH_3$
C) $2 \ CH_3CH_2CH_2CH_2I$
D)

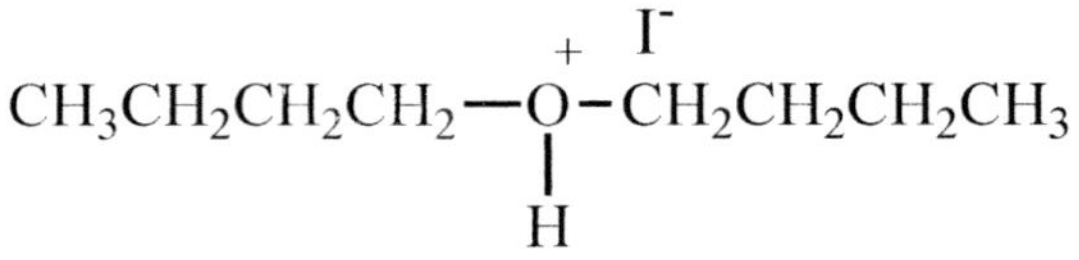

$$CH_3CH_2CH_2CH_2-\overset{\overset{+}{\underset{|}{O}}}{\underset{H}{}}-CH_2CH_2CH_2CH_3 \quad \overset{I^-}{}$$

E)   no reaction occurs

Ans: C

7. What would be the **major** organic product from the following reaction?

HCl (conc) → ?

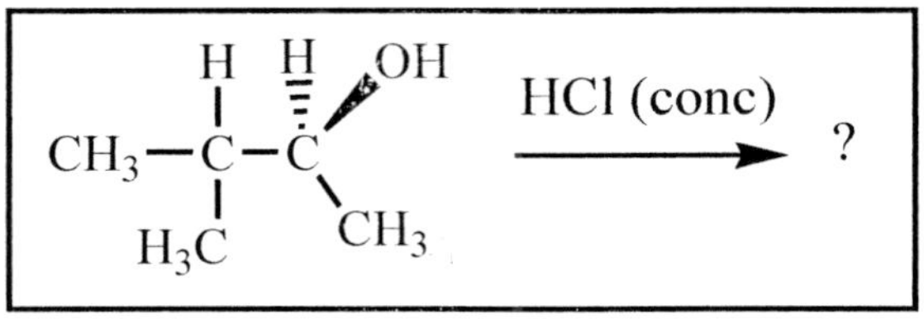

A)

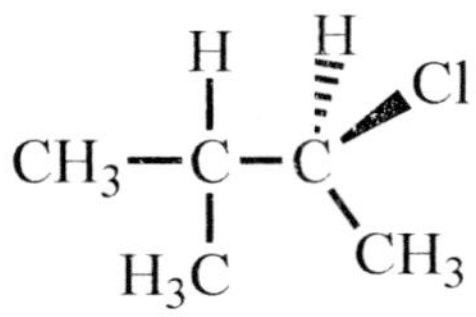

B)

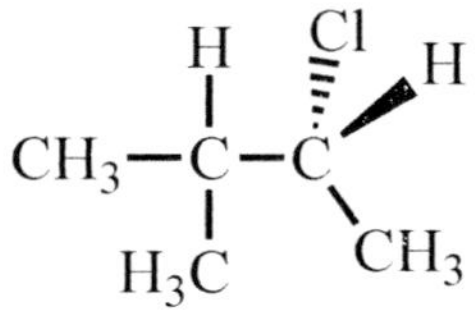

C)

$$CH_3-\underset{\underset{H_3C}{|}}{\overset{\overset{H}{|}}{C}}-\underset{\underset{CH_3}{}}{\overset{\overset{H}{|}}{C}}\diagdown Cl \quad \text{(racemic)}$$

D)

$$CH_3-\underset{\underset{H_3C}{|}}{\overset{\overset{Cl}{|}}{C}}-\underset{\underset{H}{|}}{\overset{\overset{H}{|}}{C}}-CH_3$$

E)

$$\underset{H_3C}{\overset{H_3C}{\diagdown}}C=C\underset{\diagdown CH_3}{\overset{\diagup H}{}}$$

Ans: D

8. What would be the best name of the following compound?

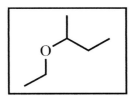

A)   3-methyl-4-oxohexane
B)   2-butoxyethane
C)   1-methy-1-ethoxypropane
D)   (1-ethyl)-diethylether
E)   2-ethoxybutane
Ans: E

9. What significant characteristic(s) does diethyl ether exhibit?
A)   It functions as an anesthetic.
B)   It is extremely flammable.
C)   It is a common solvent.
D)   It can react slowly with oxygen at room temperature.
E)   All of the above are true.
Ans: E

10. Which of the following reactions would be the best for the preparation of anisole (methoxybenzene)?

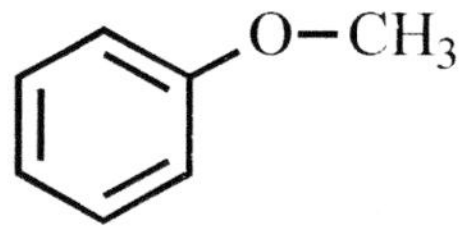

A)

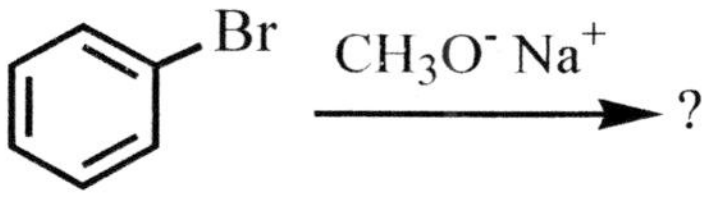

B)

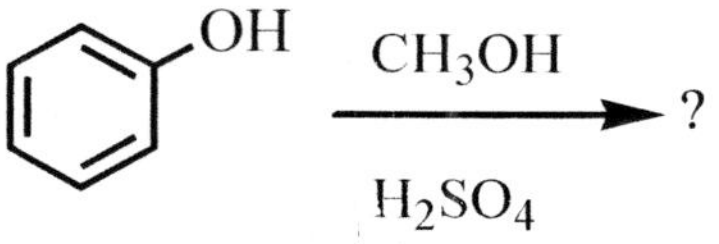

C)

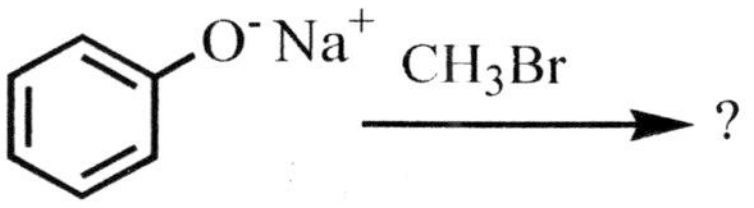

D)

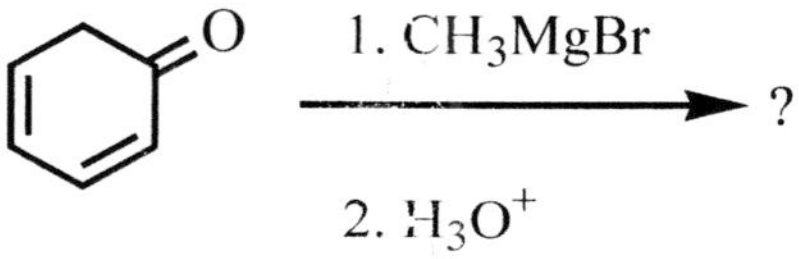

E)   None of the above would work.
Ans: C

11. Which of the following reactions would be **best** for the preparation of Nerolin II?

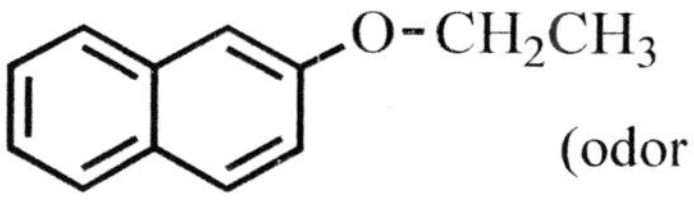

Nerolin II
(odor of orange blossoms)

A)

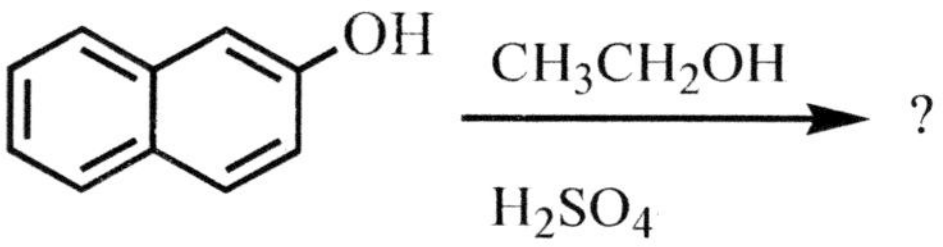

B)

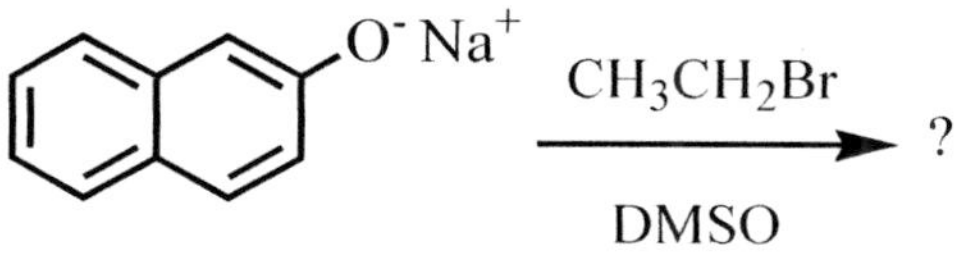

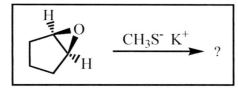

CH₃CH₂Br

DMSO

?

C)

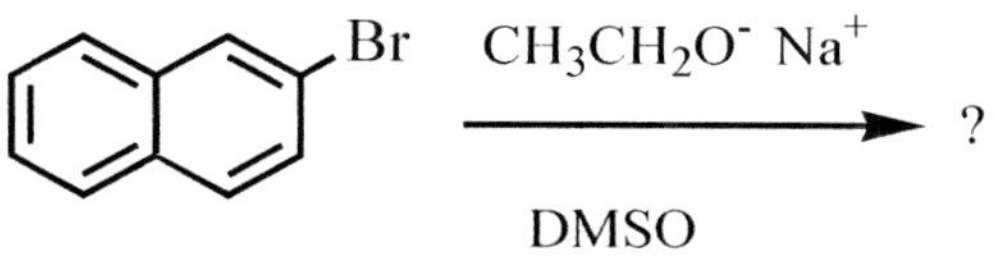

Br   CH₃CH₂O⁻ Na⁺

DMSO

?

D)   Any of the above would work.
E)   None of the above would work.
Ans: B

12. Why is the autoxidation (slow oxidation by air) of ethers important?
    A)   Several industrial chemicals are made by this method.
    B)   The heat generated often leads to open combustion.
    C)   It makes ethers unusable as anesthetics.
    D)   The products can explode upon concentration.
    E)   By absorbing all of the oxygen in closed areas, ethers pose suffocation risks.
    Ans: D

13. What would be the product of the following reaction?

CH₃S⁻ K⁺

?

A)

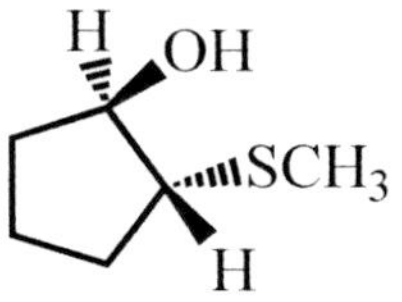

H   OH

····ⁱⁱSCH₃

H

B)

H₃CS

OH

–H

H

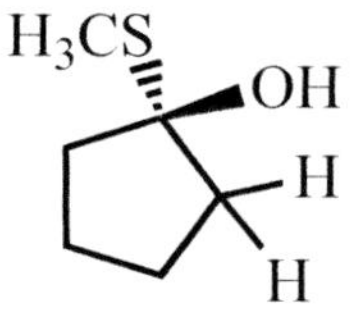

C)

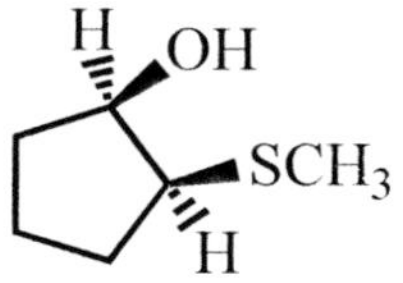

D)

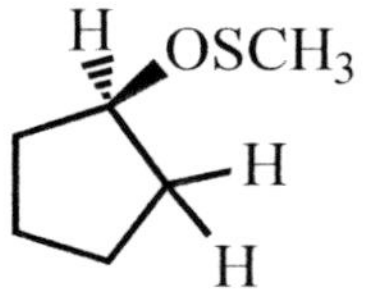

E)

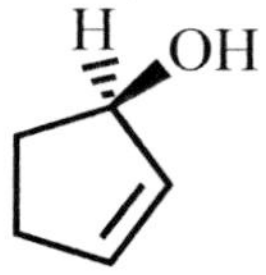

Ans: A

14. What product would result from the following reaction?

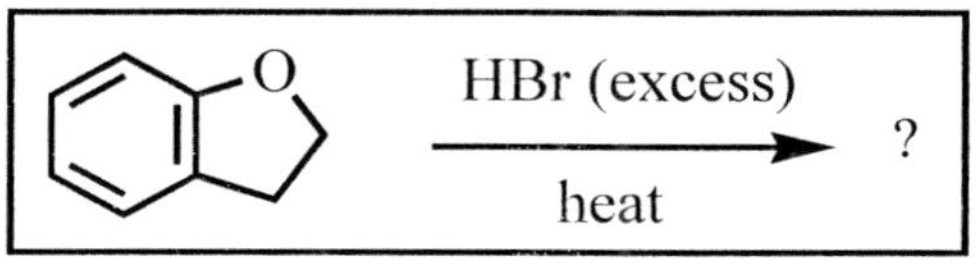

A)

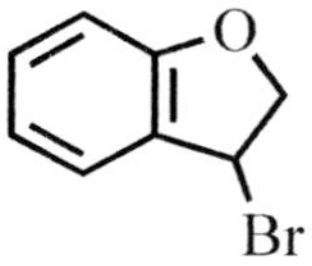

B)

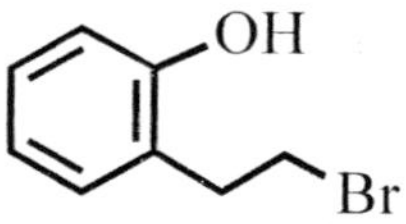

C)

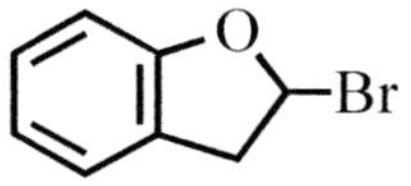

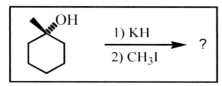

D)

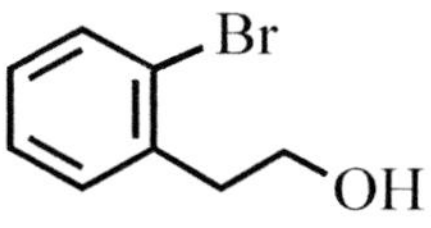

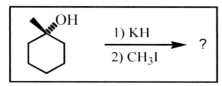

E)

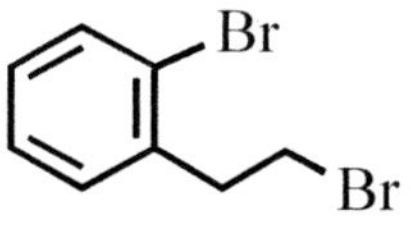

Ans: B

15. What would be the product of the following reaction?

A)

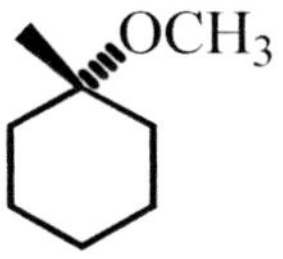

B)

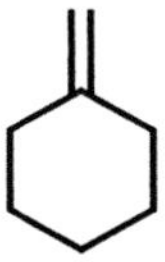

C)

D)

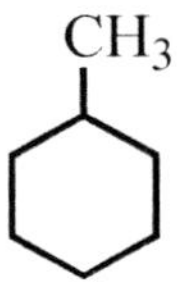

E)

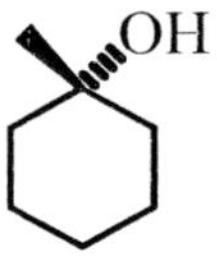

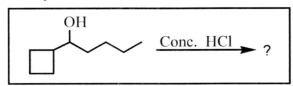

Ans: A

16. In the following reaction, an interesting rearrangement takes place. Suggest a structure for the product that is obtained.

OH

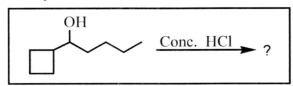

Conc. HCl ⟶ ?

A)

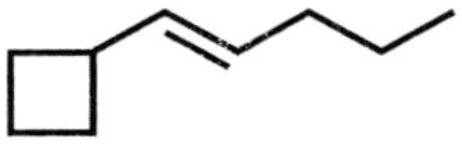

B)

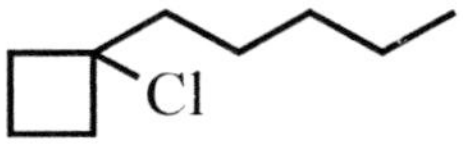

Cl

C)

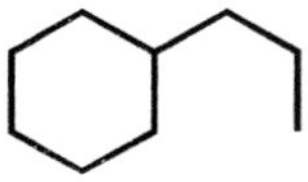

D)

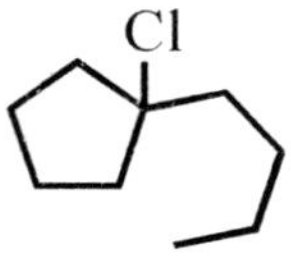

Cl

E)

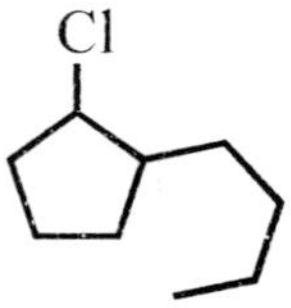

Cl

Ans: D

17. What is the product of the following reaction?

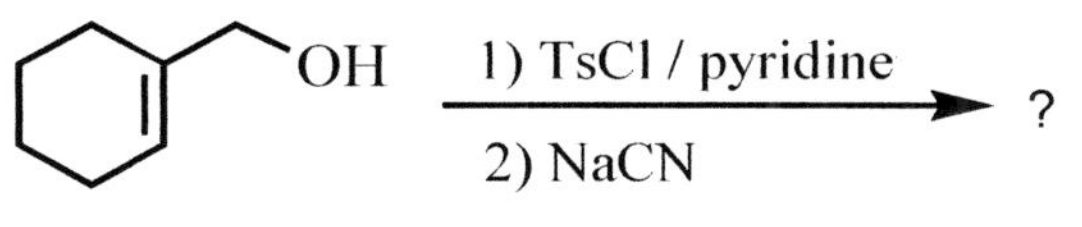

A)

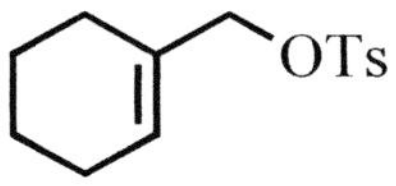

B)

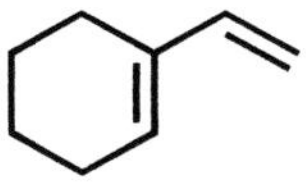

C)

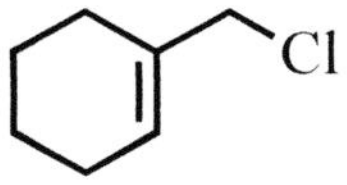

D)

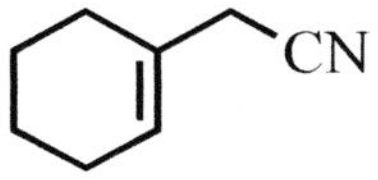

E)

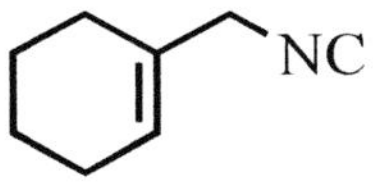

Ans: D

18. What is the **major** product of the following reaction?

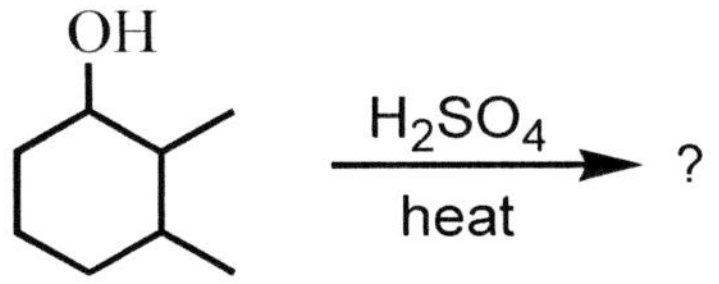

A)

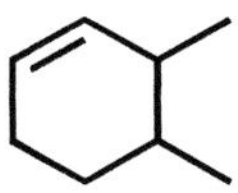

B)

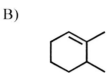

C)

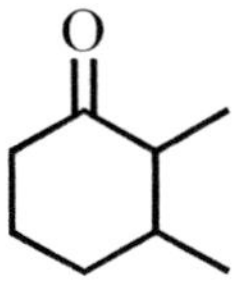

D)

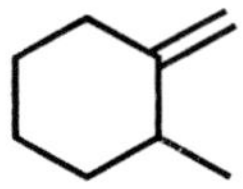

E)

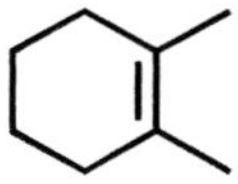

Ans: E

19. Ethers have lower boiling points than comparable alcohols because:
    A)   they are able to complex with the metal, magnesium.
    B)   they do not contain a carbonyl group.
    C)   the oxygen of the ether is sp^2 hybridized.
    D)   they are not able to hydrogen bond with themselves.
    E)   they have more acidic protons than alcohols.
    Ans: D

20. Which reagent(s) would accomplish the following reaction?

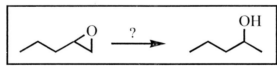

    A) H_2O, H^+
    B)   NaH
    C)   1. LiAlH$_4$
         2. H_2O
    D)   NaOH, H_2O
    E)   1. CH$_3$MgBr
         2. H_2O
    Ans: C

21. What is the **major** product of the following reaction?

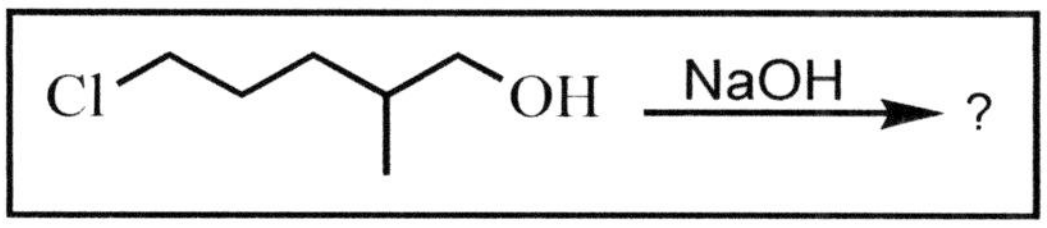

A)

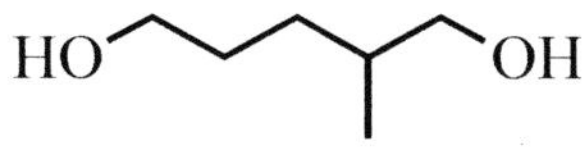

B)

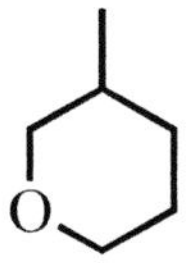

C)

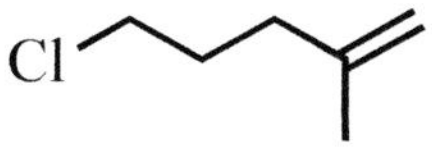

D)

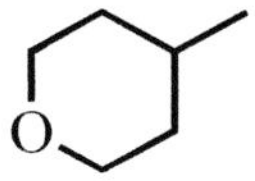

E)

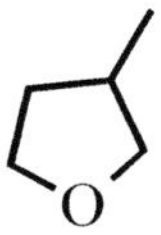

Ans: B

22. When considering the mechanism of the following reaction, which of the following statements is true?

A)   A molecule of water is lost.
B)   The mechanism involves an S_N2 reaction.
C)   A free carbocation is formed.
D)   An alkoxide is involved as a nucleophile.
E)   Both A and C are true.
Ans: E

23. What is the **major** product of the following reaction:

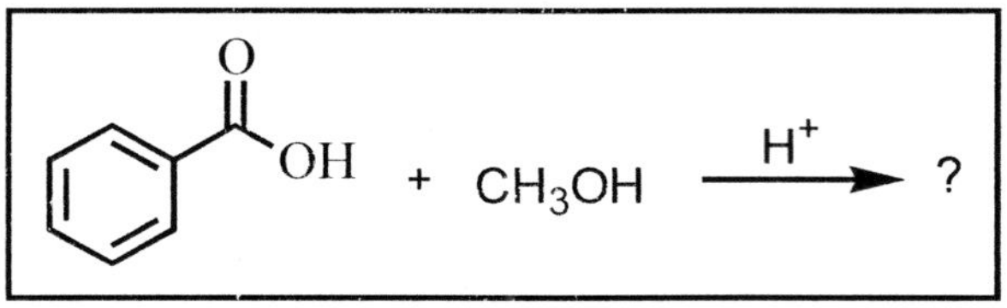

A)

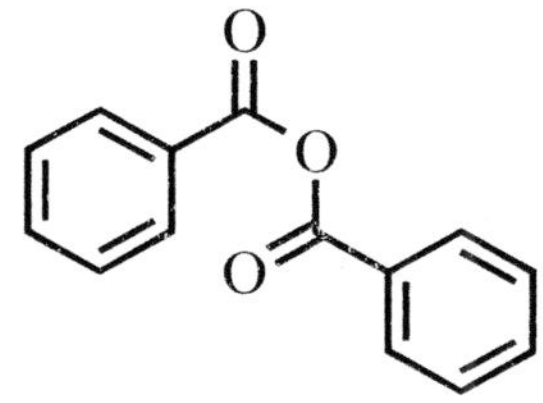

B)

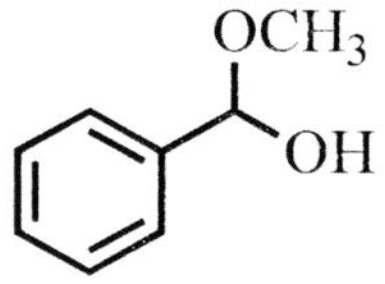

C)

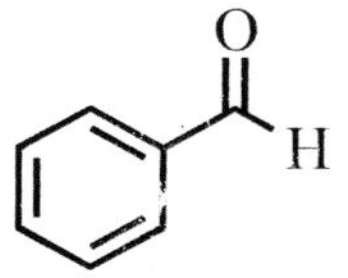

D)

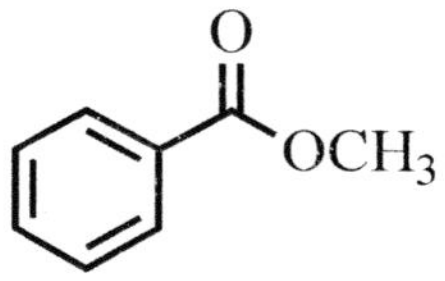

E)

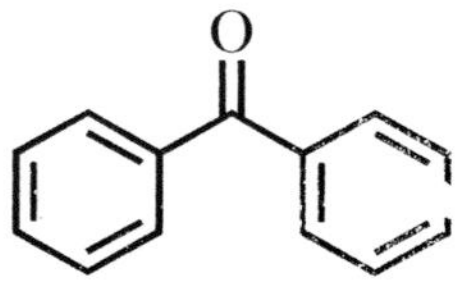

Ans: D

24. What is the **major** product of the following reaction:

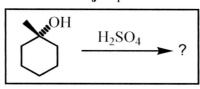

A)

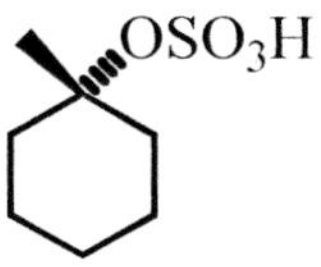

B)

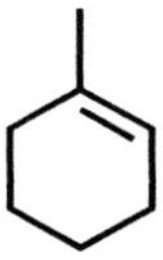

C)

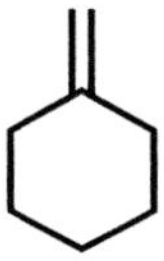

D)

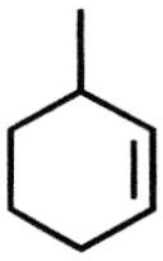

E)   none of the above
Ans: B

25. What is the **major** product of the following reaction?

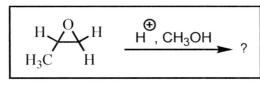

A)

HO

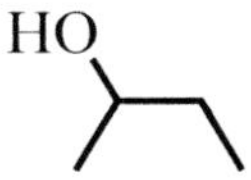

B)

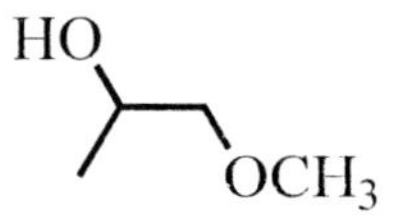

HO

OCH₃

C)

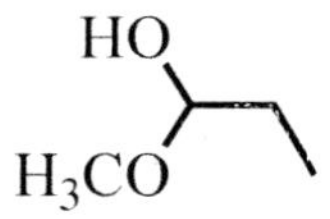

HO

H₃CO

D)

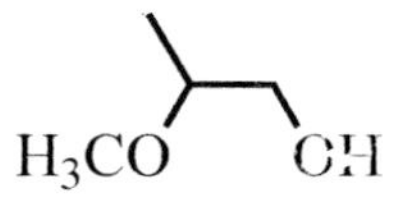

H₃CO CH

E)

OH

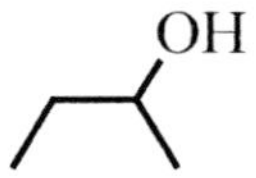

Ans: D

26. What is the **major** product of the following reaction?

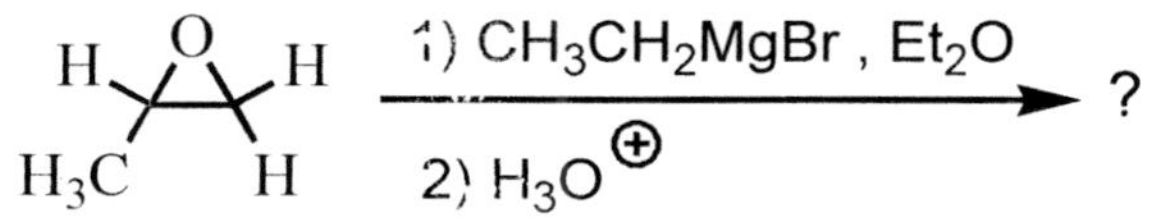

H   O   H   1) CH₃CH₂MgBr , Et₂O
H₃C   H   2) H₃O⊕   ?

A)

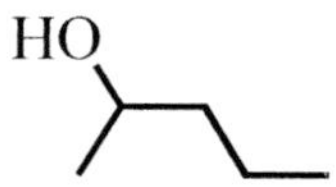

HO

B)

OH

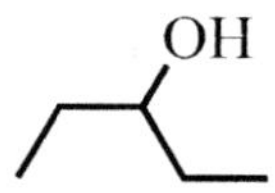

C)

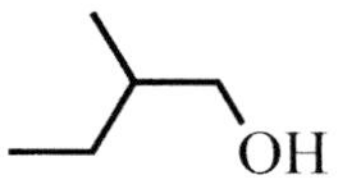

OH

D)

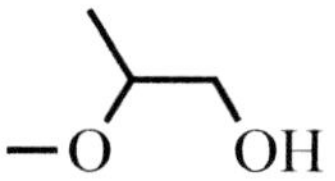

—O   OH

E)

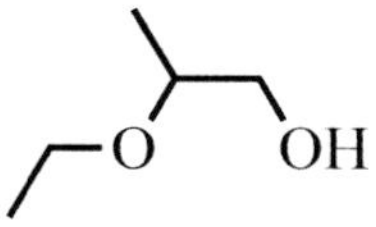

O   OH

Ans: A

27. Predict the major product of the following reaction:

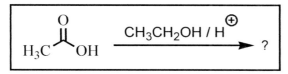

A)   methyl ethanoate
B)   ethyl propanoate
C)   phenyl ethanoate

D)   ethyl ethanoate
E)   acetic acid

Ans: D

28. Which set of reagents will effect the following transformation?

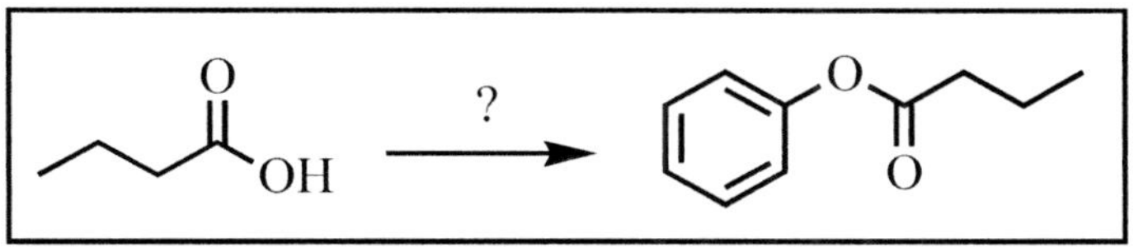

A)   benzoic acid / H_3O^+
B)

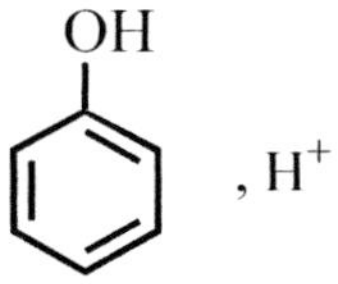

OH

, H^+

C)   MCPBA
D)   butanoic acid / H_3O^+
E) CH_3CH_2OH / H_3O^+

Ans: B

29. What is the **major** product of the following reaction?

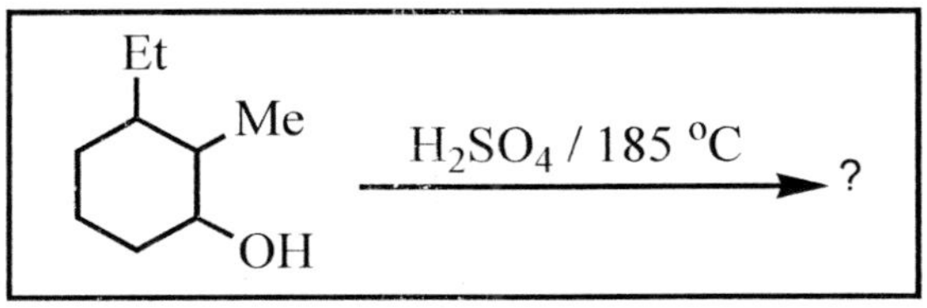

Et
Me
OH
H_2SO_4 / 185 °C → ?

A)

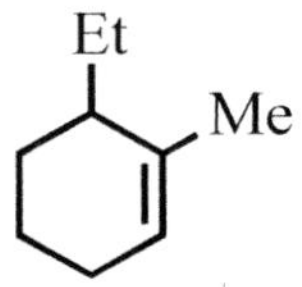

Et
Me

B)

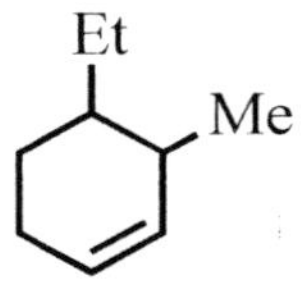

Et
Me

C)

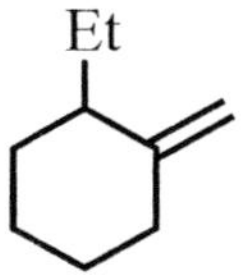

Et

D)

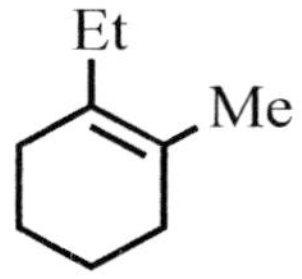

Et
Me

E)

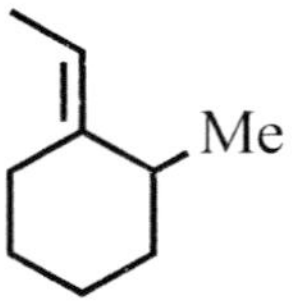

Me

Ans: D

30. What type of reaction will happen to phenol upon treatment with catalytic sulfuric acid?

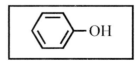
—OH

A)   E1   D)   Electrophilic elimination
B)   E2   E)   A reaction will not take place
C)   Free-radical elimination
Ans: E

31. What is the structure of THF?

A)

B)

C)

D)

E)

Ans: C

32. Which type of inorganic esters tends to be shock-sensitive (explosive)?
A) Phosphate   B) Nitrate   C) Phosphite   D) Sulfate   E) Tosylate
Ans: B

33. Diethyl ether can be dangerous for which of the following reasons:
A)   It is highly toxic.
B)   It tends to slowly accumulate hydroperoxides.
C)   It is extremely flammable.
D)   all of the above
E)   two of the above
Ans: E

34. Crown ethers are important because they
A)   have antibiotic properties.
B)   have the ability to dissolve certain salts in organic solvents.
C)   occur in marine organisms.
D)   promote the oxidation of certain organics.
E)   are used as binders in detergent formulations.
Ans: B

35. Which of the following reactions would produce diethyl ether?

A)

$$CH_3CH_2OH \xrightarrow[\text{heat}]{H_2SO_4}$$

B)

$$CH_3CH_2Br \xrightarrow{NaOH}$$

C)

$$CH_3CH_2Br \xrightarrow{CH_3CH_2ONa}$$

D) all of the above

E) two of the above

Ans: E

36. What product(s) would result from the following reaction?

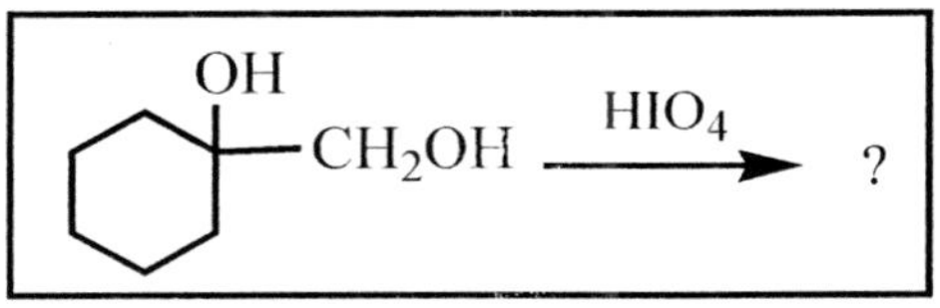

A)

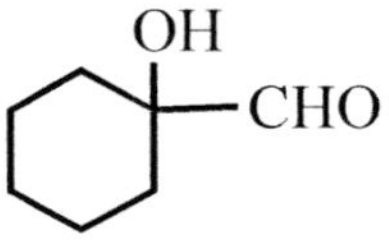

B)

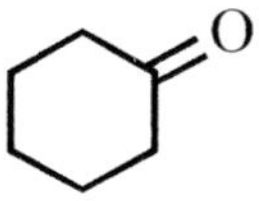

$+ CH_2=O$

C)

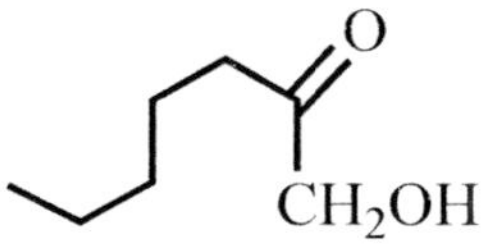

CH_2OH

D)

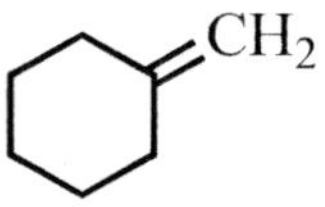

CH_2

E)

OHC CHO

Ans: B

37. Which of the following is true of thiols?
    A)   They are more acidic than alcohols.
    B)   They have lower boiling points than the corresponding alcohol.
    C)   Thiol oxidations proceed very differently than alcohol oxidations.
    D)   all of the above
    E)   two of the above
    Ans: D

38. The Merck Index reports that the odor of geosmin can be detected at 0.1 parts per billion, but that it is quickly converted to essentially odorless products in acidic solution. What is the expected major product of treatment of geosmin with sulfuric acid?

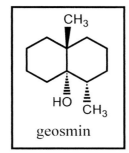

geosmin

A)

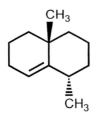

B)

C)

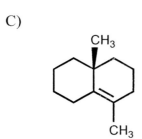

D)

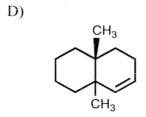

E)

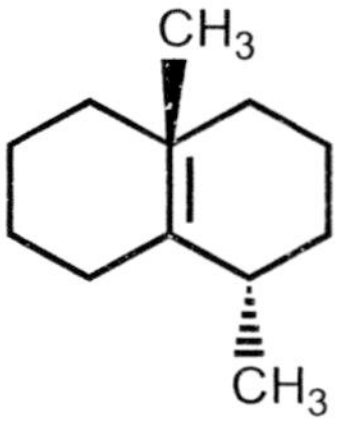

CH₃

Ans: C

39. Which of the following is a reasonable method of synthesizing methoxide?
    A)   CH₃OH + LDA
    B)   CH₃OH + nBuLi
    C)   CH₃OH + KH
    D)   Two of these are reasonable methods.
    E)   All of these would work.
    Ans: E

40. Predict the **major** product of the following reaction

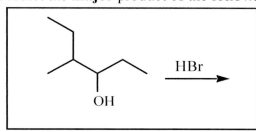

A)

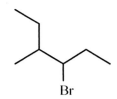

B)

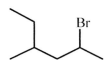

C)

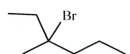

D)   A and B in equal proportions
E)   B and C in equal proportions
Ans: C

41. Predict the **major** product of the following reaction: 2,3-dimethylcyclohexanol + H₂SO₄
A)

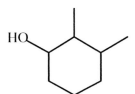

B)

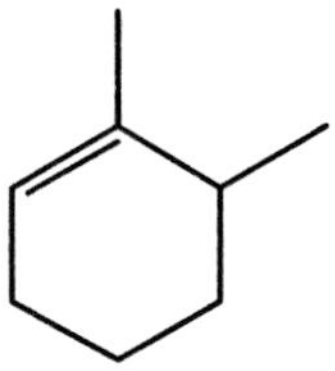

C)

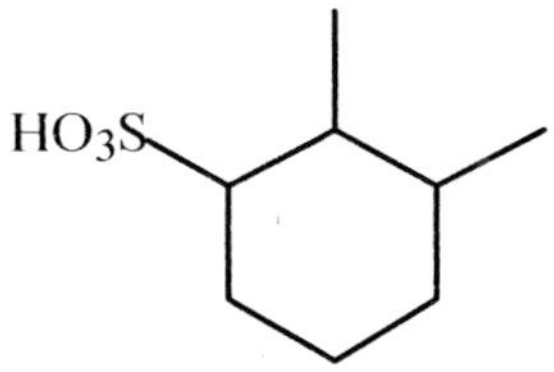

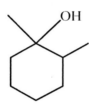

D)

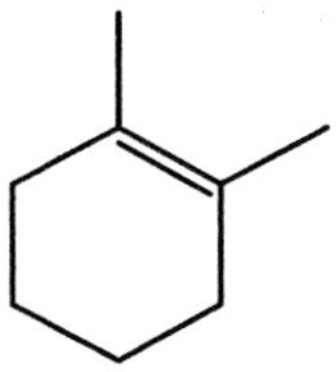

E)

Ans: D

42. Give the IUPAC name for the following compound:

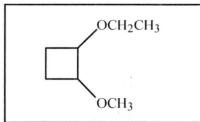

A) 1-ethoxy-2-methoxycyclobutane   D) 1-methoxy-2-ethoxycyclopropane
B) 1-ethoxy-2-methoxycyclopropane   E) 1-methoxy-2-ethoxybutane
C) 1-methoxy-2-ethoxycyclobutane
Ans: A

43. Predict the **major** product of the following reaction:

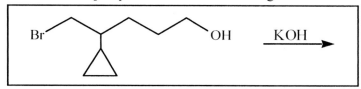

A)

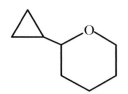

B)

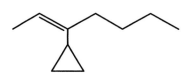

C)

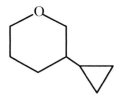

D)

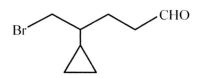

E)

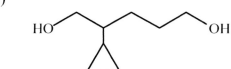

Ans: D

44. Predict the **major** product of the following reaction:

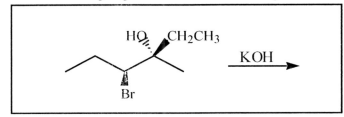

A)

B)

C)

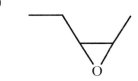

D)

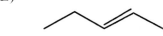

Racemic Mixture

E)

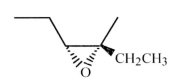

Ans: B

45. Most epoxy resins contain ____ oxacyclopropane functional groups
A) 1   B) 2   C) 3   D) 4   E) 5
Ans: B

46. For the transformations below, what is the structure of the starting material?

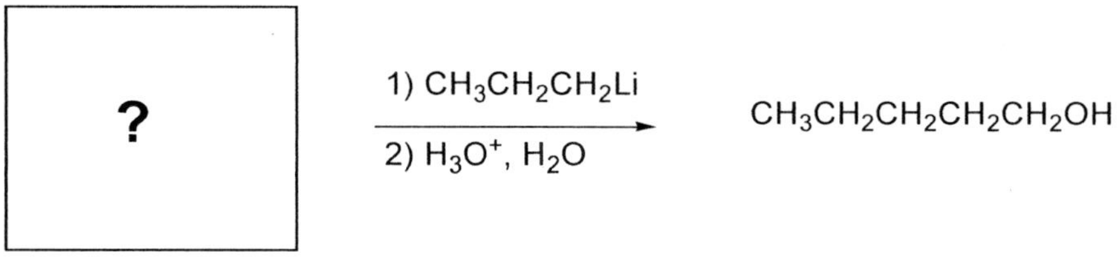

$\xrightarrow[\text{2) H}_3\text{O}^+\text{, H}_2\text{O}]{\text{1) CH}_3\text{CH}_2\text{CH}_2\text{Li}}$ CH$_3$CH$_2$CH$_2$CH$_2$CH$_2$OH

A)   CH$_3$CH$_2$OH
B)

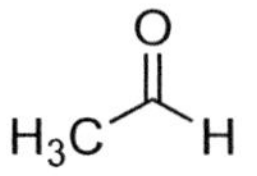

C)

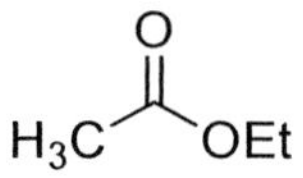

D)

E)   none of the above

Ans: D

47. For the transformations below, what is the structure of the product?

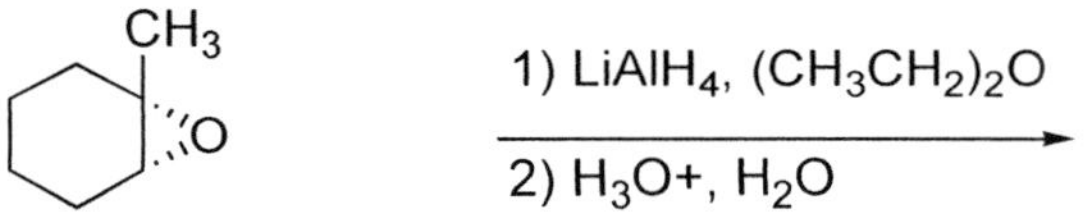

$\xrightarrow[\text{2) H}_3\text{O+, H}_2\text{O}]{\text{1) LiAlH}_4\text{, (CH}_3\text{CH}_2\text{)}_2\text{O}}$

A)

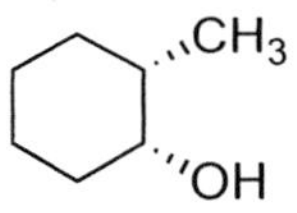

B)

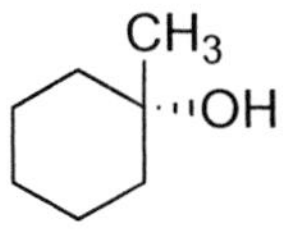

C)

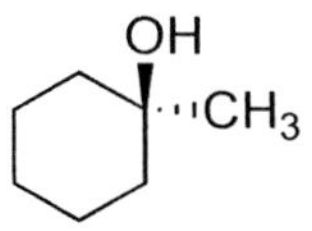

D)

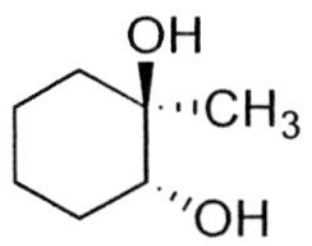

E)   none of the above

Ans: B

48. For the transformations below, what is the structure of the major product?

NaH, DMF

A)

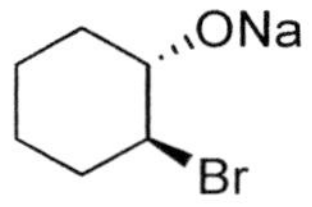

B)

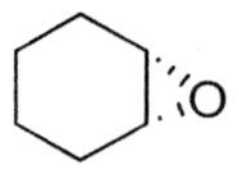

C)

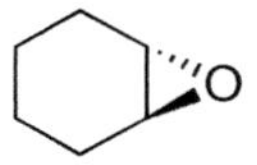

D)

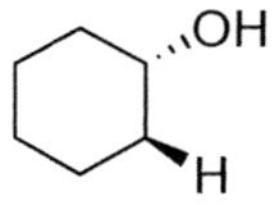

OH

H

E)

OH

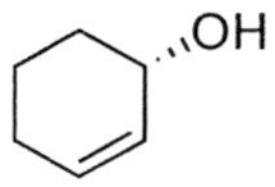

Ans: B

49. For the transformations below, what is the structure of the starting material?

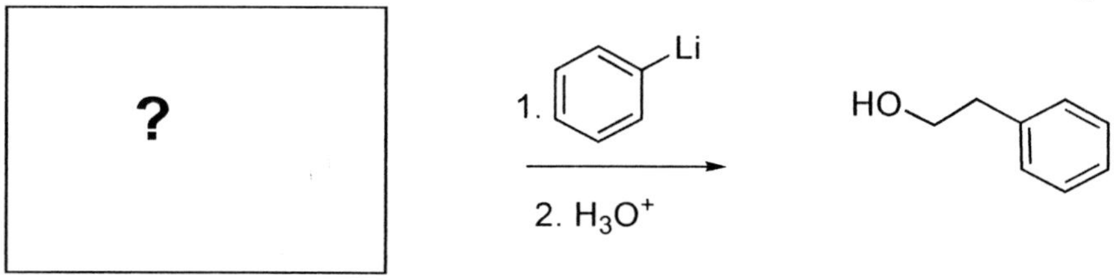

?

2. H₃O⁺

HO

A)

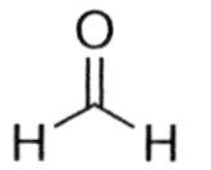

O

H   H

B)   CH₃CH₂OH

C)

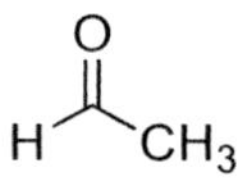

O

H   CH₃

D) 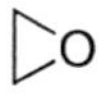   ▷O

E) 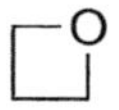   ☐O

Ans: D

Chapter 10: Using Nuclear Magnetic Resonance Spectroscopy to Deduce Structure

1. In nuclear magnetic resonance, stronger magnetic fields
   A)   give a higher sensitivity spectrum than do lower magnetic fields.
   B)   give different chemical shifts (in ppm) than would weaker magnets.
   C)   give better separation between peaks in the spectrum (in Hz) than would weaker magnets.
   D)   give different coupling constants than would be observed with weaker magnetic fields.
   E)   Both A and C are true.
   Ans: E

2. Which of the following structures of formula $C_8H_8Br_2$ would give the NMR spectrum shown below?

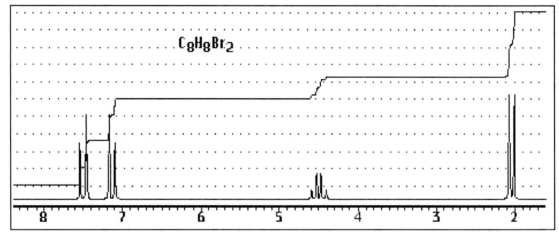

A)

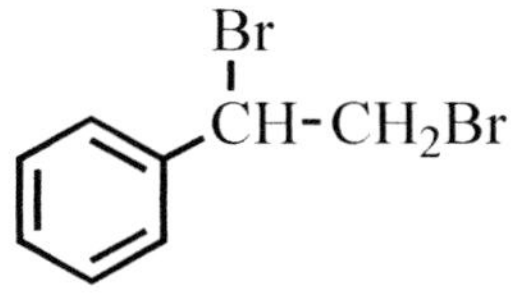

Br
|
CH–CH$_2$Br

B)

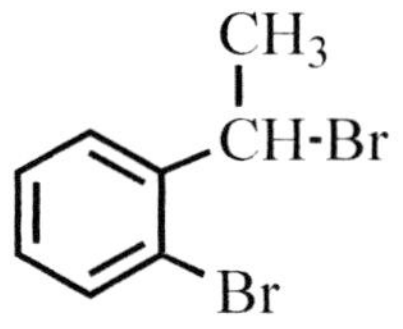

CH$_3$
|
CH·Br

Br

C)

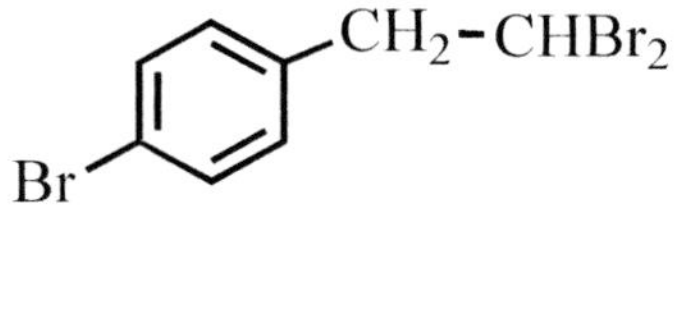

CH$_2$–CHBr$_2$

Br

D)

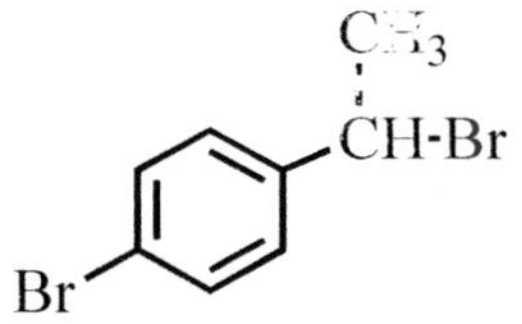

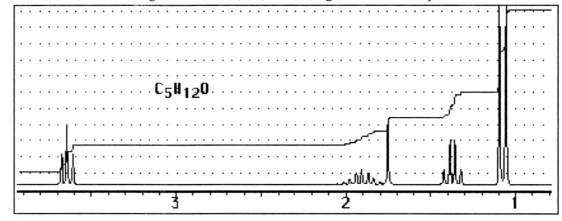

CH₃

CH-Br

Br

E)

CH₂-CH₂Br

Br

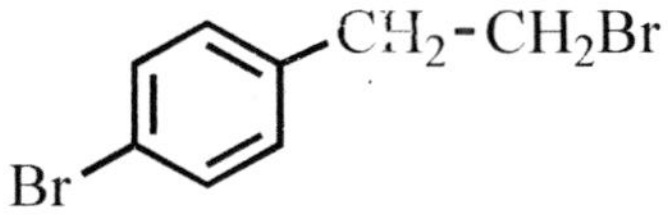

Ans: D

3. The type of electromagnetic energy required to cause nuclear magnetic resonance is
A) infrared   B) radio   C) ultraviolet   D) visible   E) microwave
Ans: B

4. Which of the following structures $C_5H_{12}O$ would give the NMR spectrum shown?

$C_5H_{12}O$

A)

$H_3C-CH_2\cdot CH_2\cdot CH_2\cdot CH_2OH$

B)

$$OH$$
$$H_3C-CH_2\cdot CH-CH_2\cdot CH_3$$

C)

$$OH$$
$$H_3C-CH_2\cdot CH_2\cdot CH-CH_3$$

D)

$$OH$$
$$CH_3\text{-}CH\text{-}CH\text{-}CH_3$$
$$CH_3$$

E)

$$CH_3\text{-}CH\text{-}CH_2\cdot CH_2OH$$
$$CH_3$$

Ans: E

5. Which of the following is **not** true of ^{13}C NMR?
   A) The sensitivity of ^{13}C NMR is much less than that of proton NMR.
   B) By simultaneously decoupling the proton region, ^{13}C peaks appear as singlets.
   C) ^{13}C chemical shifts cover a much larger range than do ^1H chemical shifts.
   D) The ^{13}C NMR spectrum can show more peaks than there are carbons in the molecular formula.
   E) The ^{13}C NMR spectrum will show one peak for each type of carbon in a molecule.
   Ans: D

6. How many **different** types of hydrogens are present in the following molecule?

$$Br \qquad Br$$
$$H_3C-CH-CH-CH-CH_3$$
$$Br$$

   A) three   B) four   C) five   D) six   E) seven
   Ans: A

7. The CH_2 group indicated would most likely appear as what in the proton NMR spectrum?

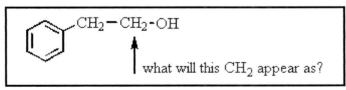

   A) singlet   B) doublet   C) triplet   D) quartet   E) pentet
   Ans: C

8. How many **different** types of carbon would be present in the following molecule?

A) three   B) four   C) five   D) six   E) eight

Ans: B

9. A bottle in a chemical stockroom was labeled simply "dichlorobenzene" without specifying which isomer was present. Capillary GC showed that it was a single pure compound, and the proton decoupled carbon NMR spectrum showed **three** peaks (not including solvent). You conclude that the bottle contained

A)

Cl
Cl
(ortho)

B)

Cl

(para)

Cl

C)

Cl

(meta)
Cl

D)   any of the dichlorobenzene isomers
E)   none of the dichlorobenzene isomers

Ans: A

10. The most downfield proton NMR signal (i.e., signal most to the left in the spectrum) in the following molecule would be

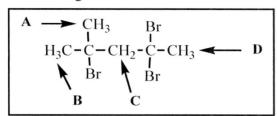

A) A   B) B   C) C   D) D   E) there is no way to tell
Ans: C

11. A very old bottle labeled only "chlorinated benzene" was found in the stockroom. Capillary GC showed (surprisingly) that the compound was pure, and a proton-decoupled ^{13}C NMR spectrum showed only two peaks. Which of the following compounds was in the bottle?
A)

B)

C)

D)

E)

Ans: D

12. How many different signals will be present in the proton NMR for ethylpropanoate? (Do not count TMS as one of the signals!)
A) 2   B) 3   C) 4   D) 5   E) 6
Ans: C

13. Which compound most likely exhibits the following proton NMR?

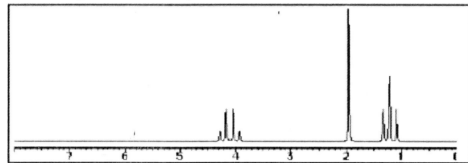

A)

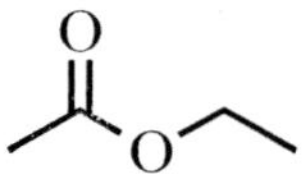

B)

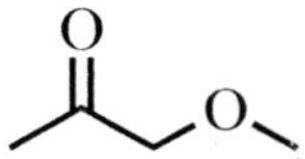

C)

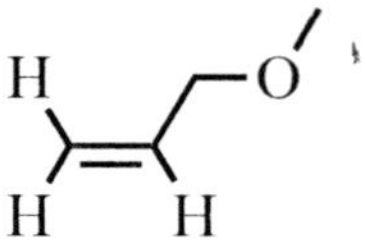

D)

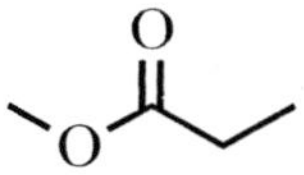

E)

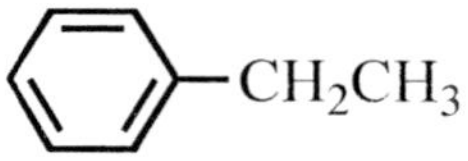

−CH₂CH₃

Ans: A

14. Which of the following structures will give **three** signals (not counting TMS) in the proton decoupled ^{13}C NMR?

A)

B)

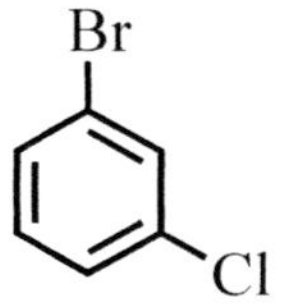

C)

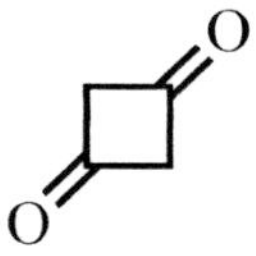

D)

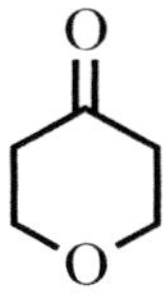

E)

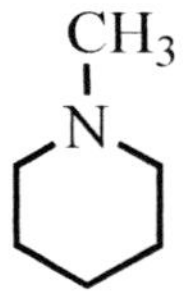

Ans: D

15. Which compound most likely matches the following proton NMR?

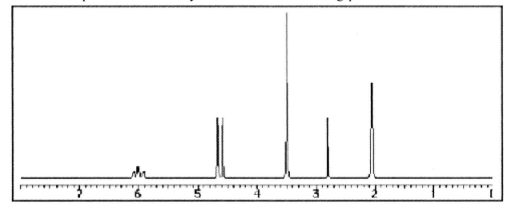

A)

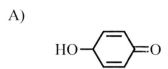

B)

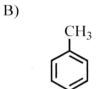

C)

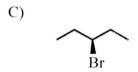

D)

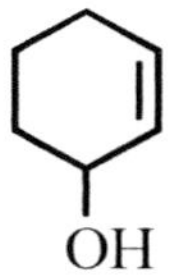

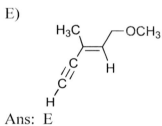

E)

H₃C   —OCH₃

Ans: E

16. 2-pentanone would show how many signals in the proton-decoupled ^{13}C NMR spectrum (not counting TMS)?
A) 1   B) 2   C) 3   D) 4   E) 5
Ans: E

17. Acetone would show how many doublets in the **proton-coupled** ^{13}C NMR spectrum?
A) 0   B) 1   C) 2   D) 3   E) 4
Ans: A

18. Heating the 4-methylbenzenesulfonate ester of the isomer shown below in 2,2,2-trifluoroethanol (a highly ionizing solvent of low nucleophilicity) leads two products with the molecular formula $C_{10}H_{18}$. The **major** product displays 10 different signals in its ^{13}C NMR spectrum. Two of them occur at relatively low field, about δ = 120 and 145 ppm, respectively. The ^{1}H NMR spectrum exhibits a multiplet near δ = 5 ppm (1 H); all other signals are upfield of δ = 3 ppm. Identify the compound.

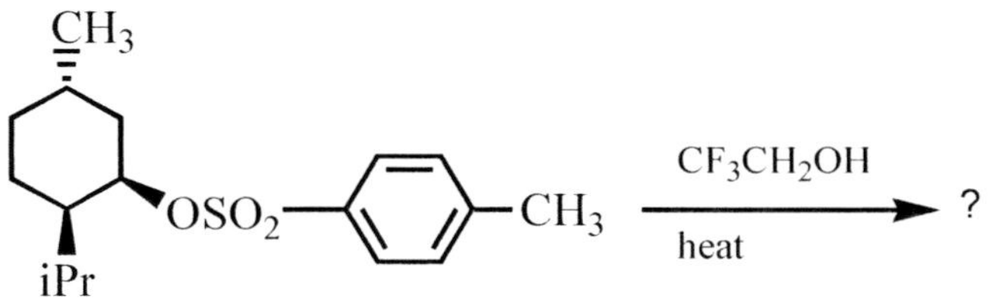

Note: ^{i}Pr = isopropyl

A)

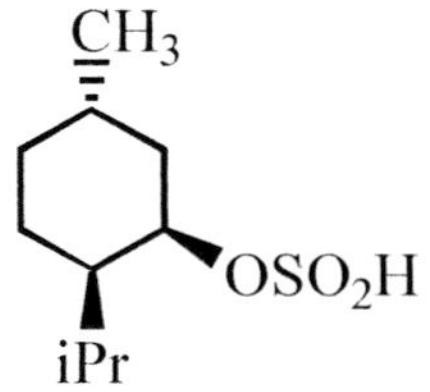

B)

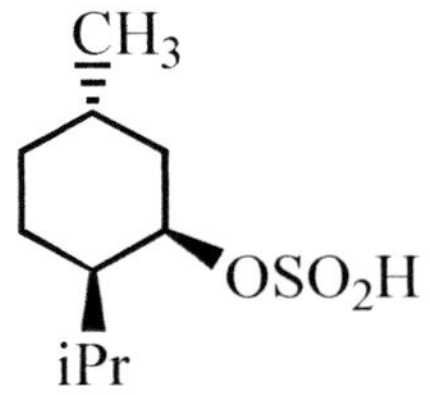

C)

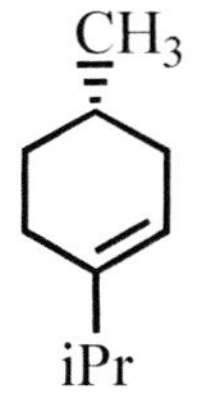

D)

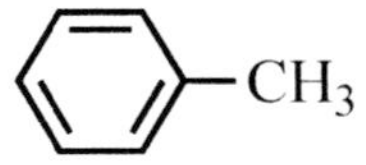

E)

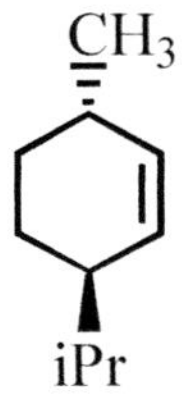

Ans: C

19. The molecular formulas and ^{13}C NMR data (in ppm) are given below. The splitting pattern of each signal, taken from the **non-decoupled** spectrum is given in parentheses. Deduce the correct structure:

C_4H_6O: 18.2 (q), 134.9 (d), 153.7 (d), 193.4 (d)

A)

B)

C)

D)

E)

Ans: C

20. The molecular formulas and ^{13}C NMR data (in ppm) are given below. The splitting pattern of each signal, taken from the **non-decoupled** spectrum is given in parentheses. Deduce the correct structure:

C_7H_{10}: 25.2 (t), 41.9 (d), 48.5 (t), 135.2 (d)

A)

B)

C)

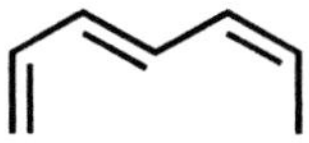

D)

E)

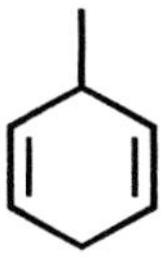

Ans: A

21. The NMR peak intensities for a first-order quartet are:
    A) 1:2:2:1   B) 1:3:3:1   C) 1:4:4:1   D) 1:1:1:1   E) none of the above
    Ans: B

22. The natural abundance of ^{13}C is
    A) 2.1%   B) 10%   C) 1.5%   D) 1.1%   E) 16%
    Ans: D

23. What structure of formula $C_3H_6Br_2$ would give the following proton NMR spectrum?

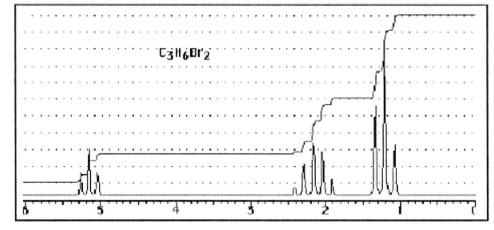

A)

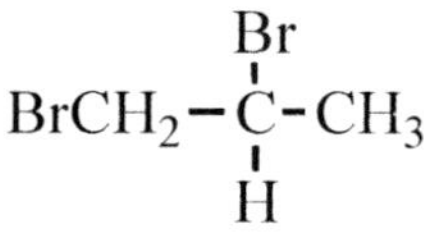

Br
|
BrCH₂−C-CH₃
|
H

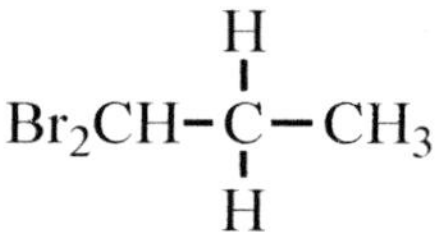

B)

H
|
Br₂CH-C−CH₃
|
H

C)

Br
|
H₃C-C-CH₃
|
Br

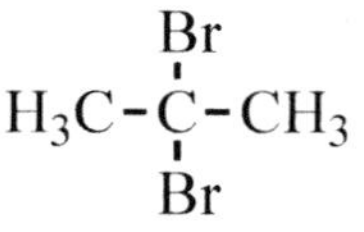

D)

H
|
BrCH₂−C-CH₂Br
|
H

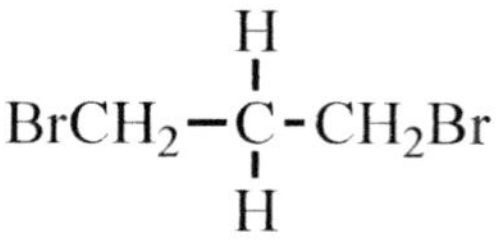

E)   none of the above

Ans: B

24. Which compound C₉H₁₁Br would give the proton NMR spectrum shown below?

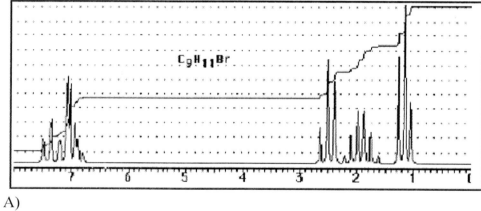

A)

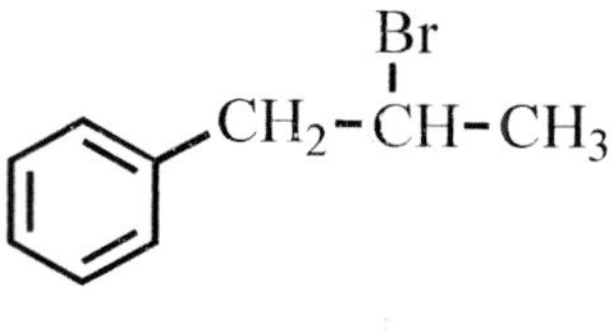

Br
|
CH₂−CH-CH₃

B)

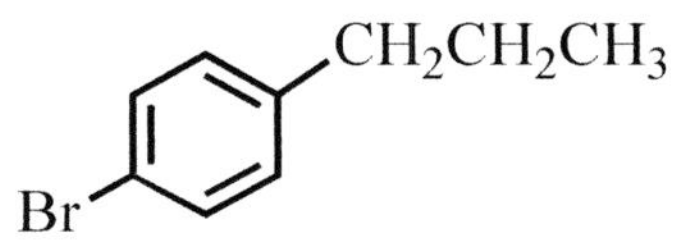

CH₂CH₂CH₃

Br

C)

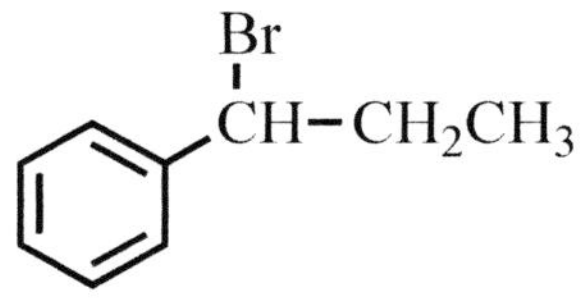

Br
|
CH−CH₂CH₃

D)

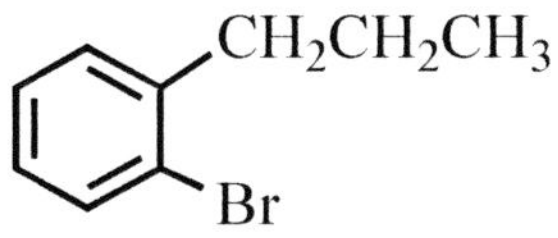

CH₂CH₂CH₃

Br

E)

CH₃
|
CH−CH₂Br

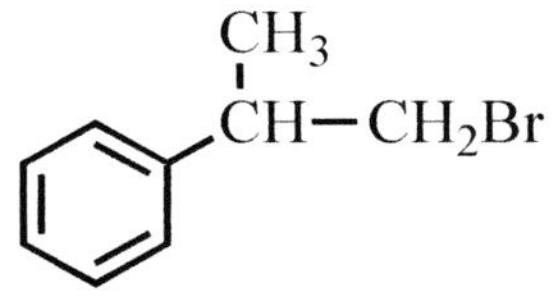

Ans: D

25. In the **proton-coupled** ^{13}C-NMR spectrum of the following molecule, how many doublets would be observed?

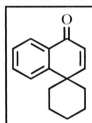

A) 2   B) 4   C) 6   D) 8   E) none of the above
Ans: C

26. The following ^{1}H-NMR spectrum was most likely obtained from which of the compounds listed below?

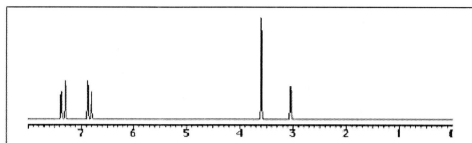

A)

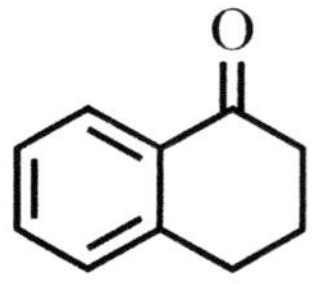

B)

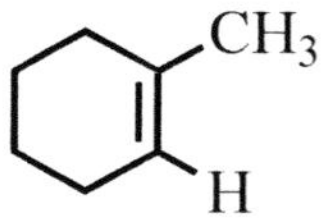

C)

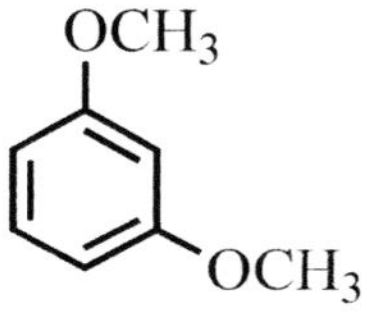

D)

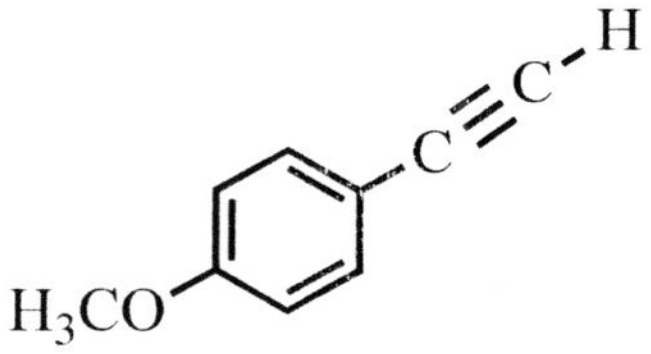

E)

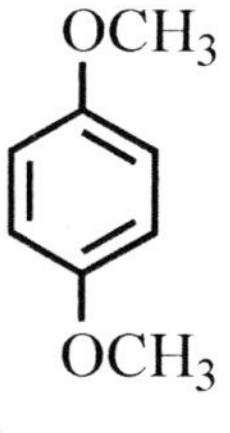

Ans: D

27. The following ^{1}H-NMR was most likely obtained from which of the compounds listed below?

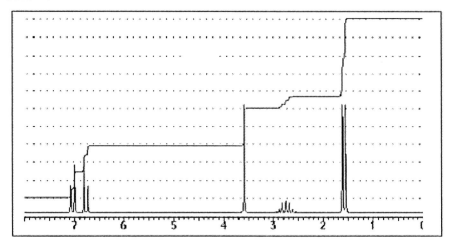

A)

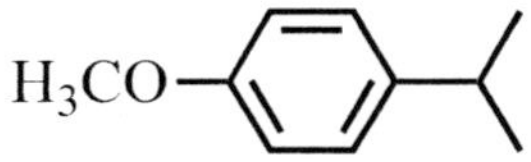

H$_3$CO—⟨benzene⟩—CH(CH$_3$)$_2$

B)

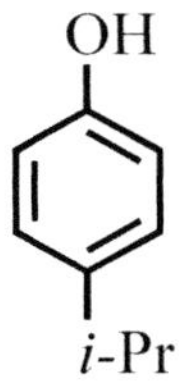

OH

i-Pr

C)

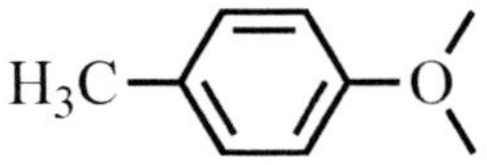

H$_3$C—⟨benzene⟩—O

D)

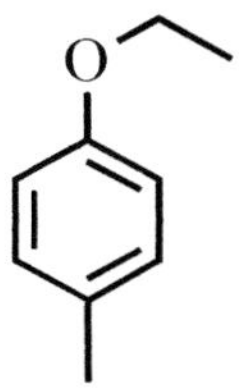

O—CH$_2$CH$_3$

E)

H$_3$C—⟨benzene⟩—O—CH(CH$_3$)$_2$

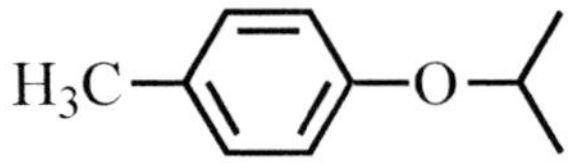

Ans: A

28. The following spectra data was most likely obtained from which compound?

IR Bands (cm^{-1})
3000
1740
1695

proton NMR	
Chemical shift (ppm)	Multiplicity
3.85	Singlet
2.70	Triplet
2.25	Triplet

Carbon-13 NMR
Chemical shift (ppm)
200
170
70
35
30

A)

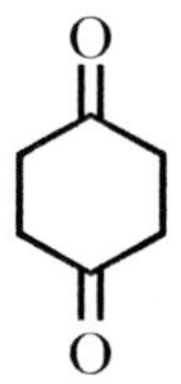

B)

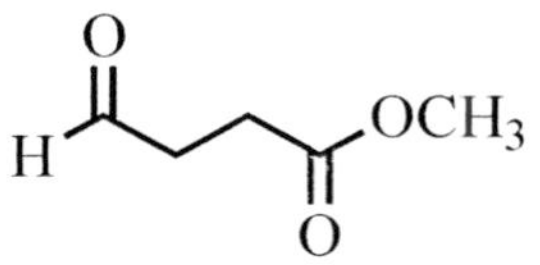

C)

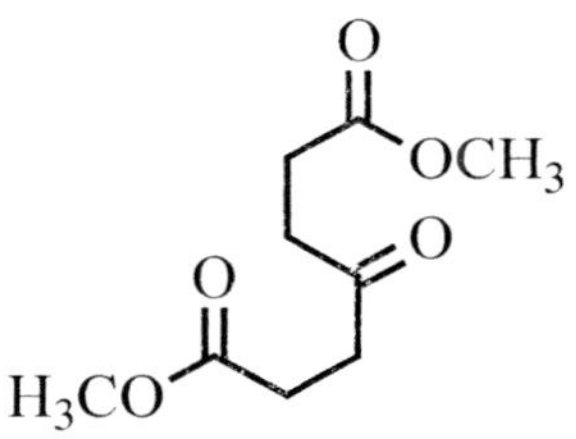

D)

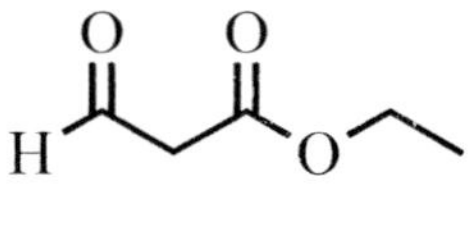

E)

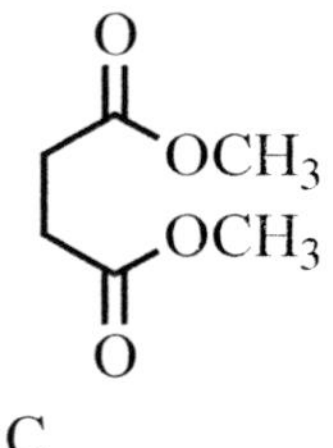

Ans: C

29. Consider the ^{1}H-NMR of the molecule shown below. Assume that $J_{CB} = 7$ Hz and $J_{CA} = 1$ Hz. What coupling pattern will H_c exhibit?

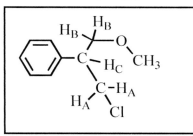

   A)   pentet   D)   triplet of triplets
   B)   quartet   E)   doublet of triplets
   C)   doublet of quartets

Ans: D

30. A seven-carbon compound which gives three signals in the ^{13}C NMR spectrum could be:
   A)   heptane   D)   2,4-dimethylpentane
   B)   2-methylhexane   E)   2,2,3-trimethylbutane
   C)   3,3-dimethylpentane

Ans: D

31. Carbon-13 NMR is
   A)   impossible since ^{13}C has no magnetic moment
   B)   complicated by ^{13}C-^{13}C splitting
   C)   impossible since ^{13}C does not occur in nature
   D)   more difficult than ^{1}H NMR
   E)   none of the above

Ans: D

32. A compound of the formula $C_{10}H_{14}$ gave the ^{1}H NMR spectrum shown below **and** exhibited three peaks in the ^{13}C NMR spectrum. What compound might it be?

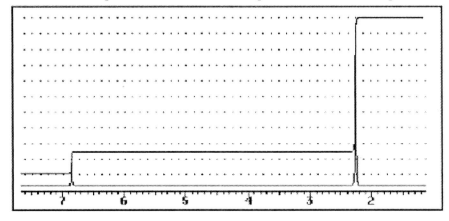

A)

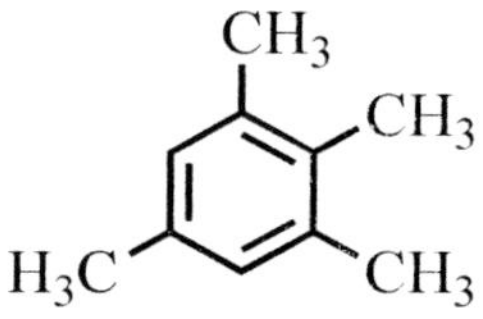
CH_3
CH_3
H_3C
CH_3

B)

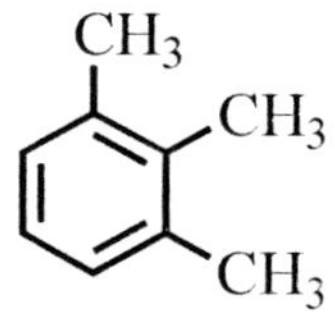
CH_3
CH_3
CH_3

C)

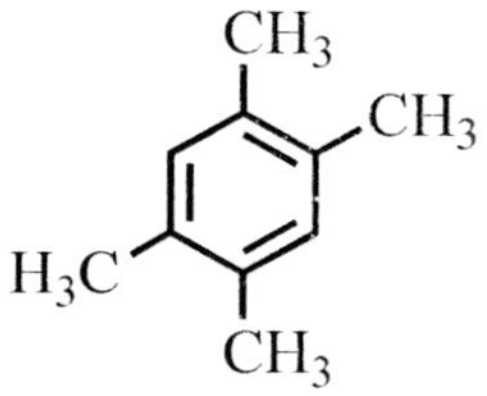
CH_3
CH_3
H_3C
CH_3

D)

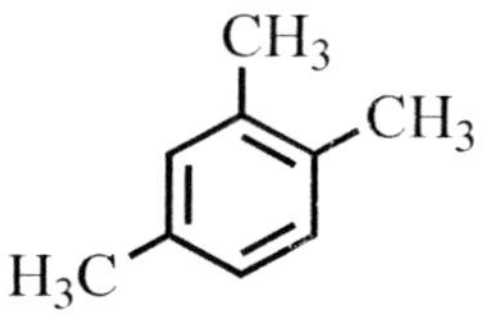
CH_3
CH_3
H_3C

E)

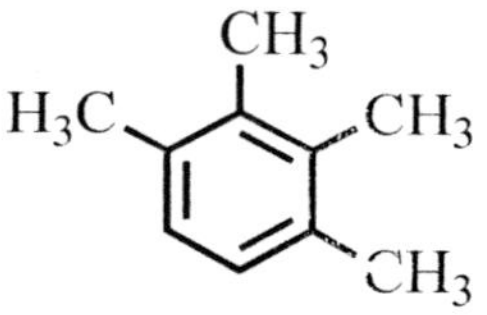
CH_3
H_3C
CH_3
CH_3

Ans: C

33. The proton NMR spectrum of a carboxylic acid, $C_{13}H_{18}O_2$, commonly sold as an over-the-counter headache remedy, is shown below. Note: the CO_2H proton is not shown, and the multiplicity of the peaks are noted (d = doublet, q = quartet, m = multiplet). Which structure is that of this pharmaceutical?

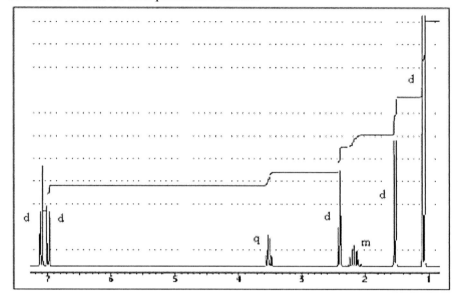

A)

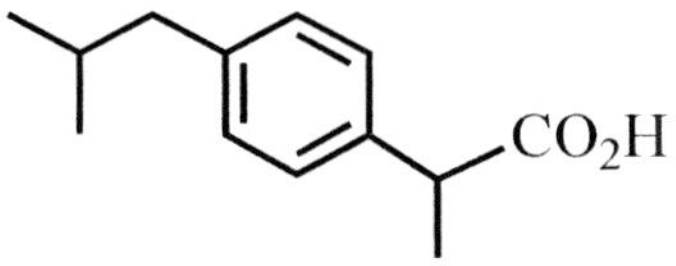

B)

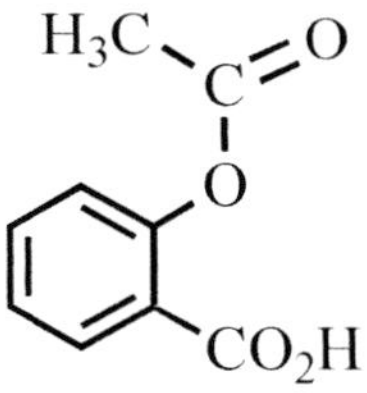

C)

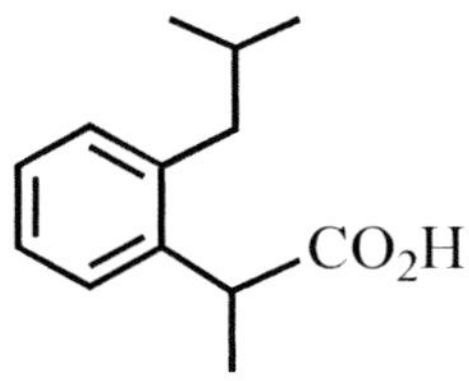

D)

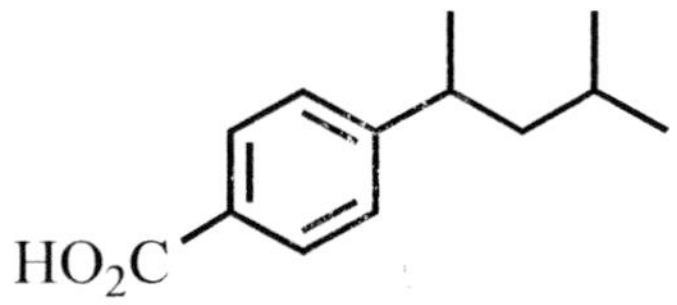

E)

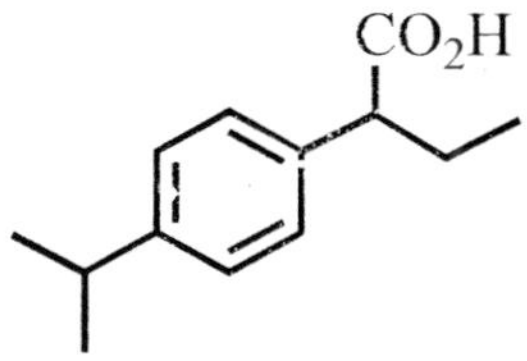

Ans: A

34. What structure would be consistent with the following NMR spectrum and data?

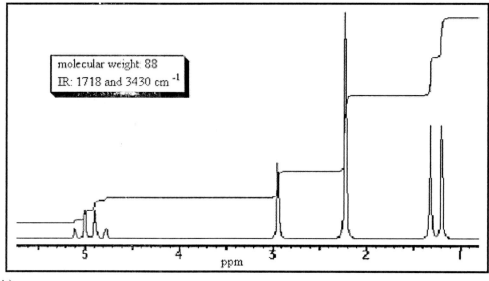

molecular weight: 88
IR: 1718 and 3430 cm $^{-1}$

ppm

A)

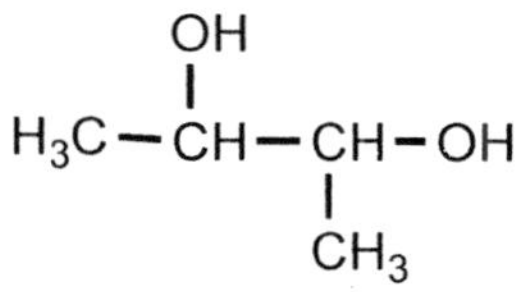

$$OH$$
$$H_3C-CH-CH-OH$$
$$CH_3$$

B)

$$H_3C \overset{O}{\underset{CH_3}{\big|\big|}} \overset{O}{\underset{}{\big|\big|}}$$

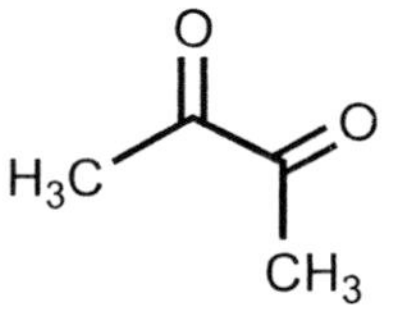

C)

$$H-\underset{\underset{O}{\|}}{C}-\underset{\underset{OH}{|}}{CH}-CH_2-CH_3$$

D)

$$H_3C-\underset{\underset{O}{\|}}{C}-\underset{\underset{CH_3}{|}}{CH}-OH$$

E)

$$H-\underset{\underset{O}{\|}}{C}-CH_2-\underset{\underset{CH_3}{|}}{CH}-OH$$

Ans: D

35. How many magnetically different **types** of hydrogens and carbons are in the following compound?

A)   6 hydrogens, 8 carbons
B)   3 hydrgens, 8 carbons
C)   6 hydrogens, 6 carbons
D)   3 hydrogens, 6 carbons
E)   3 hydrogens, 3 carbons
Ans: D

36. Typical hydrogen chemical shifts for aromatic protons occur in the range from
A) δ 0.8-2.0
B) δ 7.0-8.0
C) δ 0.5-5.0
D) δ 3.3-4.0
E)   none of the above

Ans: B

37. Which is following is **not** true about the information from a proton NMR spectrum?
    A)   It identifies the number of different types of hydrogens in a molecule.
    B)   It gives the ratios of one type of hydrogen to another.
    C)   It gives information about what environment each hydrogen is in.
    D)   It tells how many neighboring hydrogens each type of hydrogen has.
    E)   Proton NMR gives all these types of information.
    Ans: E

38. Which of the following nuclei are incapable of magnetic resonance?
    A)   Hydrogen (^{1}H)   D)   Chlorine (^{31}P)
    B)   Carbon (^{13}C)   E)   All are NMR active
    C)   Fluorine (^{19}F)
    Ans: E

39. A chemist is evaluating a proton NMR spectrum taken on a 300 MHz NMR
    spectrometer. She wishes to determine the chemical shift in ppm of a singlet that
    appears at 1140 Hz from TMS. What is the chemical shift in ppm?
    A) 0.26 ppm   B) 3.8 ppm   C) 7.6 ppm   D) 300 ppm   E) none of the above
    Ans: B

40. For the compound below give the spin-spin splitting that would be observed for each of
    the protons sets in the ^{1}H NMR spectrum.

    $$\text{H}_a-\underset{\underset{\text{H}_a}{|}}{\overset{\overset{\text{H}_a}{|}}{\text{C}}}-\overset{\overset{\text{O}}{||}}{\text{C}}-\text{O}-\underset{\underset{\text{H}_b}{|}}{\overset{\overset{\text{H}_b}{|}}{\text{C}}}-\underset{\underset{\text{H}_c}{|}}{\overset{\overset{\text{H}_c}{|}}{\text{C}}}-\text{H}_c$$

    A) H_a = triplet H_b = doublet, H_c = quartet
    B) H_a = singlet H_b = quartet, H_c = triplet
    C) H_a = singlet H_b = pentet, H_c = quartet
    D) H_a = triplet H_b = quartet, H_c = singlet
    E)   none of the above
    Ans: B

41. For the compound below give the integration ratio that would be observed for each of
    the protons sets in the ^{1}H NMR spectrum.

    $$\text{H}_a-\underset{\underset{\text{H}_a}{|}}{\overset{\overset{\text{H}_a}{|}}{\text{C}}}-\overset{\overset{\text{O}}{||}}{\text{C}}-\text{O}-\underset{\underset{\text{H}_b}{|}}{\overset{\overset{\text{H}_b}{|}}{\text{C}}}-\underset{\underset{\text{H}_c}{|}}{\overset{\overset{\text{H}_c}{|}}{\text{C}}}-\text{H}_c$$

    A) H_a = 3, H_b = 2, H_c = 1   D) H_a = 1 H_b = 1, H_c = 1
    B) H_a = 1 H_b = 2, H_c = 1   E)   none of the above
    C) H_a = 3 H_b = 2, H_c = 3
    Ans: C

42. How many signals will be present in a decoupled ^{13}C NMR spectrum for the molecule below?

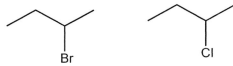

A) 7   B) 8   C) 9   D) 10   E) none of the above

Ans: C

43. Indicate how ^1H NMR spectroscopy can be used to distinguish between the following sets of structures.

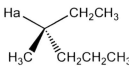

A)   The spin-spin splitting for the protons on the carbon next to the halogen will be different.

B)   The chemical shift of the resonance for the protons on the carbon attached to the chlorine atom will be shifted downfield relative to the protons on the carbon attached to the bromine atom.

C)   The chemical shift of the resonance for the protons on the carbon attached to the chlorine atom will be shifted upfield relative to the protons on the carbon attached to the bromine atom.

D)   The integration of the protons on the carbon next to the halogen will be different.

E)   none of the above

Ans: B

44. Describe the splitting that would be observed by H_a in the proton NMR spectrum, assuming H_a is coupled to all its neighboring protons in an equivalent manner.

$$Ha\diagdown \quad {}_{\diagup}CH_2CH_3$$

$$H_3C \diagup \quad \diagdown CH_2CH_2CH_3$$

A) H_a will be split into a pentet   D) H_a will be split into an octet.
B) H_a will be split into a sextet.   E)   none of the above
C) H_a will be split into a septet.

Ans: D

45. Arrange each of the following labeled hydrogens in the order of increasing chemical shift.

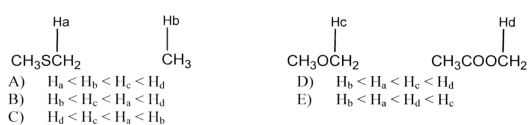

A) $H_a < H_b < H_c < H_d$
B) $H_b < H_c < H_a < H_d$
C) $H_d < H_c < H_a < H_b$
D) $H_b < H_a < H_c < H_d$
E) $H_b < H_a < H_d < H_c$

Ans: D

Chapter 11: Alkenes; Infrared Spectroscopy and Mass Spectrometry

1. What would be the name of the following compound?

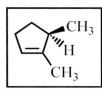

    A)   2,3-dimethylcyclopentene   D)   *cis*-1,5-dimethylcyclopentene
    B)   1,5-dimethylcyclopentene   E)   *trans*-2,3-dimethylcyclopentene
    C)   *cis*-2,3-dimethylcyclopentene

    Ans: A

2. Which of the following alkenes of the formula C_5H_{10} would you expect to be the **least** stable?

    A)

    B)

    C)

    D)

    E)

    Ans: C

3. What would be the organic product of the following reaction?

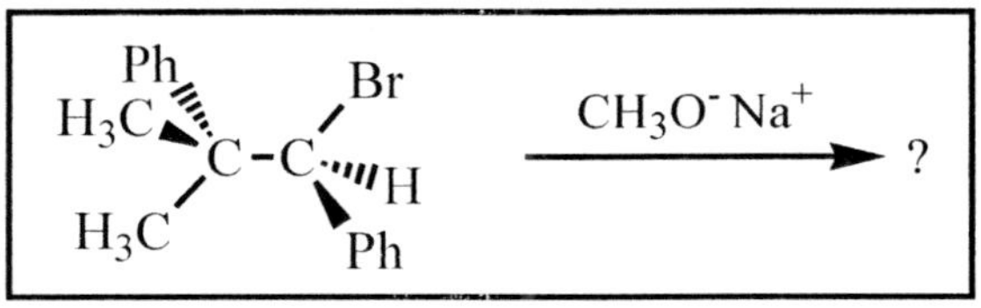

A)

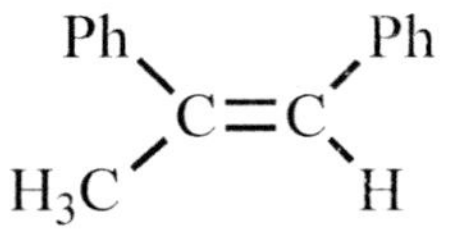

B)

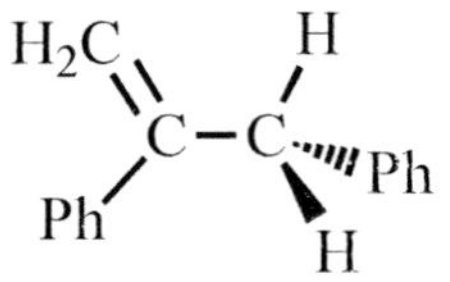

C)

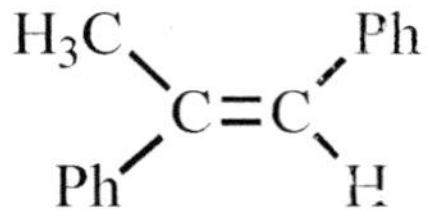

D)

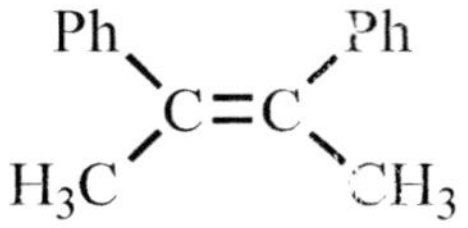

E)   none of the above

Ans: E

4. What would be the proper name of the following?

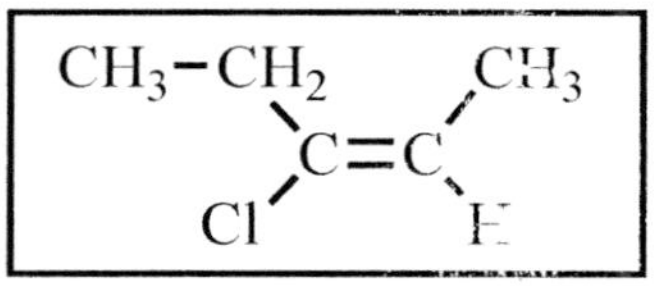

A)   (Z)-3-chloro-2-pentene   D)   (E)-3-chloro-3-pentene
B)   (Z)-3-chloro-3-pentene   E)   cis-3-chloro-3-pentene
C)   (E)-3-chloro-2-pentene

Ans: C

5. Infrared spectroscopy relies on what phenomenon?
    A)   electronic transitions   D)   molecular stretching and bending
    B)   molecular rotations   E)   conformational interconversion
    C)   nuclear alignments

Ans: D

6. The IR spectrum of a compound shows a strong absorbance peak at 1720 cm^{-1}. What functional group is indicated?
A) OH   B) C=C   C) NH   D) C=O   E) CN
Ans: D

7. A hydrocarbon with the molecular formula C_7H_{12} exhibits the following spectroscopic data: ^{1}H NMR δ = 1.3 (m, 2H), 1.7 (m, 4 H), 2.2 (m, 4H), and 4.8 (quin, J = 3 Hz, 2H) ppm; ^{13}C NMR: δ = 26.8, 28.7, 35.7, 106.9, and 149.7 ppm. The IR spectrum has key absorbances at 3072, 2950, and 1649 cm^{-1}. Hydrogenation of the compound furnishes a product with the molecular formula C_7H_{14}. Which structure is consistent with this data?
A)

B)

C)

D)

E)   none of the above
Ans: D

8. How many units of unsaturation are indicated by the following molecular formula: $C_{17}H_{18}BrI_2O_2N$?
A) 0   B) 2   C) 6   D) 8   E) 10
Ans: D

9. The following molecule contains how many units of unsaturation?

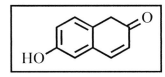

A) 2   B) 3   C) 5   D) 6   E) 7
Ans: E

10. Predict the major product of the following reaction:

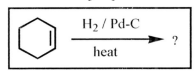

A)

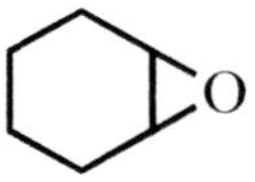

B)

C)

D)

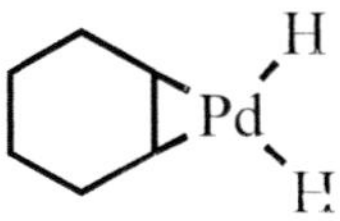

E)   none of the above
Ans: B

11. Which of the following most accurately describes the IR fingerprint region:
    A) $2200 - 3400 \text{ cm}^{-1}$ D) $1500 - 1850 \text{ cm}^{-1}$
    B) $600 - 1500 \text{ cm}^{-1}$ E) $600 - 950 \text{ cm}^{-1}$
    C) $3000 - 3500 \text{ cm}^{-1}$
    Ans: B

12. Which of the following are of **lowest** energy?
    A) radio waves   B) x-rays   C) infrared   D) ultraviolet   E) microwaves
    Ans: A

13. The following molecule contains how many units of unsaturation?

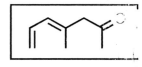

    A) 1   B) 2   C) 3   D) 4   E) 5
    Ans: C

14. What functional group would be indicated by an IR absorption at 2150 cm^{-1}?
    A) C=O   B) C=C   C) OH   D) NH   E) C≡C
    Ans: E

15. What functional group would be indicated by an IR absorption at 1650 cm^{-1}?
    A) C=O   B) C=C   C) OH   D) NH   E) C≡C
    Ans: B

16. Under special reaction conditions, α-pinene and β-pinene can be in equilibrium (caused to interconvert reversably). Using your knowledge of alkene stability, which of the following would be true at equilibrium?

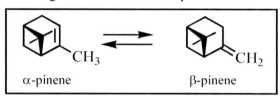

    A)   The α-isomer will predominate.
    B)   The β-isomer will predominate.
    C)   The isomers would be equally favored.
    D)   A third isomer would predominate.
    E)   None of the above is true.
    Ans: A

17. The greatest strength of infrared spectroscopy is in determining
    A)   the degree of unsaturation.
    B)   the relationships of structural fragments.
    C)   the functional groups present.
    D)   the overall structure of the molecule.
    E)   if rings are present.
    Ans: C

18. How many degrees of unsaturation are present in the following molecule?

    $C_{14}H_{13}F_3N_2O$

    A) 3   B) 5   C) 7   D) 8   E) 10
    Ans: D

19. Which of the following structures represents: (Z)-3-fluoro-3-octen-2,5-dione?

A)

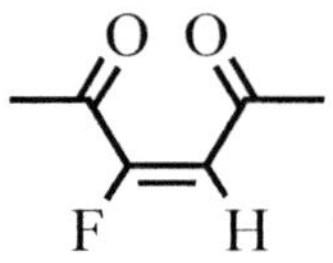

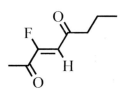

B)

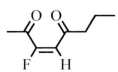

C)

D)

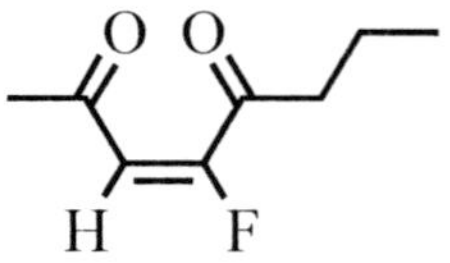

E)

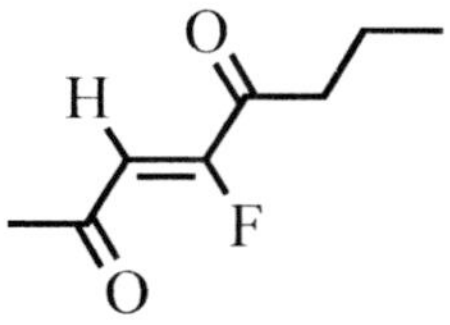

Ans: B

20. The following molecule contains how many units of unsaturation?

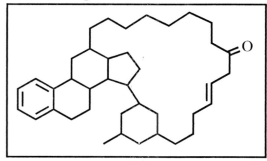

A) 7   B) 9   C) 10   D) 11   E) 15
Ans: D

21. Which of the following are (*Z*) isomers?

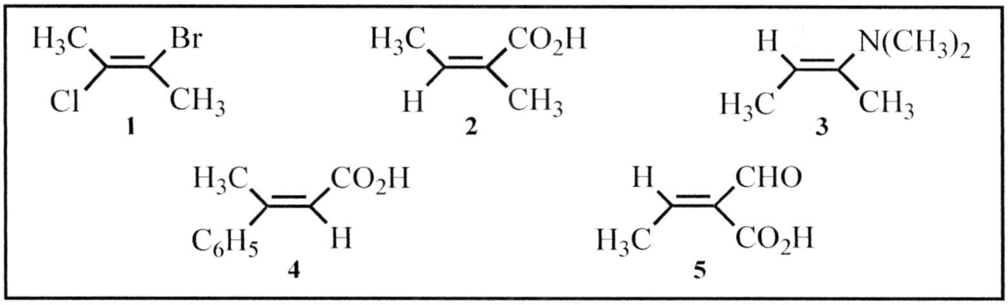

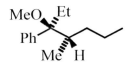

A) 1 and 5 B) 2 and 5 C) 3 and 5 D) 2 and 3 E) 2, 4 and 5

Ans: B

22. Predict the product of the following reaction:

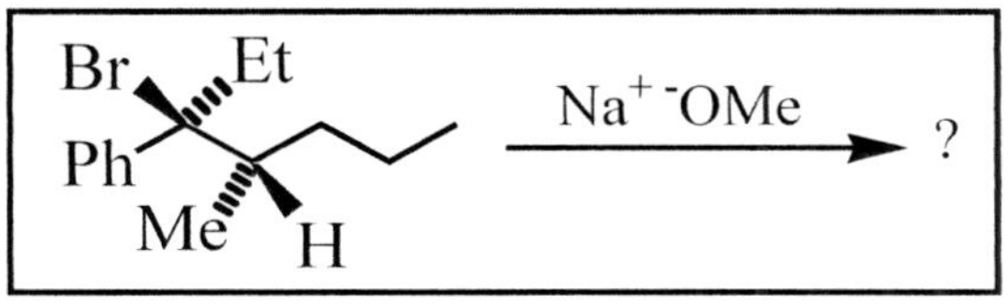

Na⁺ ⁻OMe → ?

A)

B)

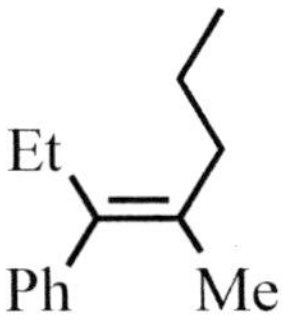

C)

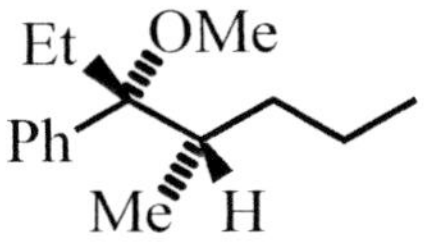

D)

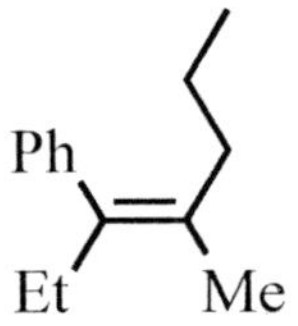

E)

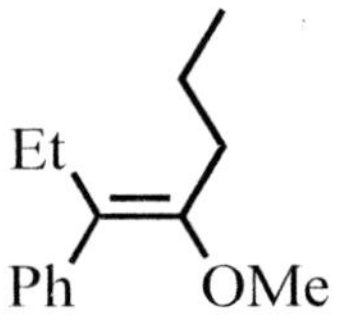

Ans: D

23. Which of the following are of **highest** energy?
    A) radio waves   B) X-rays   C) infrared   D) ultraviolet   E) microwaves
    Ans: B

24. Which is the structure of 3,7-dimethyl-2,6-octadienal?
    A)

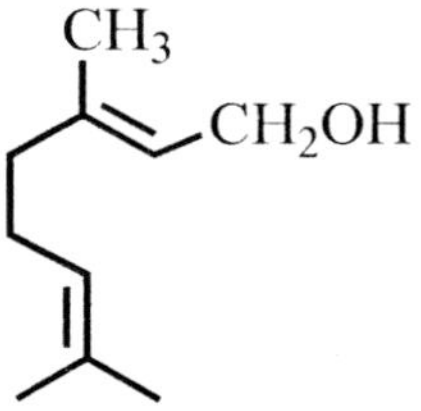

    B)

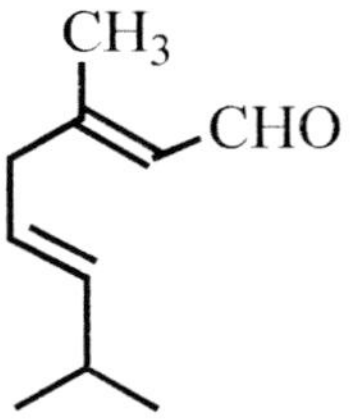

C)

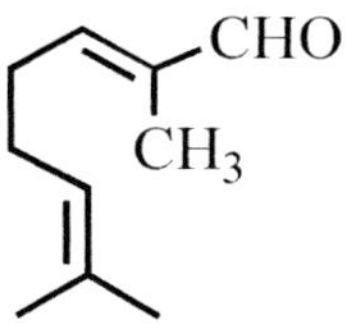

CHO

CH₃

D)

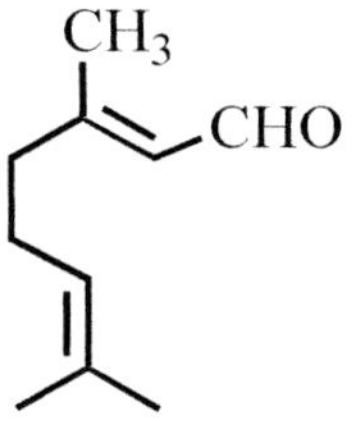

CH₃

CHO

E)

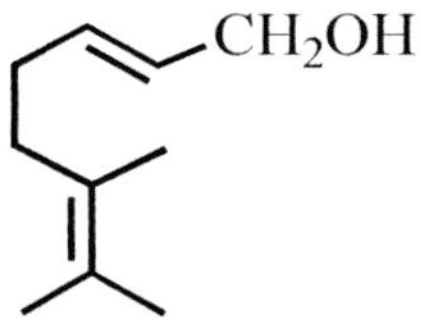

CH₂OH

Ans: D

25. The IUPAC name for piperitone is

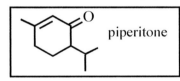

piperitone

A)   6-isopropyl-3-methyl-2-cyclohexenone.
B)   2-isopropyl-5-methyl-5-cyclohexenone.
C)   6-isopropyl-3-methylcyclohexanone.
D)   1-methyl-4-isopropylcyclohexen-3-one.
E)   6-isopropyl-3-methyl-3-cyclohexenone.
Ans: A

26. Which structure would be named 3-bromo-5-methylcyclohexene?

    A)

    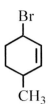

    B)

    C)

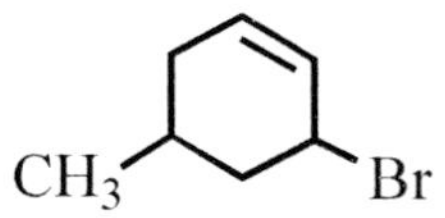

    D)

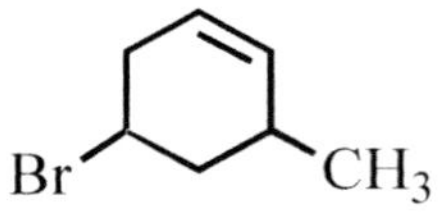

    E)   none of the above

    Ans: C

27. Which of the following are (*E*) isomers?

    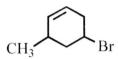

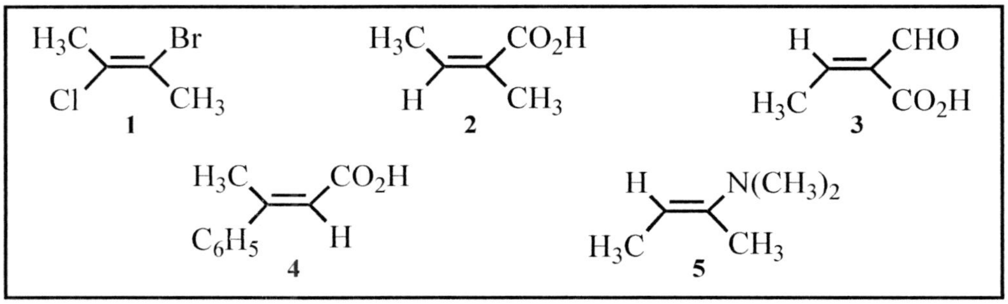

    A) 1, 3, and 5   B) 2, 4, and 5   C) 1, 4, and 5   D) 1, 2, and 4   E) 2, 3, and 4

    Ans: C

28. What product, if any, would result from the reaction shown below?

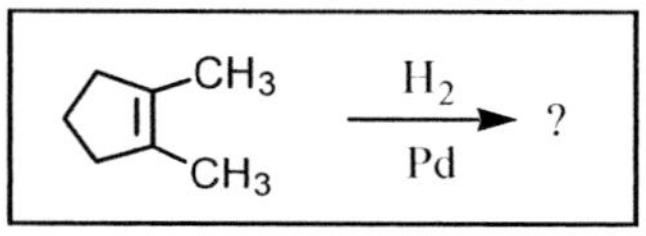

A)

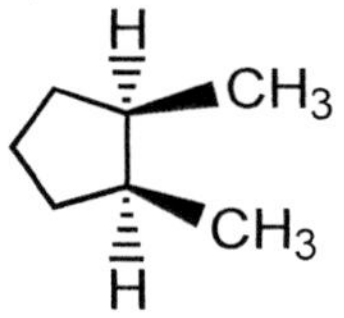

B)

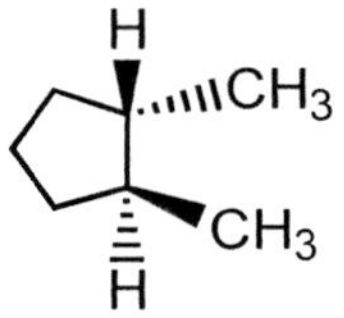

C)

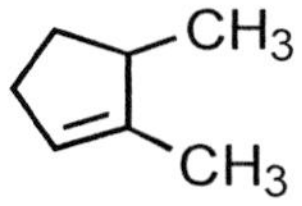

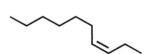

D)   both A and B
E)   no reaction occurs
Ans: A

29. Which of the alkenes shown below would be expected to have the **lowest** melting point?
A)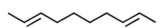
B)

C)

D)

E)   There is no basis for such a prediction.
Ans: C

30. What reagent would give the highest yield of the product shown below?

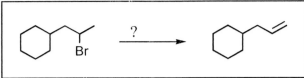

A) K⁺⁻OtBu   B) NaCN   C) CH₃S⁻Na⁺   D) NaOH   E) CH₃O⁻Na⁺

Ans: A

31. If you could have **only one** of the following to use to identify the entire structure of a *previously unknown* organic compound, which would be the best?
    A)   melting point
    B)   IR spectrum
    C)   molecular weight
    D)   NMR spectrum
    E)   boiling point

Ans: D

32. Which reagent(s) would you expect to give the highest yield of the product shown?

A) K⁺⁻OᵗBu   B) CH₃S⁻ Na⁺   C) H₂SO₄   D) CH₃O⁻ Na⁺   E) K⁺⁻CN

Ans: D

33. Which alkene would you expect to release the **least** amount of heat upon hydrogenation?
    A)

    B)

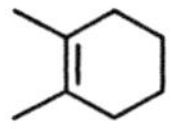

    C)

    D)

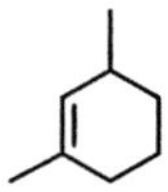

    E)

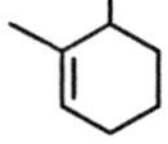

Ans: B

34. Which sets of arrows correctly represents the electron movements during an E2 reaction?

A)

B)

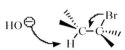

C)

D)

E)

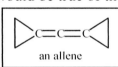

Ans: B

35. Based on what you know about carbon-carbon double bonds, which of the following would be true of the allene shown?

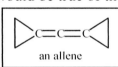

an allene

A) The two rings would be in the same plane.
B) The two rings would be in perpendicular planes.
C) There is no way to tell what geometric relationship the rings would have.
D) The three carbons shown would not be co-linear.
E) Allenes cannot exist.
Ans: B

36. Which of the following are E isomers?

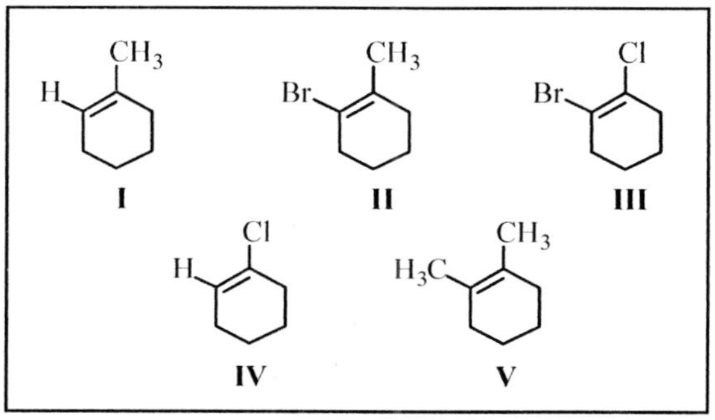

A) III and V   B) II and IV   C) I, III, and V   D) II and III   E) I, II, and IV

Ans: B

37. What product would you expect from the reaction shown below?

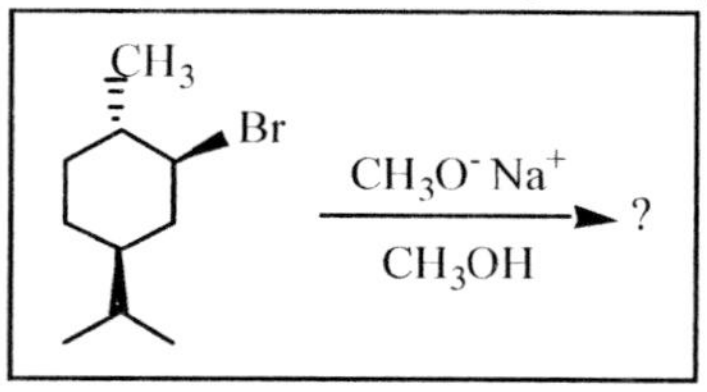

A)

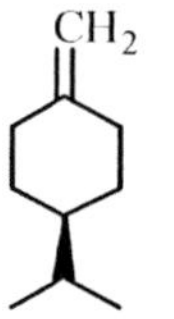

B)

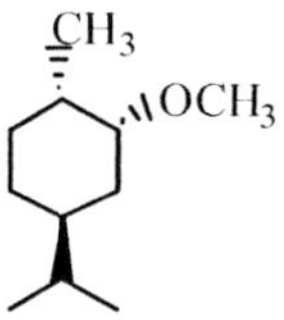

C)

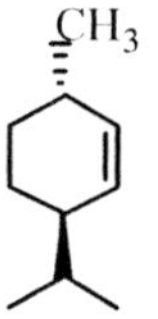

D)

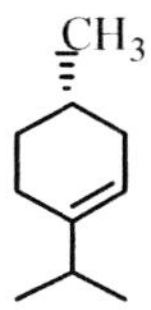

E)

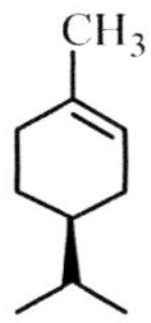

Ans: C

38. Which is the correct order of stabilities of alkenes listed from least stable to most stable?

A)

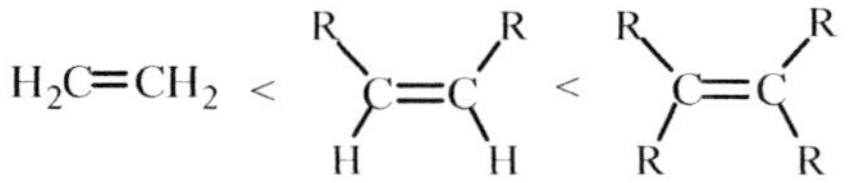

B)

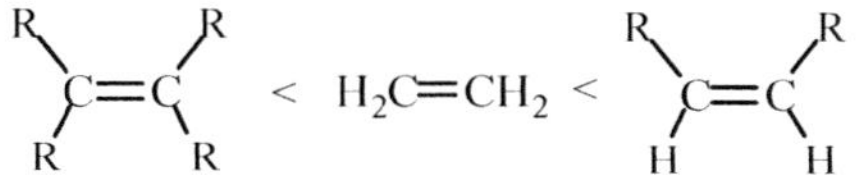

C)

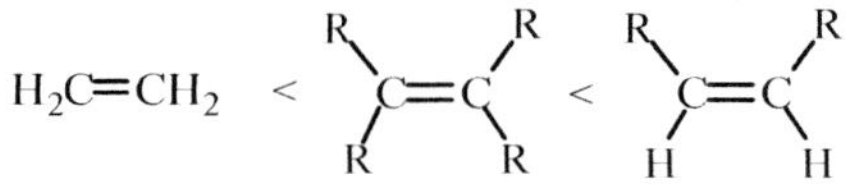

D)

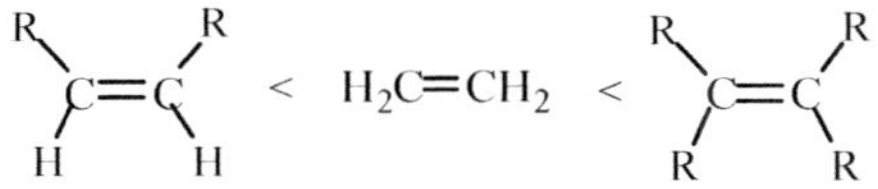

E)

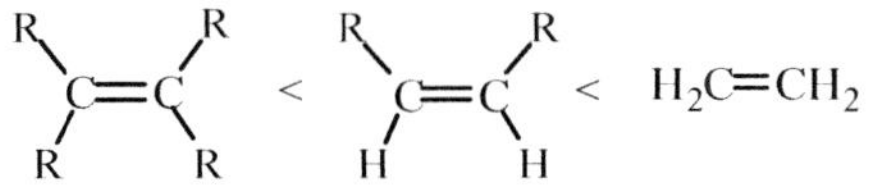

Ans: A

39. What would be the MAJOR organic product of the following reaction?

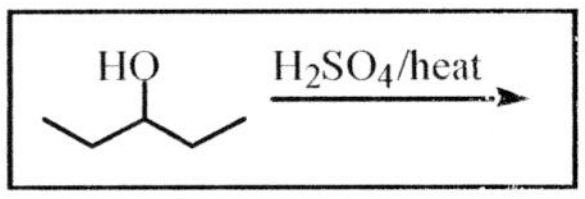

A)  ⌇⌇⌇

B) 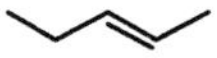 ⌇⌇⌇

C)  ⌇⌇⌇

D)

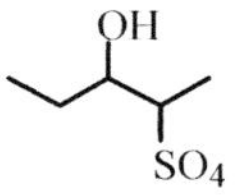

OH

SO₄

E)

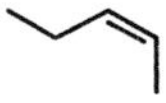

Ans: B

40. A chiral compound, C_5H_8, upon simple catalytic hydrogenation yields an achiral compound. What is the best name for the former?
   A)   1-methylcyclobutene
   B)   3-methylcyclobutene
   C)   1,2-dimethylcyclopropene
   D)   cyclopentene
   E)   none of the above
   Ans: B

41. What is the degree of unsaturation in cyclobutene
   A) zero   B) one   C) two   D) three   E) This molecule is not unsaturated.
   Ans: C

42. Choose the name of the following compound.

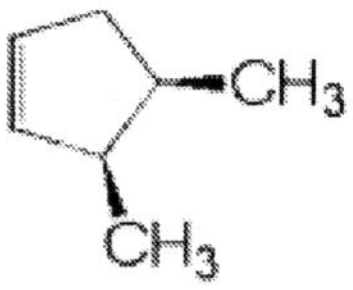

   CH₃

   CH₃

   A)   cis-4,5-dimethylcyclopentene
   B)   cis-1,2-dimethylcyclopent-3-ene
   C)   cis-2,3-dimethycyclopentene
   D)   cis-3,4-dimethylcyclopentene
   E)   cis-1,2-dimethylcyclopent-4-ene
   Ans: D

43. A compound which shows a molecular ion at m/z 84 could plausibly have what formula?
   A) $C_5H_{10}N$ B) $C_4H_{20}O$ C) C_6H_{12} D) C_5H_{24} E) $C_5H_{10}O$
   Ans: C

44. Enanthotoxin is an extremely poisonous organic compound found in the hemlock water dropwart, which is reputed to be the most poisonous plant in England. It is believed that no British plant has been responsible for more fatal accidents. The most poisonous part of the plant is the roots, which resemble small white carrots, giving the plant the name "five finger death." Also poisonous are its leaves, which look like parsley. Enanthotoxin is thought to interfere with the sodium ion current in nerve cells which leads to convulsions and death. How many steroisomers are possible for enanthotoxin?

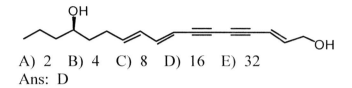

A) 2   B) 4   C) 8   D) 16   E) 32
Ans: D

45. Select the product for the following reaction.

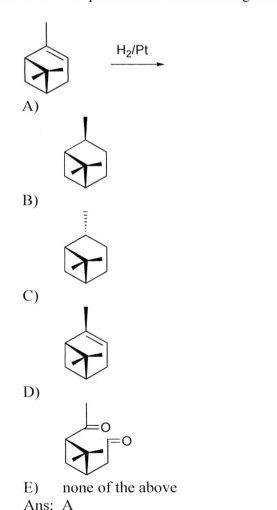

A)

B)

C)

D)

E)   none of the above
Ans: A

46. Label each of the alkenes as either *E* or *Z*.

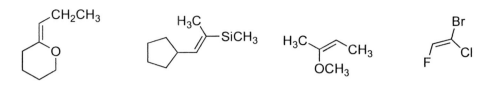

A   B   C   D

A)   A = *E*, B = *Z*, C = *E*, D = *Z*   D)   A = *E*, B = *E*, C = *E*, D = *E*
B)   A = *Z*, B = *E*, C = *Z*, D = *E*   E)   none of the above
C)   A = *Z*, B = *E*, C = *Z*, D = *Z*
Ans: B

47. How many degrees of unsaturation are present in the following molecule?

A) 4   B) 5   C) 6   D) 7   E) 8
Ans: D

48. The mass spectrum of 1-pentanol gives a large peak at m/z = 68. This peak can be characterized as?
    A)   the parent ion   D)   the parent ion plus a proton
    B)   the parent ion minus hydroxide   E)   none of the above
    C)   the parent ion minus water
    Ans: C

49. The mass spectrum of isopropylbenzene gives a large peak at m/z = 105. This peak can be characterized as?
    A)   the parent ion   D)   the parent ion minus a methyl group
    B)   the parent ion minus a proton   E)   none of the above
    C)   the parent ion minus water
    Ans: C

Chapter 12: Reactions of Alkenes

1. What type of reaction is the following?

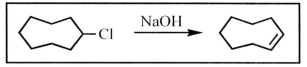

A) elimination   B) substitution   C) addition   D) rearrangement   E) reduction
Ans: A

2. What would be the major organic product of the following reaction?

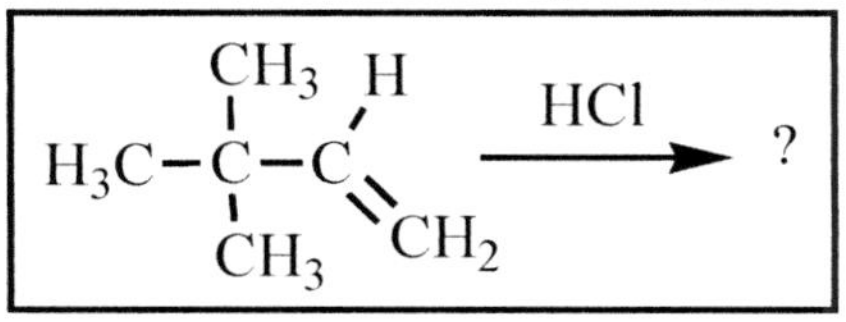

$$H_3C-\overset{\overset{\displaystyle CH_3}{|}}{\underset{\underset{\displaystyle CH_3}{|}}{C}}-\overset{H}{\underset{}{C}}\diagdown \overset{}{\underset{CH_2}{}} \quad \xrightarrow{\quad HCl \quad} \quad ?$$

A)

$$H_3C-\overset{\overset{\displaystyle H_3C}{|}}{\underset{\underset{\displaystyle H_3C}{|}}{C}}-\overset{\overset{\displaystyle H}{|}}{\underset{\underset{\displaystyle H}{|}}{C}}-CH_2Cl$$

B)

$$H_3C-\overset{\overset{\displaystyle H_3C}{|}}{\underset{\underset{\displaystyle H_3C}{|}}{C}}-\overset{\overset{\displaystyle Cl}{|}}{\underset{\underset{\displaystyle H}{|}}{C}}-CH_3$$

C)

$$H_3C-\overset{\overset{\displaystyle Cl}{|}}{\underset{\underset{\displaystyle H_3C}{|}}{C}}-\overset{\overset{\displaystyle H}{|}}{\underset{\underset{\displaystyle CH_3}{|}}{C}}-CH_3$$

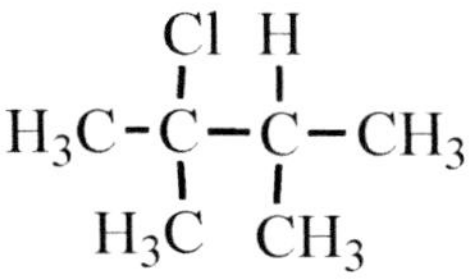

D)

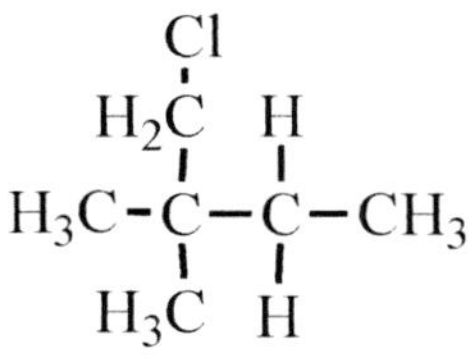

$$H_3C-\overset{\overset{\displaystyle H_2C-Cl}{|}}{\underset{\underset{\displaystyle H_3C}{|}}{C}}-\overset{\overset{\displaystyle H}{|}}{\underset{\underset{\displaystyle H}{|}}{C}}-CH_3$$

E)

$$H_3C-\overset{\overset{\displaystyle H_3C}{|}}{\underset{\underset{\displaystyle H_3C}{|}}{C}}-\overset{\overset{\displaystyle Cl}{|}}{\underset{\underset{\displaystyle H}{|}}{C}}-\overset{Cl}{\underset{}{C}}H_2$$

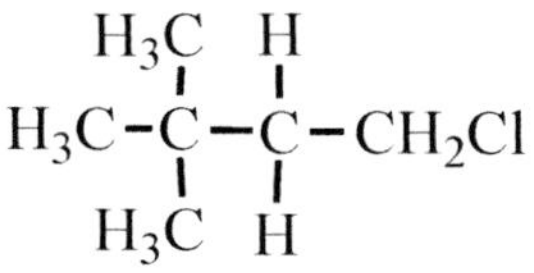

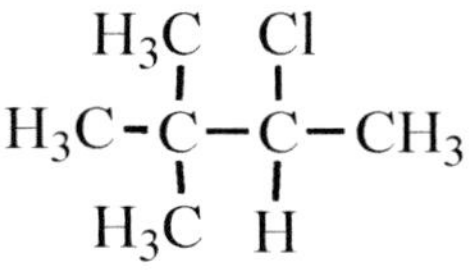

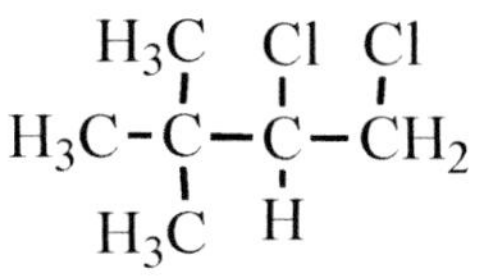

Ans: C

3. What would be the **major** organic product of the following reaction?

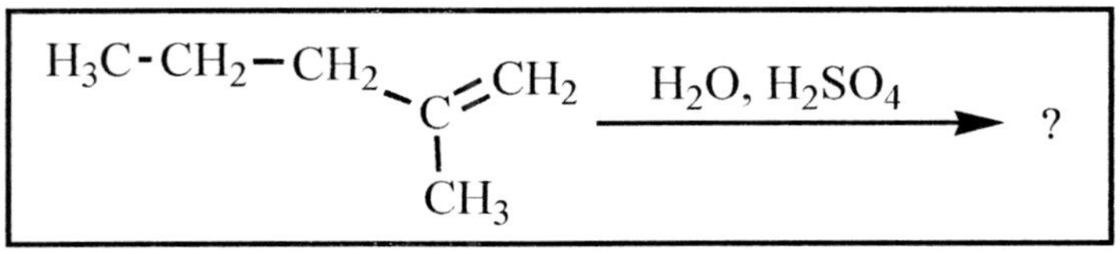

$$H_3C\text{-}CH_2\text{-}CH_2\text{-}\underset{\underset{CH_3}{|}}{C}\text{=}CH_2 \quad \xrightarrow{H_2O, H_2SO_4} \quad ?$$

A)

$$H_3C\text{-}CH_2\text{-}CH_2\text{-}\underset{\underset{CH_3}{|}}{\overset{\overset{H}{|}}{C}}\text{-}CH_2\text{-}OH$$

B)

$$H_3C\text{-}CH_2\text{-}CH_2\text{-}\underset{\underset{CH_3}{|}}{\overset{\overset{OH}{|}}{C}}\text{-}CH_3$$

C)

$$H_3C\text{-}CH_2\text{-}CH_2\text{-}\underset{\underset{CH_3}{|}}{\overset{\overset{H}{|}}{C}}\text{-}CH_2\text{-}OOH$$

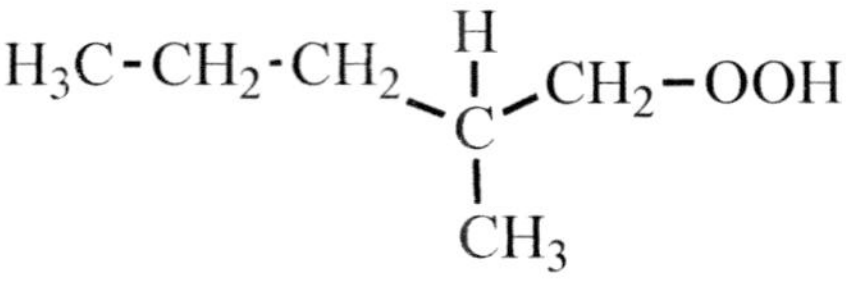

D)

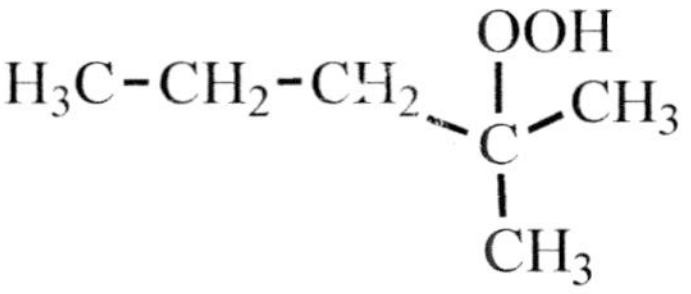

$$H_3C\text{-}CH_2\text{-}CH_2\text{-}\underset{\underset{CH_3}{|}}{\overset{\overset{OOH}{|}}{C}}\text{-}CH_3$$

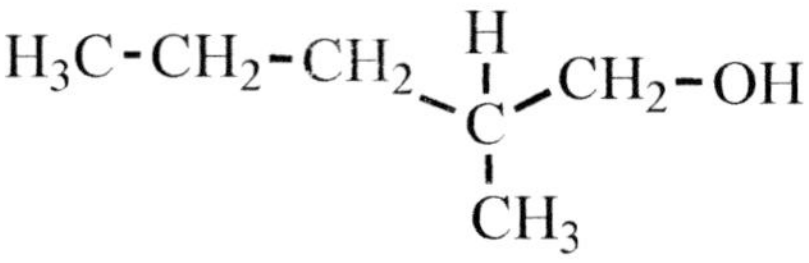

E)

$$H_3C\text{-}CH_2\text{-}CH_2\text{-}\underset{\underset{CH_3}{|}}{\overset{\overset{H}{|}}{C}}\text{-}\overset{\overset{O}{\|}}{C}\text{-}H$$

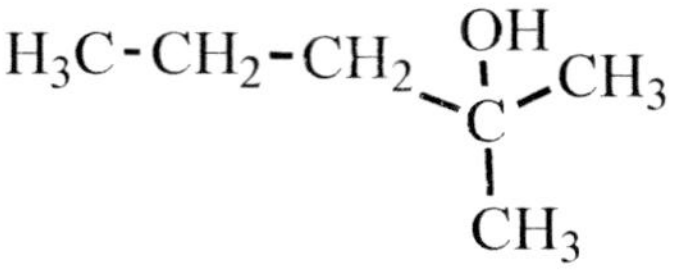

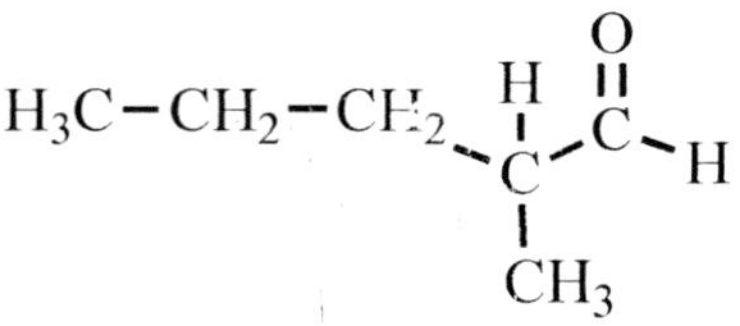

Ans: B

4. Reaction with ozone, followed by treatment with $(CH_3)_2S$, of which of the following would not yield **any** CH_3CHO?

A)

$$\underset{H}{\overset{H}{\diagdown}}C=C\underset{CH_3}{\overset{CH_3}{\diagup}}$$

B)

$$\underset{H_3C}{\overset{H}{\diagdown}}C=C\underset{CH_3}{\overset{H}{\diagup}}$$

C)

$$\underset{H}{\overset{H_3C}{\diagdown}}C=C\underset{CH_3}{\overset{CH_3}{\diagup}}$$

D)

$$\underset{H_3C}{\overset{H}{\diagdown}}C=C\underset{H}{\overset{CH_3}{\diagup}}$$

E)   Both B and D

Ans: A

5. Which of the following sets of reagents would convert 1-methylcyclohexene into *trans*-1-methyl-1,2-cyclohexanediol?

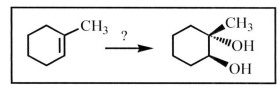

A)   1. CH_3CO_3H
     2. CH_3ONa, CH_3OH
B) $KMnO_4, H_2O, {}^-OH$
C)   1. CH_3CO_3H
     2. H_3O^+
D)   1. OsO_4
     2. H_2S, H_2O
E)   1. O_3
     2. $(CH_3)_2S$

Ans: C

6. What reagent(s) would accomplish the following transformation?

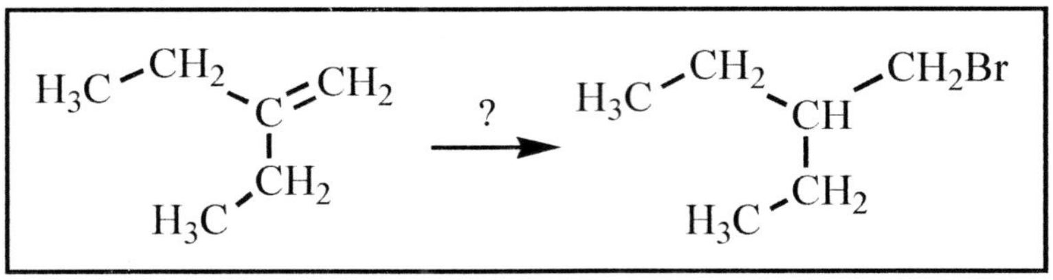

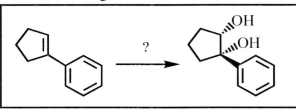

A) Br_2, hv   B) HBr   C) PBr_3 D) HBr + peroxides   E) $HgBr_2$ + $NaBH_4$
Ans: D

7. Which of the reagents below would best accomplish the following transformation?

A) H_2O + cat. H_2SO_4 D) O_3 then Zn + HCl
B) CH_3CO_3H, then NaOH + H_2O E) $KMnO_4$ + $^-$OH/ H_2O
C) Br_2 + H_2O

Ans: E

8. What would be the product of the following reaction?

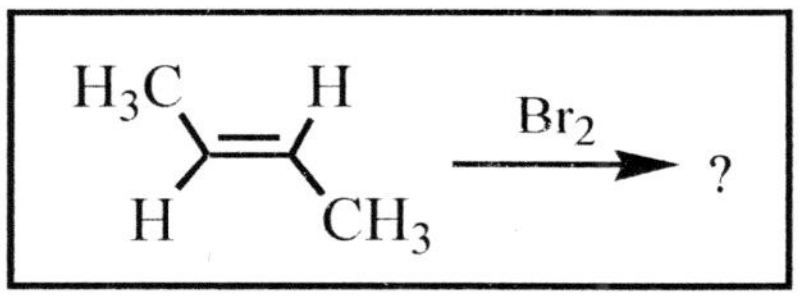

A)

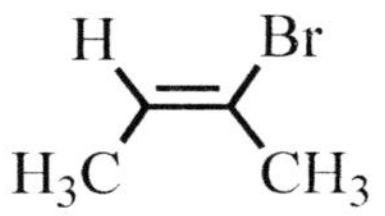

B)

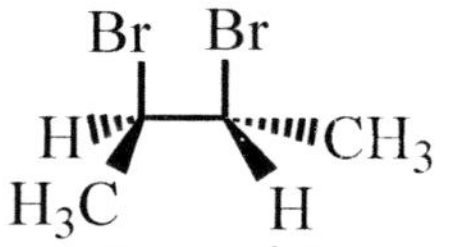

(racemic)

C)

Br   H

H_3C CH_3

D)

Br Br

H   H

H_3C CH_3

E)

H   H

H_3C CH_2Br

Ans: D

9. Which of the following reagents would best accomplish the following transformation?

A) $NaBH_4$ B) $LiAlH_4$ C) BH_3, $NaBH_4$ D) H_2SO_4 E) H_2, Pd
Ans: E

10. Polymerization reactions are thermodynamically favorable (exothermic) because
   A)   large molecules are more stable than small ones.
   B)   polymers precipitate, which shifts the equilibrium.
   C)   a sigma bond is more stable than a π bond.
   D)   crosslinking stabilizes the product.
   E)   alkenes are too unstable to store.
   Ans: C

11. Radical polymerization of styrene produces what polymer? (*n* = large number)

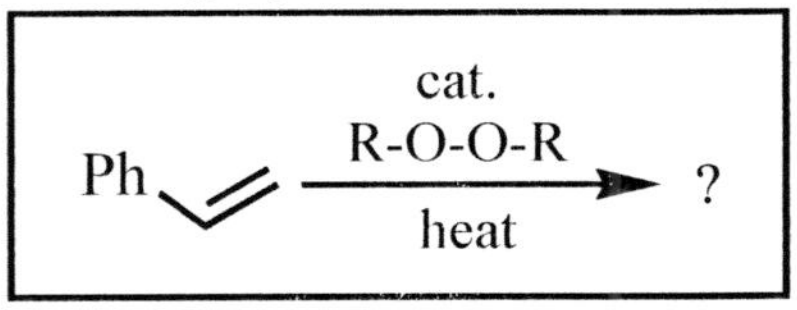

A)

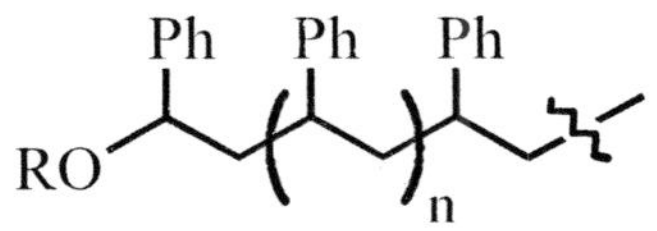

B)

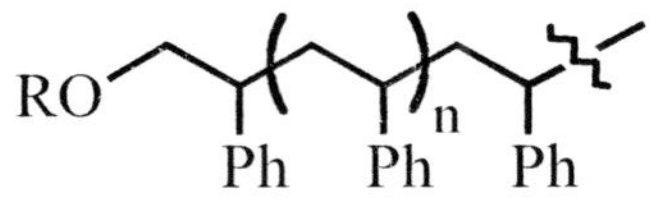

C)

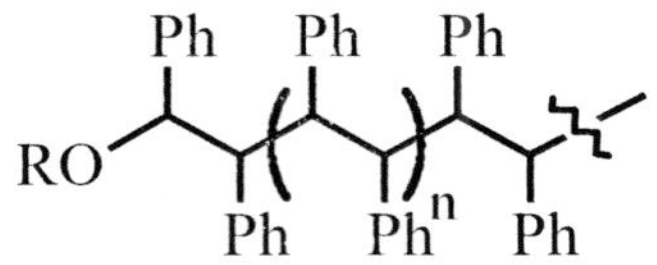

D)

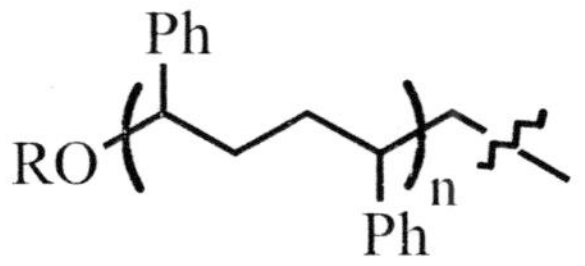

E)   none of the above

Ans: B

12. What would be the expected product of the following reaction?

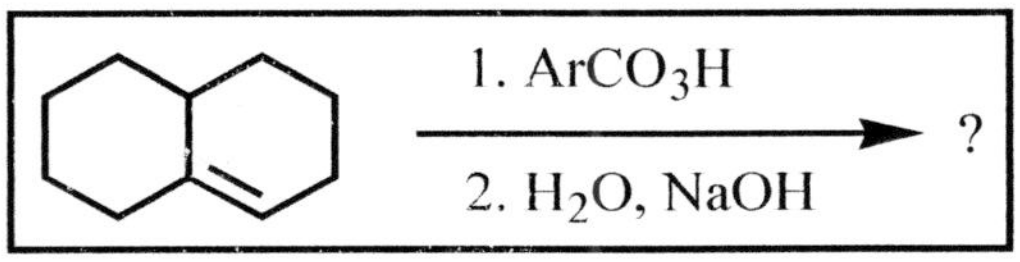

A)

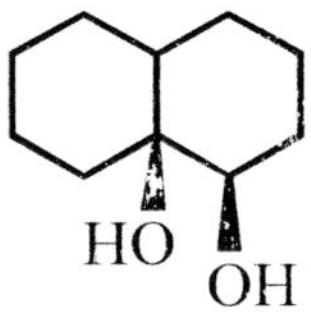

B)

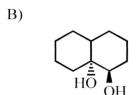

C)

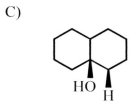

D)

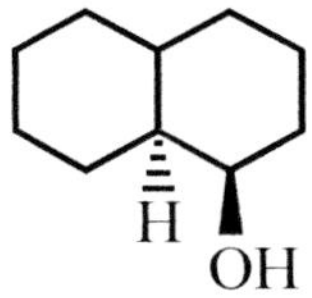

E)

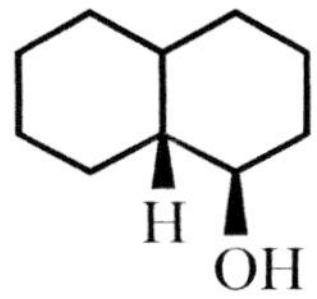

Ans: B

13. Based on your knowledge of the mechanisms involved, which of the reagents below would you expect to accomplish the following reaction? (Think through the mechanism!)

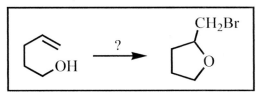

A) HBr   B) Br₂   C) PBr₃   D) NaBr   E) HBr + peroxides
Ans: B

14. What type of reaction is the following?

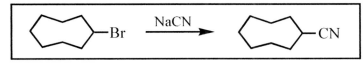

A) elimination   B) addition   C) substitution   D) rearrangement   E) reduction
Ans: C

15. Which of the following rearrangements would you **not** expect the cation below to undergo to any significant extent?

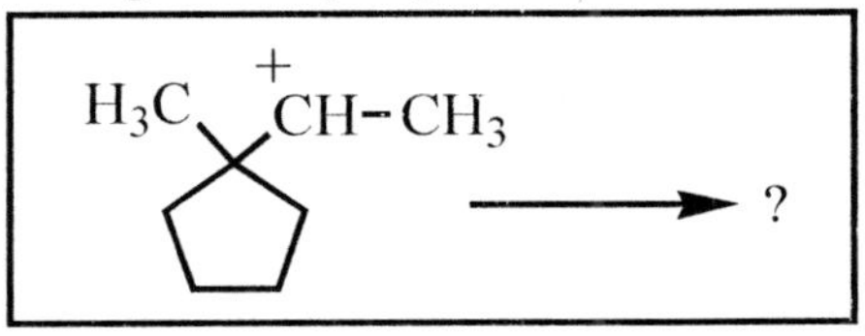

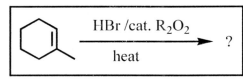

A)

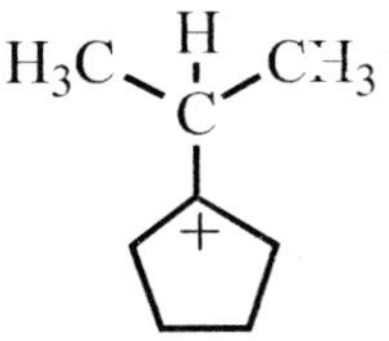

H₃C— C(H)—CH₃ (cyclopentyl cation)

B)

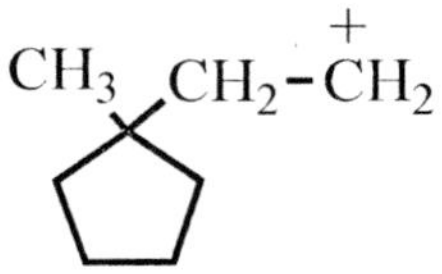

C)

CH₃
CH₃ (methylcyclohexyl cation)

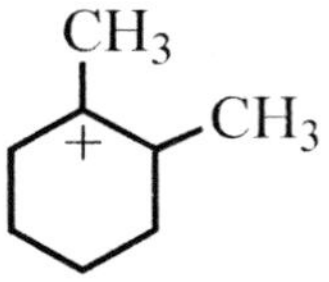

D)   None of the above would occur to a significant extent.
E)   All of the above would be significant.
Ans: B

16. What is the **major** product of the following reaction?

HBr /cat. R₂O₂
─────────────→ ?
heat

A)

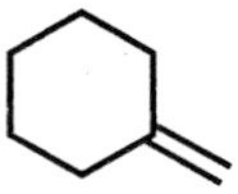

(methylenecyclohexane)

B)

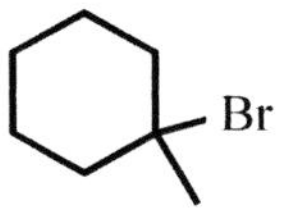

C)

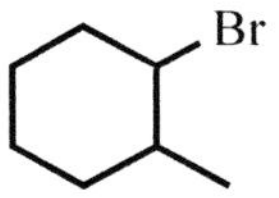

Br

D)

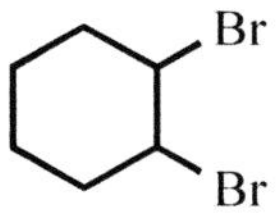

Br

Br

E)

CH₂Br

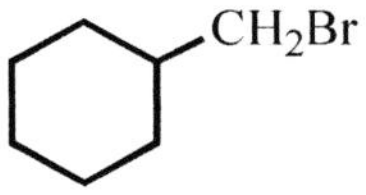

Ans: C

17. Predict the **major** product of the following reaction:

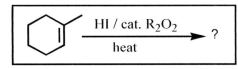

A)

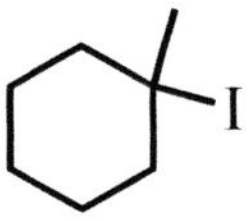

I

B)

I

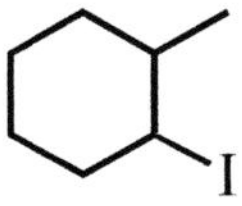

C)

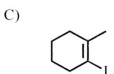

D)

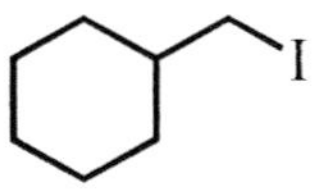

E)

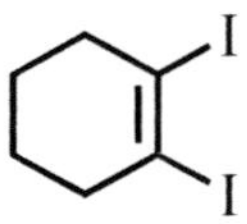

Ans: A

18. What reagent(s) might cause the following conversion?

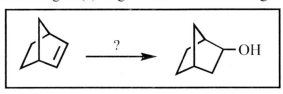

A)   1. Br₂ 2. H₂O   D)   1. BH₃ 2. H₂O₂, NaOH
B)   NaOH, H₂, Pd   E)   Br₂, H₂O
C)   H₂SO₄
Ans: D

19. What reagent(s) would accomplish the following reaction?

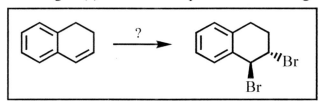

A) Br₂   B) NBS   C) Br₂ + light   D) Br₂ + FeBr₃   E) HBr
Ans: A

20. What reagents would be required to accomplish the following transformation?

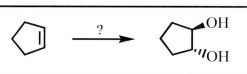

   A) $KMnO_4$, ⁻OH, H_2O D) OsO_4, ᵗBuOOH, H_2O

   B) BH_3 then H_2O_2 E) Br_2, H_2O

   C) CH_3CO_3H then H_2O, H^+

   Ans: C

21. Which reagents would you expect to accomplish the following transformation?

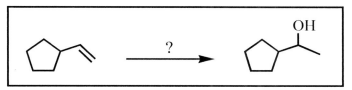

   A) BH_3 then H_2O_2, ⁻OH

   B) $Hg(O_2CCH_3)_2$,

          H_2O then $NaBH_4$

   C) H_2O, H^+

   D) $KMnO_4$, H_2O, cold

   E)   cat. OsO_4, H_2O_2

   Ans: B

22. Considering the following reactions, you conclude that the stereochemistry of reactions #1 and #2 is:

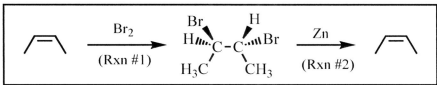

   A)   *anti* and *syn*, repectively   D)   *syn* and *syn*, repectively

   B)   *syn* and *anti*, repectively   E)   none of the above

   C)   *anti* and *anti*, repectively

   Ans: C

23. Based on your knowledge of the mechanisms involved, which of the reagents below would you expect to accomplish the following reaction? (Think through the mechanism!)

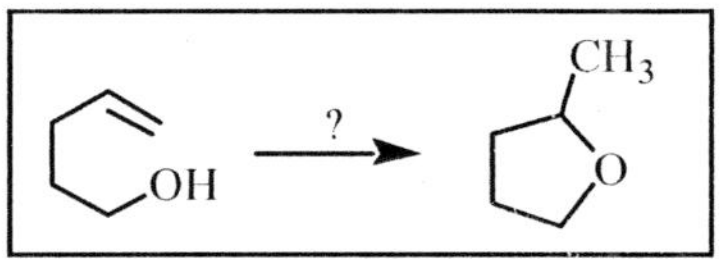

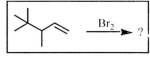

A) H₂/Pd   B) Br₂   C) PBr₃   D) H₂SO₄   E) NaBH₄

Ans: D

24. What would be the expected product from the reaction shown?

A)

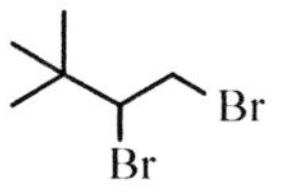

B)

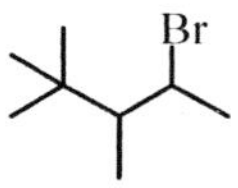

C)

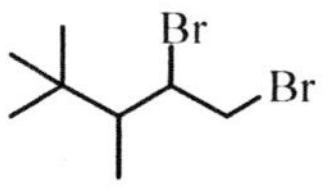

D)

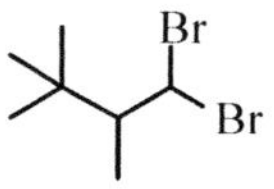

E)

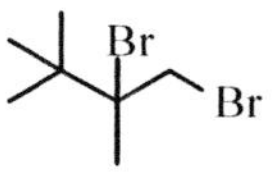

Ans: C

25. What reactant and product types would be **most** appropriate for the reagents shown?

```
        1. OsO₄
  ? ─────────────→ ?
        2. H₂S, H₂O
```

A)   alkene/alcohol   D)   alkyne/ketone
B)   alkene/*anti*-1,2-diol E)   alkyne/aldehyde
C)   alkene/*syn*-1,2-diol

Ans: C

26. What reactant and product types would be **most** appropriate for the reagents shown?

A) alkene/Markovnikov alcohol
B) alkene/anti-Markovnikov alcohol
C) alkene/1,2-diol

D) alkyne/1,2-diol
E) alcohol/alkene

Ans: A

27. What reactant and product types would be **most** appropriate for the reagents shown?

A) alkene/Markovnikov alkyl bromide
B) alkene/anti-Markovnikov alkyl bromide
C) alkene/*syn*-1,2-dibromide
D) alkyne/*anti*-1,2-dibromide
E) alcohol/alkene

Ans: A

28. What reactant and product types would be **most** appropriate for the reagents shown?

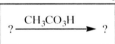

A) alkene/Markovnikov alcohol
B) alkene/anti-Markovnikov alcohol
C) alkene/*syn*-1,2-diol

D) alkyne/*anti*-1,2-diol
E) alkene/epoxide

Ans: E

29. What reactant and product types would be **most** appropriate for the reagents shown?

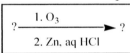

A) alkene/*syn*-1,2-diol
B) alkene/*anti*-1,2-diol
C) alkene/alcohol

D) alkene/aldehydes and/or ketones
E) alkene/epoxide

Ans: D

30. What reactant and product types would be **most** appropriate for the reagents shown?

A) alkene/*syn*-1,2-dibromide
B) alkene/*anti*-1,2-dibromide
C) alkene/2-bromoalcohol

D) alkene/1,2-diol
E) alkene/epoxide

Ans: C

31. Which reagents would be appropriate for the chemical transformation shown below?

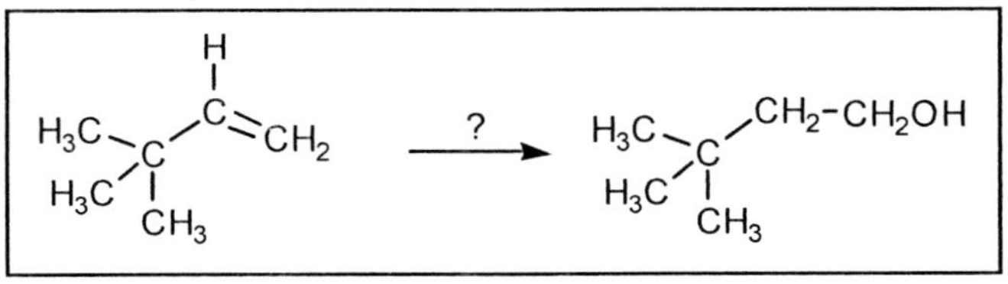

A) H_2O, H_2SO_4 D) $NaBH_4$, CH_3OH
B) BH_3, then H_2O_2, ^-OH E) PCC
C) $Hg(OAc)_2$, H_2O, then $NaBH_4$

Ans: B

32. Which reagents would be appropriate for the chemical transformation shown below?

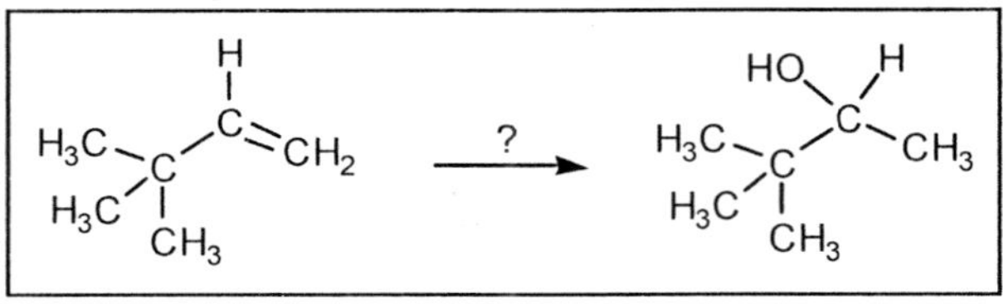

A) H_2O, H_2SO_4 D) $NaBH_4$, CH_3OH
B) BH_3, then H_2O_2, ^-OH E) PCC
C) $Hg(OAc)_2$, H_2O, then $NaBH_4$

Ans: C

33. Which reagents would be appropriate for the chemical transformation shown below?

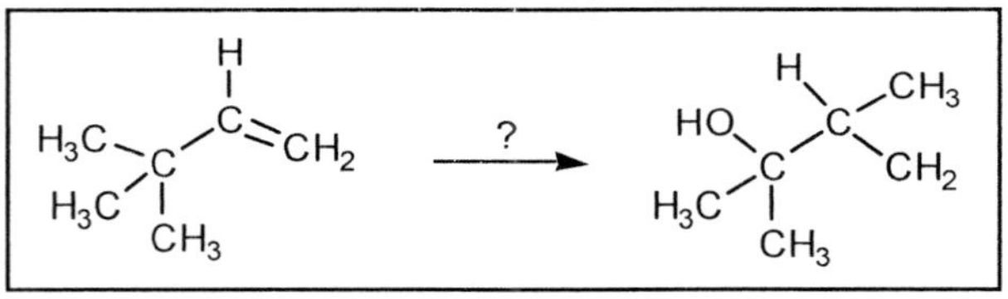

A) H_2O, H_2SO_4 D) $NaBH_4$, CH_3OH
B) BH_3, then H_2O_2, ^-OH E) PCC
C) $Hg(OAc)_2$, H_2O, then $NaBH_4$

Ans: A

34. Predict the product of the following reaction:

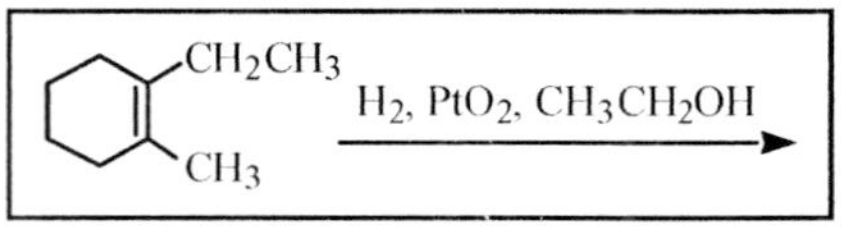

A)

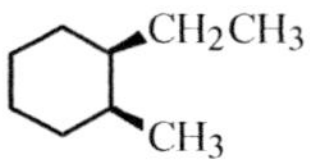

B)

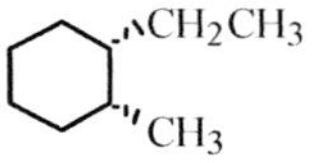

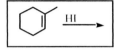

C)

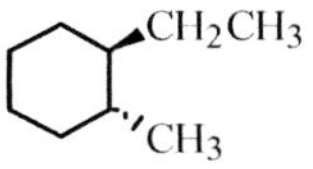

CH₂CH₃
CH₃

D)

CH₂CH₃
CH₃

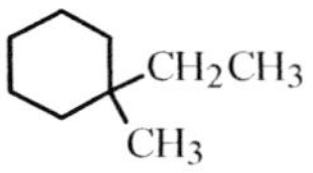

E)   Equal amounts of A and B

Ans: E

35. What is the **major** product of the following reaction?

HI

A)

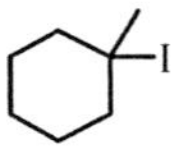

I

B)

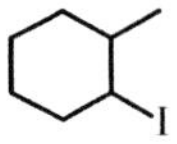

I

C)

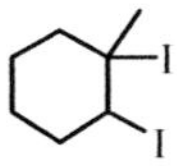

I
I

D)   No reaction

E)

I

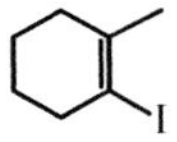

Ans: A

36. Predict the **major** product of the following reaction:

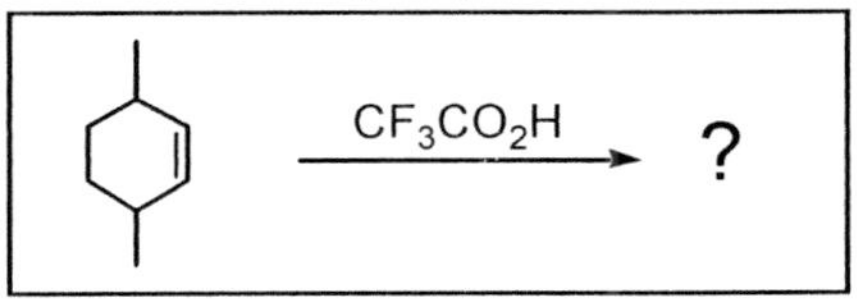

CF_3CO_2H → **?**

A)

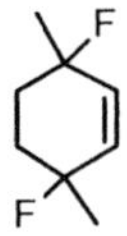

B)

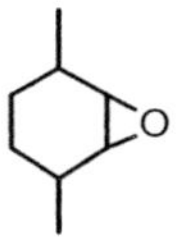

C)

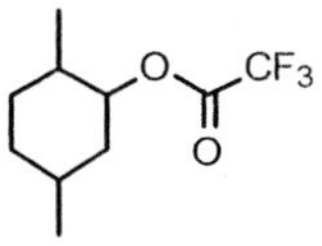

D)

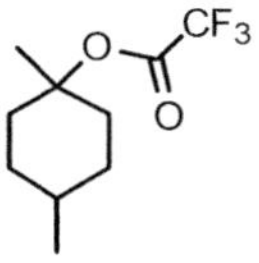

E)

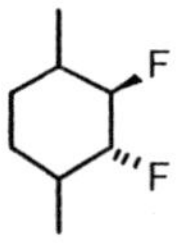

Ans: D

37. How many products are possible in the reaction of *trans*-2-butene with Br_2?
    A) 0 B) 1 C) 2 D) 3 E) 4
    Ans: B

38. What is the best method to convert alkenes into alcohols following Markovnikov's Rule?
    A) PCC   D) oxymercuration-demercuration
    B) H_2O E) none of the above
    C) hydroboration/oxidation
    Ans: D

39. Which of the following reagents will achieve the following reaction:

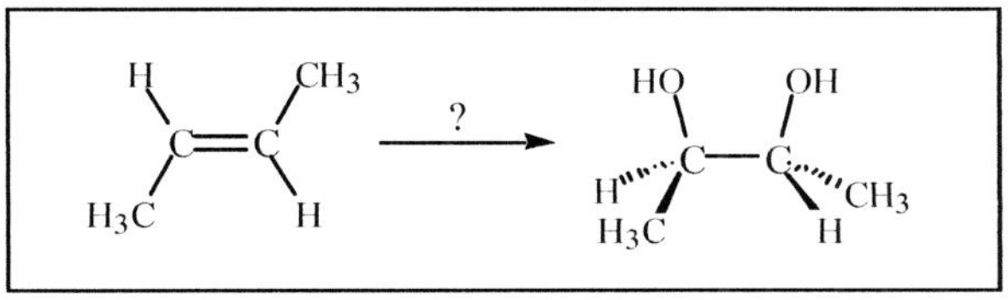

A) 1. MCPBA, CH$_2$Cl$_2$
   2. H$^+$, H$_2$O
B) 1. OsO$_4$, THF, 25° C
   2. H$_2$S
C) PCC
D) 1. O$_3$/CH$_2$Cl$_2$
   2. Zn/CH$_3$CO$_2$H
E) any of the above
Ans: B

40. Which of the following products is most likely to form under the reaction conditions?

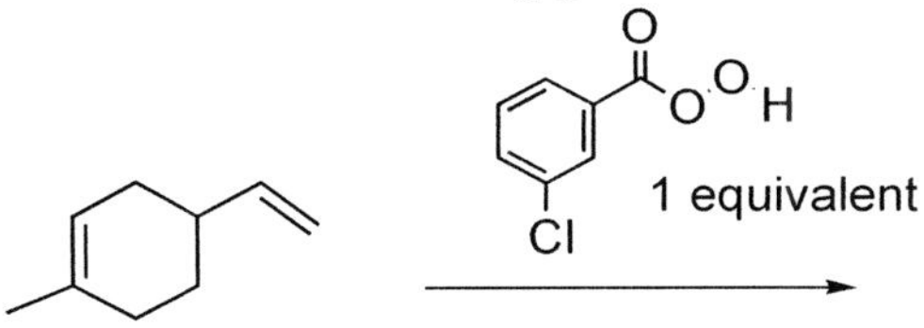

1 equivalent

A)

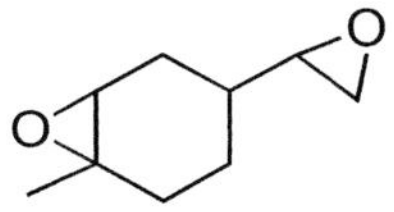

B)

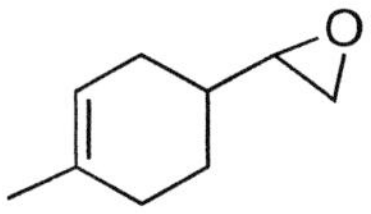

C)

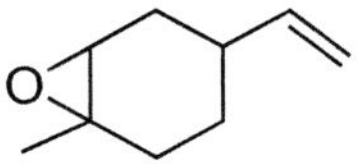

D)

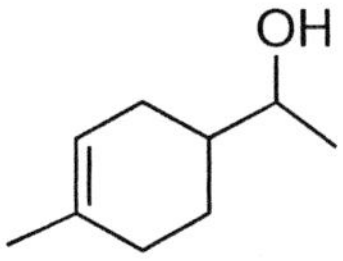

E)

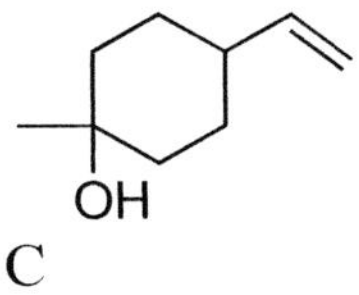

Ans: C

41. Which of the following starting materials are most likely to give the product under the reaction conditions?

 $\dfrac{\text{1. O}_3}{\text{2. Zn, CH}_3\text{COOH}}$ 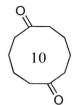 10

A)

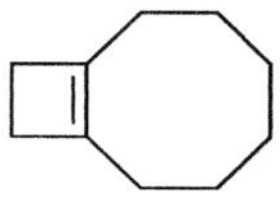

B)

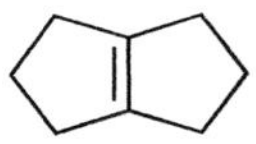

C)

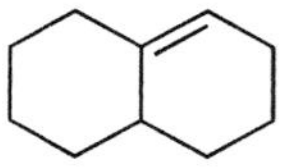

D)

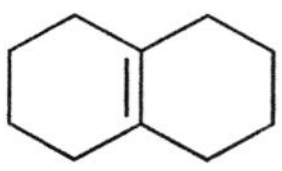

E)

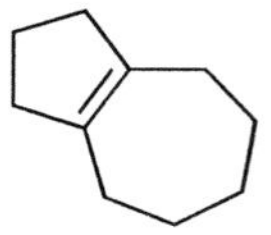

Ans: D

42. Which of the following products is most likely to form under the reaction conditions?

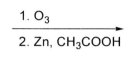 $\dfrac{\text{1. BH}_3}{\text{2. H}_2\text{O}_2, \text{NaOH, H}_2\text{O}}$

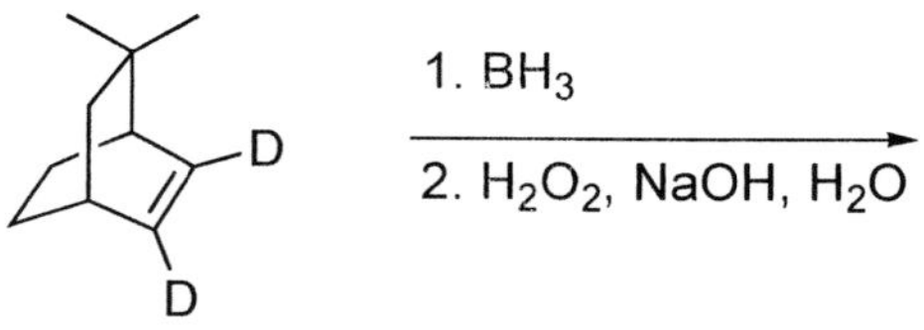

A)

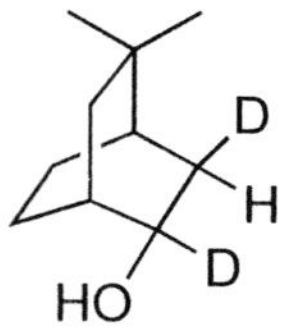

B)

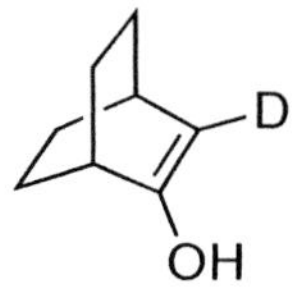

C)

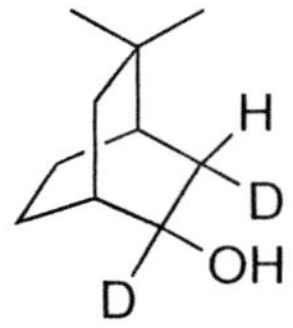

D)

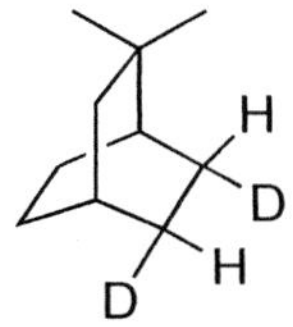

E)   none of the above

Ans: A

43. Which of the following products is most likely to form under the reaction conditions?

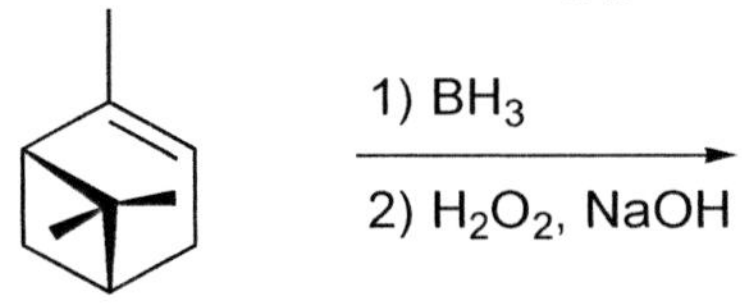

1) BH$_3$

2) H$_2$O$_2$, NaOH

A)

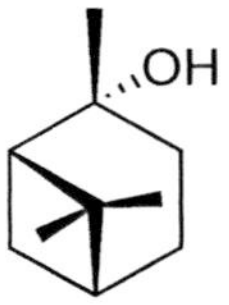

B)

C)

D)

E)

Ans: E

44. Cholesterol is a major lipid component of athersclerotic plaques and can be present at such high concentrations that it forms a crystalline phase within a diseased artery. In addition to cholesterol, the 5,6-secosterol compound has also been isolated. 5,6-secostereol has been shown to be the product of an unforeseen oxidation reaction in the body. Which one of these reagents could be used convert cholesterol to the 5,6-secosterol? (*Science* 2003, *302*, 1053)

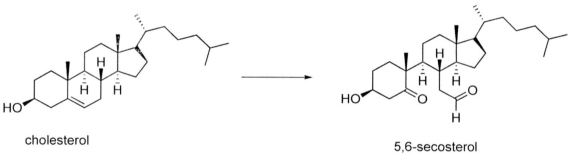

cholesterol

5,6-secosterol

A) $K_2Cr_2O_7$ B) O_3 C) $(CH_3)_2S$ D) HOOH   E) LiOH
Ans: B

45. Select the **major** product of the olefin metathesis reaction ?

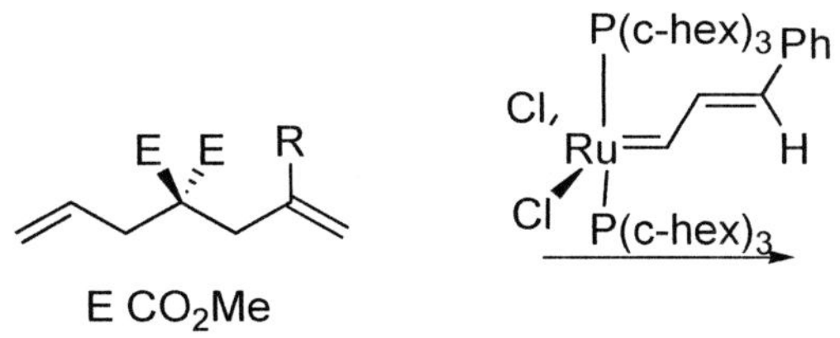

A)

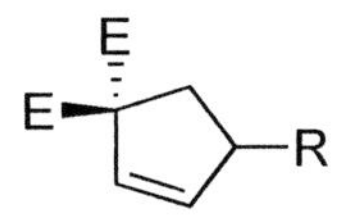

B)

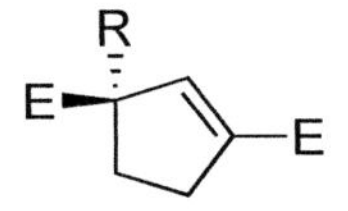

C)

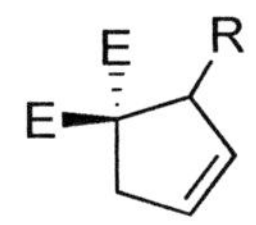

D)

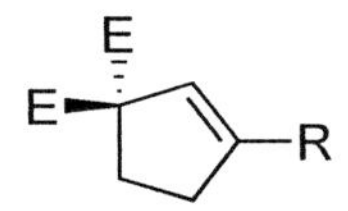

E)

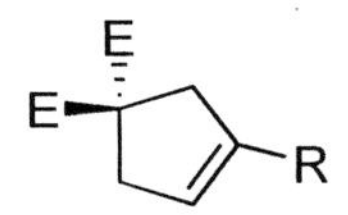

Ans: E

Chapter 13: Alkynes: The Carbon-Carbon Triple Bond

1. What would be the proper name of the following compound?

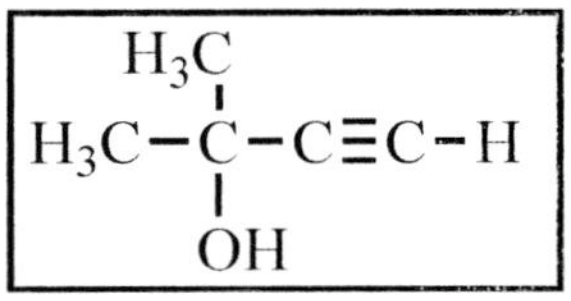

$$H_3C-\underset{\underset{OH}{|}}{\overset{\overset{H_3C}{|}}{C}}-C\equiv C-H$$

   A) 1,1-dimethyl-2-propyn-1-ol
   B) 3-methyl-1-butyn-3-ol
   C) 3-hydroxy-3-methyl-1-propyne
   D) 2-methyl-3-butyn-2-ol
   E) 2-ethynyl-2-propanol

   Ans: D

2. What would be the product of the following reaction sequence?

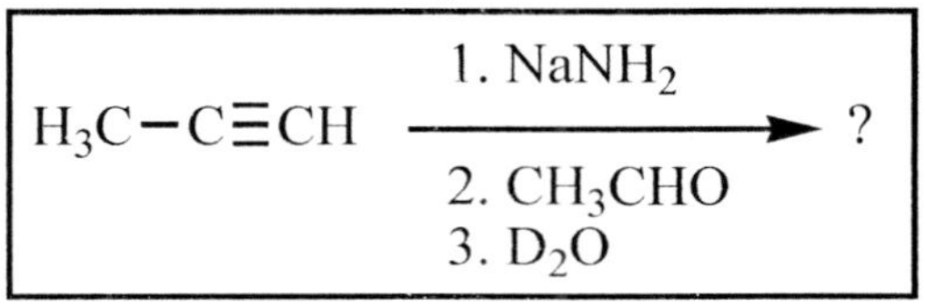

$$H_3C-C\equiv CH \xrightarrow[\substack{2.\ CH_3CHO \\ 3.\ D_2O}]{1.\ NaNH_2} ?$$

   A)

$$DO-\underset{\underset{CH_3}{|}}{\overset{\overset{H}{|}}{C}}-CH_2-C\equiv CH$$

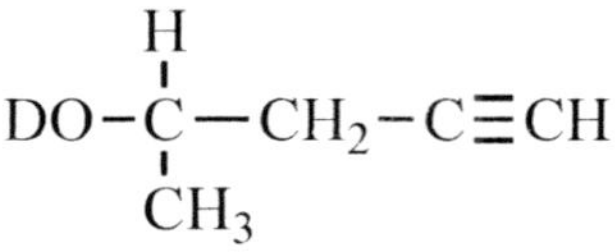

   B) $H_3C-C\equiv CD$

   C) $H_3C-C\equiv C-CH_2-CH_2-OD$

   D)

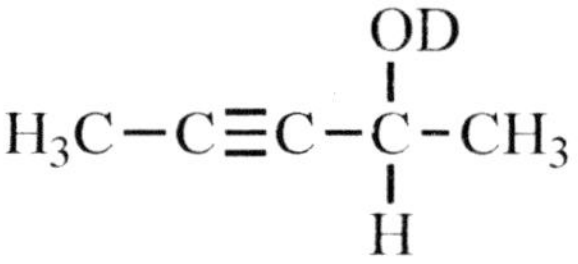

$$H_3C-C\equiv C-\underset{\underset{H}{|}}{\overset{\overset{OD}{|}}{C}}-CH_3$$

   E)

$$HO-\underset{\underset{CH_3}{|}}{\overset{\overset{H}{|}}{C}}\cdot CH_2-C\equiv CD$$

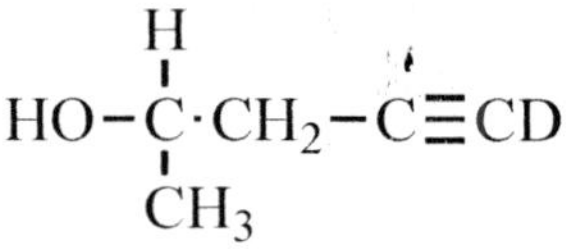

   Ans: D

3. What would be the product of the following reaction?

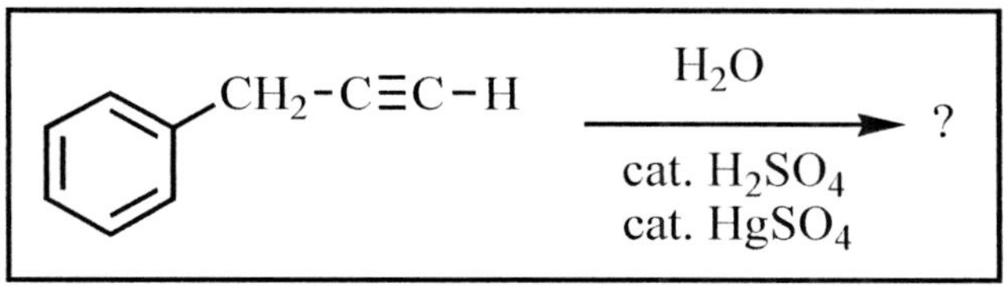

$$CH_2-C\equiv C-H \xrightarrow[\substack{\text{cat. } H_2SO_4 \\ \text{cat. } HgSO_4}]{H_2O} \ ?$$

A)

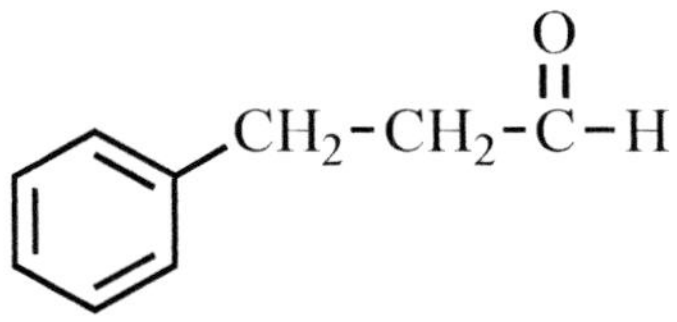

$$CH_2-CH_2-\overset{\overset{\displaystyle O}{\|}}{C}-H$$

B)

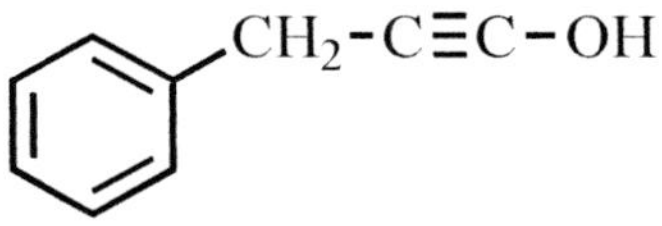

$$CH_2-C\equiv C-OH$$

C)

$$CH_2-\underset{\underset{\displaystyle OH}{|}}{CH}-\underset{\underset{\displaystyle OH}{|}}{CH_2}$$

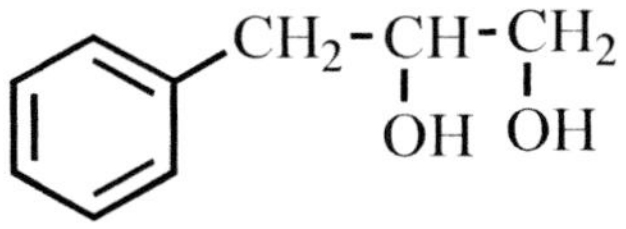

D)

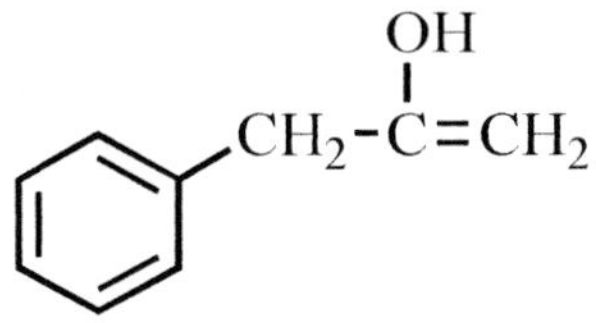

$$CH_2-\overset{\overset{\displaystyle OH}{|}}{C}=CH_2$$

E)

$$CH_2-\overset{\overset{\displaystyle O}{\|}}{C}-CH_3$$

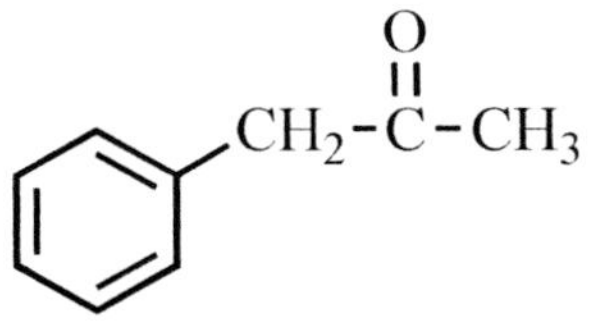

Ans: E

4. What would be the product of the following reaction?

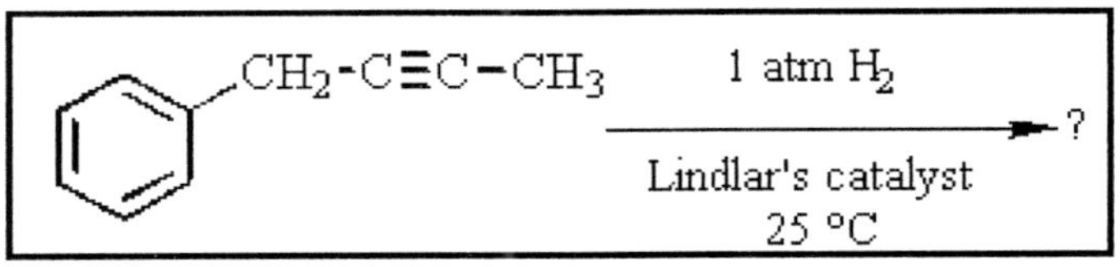

CH$_2$-C≡C−CH$_3$ 1 atm H$_2$

Lindlar's catalyst
25 °C   ?

A)

CH$_2$·CH$_2$·CH$_2$·CH$_3$

B)

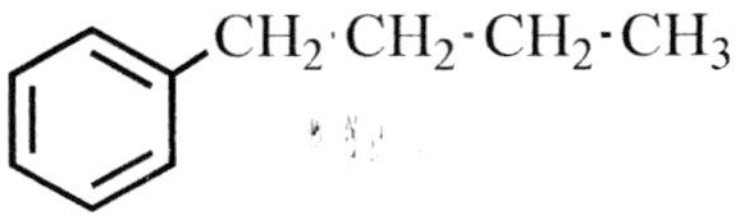

H   CH$_3$
C=C
−CH$_2$ H

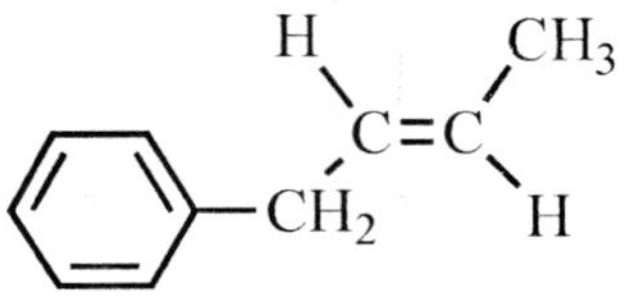

C)

CH$_2$-C≡C−H

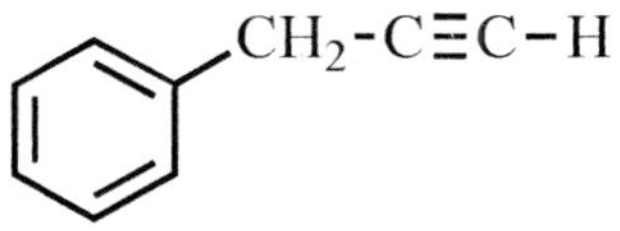

D)

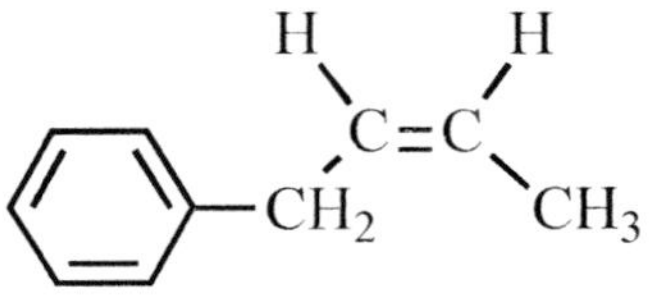

H   H
C=C
−CH$_2$ CH$_3$

E)

CH$_2$·CH$_2$·CH$_2$·CH$_3$

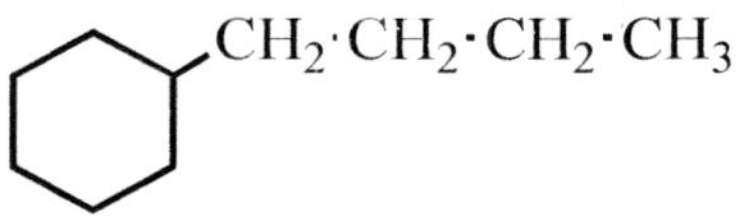

Ans: D

5. What would be the product of the following reaction sequence?

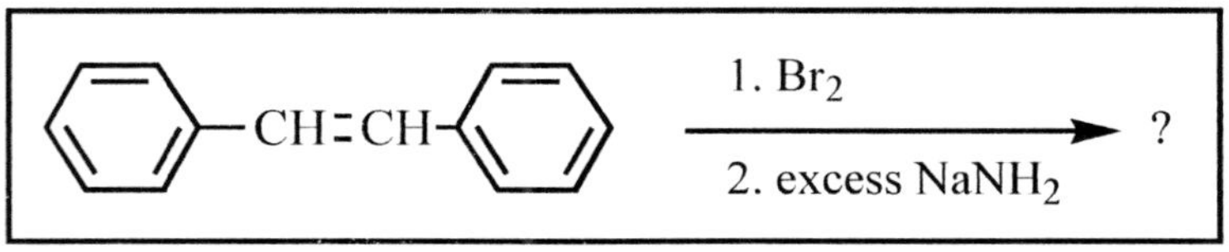

−CH=CH−   1. Br$_2$?

2. excess NaNH$_2$

A)

Ph   Br
H''·C−C''·H
Br   Ph

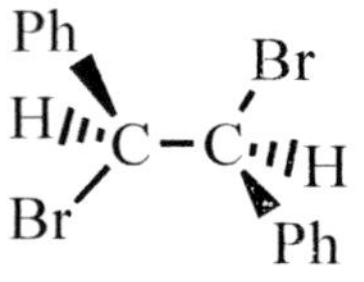

(racemic)

B)

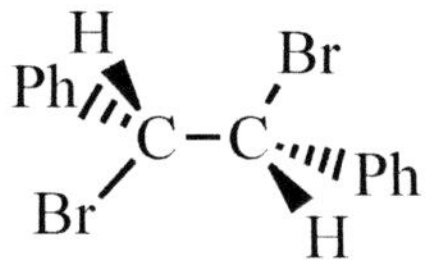

H   Br
Ph///C—C.//Ph
Br   H

(meso)

C)   Ph–C≡C–Ph

D)

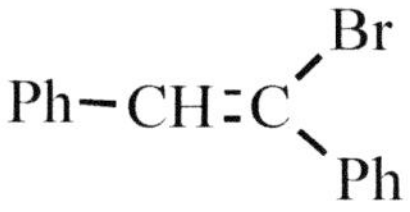

Br
Ph–CH≡C
Ph

E)

Ph   NH₂
CH-CH
NH₂   Ph

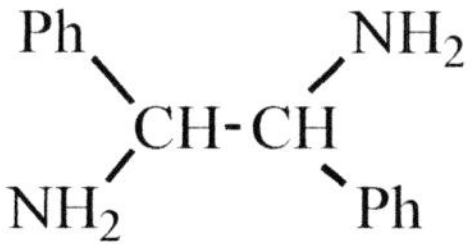

Ans: C

6. Given separate pure samples, in what way(s) could you quickly distinguish between the two alkynes below?

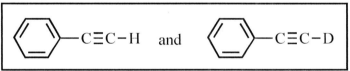

A)   gas chromatography   D)   NMR spectroscopy
B)   infrared spectroscopy   E)   both B and D
C)   ultraviolet spectroscopy

Ans: E

7. What would be the **major** product expected from the following reaction? (Notice the D isotope.)

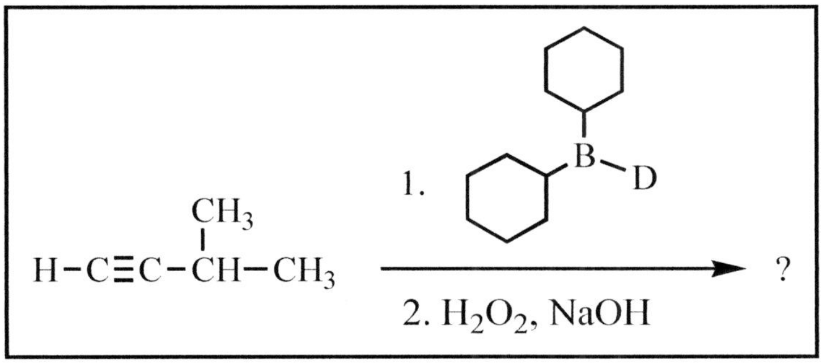

CH₃
|
H–C≡C–CH–CH₃

1. [dicyclohexylborane–D]

2. H₂O₂, NaOH

→ ?

A)

CH₃
|
H   CH–CH₃
C=C
HO   D

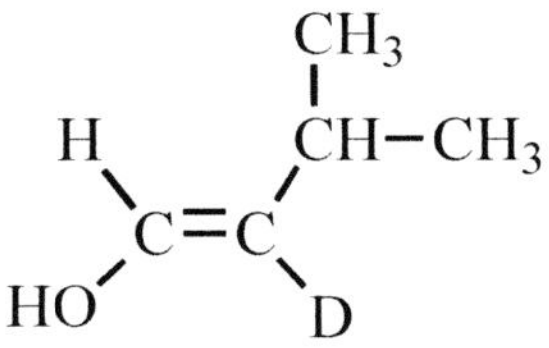

B)

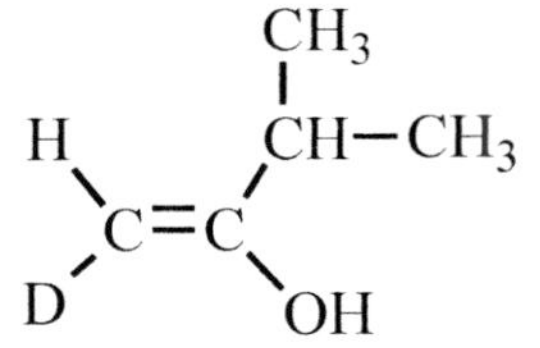

$$H_3C-CH-CH_3$$
(structure with CH_3 on top, $C=C$ with H and D on left carbon, OH on right)

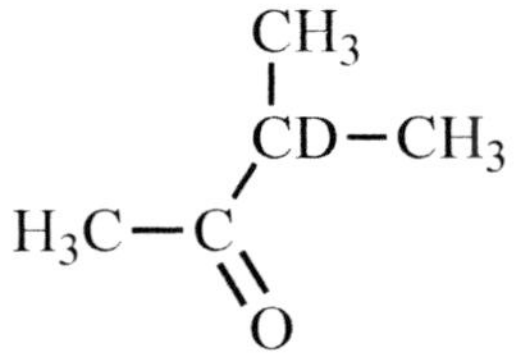

C)

(structure with CH_3 on top, $CD-CH_3$, H_3C-C with $=O$ below)

D)

(structure with O double bonded to C, H, $-CHD-CH-CH_3$ with CH_3 on top)

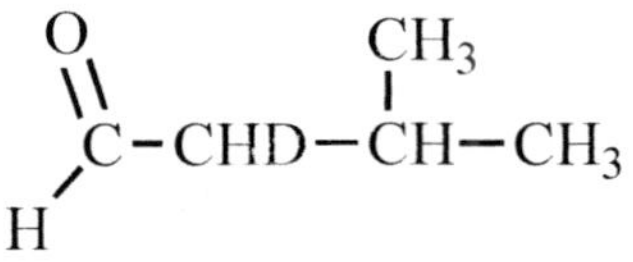

E)

(structure with CH_3 on top, $CH-CH_3$, DH_2C-C with $=O$ below)

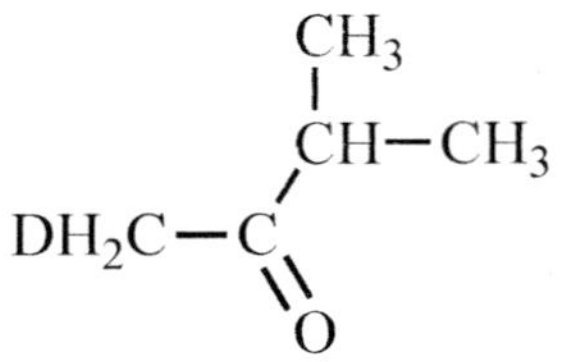

Ans: D

8. What would you expect the **major** product of the following reaction sequence to be?

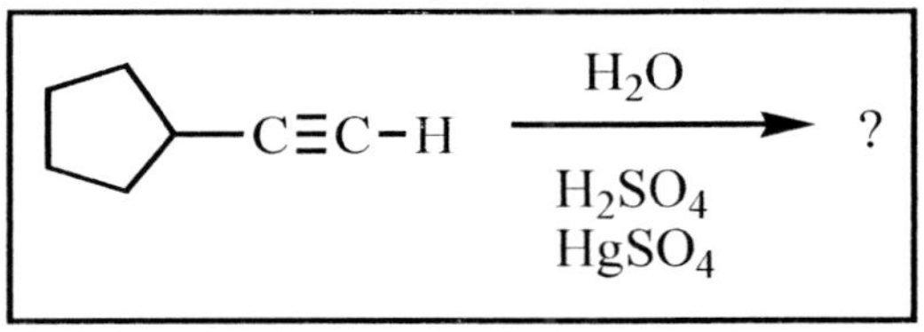

(cyclopentane)$-C\equiv C-H \xrightarrow[\begin{array}{c}H_2SO_4\\HgSO_4\end{array}]{H_2O}$?

A)

(cyclopentane)$-CH_2-\overset{\overset{\textstyle O}{\|}}{C}-CH_3$

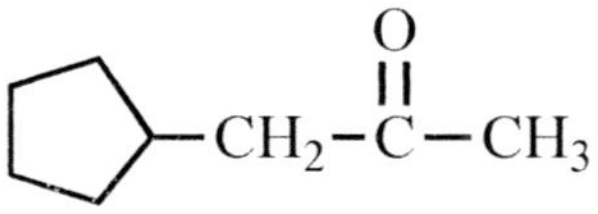

B)

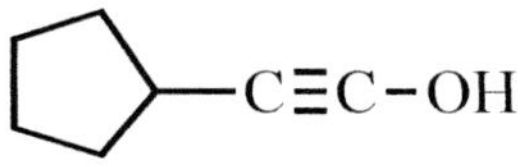

Cyclopentyl—C≡C—OH

C)

Cyclopentyl—C=C—OH
        | |
        H H

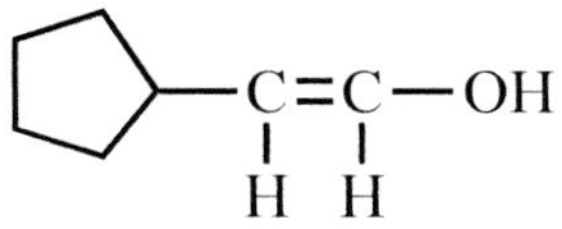

D)

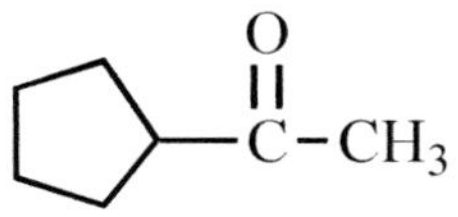

Cyclopentyl—C(=O)—CH₃

E)

Cyclopentyl—CH₂—C(=O)—H

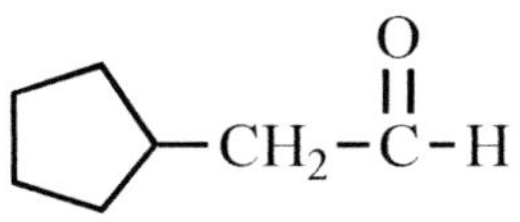

Ans: D

9. What is the **major** product expected from the following reaction?

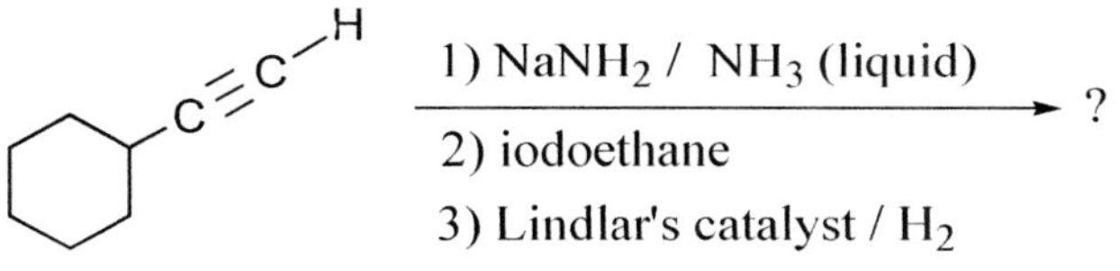

Cyclohexyl—C≡C—H

1) NaNH₂ / NH₃ (liquid)

2) iodoethane

3) Lindlar's catalyst / H₂

→ ?

A)

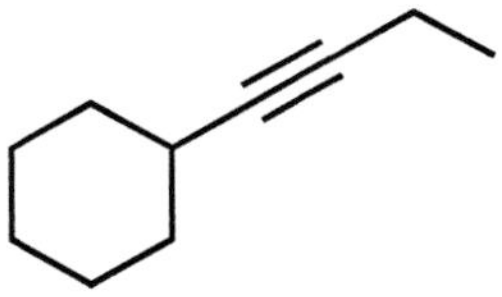

B)

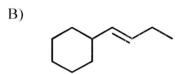

C)

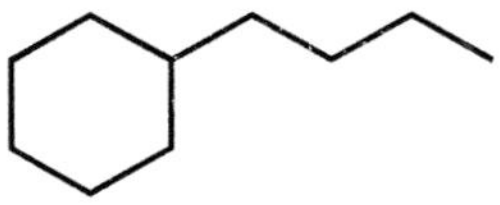

D)

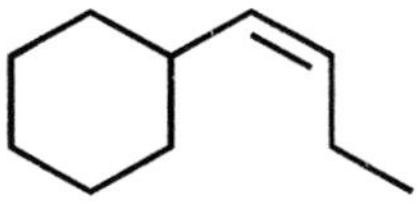

E)

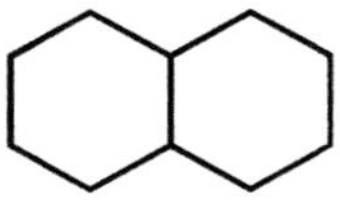

Ans: D

10. Considering the mechanism of the following reaction, which of the intermediates shown below is **not** likely to form along the reaction pathway?

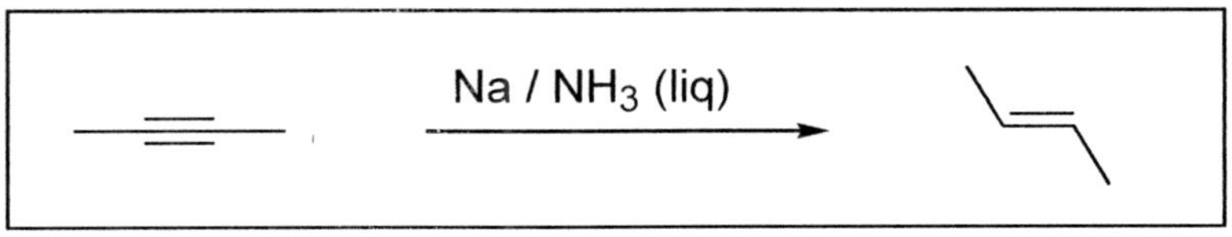

$$\text{———} \xrightarrow{\text{Na / NH}_3 \text{ (liq)}} \text{———}$$

A)

$$H_3C-C\overset{\cdot}{=}\overset{\oplus}{C}-CH_3$$

B)

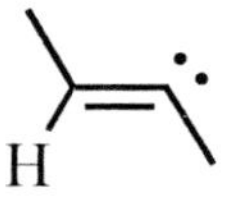

C)

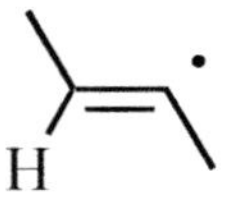

D)

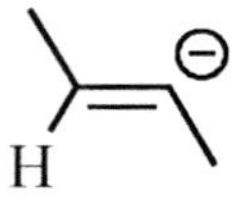

E)

$$H_3C-C\overset{\cdot}{=}\overset{\ominus}{C}-CH_3$$

Ans: A

11. What major product(s) are expected from the reaction shown below?

$$H_3C—C≡C—CH_3 \xrightarrow{\text{HBr (excess)}} ?$$

A)

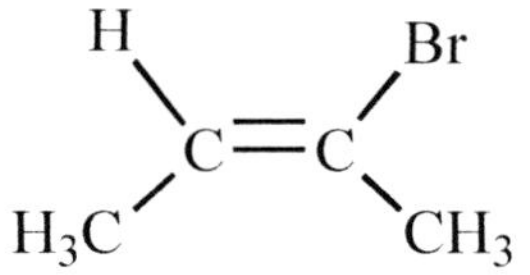

B)

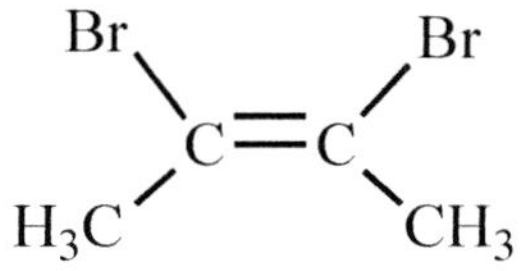

C)

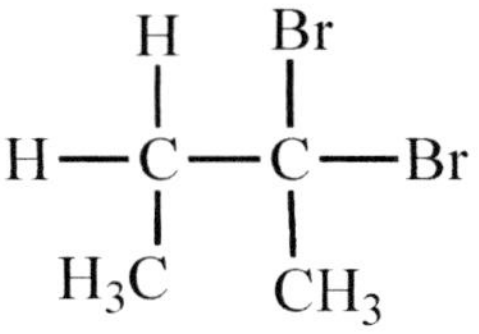

D)

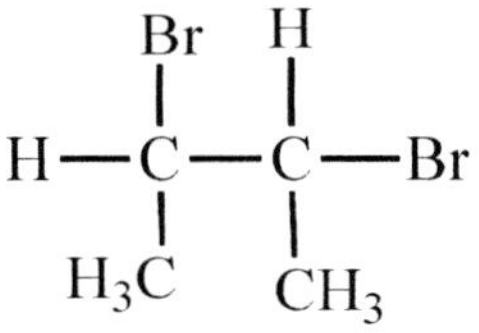

E)   more than one of the above

Ans: C

12. What organic product results from the reaction shown below?

$$CaC_2 + H_2O \longrightarrow ?$$

A) CH_4

B) $Ca(CH_3)_2$

C) $CH_3CH_3 + Ca(OH)_2$

D) $HC≡CH$

E)

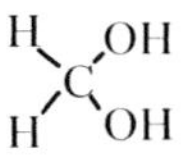

Ans: D

13. What is the **major** product of the following reaction?

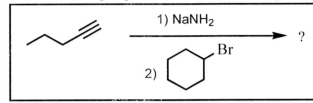

A)

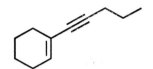

B)

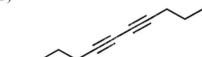

C)

D)

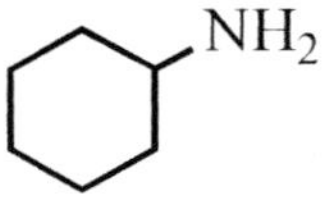

E)

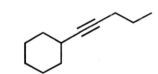

Ans: C

14. Which, if either, of the following hydrogenations would be the **more** exothermic?

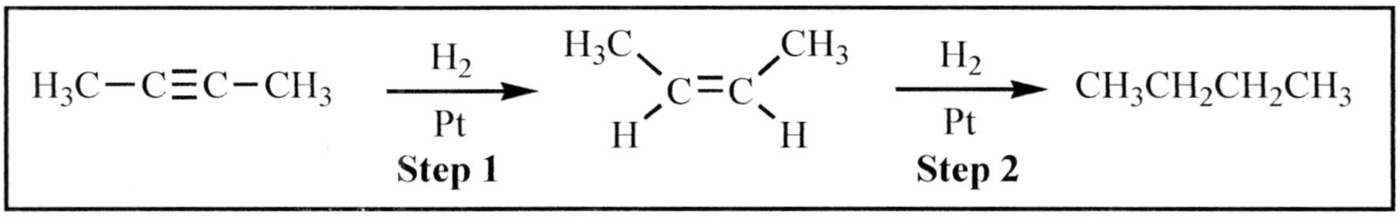

$$H_3C-C{\equiv}C-CH_3 \quad \xrightarrow[\text{Pt}]{H_2} \quad \underset{\text{Step 1}}{} \quad \overset{H_3C}{\underset{H}{}}C{=}C\overset{CH_3}{\underset{H}{}} \quad \xrightarrow[\text{Pt}]{H_2} \quad CH_3CH_2CH_2CH_3$$

Step 1   Step 2

A)   Step 1   D)   neither is exothermic
B)   Step 2   E)   there is no way to predict this
C)   both are equally exothermic
Ans: A

15. What product do you expect from the following reaction sequence?

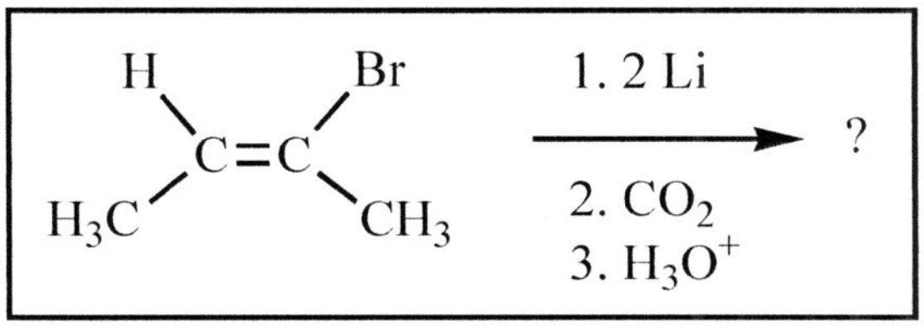

A)

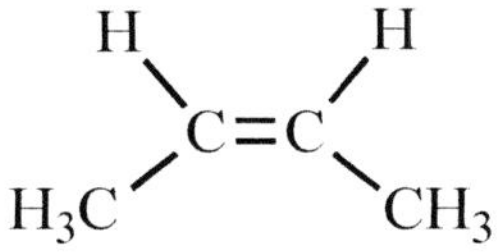

B)

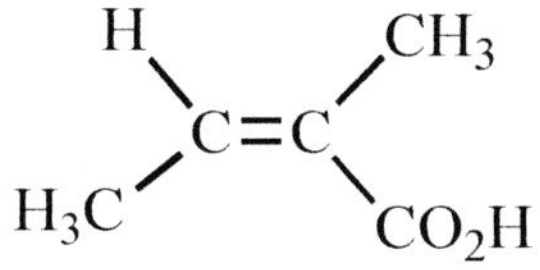

C)

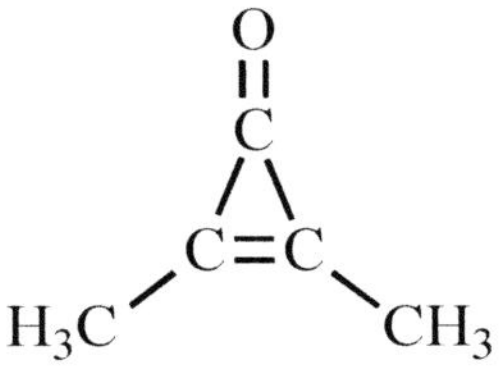

D)

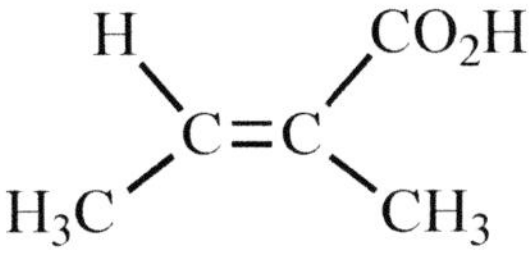

E)

$H_3C-C\equiv C-CH_3$

Ans: D

16. What major product(s) are expected from the reaction shown below?

$$H_3C-C\equiv C-H \xrightarrow{\text{HI (excess)}} ?$$

A)

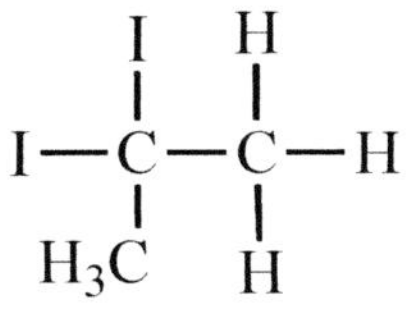

B)

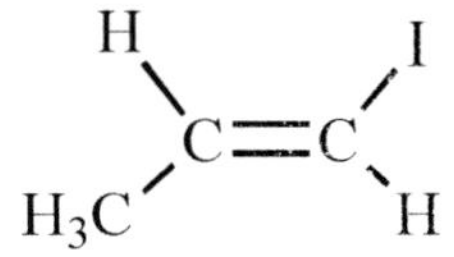

C)

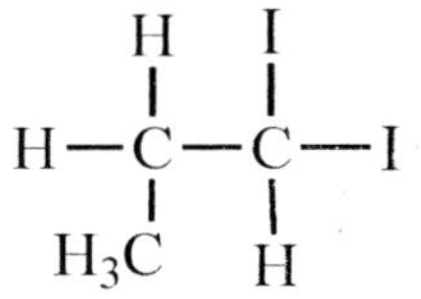

D)

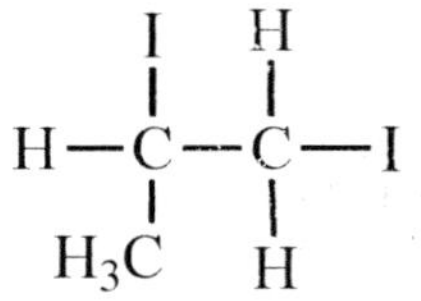

E)

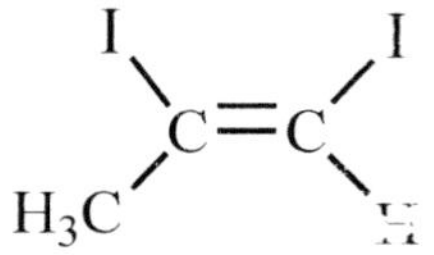

Ans: A

17. What reagent(s) would be required to accomplish the transformation shown?

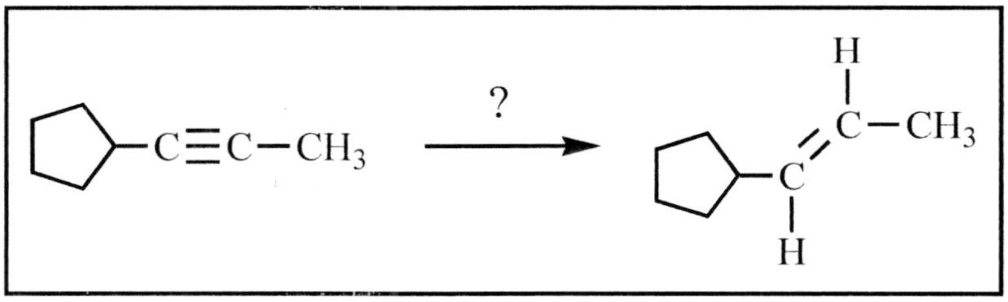

A) H_2, Pt   D) $LiAlH_4$ then H_2O
B) H_2, Lindlar's catalyst   E)   none of these would accomplish this
C)   Na, liq. NH_3, then H_2O
Ans: C

18. What would be the **major** product of the following reaction?

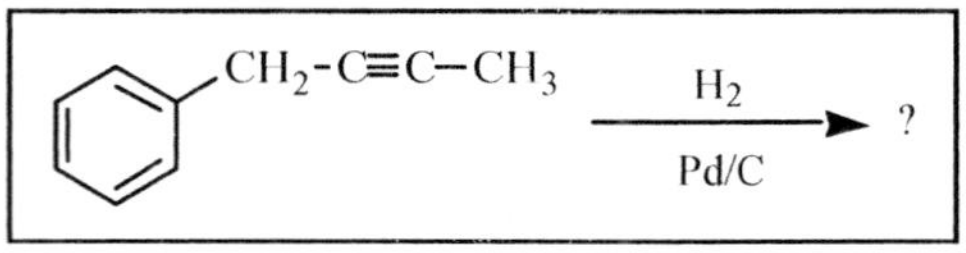

A)

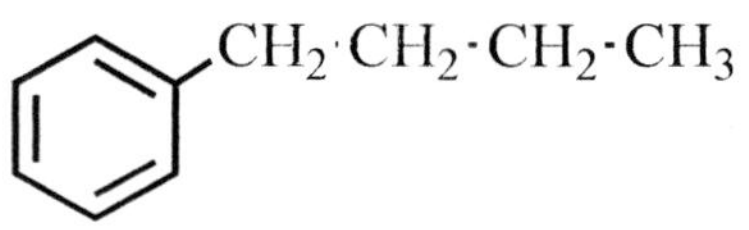

B)

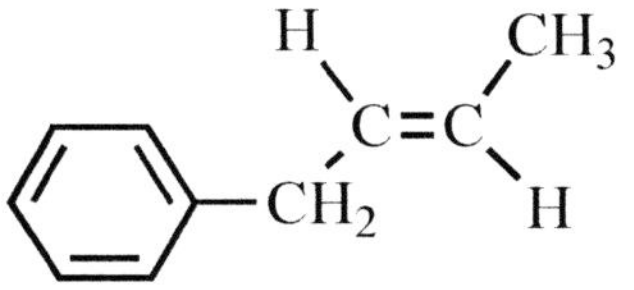

H   CH₃
 \   /
  C=C
 /   \
CH₂   H

C)

CH₂-C≡C-H

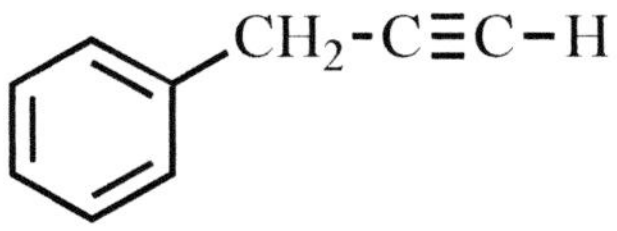

D)

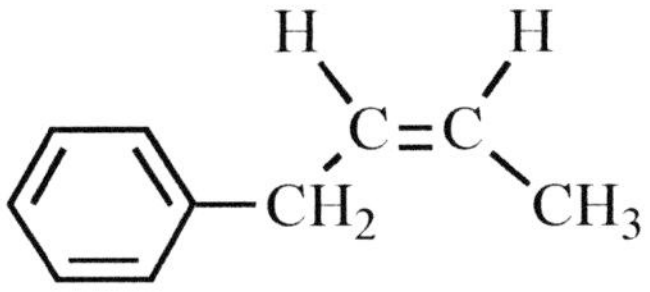

H   H
 \   /
  C=C
 /   \
CH₂   CH₃

E)

CH₂·CH₂·CH₂·CH₃

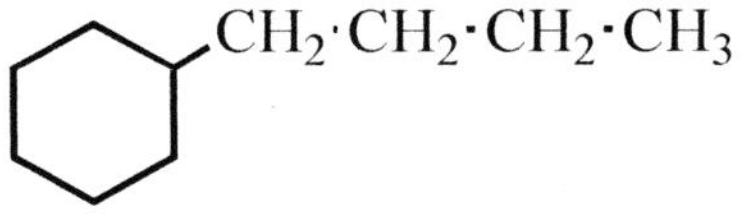

Ans: A

19. What reagent(s) would be required to accomplish the process shown below?

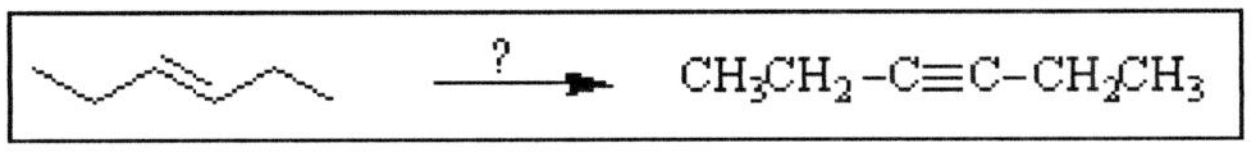

$$\xrightarrow{?}\quad CH_3CH_2-C\equiv C-CH_2CH_3$$

A)   1. HBr
       2. NaOH
B)   1. Br₂
       2. NaNH₂ (xs)
C)   1. Br₂
       2. NaOH
D)   H₂SO₄
       (catalytic)
E)   1. NaNH₂
       2. H₂O
Ans: B

20. Which metal acts as a **poison** for hydrogenation catalysts?
    A) Pd   B) Pt   C) Ni   D) Pb   E) Hg
    Ans: D

21. What reactant and product types would be **most** appropriate for the reagents shown?

    $$? \xrightarrow[\text{2. } H_2O_2, \text{ NaOH}]{\text{1. } BH_3} ?$$

    A) alkene/Markovnikov alcohol
    B) alkene/anti-Markovnikov alcohol
    C) alkyne/aldehyde or ketone
    D) both A and B
    E) both B and C

    Ans: E

22. What is $NaNH_2$ mainly used for in organic chemistry?
    A) as a nucleophile
    B) as a weak base
    C) as a strong base
    D) as a weak acid
    E) as a strong acid

    Ans: C

23. What reagent(s) are required to accomplish the transformation shown?

    A) 1. NaD
    B) 1. Mg/THF
        2. D_2O
    C) D_2O/peroxides
    D) D_2/catalyst
    E) DBr/peroxides

    Ans: B

24. What reagent(s) would be required to accomplish the transformation shown?

    A) H_2, Pt
    B) H_2, Lindlar's catalyst
    C) Na, liq. NH_3, then H_2O
    D) $LiAlH_4$ then H_2O
    E) none of the above would accomplish this

    Ans: B

25. What is the **major** product from the following reaction?

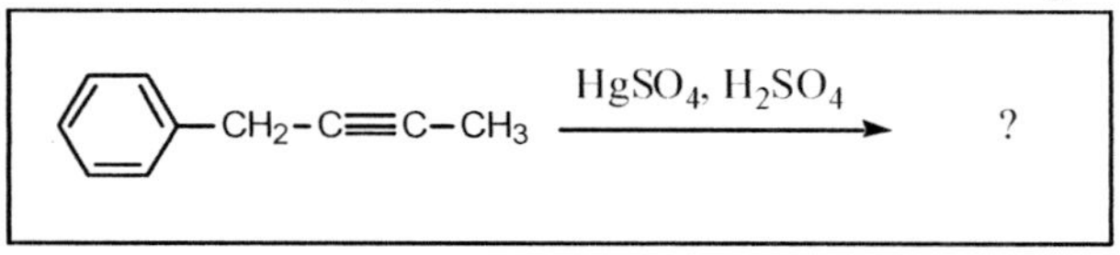

A)

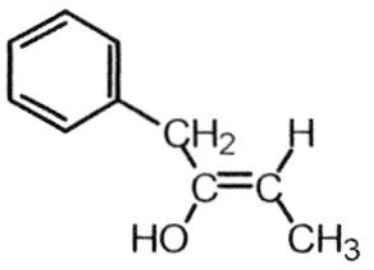

B)

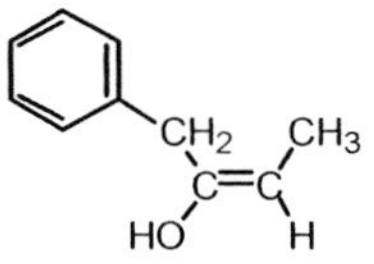

C)

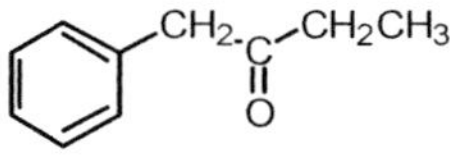

D)

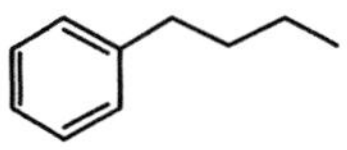

E) no reaction

Ans: C

26. What major product(s) are expected from the reaction shown below?

$$H_3C-C\equiv C-CH_2CH_3 \xrightarrow[\text{2. } H^+]{\text{1. } KMnO_4/NaOH} ?$$

A)

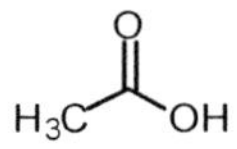

B)

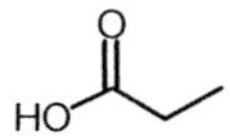

C)

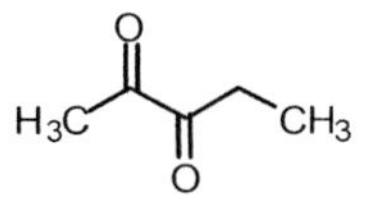

D)

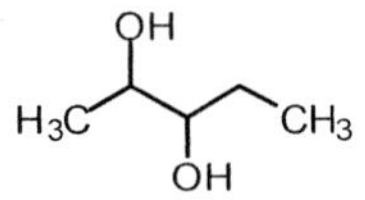

E) Both A and B

Ans: E

27. Infrared spectroscopy is a useful technique in identifying terminal alkynes. What is/are the characteristic stretching band(s) for a terminal alkyne?
    A)   3260-3330 cm^{-1}
    B)   1550-1680 cm^{-1}
    C)   2100-2260 cm^{-1}
    D)   both A and B
    E)   both A and C
    Ans: E

28. What is the major product of the following reaction?

    $H_3C-C\equiv C-CH_3$ $\xrightarrow[\text{2. } D_2O]{\text{1. NaOH}}$?

    A) $H_3C-C\equiv C-CH_2D$
    B) $H_3C-C\equiv C-CHD_2$
    C) $DH_2C-C\equiv C-CH_2D$
    D) $D_3C-C\equiv C-CD_3$
    E)   no reaction
    Ans: E

29. What is the expected product from the following reaction?

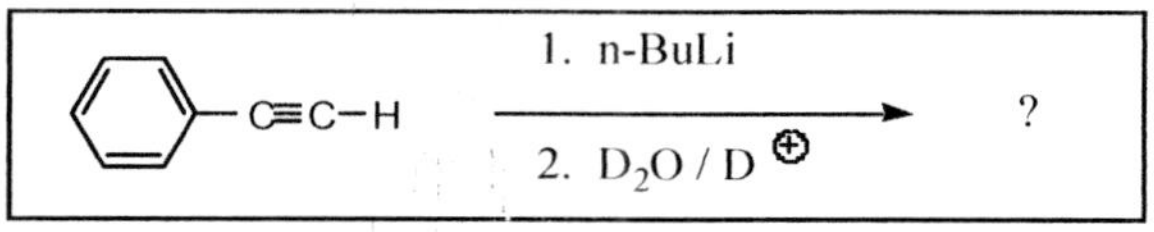

    Ph$-C\equiv C-H$ $\xrightarrow[\text{2. } D_2O / D^{\oplus}]{\text{1. n-BuLi}}$?

    A) 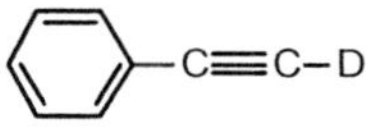
    Ph$-C\equiv C-D$

    B) 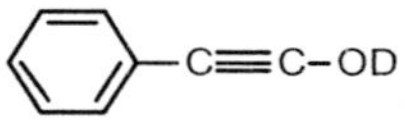
    Ph$-C\equiv C-OD$

    C) 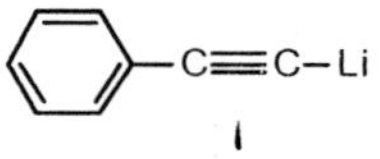
    Ph$-C\equiv C-Li$

    D)
    Ph$-C\equiv C-C\equiv C-$Ph

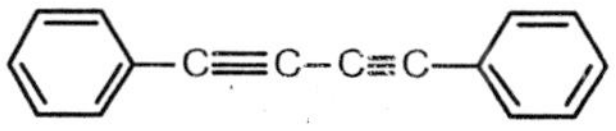

    E)   no reaction
    Ans: A

30. The following is an example of intramolecular Heck reaction. Which product is the most likely to form?

$$\text{1 mol\%Pd(OAc)}_2$$

PPh₃, NEt₃, MeCN
3h, reflux

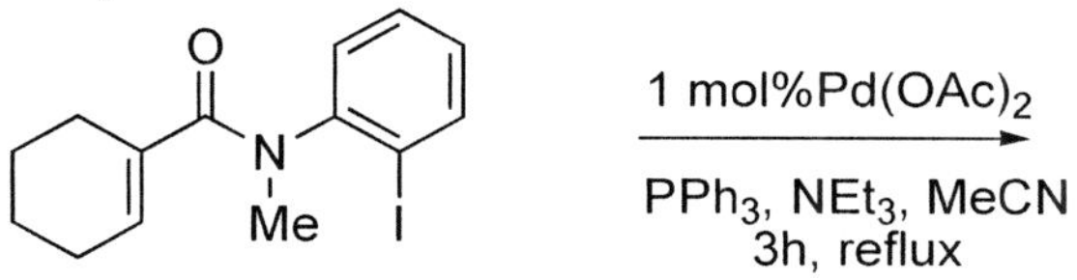

A)

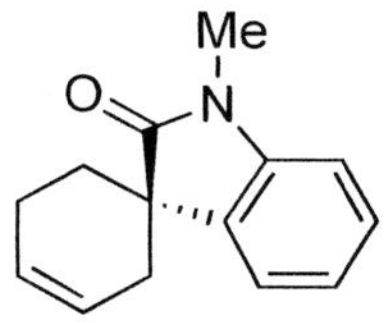

B)

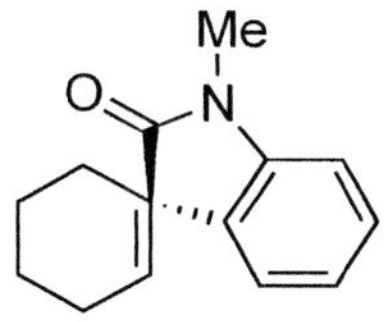

C)

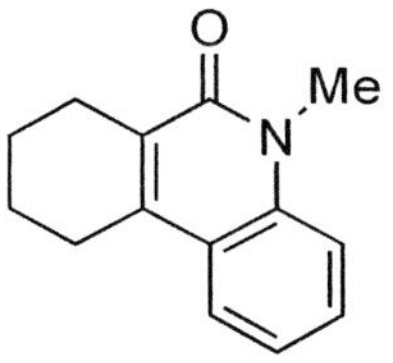

D)

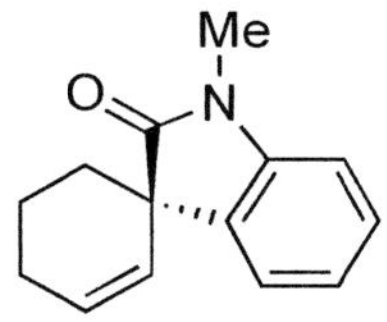

E)

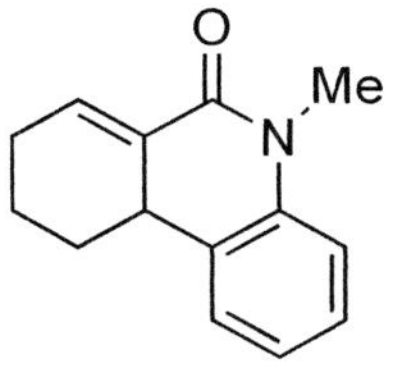

Ans: D

31. Which product is the most likely to form?

$$\text{H}_2$$

Lindlar's catalyst

A)

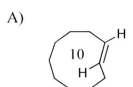

H
10
H

B)

10

C)

H
10
H

D)

H
10
Lindlar's

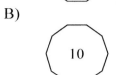

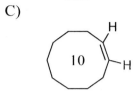

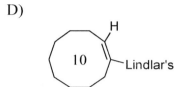

E) All of the above will form in nearly equal amounts.
Ans: C

32. Schwartz' reagent reacts with alkynes in a manner similar to that of R_2BH. With this information which product would you expect to be formed predominantly from the reaction below?

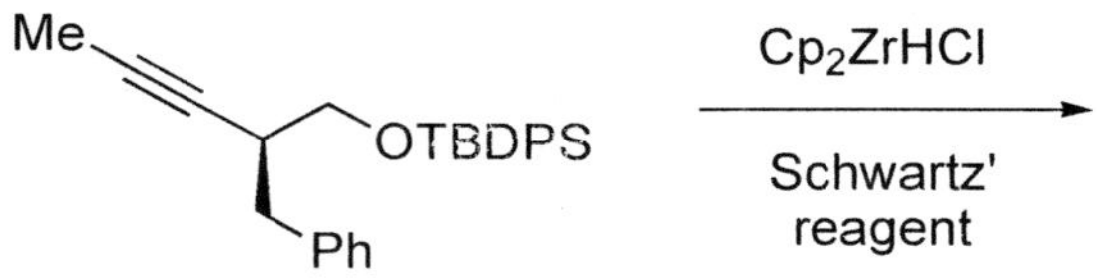

Me
OTBDPS
Ph
Cp2ZrHCl
Schwartz'
reagent

A)

H
Cp2ClZr
OTBDPS
Me
Ph

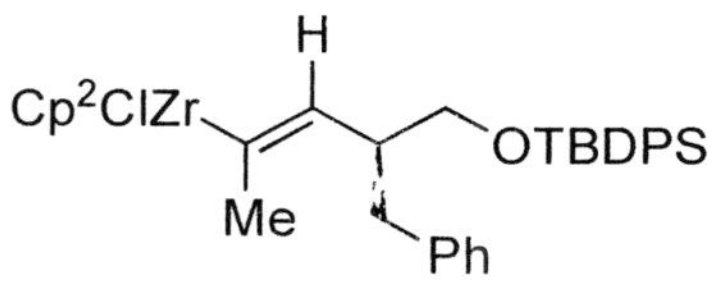

B)

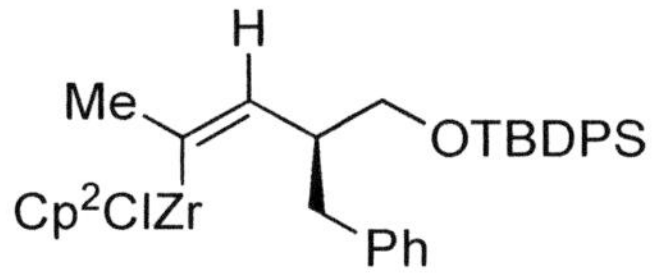

C)

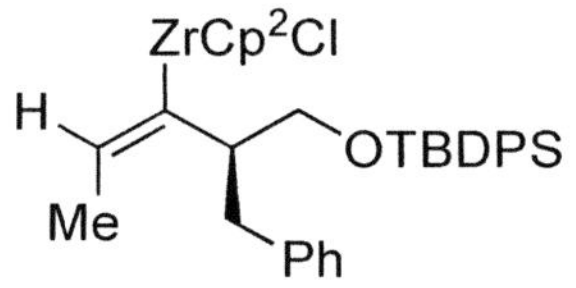

D)

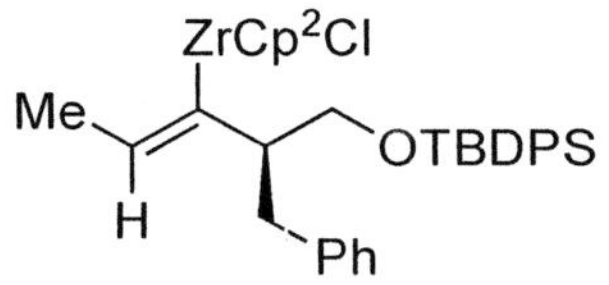

E)   All of the above will form in nearly equal amounts.

Ans: A

33. Subjecting hexyne to Electron Impact Ionization Mass spectrometry produces two characteristic ionization peaks as a result of what two bonds breaking?

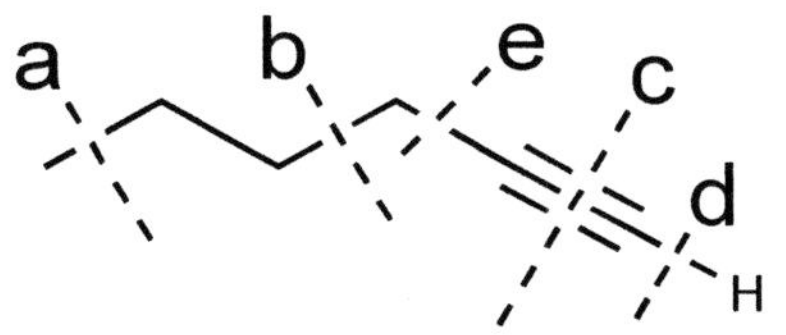

A) a and d   B) b and c   C) c and d   D) b and d   E) e and d

Ans: D

Chapter 14: Delocalized Pi Systems: Investigation by Ultraviolet and Visible Spectroscopy

1. What product(s) would you expect the following radical reaction to provide in reasonable yields?

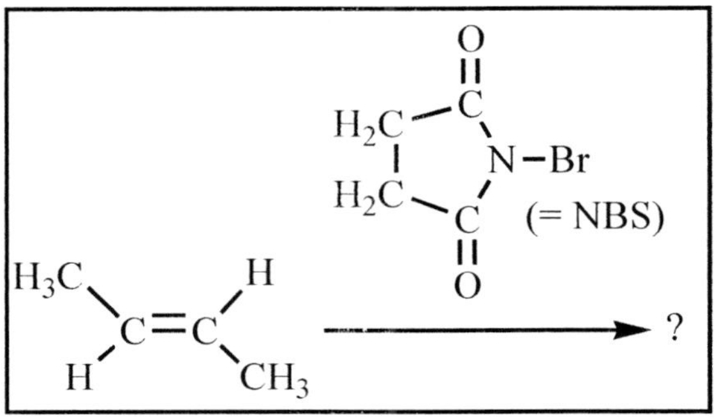

$$H_3C-C(=O)-N(Br)-C(=O) \text{ (5-membered ring)} \quad (= NBS)$$

H₂C—C(=O)
| N–Br
H₂C—C(=O)   (= NBS)

$$H_3C, H \quad C=C \quad H, CH_3 \longrightarrow ?$$

A)

HOCH₂, H
       C=C
H,   CH₃

B)

H₃C—CH=C
       H
       CH₂Br

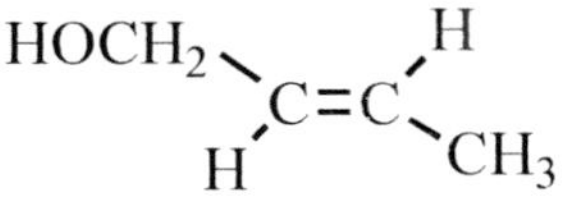

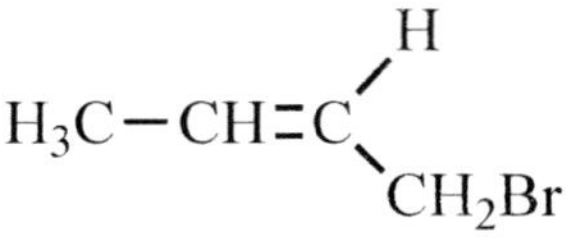

C)

H₃C   H
  | /
H–C–C
  | \\
  Br   CH₂

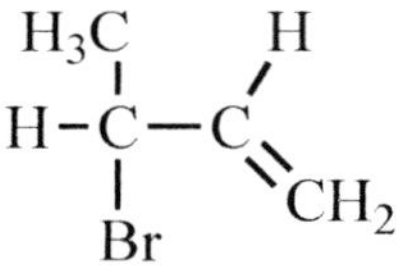

D)   both B and C
E)   both A and C

Ans: D

2. What would be the product of the following reaction?

2 (cyclopentadiene) ⟶ ?

A)

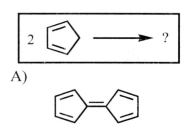

B)

C)

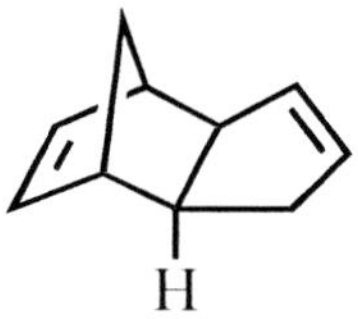

D)

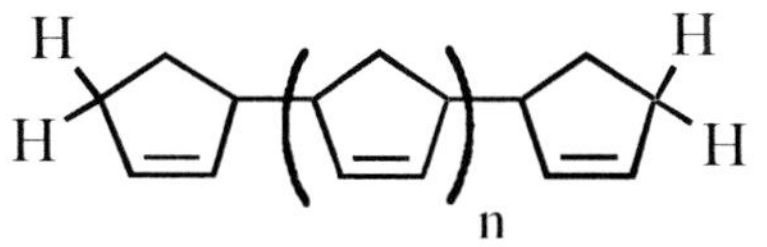

E)   No reaction occurs

Ans: B

3. What product(s) would you expect from the following reaction?

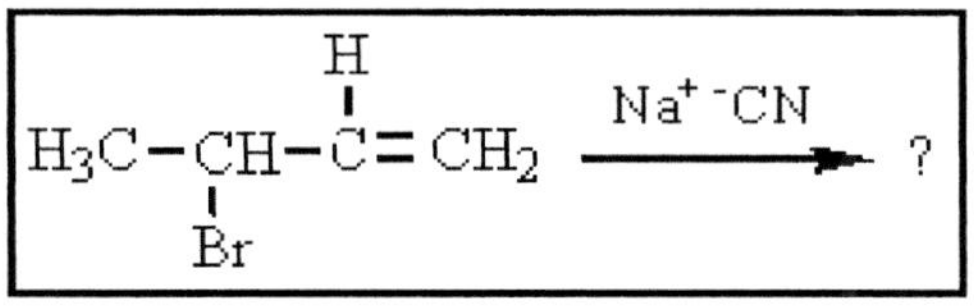

$$H_3C-\underset{\underset{Br}{|}}{CH}-\overset{\overset{H}{|}}{C}=CH_2 \xrightarrow{Na^+\;{}^-CN} \;\;?$$

A)

$$H_3C-\underset{\underset{CN}{|}}{CH}-\overset{\overset{H}{|}}{C}=CH_2$$

B)

$$H_3C-CH_2-\overset{\overset{CN}{|}}{C}=CH_2$$

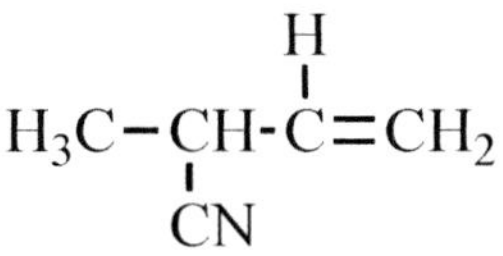

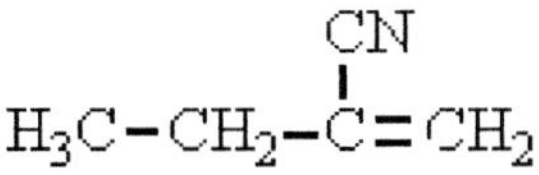

C)

$$H_3C-CH=\overset{\overset{H}{|}}{C}-CH_2CN$$

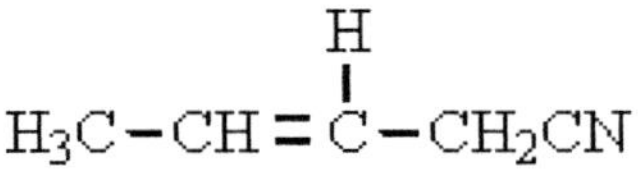

D)   both A and B

E)   both A and C

Ans: E

4. In order of decreasing reactivity, how would the bromides below rank in the following reaction?

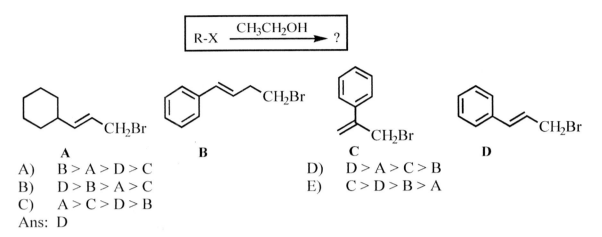

A)   B > A > D > C   D)   D > A > C > B
B)   D > B > A > C   E)   C > D > B > A
C)   A > C > D > B
Ans: D

5. What would be the final product(s) of the following reactions?

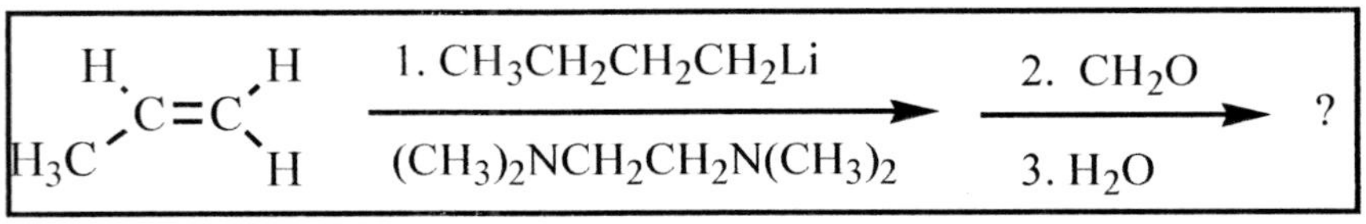

$$
\underset{H_3C}{\overset{H}{>}}C=C\underset{H}{\overset{H}{<}} \quad \xrightarrow[\text{(CH}_3)_2\text{NCH}_2\text{CH}_2\text{N(CH}_3)_2]{1.\ CH_3CH_2CH_2CH_2Li} \quad \xrightarrow[\text{3. H}_2\text{O}]{2.\ CH_2O} \quad ?
$$

A)

$$
\underset{H}{\overset{HOCH_2}{>}}C=C\underset{CH_3}{\overset{H}{<}}
$$

B)

$$
\underset{H}{\overset{H}{>}}C=C\underset{CH_2-CH_2OH}{\overset{H}{<}}
$$

C)

$$
\underset{H_2C}{>}C\underset{CH_3}{\overset{CH_2OH}{<}}
$$

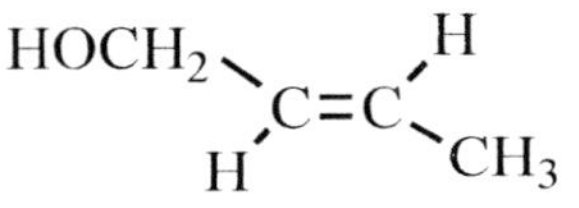

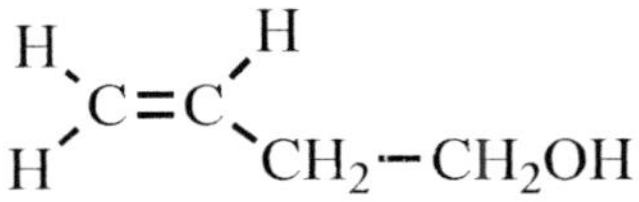

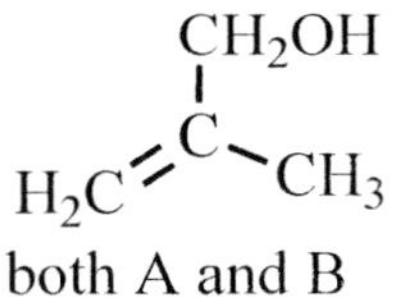

D)   both A and B
E)   both A and C
Ans: B

6. Which one of the following dienes would you expect to be the **most** stable?

A)

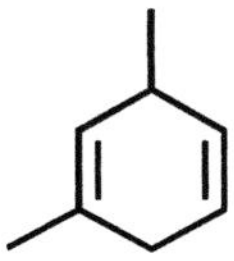

B)

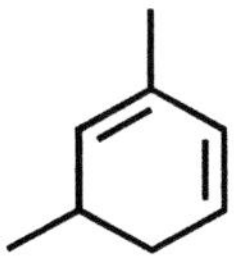

C)

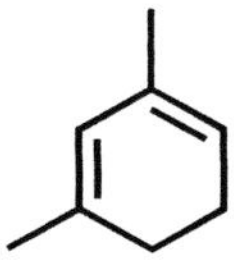

D)

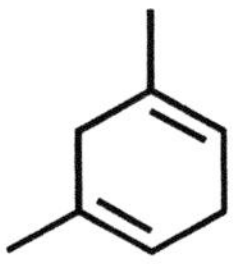

E)

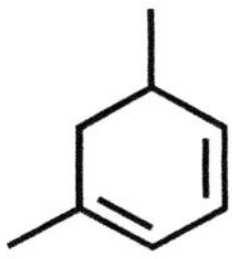

Ans: C

7. What product(s) would **NOT** be formed from the reaction of 1,3-butadiene with HCl?

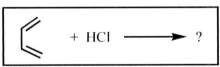

A) $ClCH_2-CH_2-CH:CH_2$ D)   neither A nor C

B) $H_3C-CHCl-CH=CH_2$ E)   neither B nor C

C) $ClCH_2-CH=CH-CH_3$

Ans: A

8. What would be the major product of the following reaction?

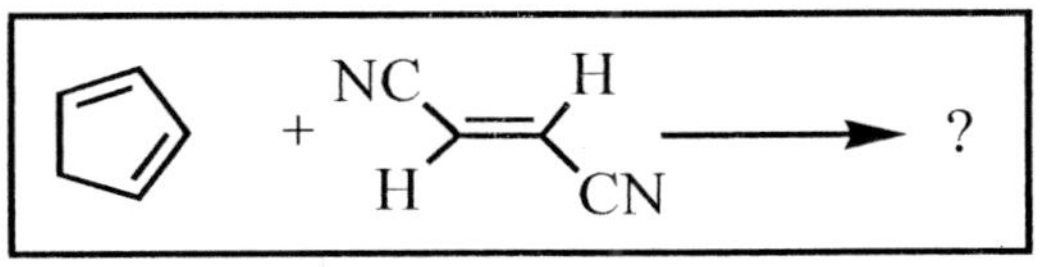

A)

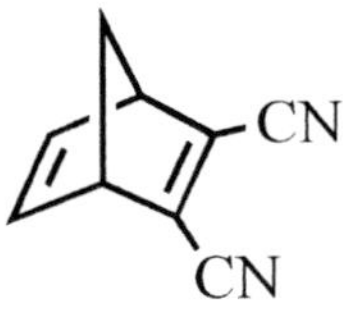

B)

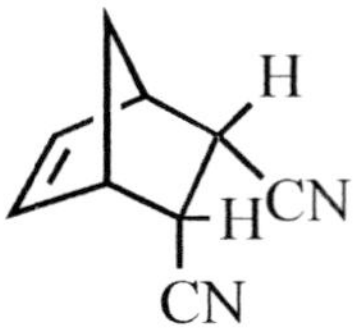

C)

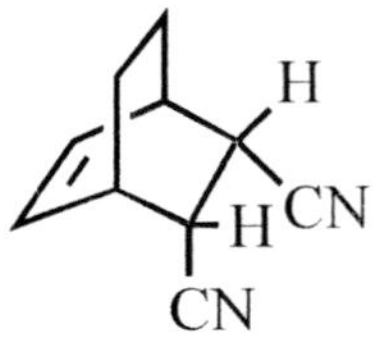

D)

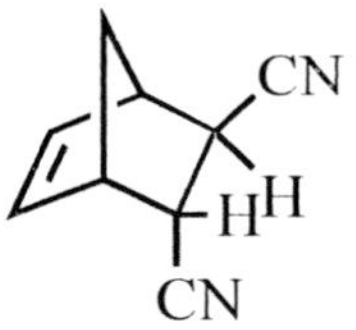

E)

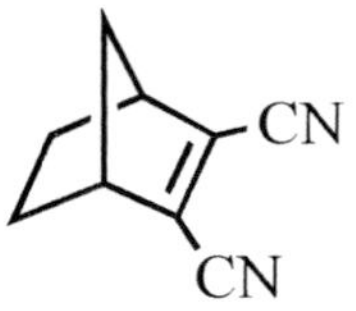

Ans: D

9. UV-visible spectroscopy involves what type of phenomenon?

A) Binding of chemical bonds
B) Electron transitions between orbitals
C) Molecular rotations
D) Nuclear spin transitions
E) Stretching of chemical bonds

Ans: B

10. The reaction of butadiene with acrolien would yield what product?

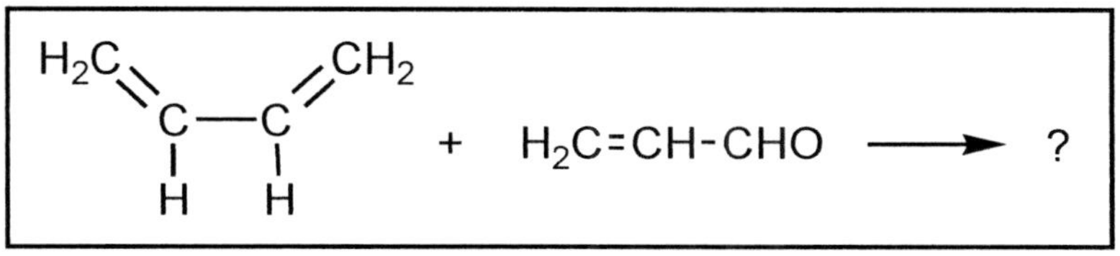

    + $H_2C=CH-CHO$ ⟶ ?

A)

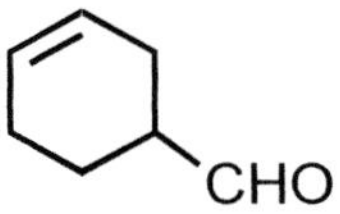

CHO

B)

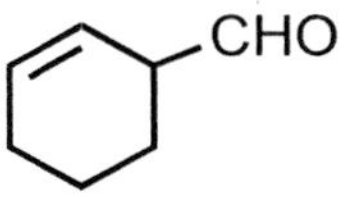

CHO

C)

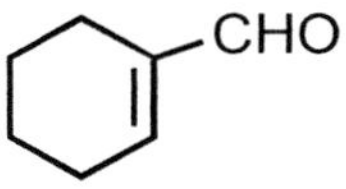

CHO

D)

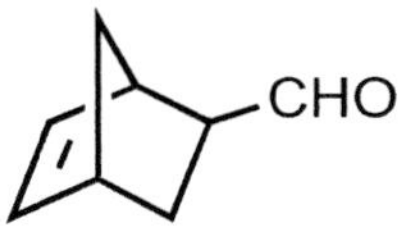

CHO

E)   None of these

Ans: A

11. What would be the expected major product of the following reaction sequence?

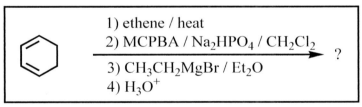

1) ethene / heat
2) MCPBA / Na_2HPO_4 / CH_2Cl_2
3) CH_3CH_2MgBr / Et_2O
4) H_3O^+

?

A)

B)

C)

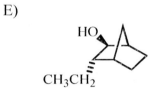

D)

E)

Ans: D

12. The LUMO of 1,3,5-hexatriene is:

A) $\psi 1$ B) $\psi 2$ C) $\psi 3$ D) $\psi 4$ E) $\psi 5$
Ans: D

13. A typical Diels-Alder reaction involves
    A)   an electron-rich diene and an electron-rich dienophile.
    B)   an electron-poor diene and an electron-rich dienophile.
    C)   an electron-rich diene and an electron-poor dienophile.
    D)   an electron-poor diene and an electron-poor dienophile.
    E)   a non-substituted diene and a non-substituted dienophile.
Ans: C

14. What would be the major product of the following reaction?

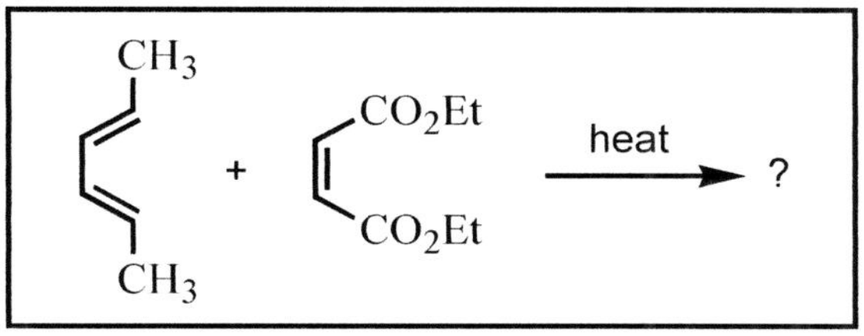

A)

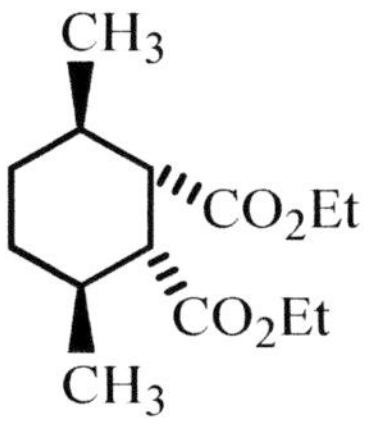

B)

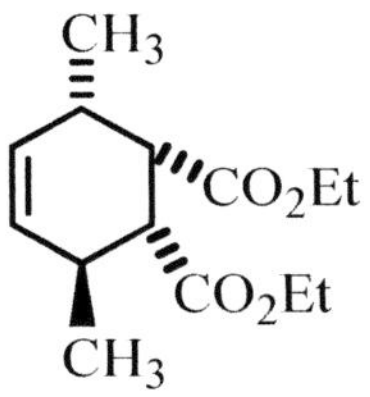

C)

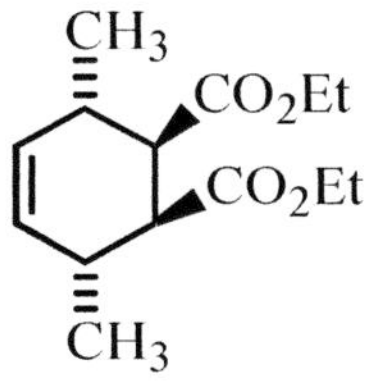

D)

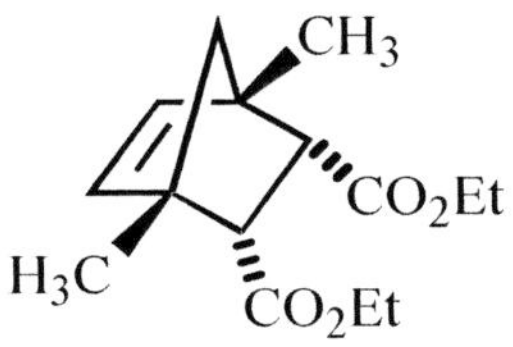

E)   None of these

Ans: C

15. The presence of a bromine WHERE in the following carbon chain would give the most reactive material for an S_N2 reaction with a nucleophile (all other bonds would be to hydrogen)?

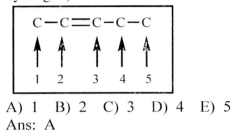

A) 1 B) 2 C) 3 D) 4 E) 5
Ans: A

16. What would be the major product from the following reaction?

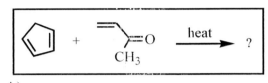

A)

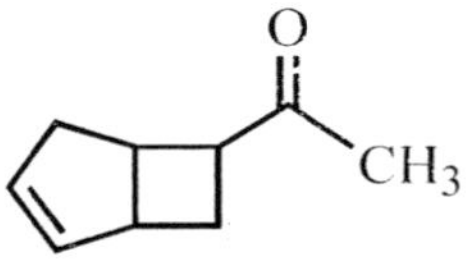

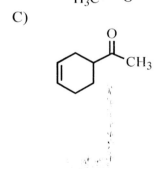

B)

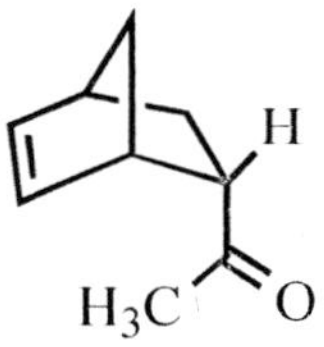

C)

D)

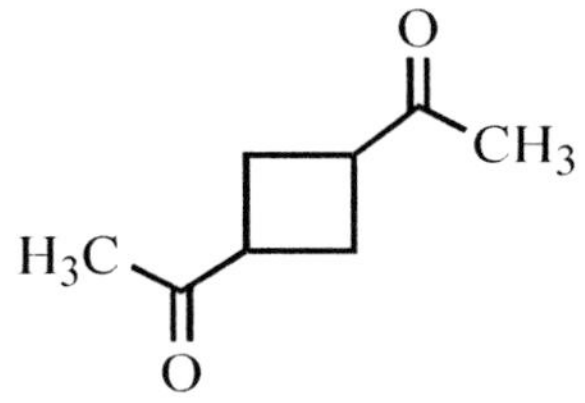

E)

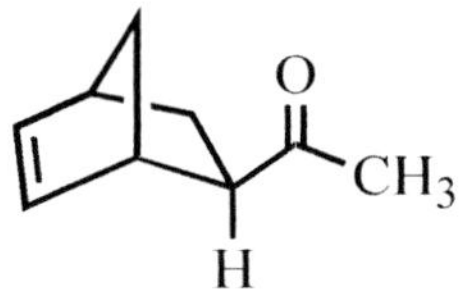

Ans: B

17. What major product would result from the following sequence of reactions?

A)

B)

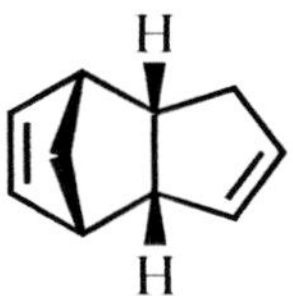

C)

D)

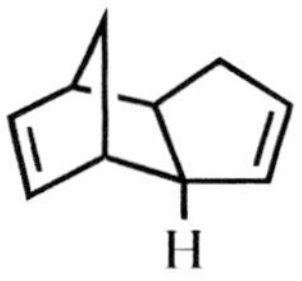

E)

Ans: E

18. What would be the expected **major** product of the following reaction?

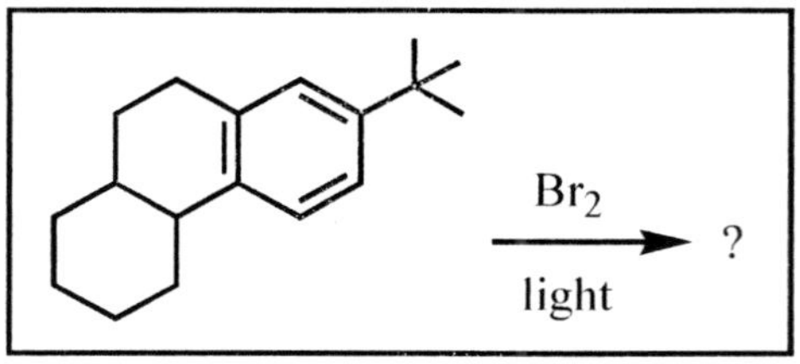

A)

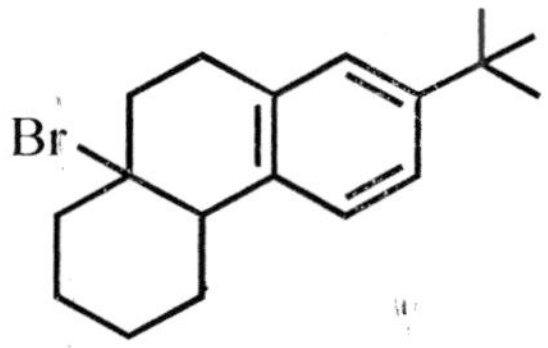

B)

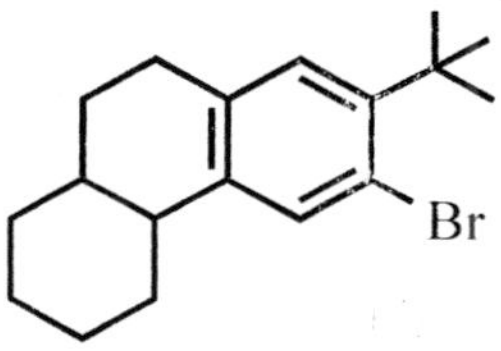

C)

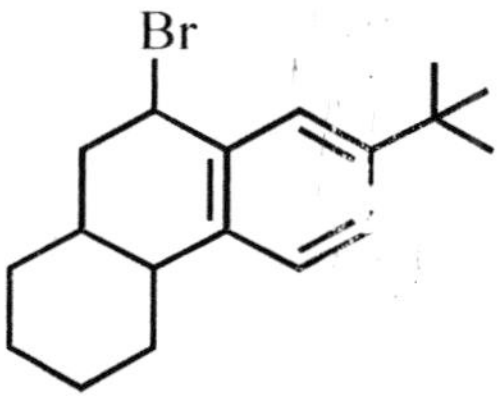

D)

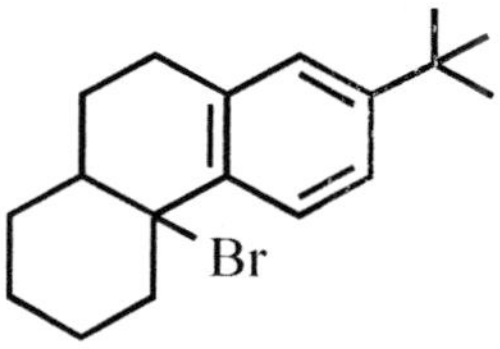

E)

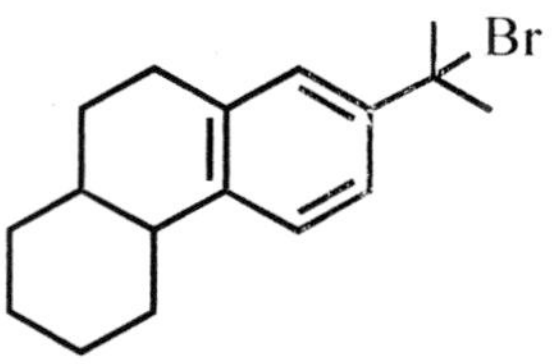

Ans: D

19. Which of the following dienes would you expect to be the most reactive in Diels-Alder reactions?

A)

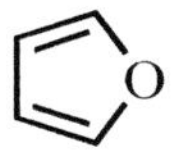

B)

C)

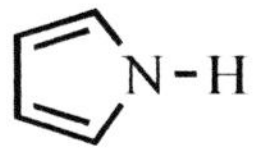

N−H

D)

E)

H₂C

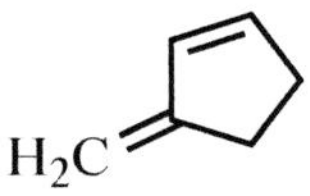

Ans: B

20. What product would you expect from the following reaction?

 + H−C—C(=O)—OCH₃ (with CH₂ double bond) ⟶ ?

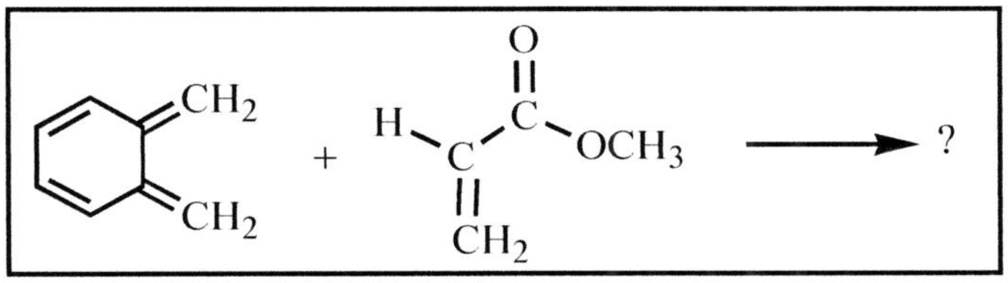

A)

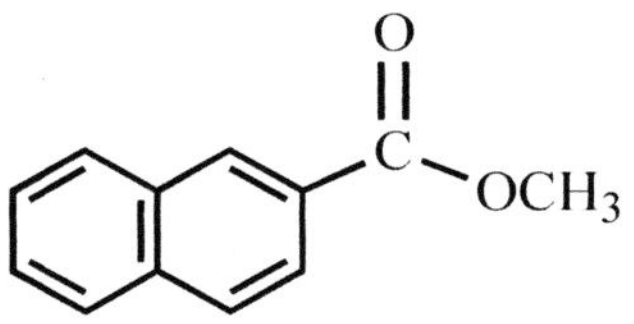

(naphthalene)—C(=O)—OCH₃

B)

(benzene)—C(=O)—OCH₃

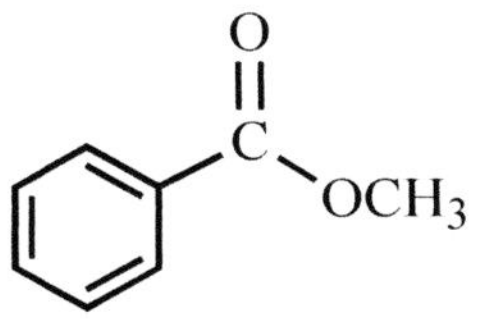

C)

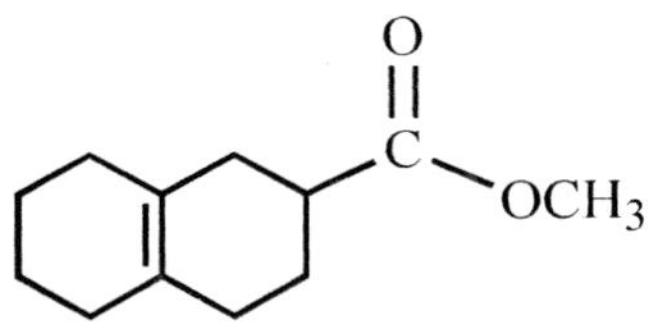

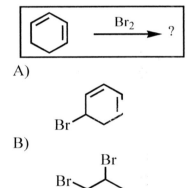

D)

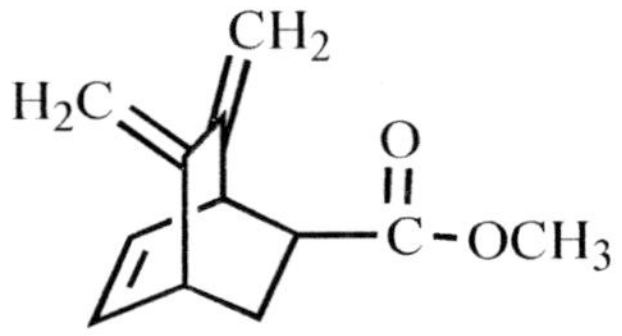

E)

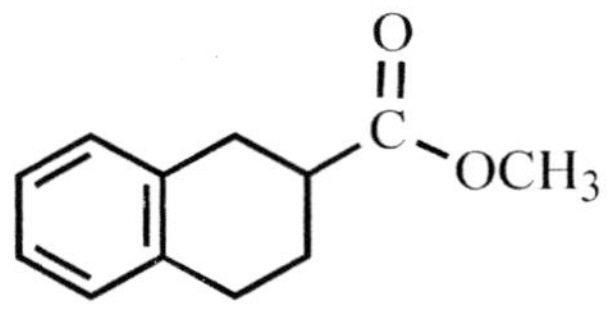

Ans: E

21. The reaction shown below is expected to produce which product(s)?

Br$_2$ → ?

A)

Br

B)

Br

Br

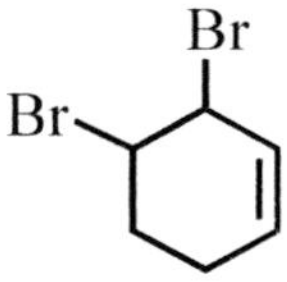

C)

D)

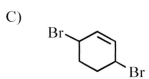

E)   more than one of these

Ans: E

22. The pi electrons in 1,3-butadiene are distributed as follows:
    A)   One in each of 4 bonding orbitals
    B)   Two in bonding orbitals, two in non-bonding orbitals
    C)   Two in each of 2 bonding orbitals
    D)   One in each of 4 non-bonding orbitals
    E)   None of these
    Ans: C

23. Predict the product of the hydrolysis of (S)-4-bromo-2-pentene
    A)   (R)-2-pentene-4-ol   D)   Racemic-3-hydroxy-3-pentene
    B)   Racemic 3-pentene-2-ol   E)   (S)-2-hydroxy-3-pentene
    C)   (R)-2-hydroxy-3-pentene
    Ans: B

24. What is the IUPAC name for the following compound?

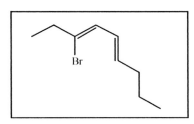

A)   (3E,5E)-7-Bromo-4,6-nonadiene   D)   (3Z,5E)-3-Bromo-3,5-nonadiene

B)   (3E,5E)-3-Bromo-3,5-nonadiene   E)   (3Z,5Z)-3-Bromo-3,5-nonadiene

C)   (3E,5Z)-7-Bromo-4,6-nonadiene

Ans: D

25. Which is the MAJOR product of combining 1,3-butadiene with HBr at 25 °C?
    A)   1-bromo-2-butene   D)   2,3-dibromobutene
    B)   3-bromobutene   E)   3,3-dibromobutene
    C)   1,3-dibromobutadiene

    Ans: B

26. Predict the MAJOR product of the following reaction:

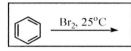

    A)

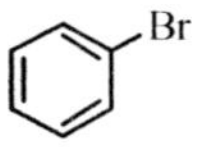

    B)

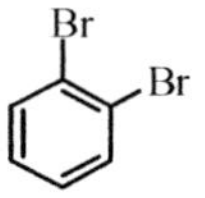

    C)

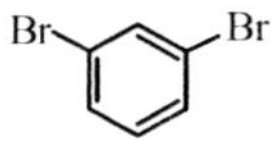

    D)

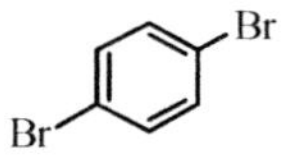

    E)   No reaction

    Ans: E

27. The UV spectrum of the following molecule is useful for determining _____.

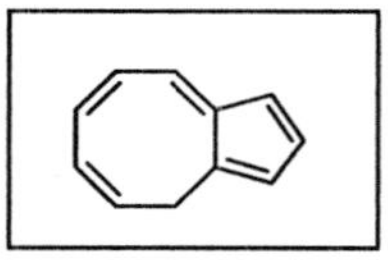

    A)   coupling constants between hydrogen atoms
    B)   molecular weight
    C)   conjugation resulting in electronic transitions
    D)   molecular formula
    E)   two of these are correct

    Ans: C

28. Predict the product of the following reaction:

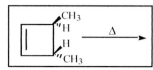

A)

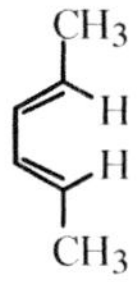

CH₃
H
H
CH₃

B)

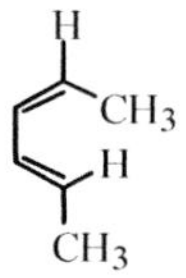

H
CH₃
H
CH₃

C)

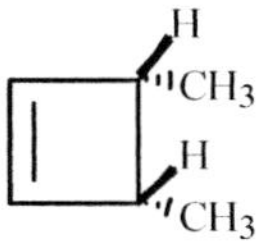

H
CH₃
H
CH₃

D)

CH₃
H
CH₃
H

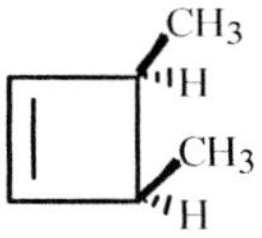

E)   No reaction

Ans: A

29. What is the proper IUPAC name for the following molecule:

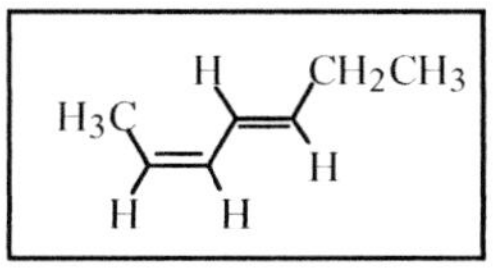

H₃C   H   CH₂CH₃
              H
     H   H

A)   (2*E*,4*Z*)-2,4-heptadiene   D)   (2*E*,4*Z*)-2,4-hexadiene
B)   (2*E*,3*Z*)-2,3-heptadiene   E)   (2*Z*,3*E*)-2,3-hexadiene
C)   (2*Z*,4*E*)-2,4-heptadiene

Ans: C

30. Which of the following are most favored thermodynamically?

A)   Br Br   D)   All of these

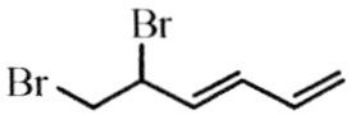

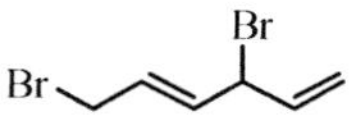

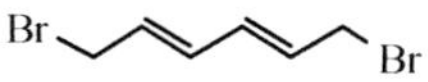

B)   Br Br   E)   None of these

C)   Br ~~~ Br

Ans: C

31. When reacted with Br_2 and light, which C-H bond 2-pentene will preferentially dissociate to give a radical?

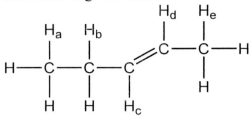

A) The C-H_a bond
B) The C-H_b bond
C) The C-H_c bond
D) The C-H_d bond
E) The C-H_e bond

Ans: E

32. Which of the structures below do not benefit from resonance stabilization?

A) $H_2C=CH-\overset{\bullet}{C}H_2$

B) $H_2C=CH-\overset{\oplus}{C}H_2$

C) $H_2C=CH-\overset{\ominus}{C}H_2$

D) $H_2C=CH-CH_3$

E) None of the above

Ans: D

33. Which of the following alkylbromides **cannot** be a product of the allylic bromination of 1-methylcyclopentene with NBS?

A)

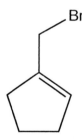

B)

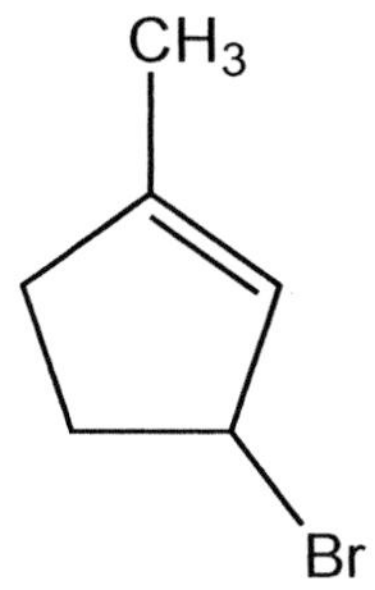

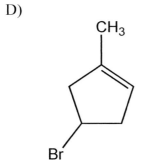

C)

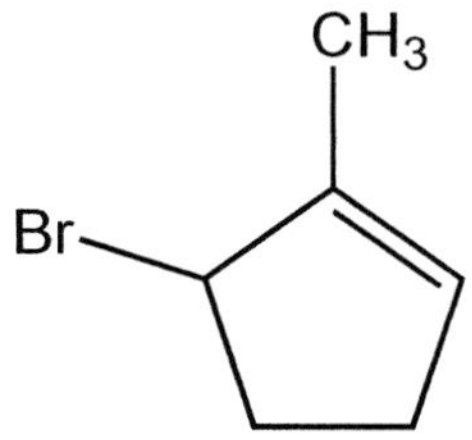

D)

E)   All of the above can be a product from the reaction.

Ans: D

34. Which of the following electrocyclic reactions occurs via a conrotatory process?

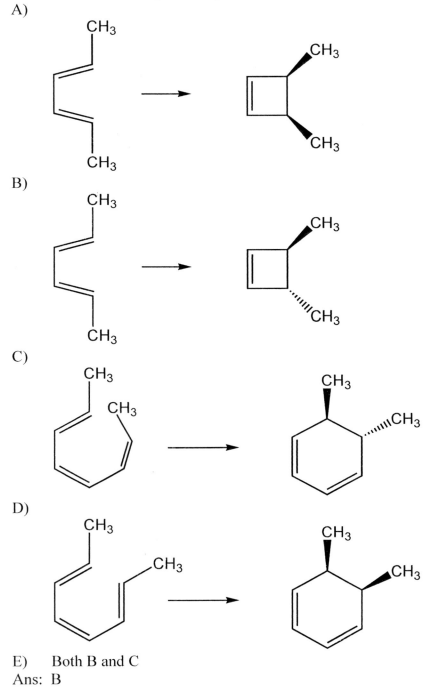

A)

B)

C)

D)

E) Both B and C

Ans: B

Chapter 15: Benzene and Aromaticity: Electrophilic Aromatic Substitution

1. Which of the following would **not** be aromatic (i.e., which would **not** be unusually stable)?

   A)

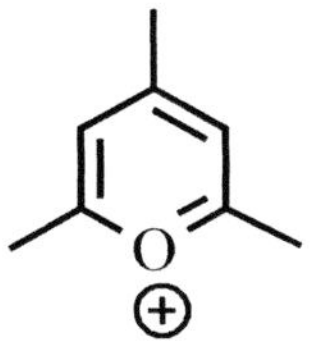

   B)

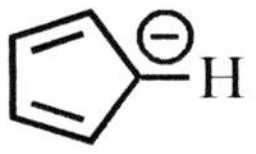

   C)

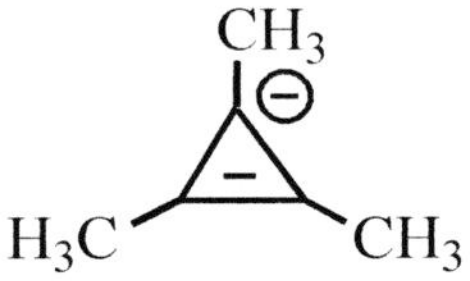

   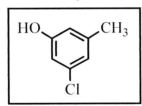

   D)

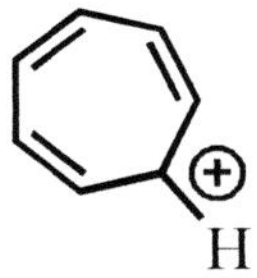

   E)

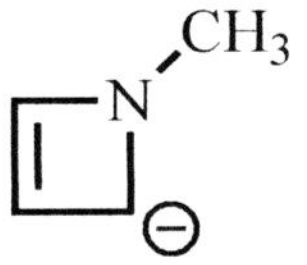

   Ans: C

2. How would you name the following?

   A) 3-chloro-5-methylphenol
   B) 3-hydroxy-5-chlorotoluene
   C) 1-chloro-3-hydroxy-5-methylbenzene
   D) Meta-methy-meta-hydroxytoluene
   E) 3-hydroxy-5-methylchlorobenzene
   Ans: A

3. Which of the following would you expect to be aromatic?
   A)

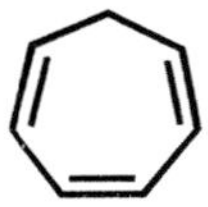

   B)

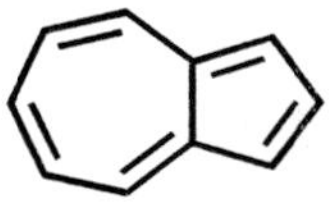

   C)

   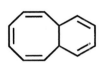

   D)

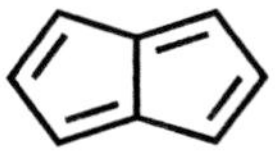

   E)

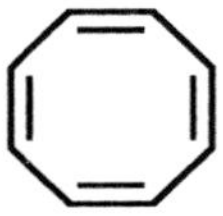

   Ans: B

4. The best **experimental** proof of aromaticity is
   A)   a pleasant odor.   D)   presence of resonance structures.
   B)   infrared CH absorption frequency.   E)   presence of conjugation.
   C)   NMR chemical shifts.
   Ans: C

5. Which of the following reactions of aromatics is reversible?
   A)   Nitration   D)   Sulfonation
   B)   Bromination   E)   F-C acylation
   C)   F-C alkylation
   Ans: D

6. What reagents are typically required to accomplish bromination of an aromatic ring?
   A) Br_2 + HBr   D) Br_2 + $FeBr_3$
   B) Br_2 + heat   E) Br_2 + H_2SO_4
   C) Br_2 + light
   Ans: D

7. Which of the following is **not** a resonance structure involved in electrophilic aromatic bromination?

    A)

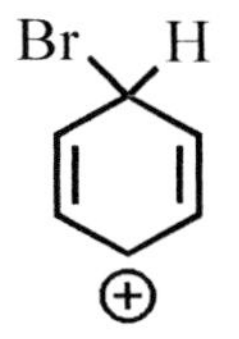

    B)

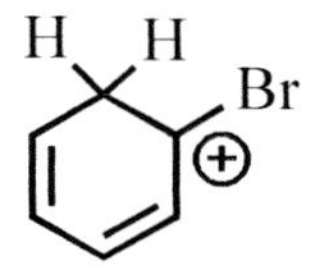

    C)

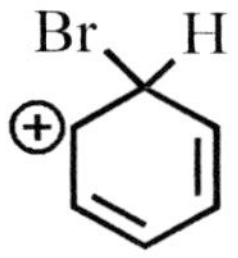

    D)

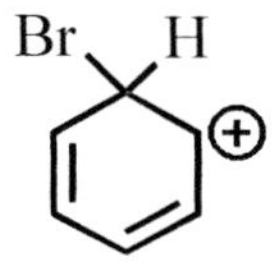

    E)   All of these are valid resonance structures.

    Ans: B

8. What would be the product of the following reaction?

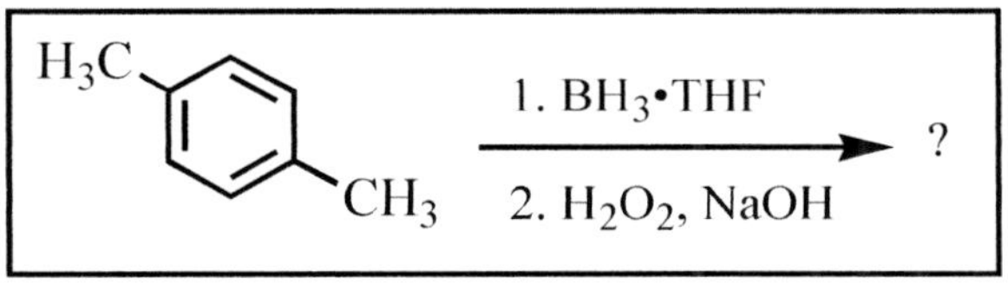

    $\xrightarrow[\text{2. } H_2O_2, \text{NaOH}]{\text{1. } BH_3 \cdot THF}$?

    A)

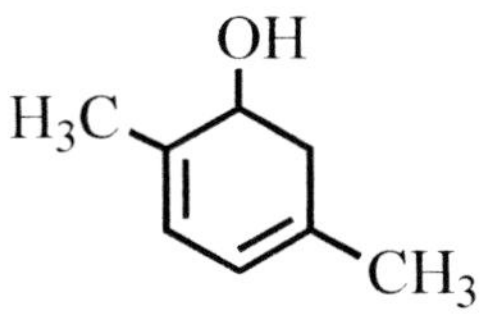

B)

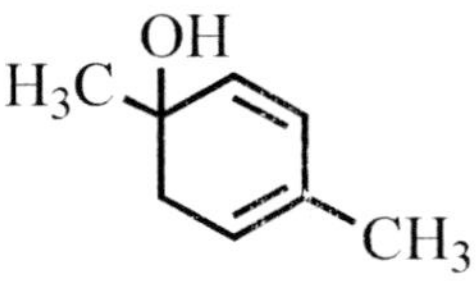
OH
H3C
CH3

C)

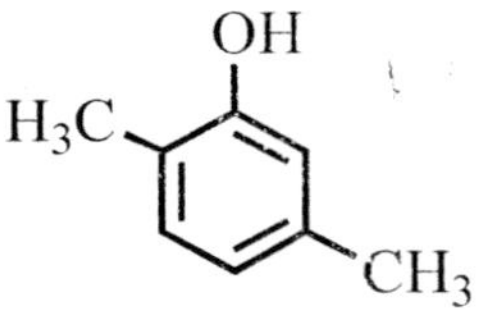
OH
H3C
CH3

D)

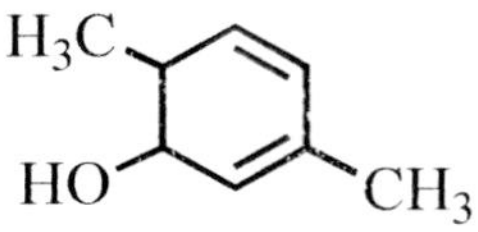
H3C
HO
CH3

E) No reaction occurs
Ans: E

9. What would be the expected product of the following reactions?

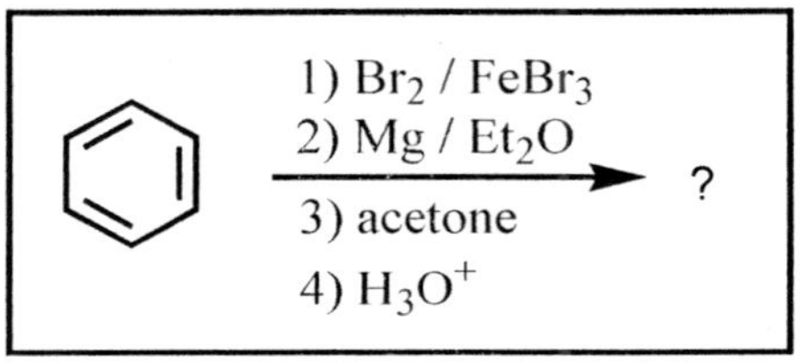
1) Br2 / FeBr3
2) Mg / Et2O
3) acetone
4) H3O+
?

A)

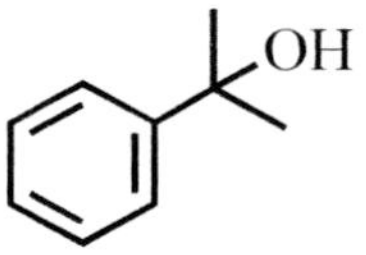
OH

B)

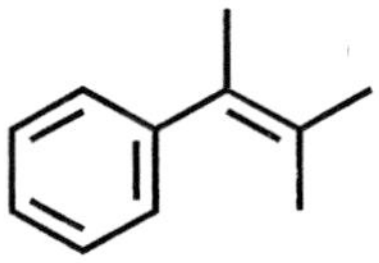

C)

Br

D)

H OH Ph

E)

Ans: A

10. The reagents listed below all react readily with alkenes. Which one can react (slowly) irreversibly with an aromatic ring?
    A) HBr + peroxides   B) CH_3CO_3H C) HBr   D) H_2/catalyst   E) H_2O, H^+
    Ans: D

11. How many mononitrated (on the aromatic ring) derivatives of meta-xylene (= 1,3-dimethylbenzene) are **possible**? (Don't worry about how they might be made or which would be the major product.)
    A) 1   B) 2   C) 3   D) 4   E) 5
    Ans: C

12. Which of the reagents given below would accomplish the reaction shown?

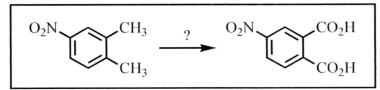

    A) H_2O_2, KOH, heat   D) O_3, then H_2O
    B) $Na_2Cr_2O_7$, H^+, heat   E)   none of these
    C) $ClCO_2H$, $AlCl_3$
    Ans: B

13. Which of the following would you expect to react fastest in an S_N1 reaction (consider the mechanism)?

A)

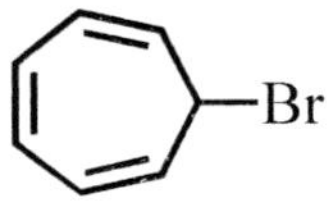

B)

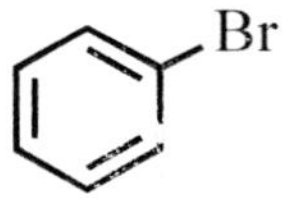

C)

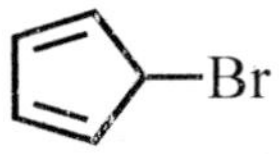

D) all would react rapidly
E) none would react
Ans: A

14. One of the double bonds in phenanthrene, shown below, is much more reactive than the others. Which one is it?

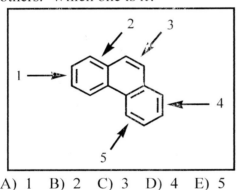

A) 1   B) 2   C) 3   D) 4   E) 5
Ans: C

15. Which of the following carbocations would you expect to be **most** stable?

A)

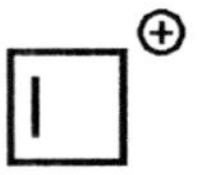

B)

C)

D)

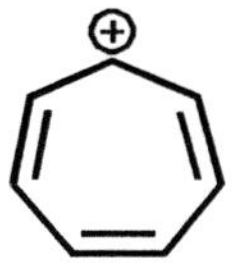

E)

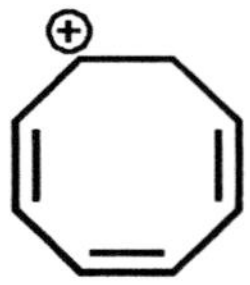

Ans: D

16. Which of the following molecules would you predict to be aromatic?
    A)

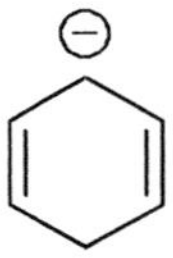

    B)

C)

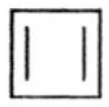

D)

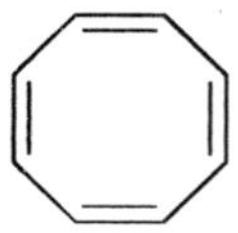

E)

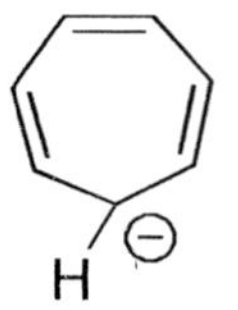

Ans: B

17. Which would be the best systematic name of vanillan, the primary flavoring ingredient in vanilla?

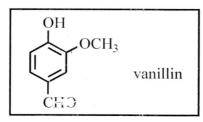

A)   4-formyl-2-methoxyphenol   D)   5-formyl-2-hydroxyanisole
B)   3-formyl-6-hydroxyanisole   E)   4-formyl-5-methoxyphenol
C)   4-hydroxy-3-methoxybenzaldehyde
Ans: C

18. Which of the following reactions has an aromatic transition state with $(4n + 2)$ electrons involved?
A)

permanganate
addition:

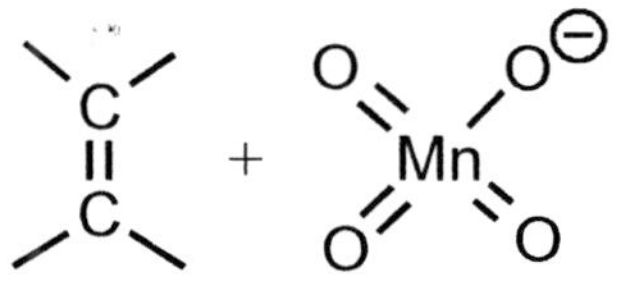

B)

Diels-Alder reaction:

C)

ozonolysis: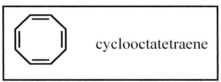

D)   two of these
E)   all of these
Ans: E

19. Which of the following best describes the electronic nature of cyclooctatetraene?

cyclooctatetraene

A)   This compound is predicted to be aromatic.
B)   This compound is anti-aromatic and very unstable.
C)   This compound is non-planar and non-aromatic.
D)   Not all of the carbon atoms possess the π-orbital required for conjugation.
E)   None of these are true.
Ans: C

20. What is the common name for the following compound?

A) Toluene   B) Anisole   C) Aniline   D) Phenol   E) Cresol
Ans: B

21. What is/are the major product(s) in the following reaction?

CH3
CH2(CH2)2CH2Cl
AlCl3
?

A)

CH3

B)

CH3

C)

CH3

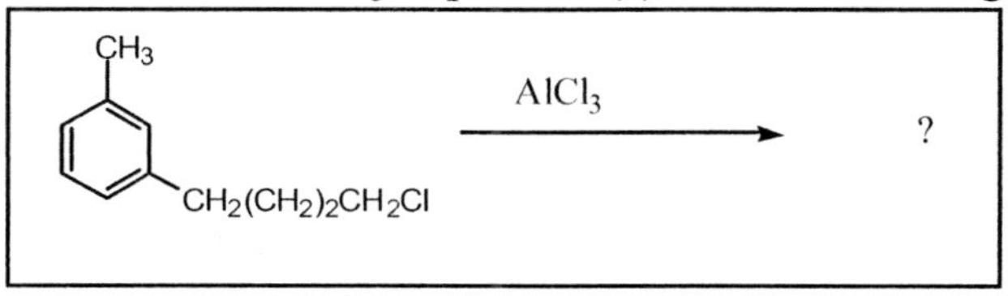

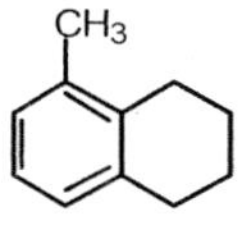

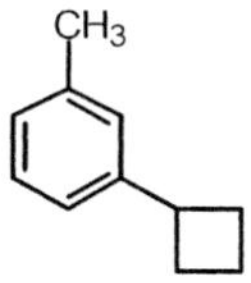

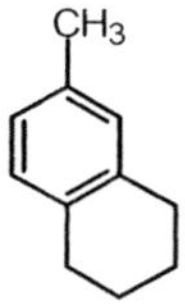

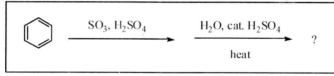

D) Both A and C
E) No Reaction
Ans: D

22. What is/are the product(s) from the following reaction?

SO3, H2SO4
H2O, cat. H2SO4
heat
?

A)

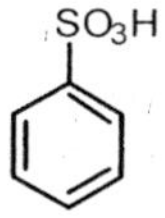

SO3H

B)

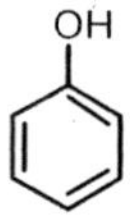

OH

C)

D)

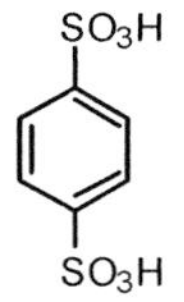

E)

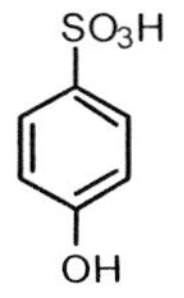

Ans: C

23. What is/are the product(s) in the following Friedel-Crafts Reaction?

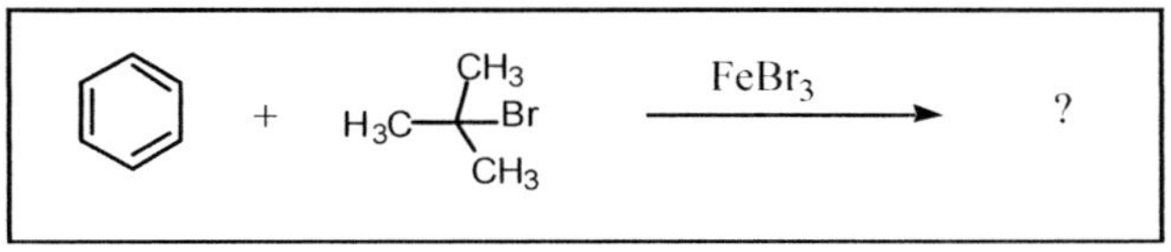

A)

B)

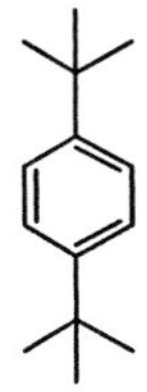

C)

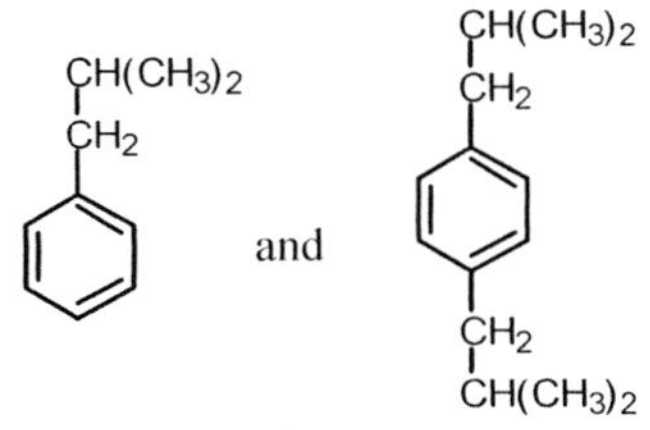

D)   both A and B
E)   all of the above
Ans: D

24. What is the major product of the following reaction?

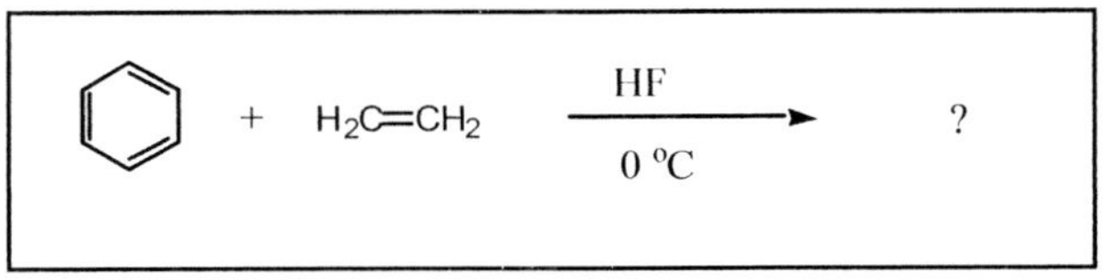

 + $H_2C=CH_2$ $\xrightarrow[\text{0 °C}]{\text{HF}}$?

A)

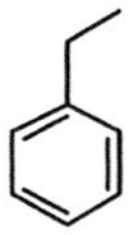

B)

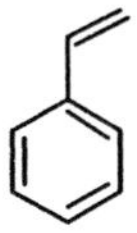

C)

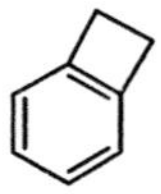

D)

CH₃

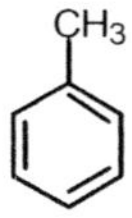

E)   no reaction
Ans: A

25. Which of the following is not an allotrope of carbon?
    A) Graphite   B) Diamond   C) Coal   D) C_{60} E) All are allotropes of carbon.
    Ans: E

26. Which of the following statements are **not** true of benzene?
    A)   The carbon-carbon bond lengths alternated between single bonds and double bonds.
    B)   All carbons are sp^2 hybridized.
    C)   The delocalized electrons form a circular pi-cloud above and below the ring.
    D)   It is especially stable according to heats of hydrogenation data.
    E)   All of these statements are true.
    Ans: A

27. If the heat of hydrogenation of the hypothetical 1,3,5-cyclohexatriene is –78.9 kcal/mol, but the heat of hydrogenation of benzene is –49.3 kcal/mol, what is the stabilization energy attributed to the resonance in benzene?
    A) –49.3 kcal/mol + (–78.9 kcal/mol) = –128.2 kcal/mol
    B) –49.3 kcal/mol – (–78.9 kcal/mol) = 29.6 kcal/mol
    C) –49.3 kcal/mol
    D) –78.9 kcal/mol
    E) none of the above
    Ans: B

28. Which of the following molecular orbitals corresponds to the Ψ_1 molecular orbital of benzene?
    A)

    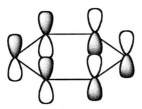

    B)

    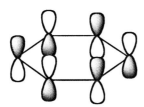

    C)

    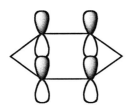

    D)

    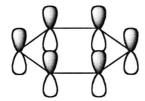

    E) none of the above
    Ans: A

29. The infrared spectrum of a dimethylbenzene has a band at 738 cm^{-1}. What is the most likely structure of the compound?

    A)   1,2-dimethylbenzene
    B)   1,3-dimethylbenzene
    C)   1,4-dimethylbenzene

    D)   1,5-dimethylbenzene
    E)   Not enough information to determine

    Ans: A

30. Which of the following mechanisms best describes electrophilic aromatic substitution of benzene with bromine?

    A)

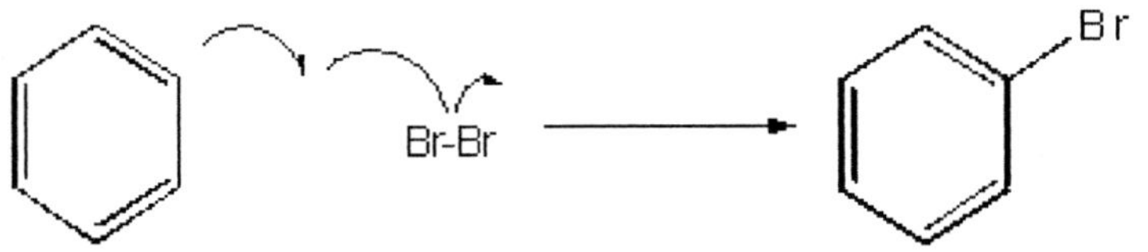

    B)

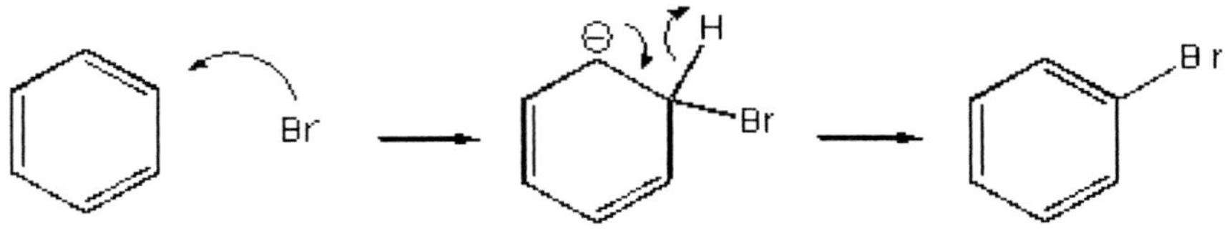

    C)

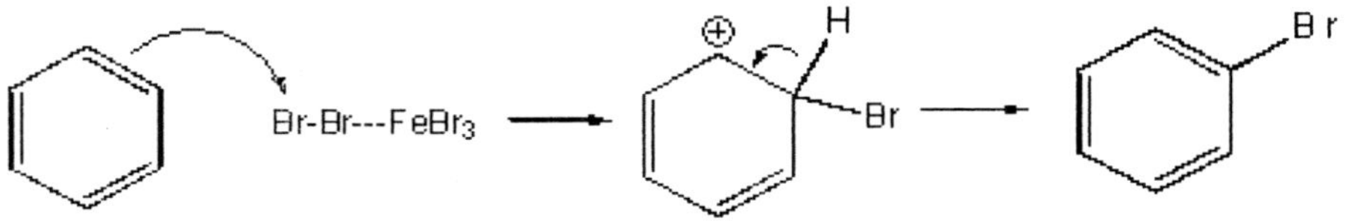

    D)

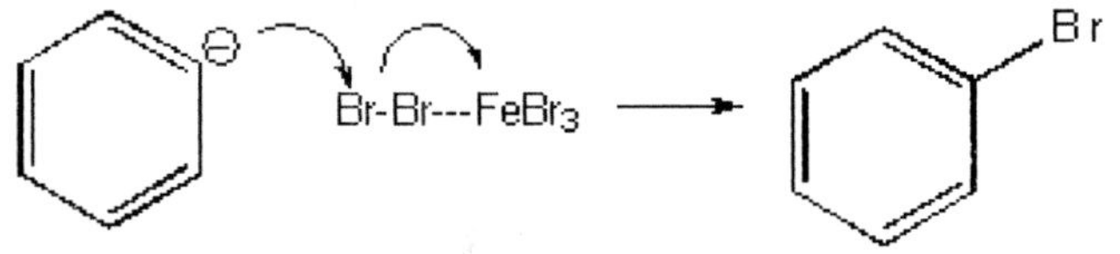

    E)   none of the above

    Ans: C

Chapter 16: Electrophilic Attack on Derivatives of Benzene: Substituents Control Regioselectivity

1. What **major** product(s) would you expect from the following reaction?

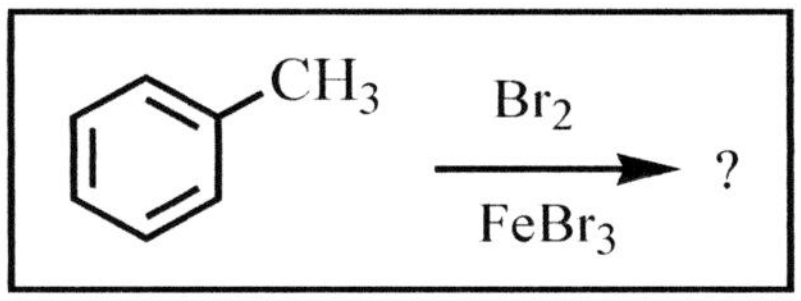

A)

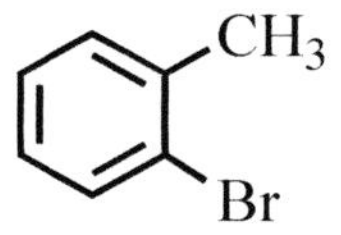

B)

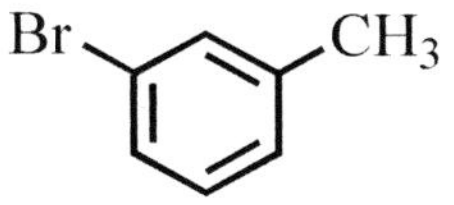

C)

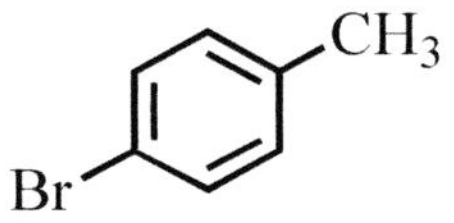

D)

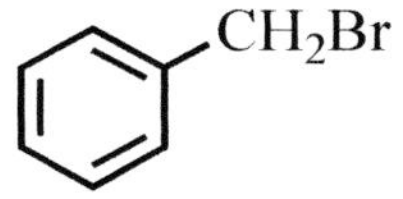

E)   both A and C

Ans: E

2. What **major** product(s) would you expect from the following reaction?

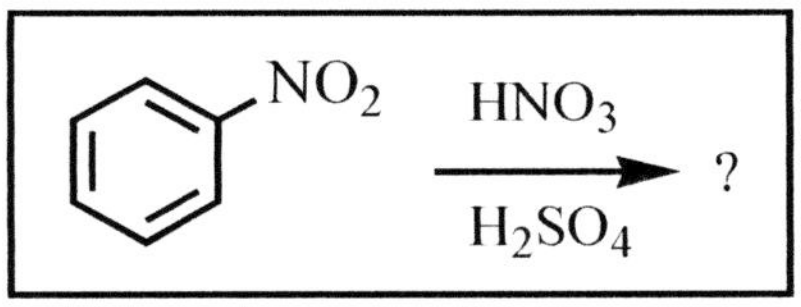

A)

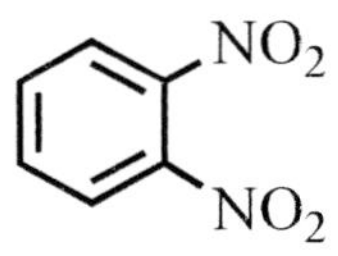

B)

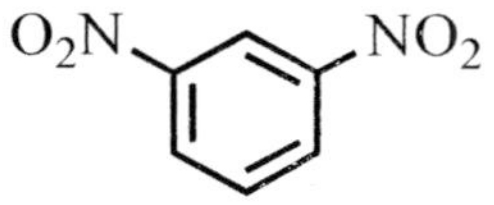

C)

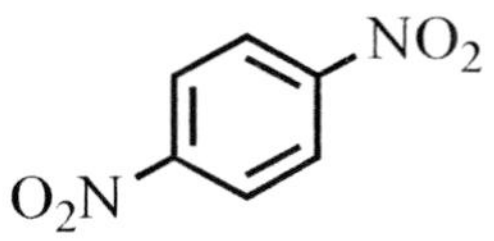

D)

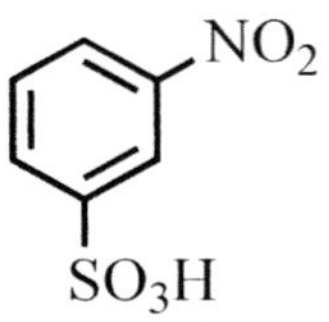

E)   both A and C

Ans: B

3. What **major** product would you expect from the following reaction?

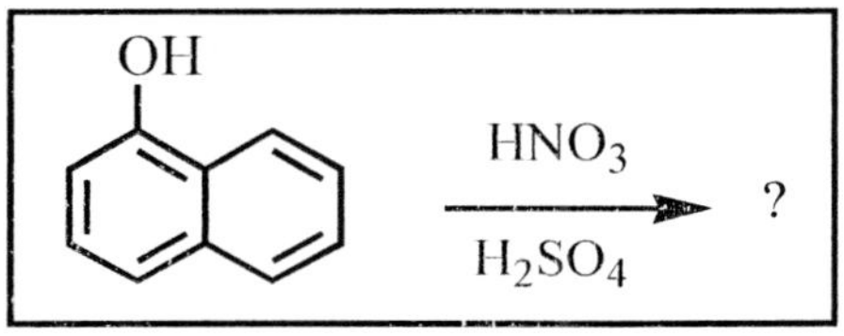

A)

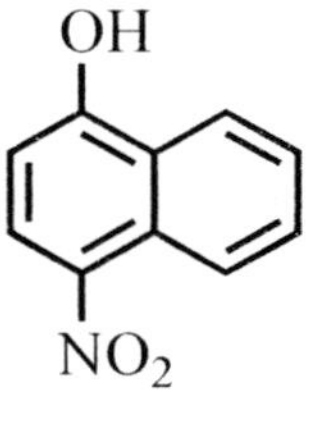

B)

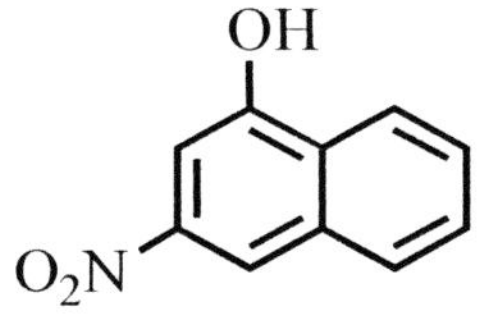

C)

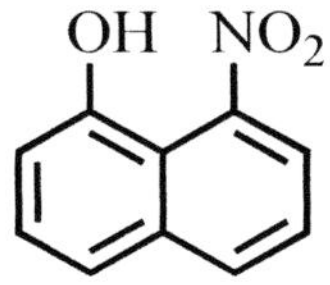

D)

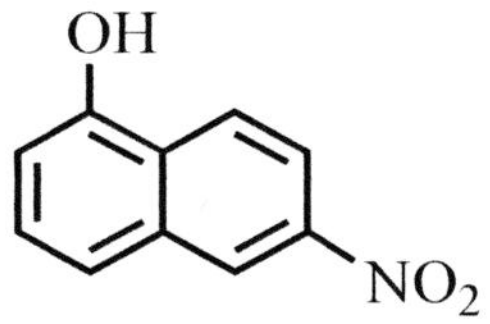

E)

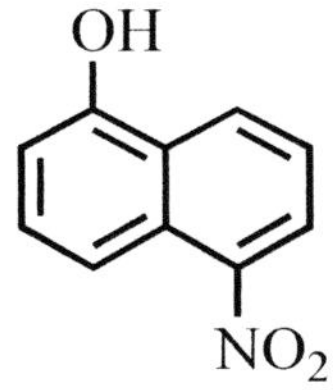

Ans: A

4. What **major** product(s) would you expect from the following reaction?

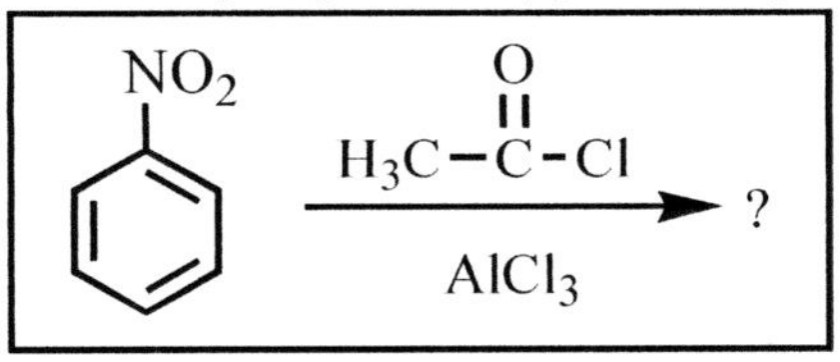

A)

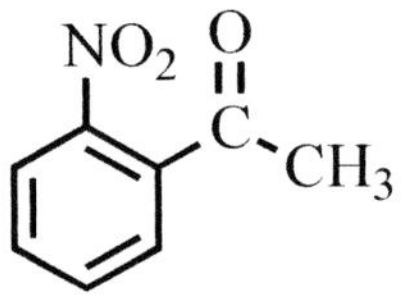

B)

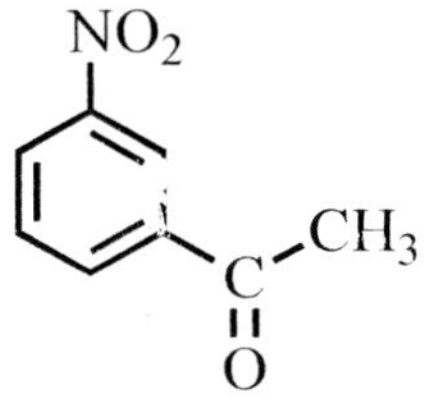

C)

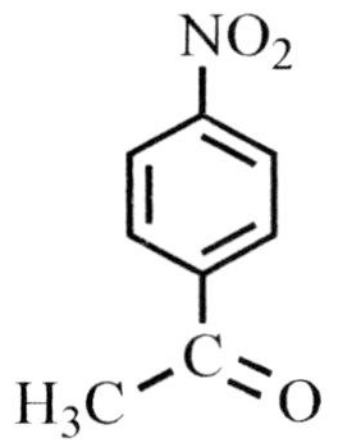

D)   both A and C
E)   no reaction occurs
Ans: E

5. Which of the following sequences of reactants would you expect to convert benzene to the substituted aromatic shown below?

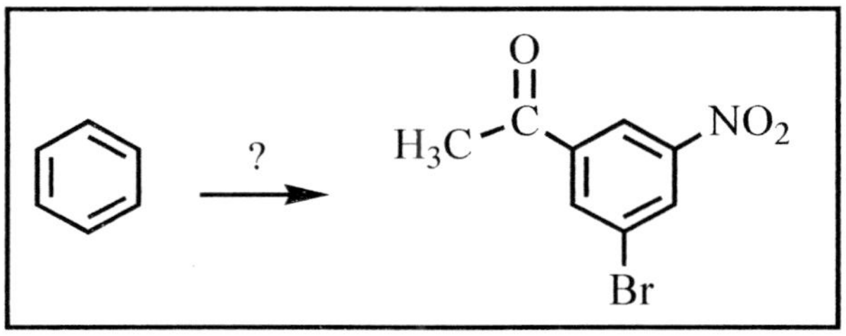

A)
        1. HNO$_3$, H$_2$SO$_4$
        2. Br$_2$, FeBr$_3$
        3. CH$_3$COCl, AlCl$_3$

B)
        1. Br$_2$, FeBr$_3$
        2. CH$_3$COCl, AlCl$_3$
        3. HNO$_3$, H$_2$SO$_4$

C)
        1. CH$_3$COCl, AlCl$_3$
        2. HNO$_3$, H$_2$SO$_4$
        3. Br$_2$, FeBr$_3$

D)   both A and B
E)   both B and C
Ans: C

6. Rank the following aromatics in order of decreasing reactivity toward electrophilic aromatic substitution (most reactive > least reactive).

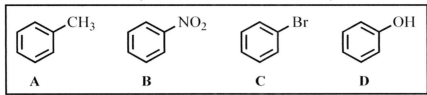

A) A > C > D > B
B) D > C > A > B
C) B > C > A > D
D) D > A > C > B
E) C > A > D > B

Ans: D

7. What would be the proper name of the molecule below?

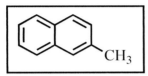

A) benzotoluene
B) 3-methylnapthalene
C) 3-methyldibenzene

D) 2-methylnapthalene
E) 1-methylnapthalene

Ans: D

8. What product(s) would you expect from the following reaction?

A)

B)

C)

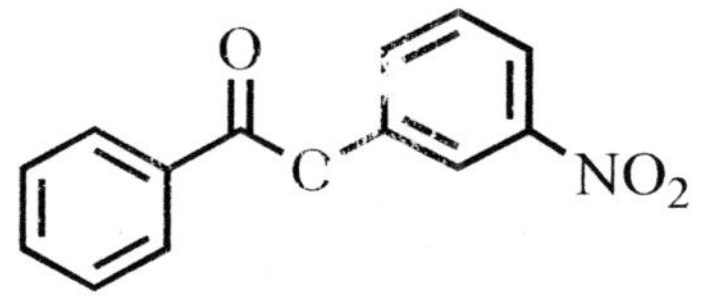

D)

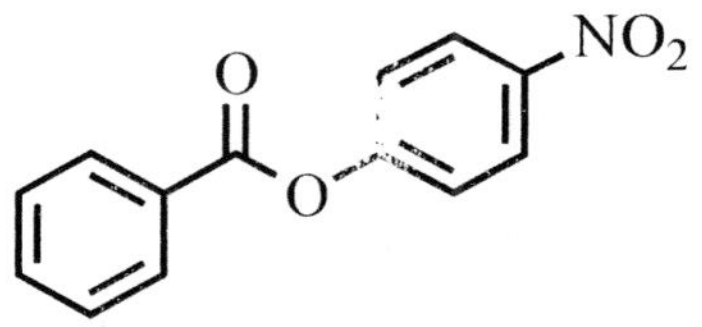

E)   both B and D
Ans: E

9. The explosive TNT is an isomer of trinitrotoluene. Given what you know about
    electrophilic aromatic substitution, which isomer is it most likely to be?
    A)

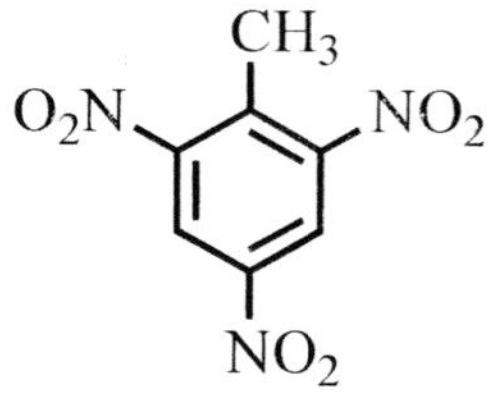

    B)

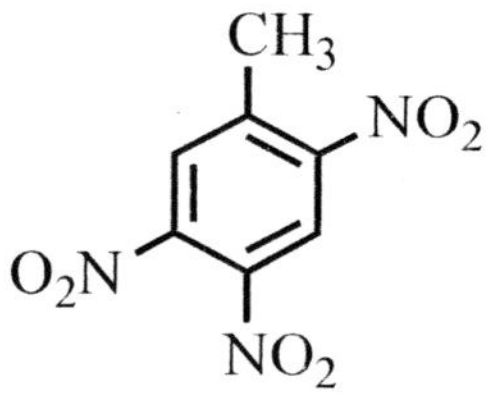

C)

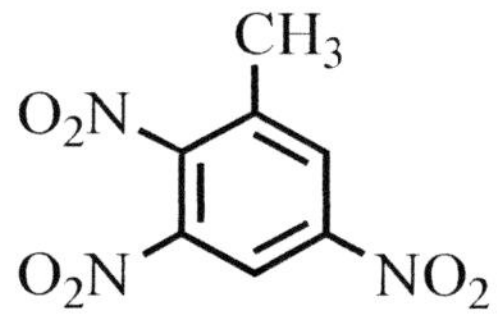

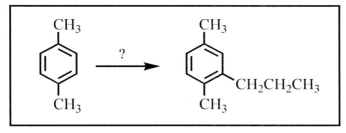

D)

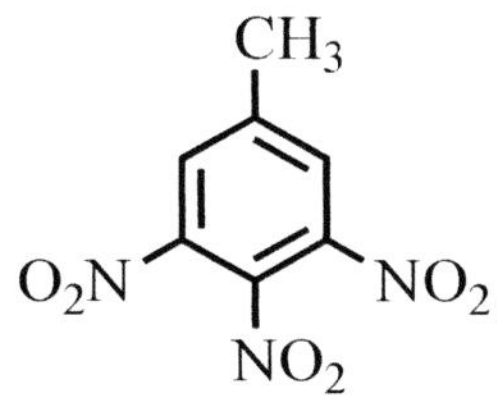

E)

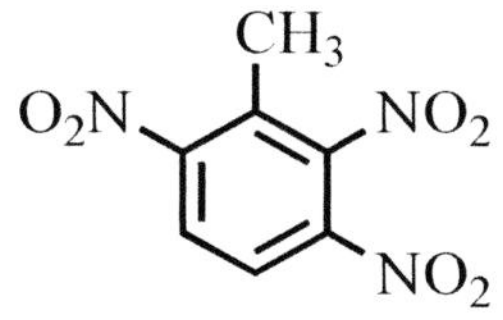

Ans: A

10. What reagent(s) would be required to accomplish the following reaction?

A) $CH_3CH_2C(=O)Cl$, $AlCl_3$
B) $CH_3CH_2CH_2Cl$, $AlCl_3$
C) Reagents in A, followed by H_2NNH_2, KOH, Δ
D) Reagents in B followed by zinc and HCl
E) $CH_3CH=CH_2$, H_2SO_4

Ans: C

11. In which electrophilic aromatic substitution reaction can unintended poly-substitution (i.e., disubstitution, trisubstitution, etc.) be a problem?
A) Nitration   D) Friedel-Crafts alkylation
B) Friedel-Crafts acylation   E) Chlorination
C) Bromination

Ans: D

12. One of the interesting aspects of azulenes is that they are soluble in strong aqueous acids because of a reaction with H^+. Which of the structures below would represent the most stable form of protonated azulene?

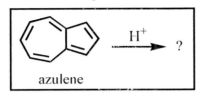

A)

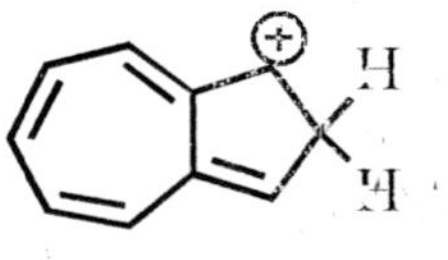

B)

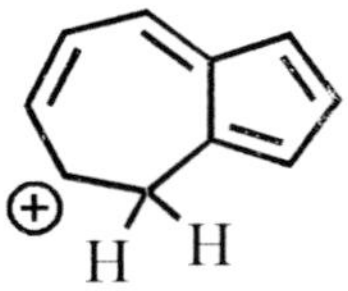

C)

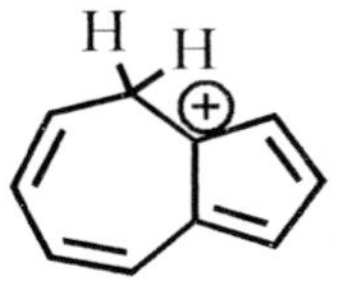

D)

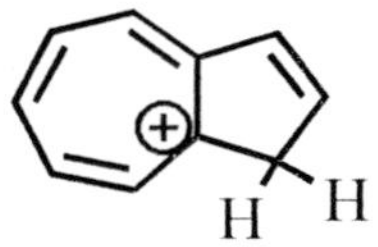

E)

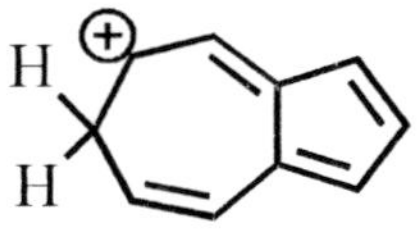

Ans: D

13. Which of the following statements is **not** true of the process shown below?

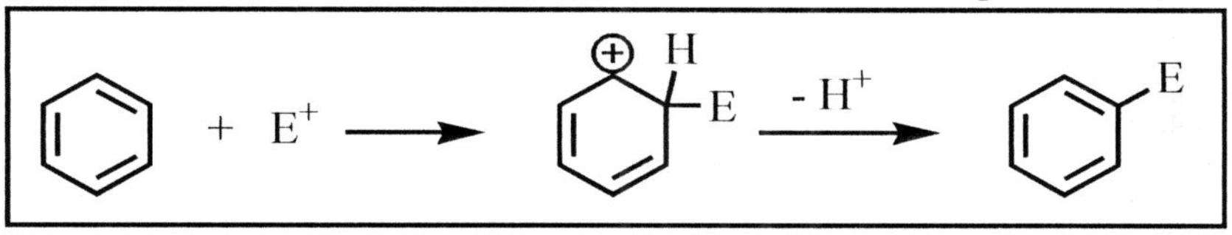

A) Benzene is less reactive with E^+ than other alkenes are.
B) The overall process is a substitution reaction.
C) There are three resonance structures of the intermediate possible.
D) The first step is rate determining.
E) All these statements are true.

Ans: E

14. Carefully consider the effect of the nitro groups on the stability of the intermediates involved as you decide which product(s) the reaction shown provides.

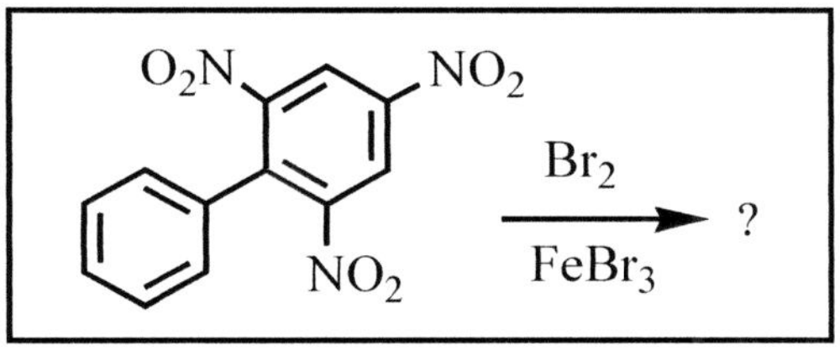

A)

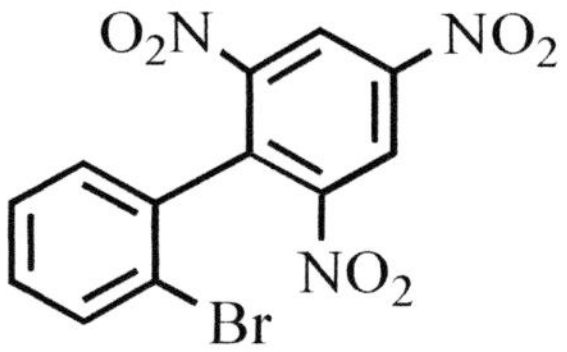

B)

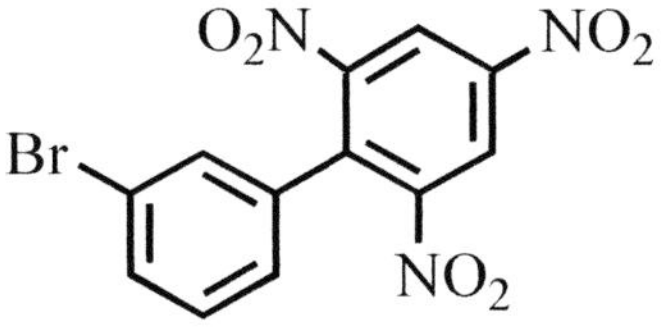

C)

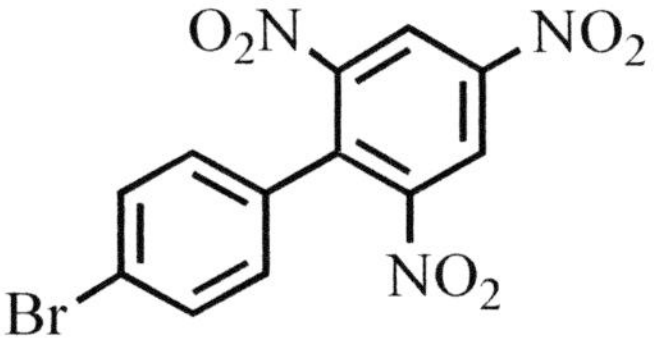

D) both A and C
E) none of these would be formed

Ans: B

15. What **major** product(s) would you expect from the reaction shown?

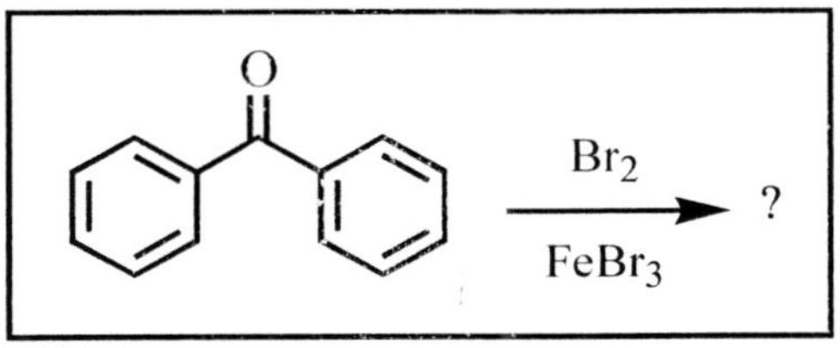

A)

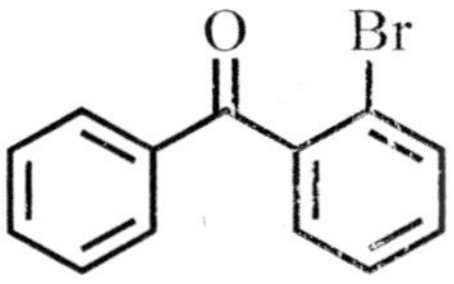

B)

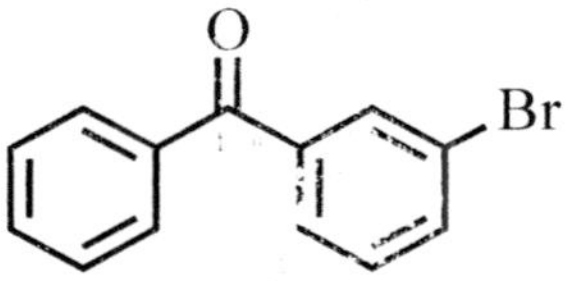

C)

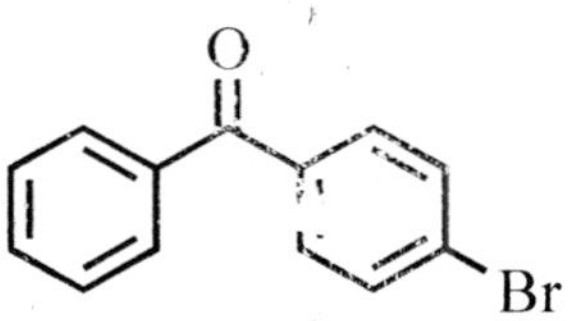

D)

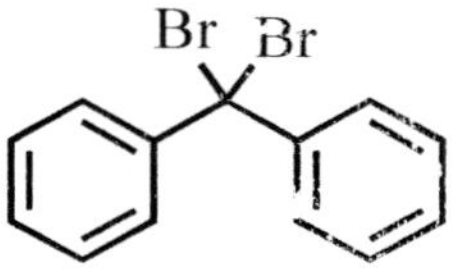

E)   both A and C
Ans: B

16. Which of the following resonance structures is the most stable?
A)

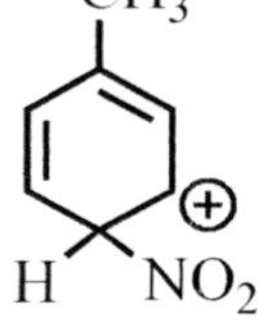

B)

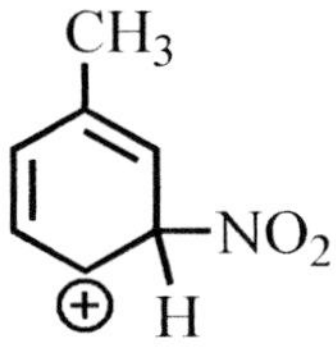

CH₃

⊕ H NO₂

C)

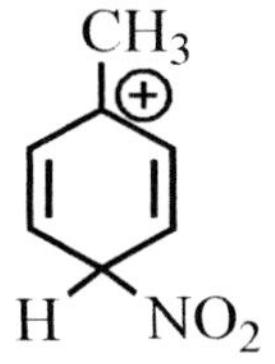

CH₃ ⊕

H NO₂

D)

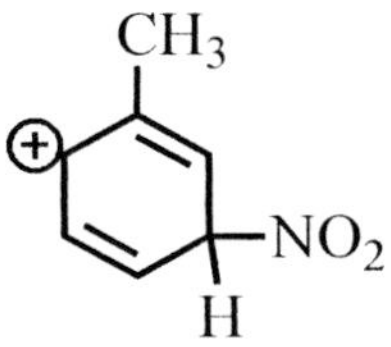

CH₃

⊕ NO₂

H

E)

CH₃

⊕ H NO₂

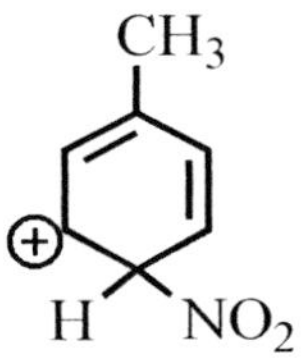

Ans: C

17. Rank the following in order of **decreasing** reactivity toward nitration (more reactive > less reactive).

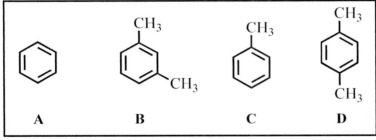

| A | B | C | D |

A)   **D > C > B > A**   D)   **C > D > B > A**
B)   **B > D > C > A**   E)   **A > C > D > B**
C)   **D > B > C > A**
Ans: B

18. What would be the best way to prepare the ketone shown below?

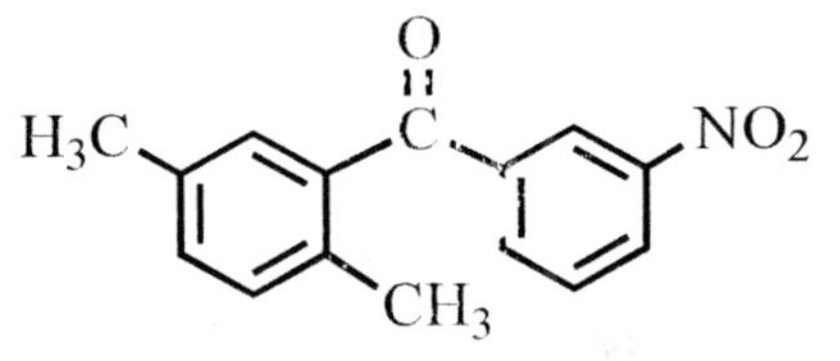

A)

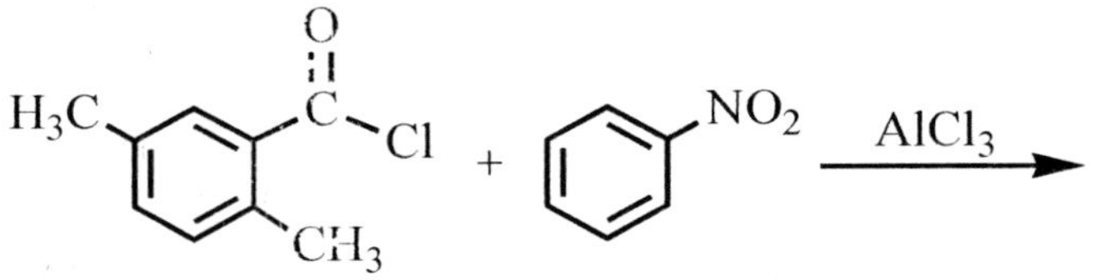

B)

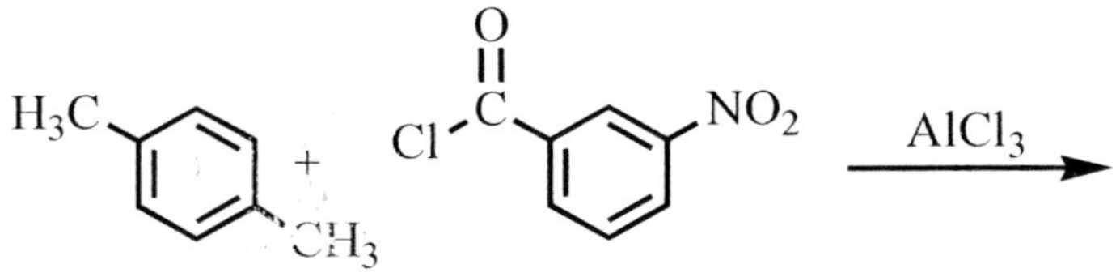

C)

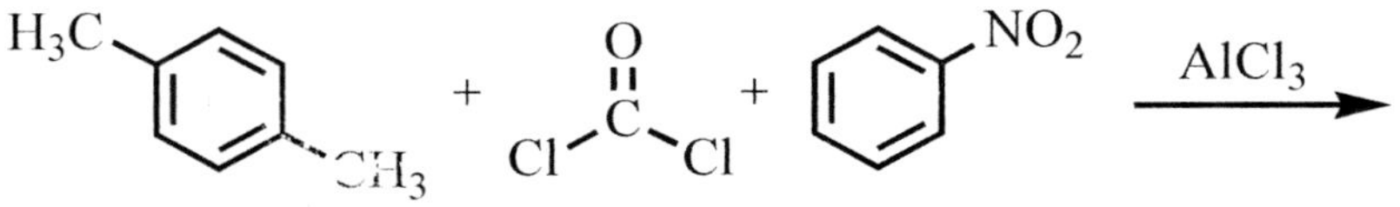

D)   Any of these would work.
E)   None of these would work.
Ans: B

19. What significant product(s) would **not** be formed in the following reaction?

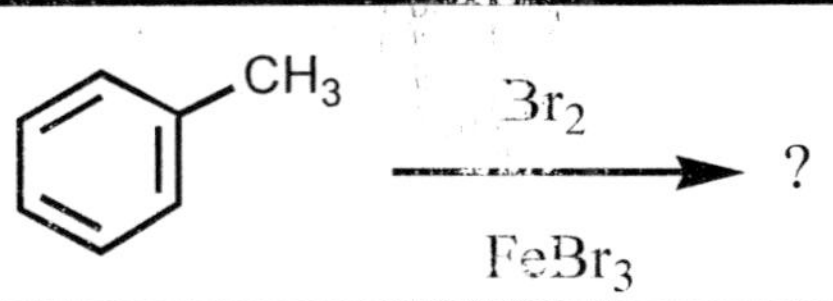

A)

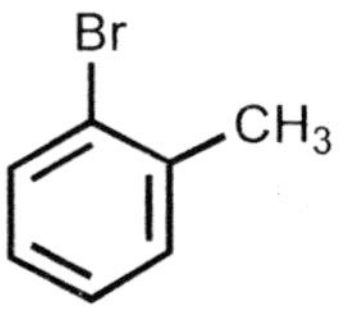

B)

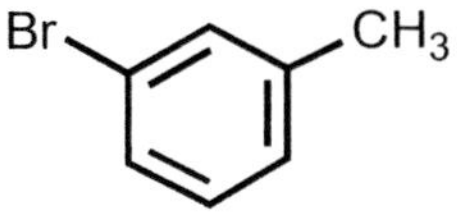

C)

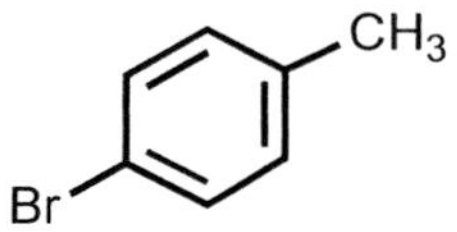

D)   neither A nor B would be formed
E)   neither A nor C would be formed
Ans: B

20. Predict the major organic product of the following reaction.

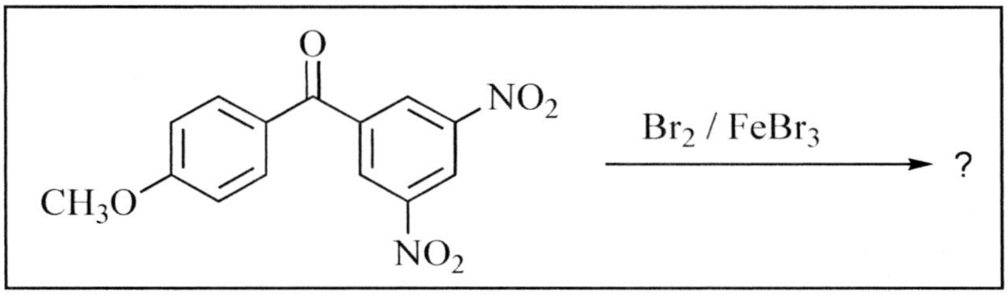

A)

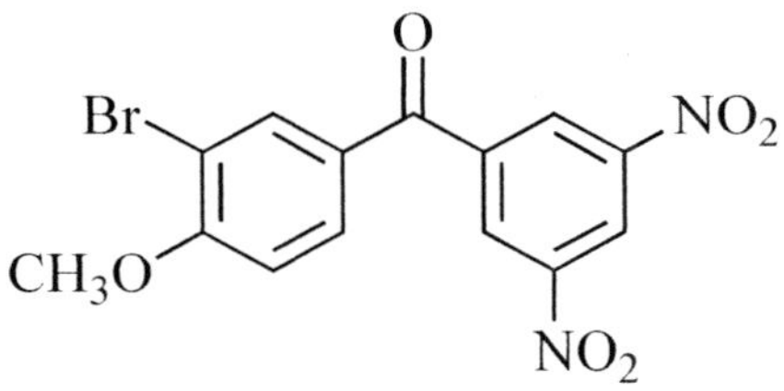

B)

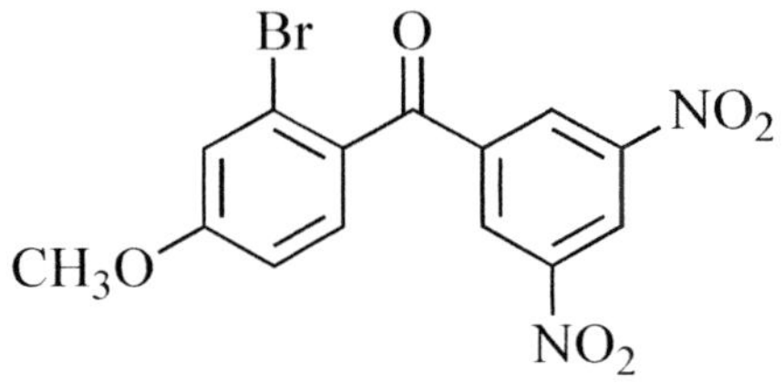

C)

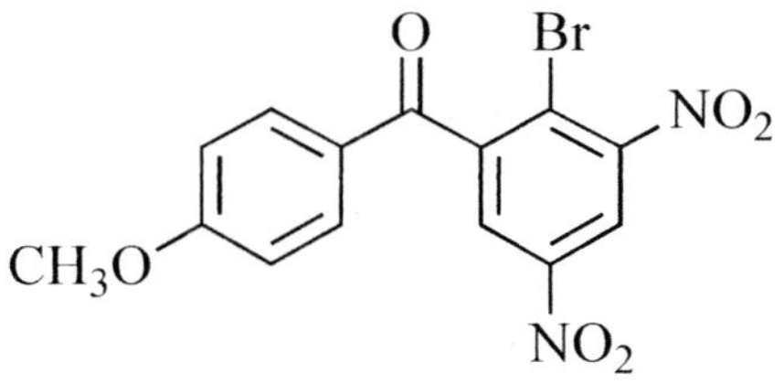

D)

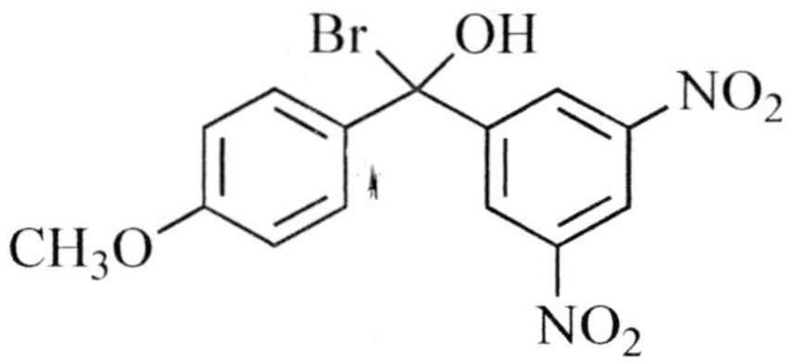

E)

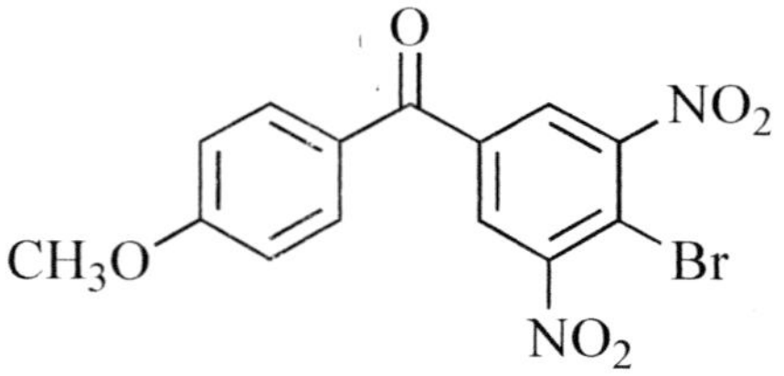

Ans: A

21. Which of the following aromatics could you expect to make from benzene in the **highest yield**?

A)

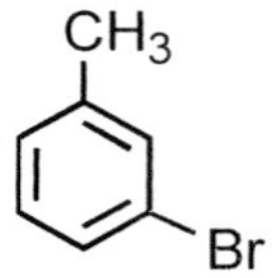

B)

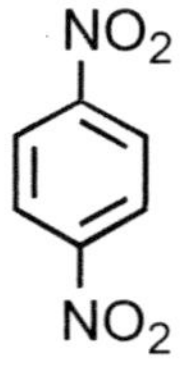

C)

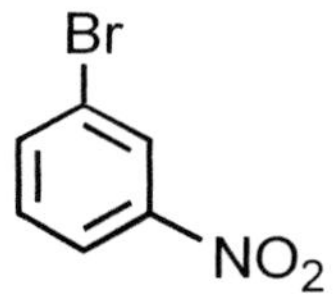

Br

NO$_2$

D)

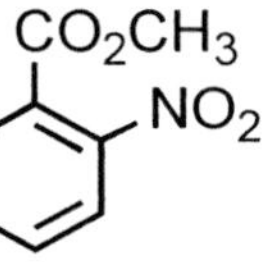

CO$_2$CH$_3$
NO$_2$

E)

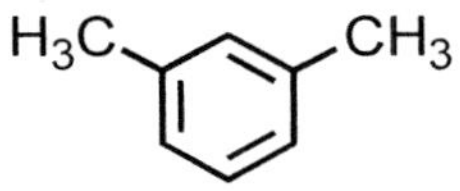

H$_3$C   CH$_3$

Ans: C

22. Which of the following are **not** electron-withdrawing groups?
    A) Carbonyl   B) Cyano   C) Alkyl   D) Sufonyl   E) Nitro
    Ans: C

23. Predict the **major** product of the following reaction:

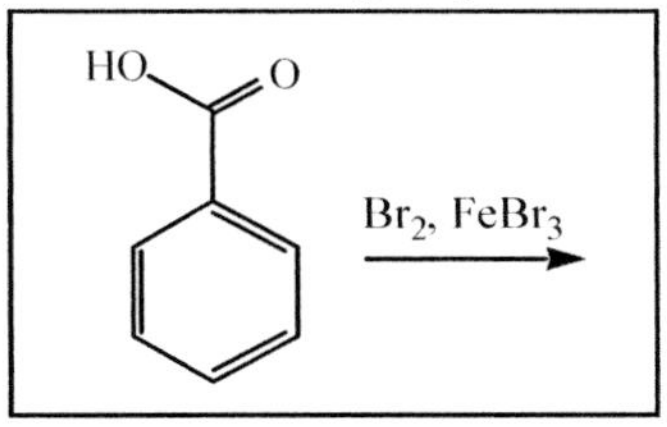

HO   O

Br$_2$, FeBr$_3$

A)

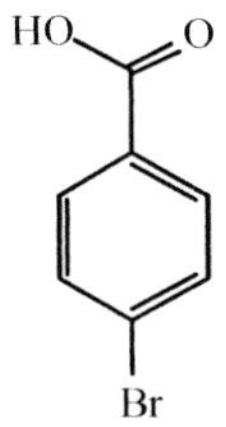

HO   O

Br

B)

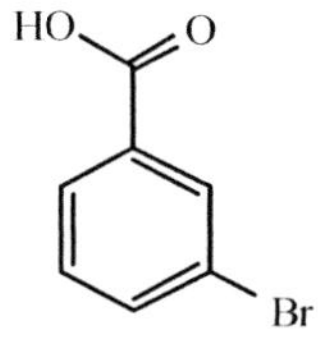

HO   O

Br

C)

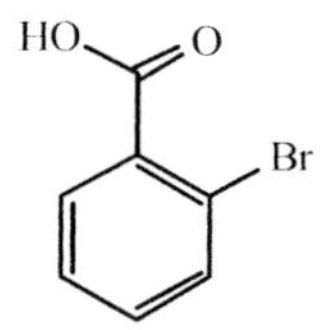

HO—C(=O), Br (ortho-bromobenzoic acid)

D)

HO—C(=O), Br, Br (3,5-dibromobenzoic acid)

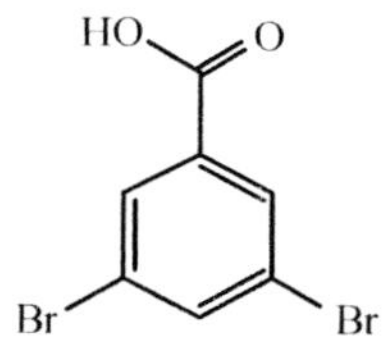

E)   none of these

Ans: B

24. Choose the appropriate reagents necessary to achieve this reaction:

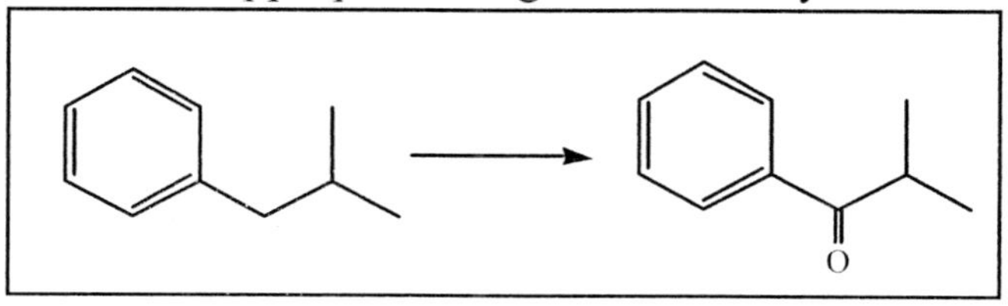

A) H_2, Pd, ⟋⟍OH   D) CrO_3, H^+, H_2O

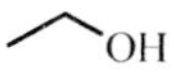

B)   Zn(Hg). HCl, Δ E)   None of these

C)   Fe, HCl

Ans: D

25. Predict the product of the following reaction:

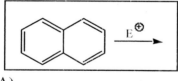

A)

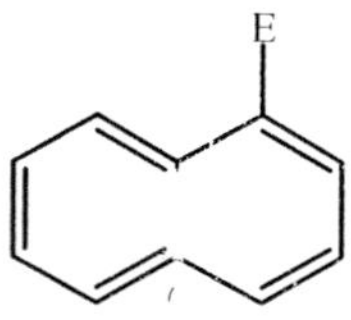

B)

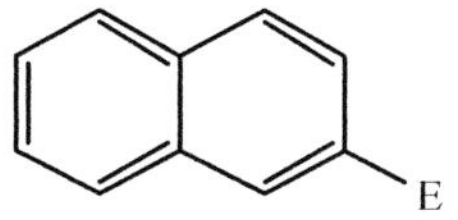

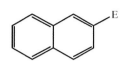

C)

D)

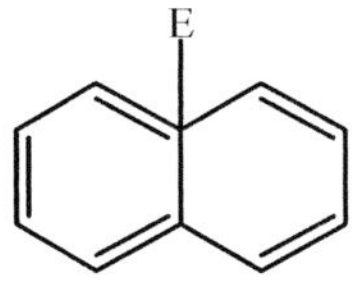

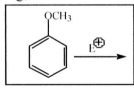

E)   none of these

Ans: A

26. Rank the following in order of increasing reactivity toward electrophilic substitution:

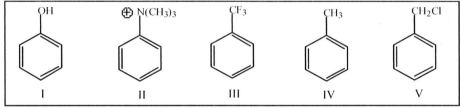

A)   I, IV, V, II, III
B)   II, III, V, IV, I
C)   III,V,IV,I,II

D)   II,V, IV, III, I
E)   V, IV, II, III, I

Ans: B

27. Considering the intermediate formed upon addition of an electrophile to this aromatic ring, which of the following is **not** a correct resonance structure:

A)

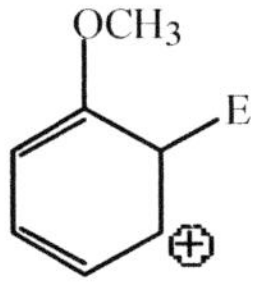

OCH₃

B)

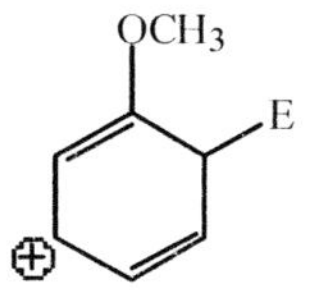

C)

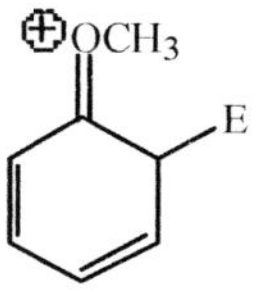

D)

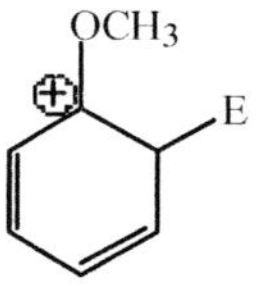

E)   All of these are correct.

Ans: E

28. What would be the **major** product from the following reaction sequence?

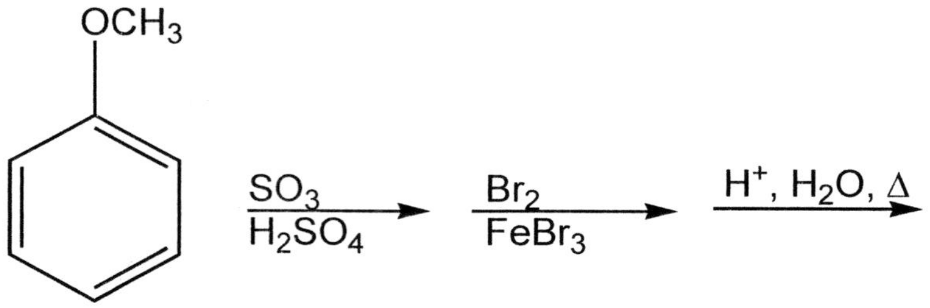

A)

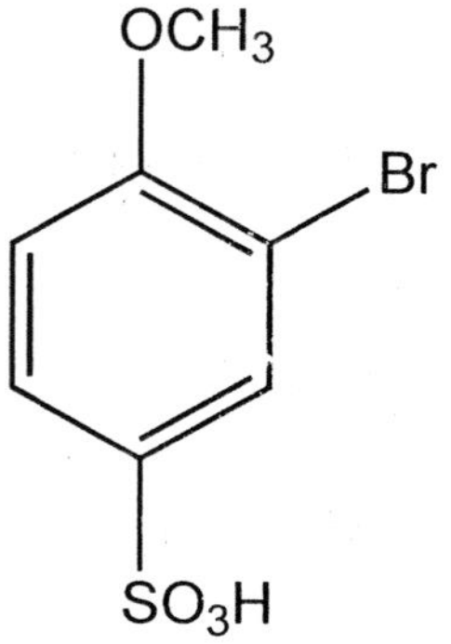

B)

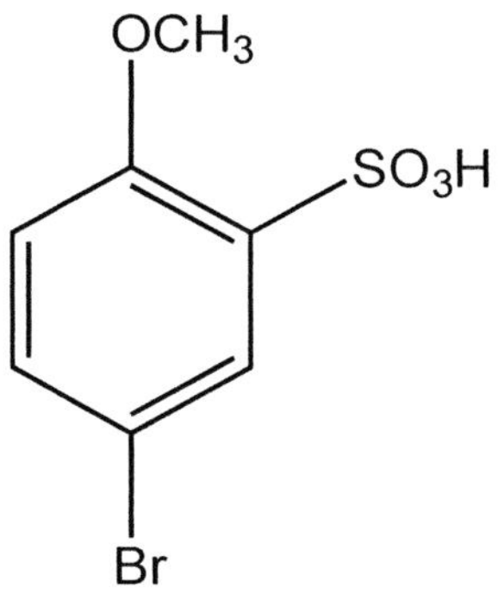

OCH$_3$

SO$_3$H

Br

C)

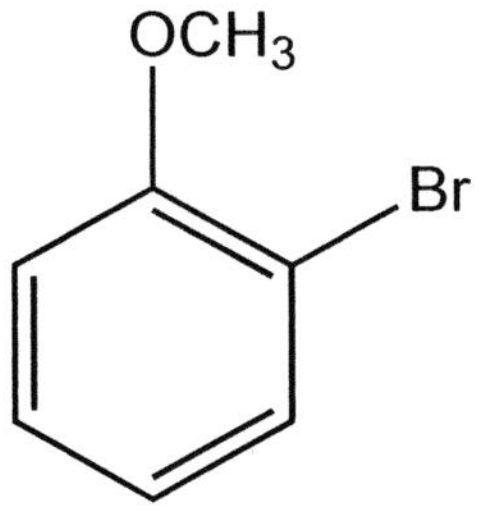

OCH$_3$

Br

D)

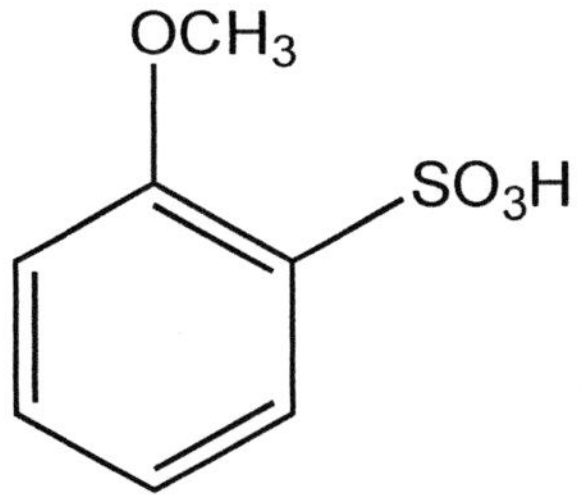

OCH$_3$

SO$_3$H

E)

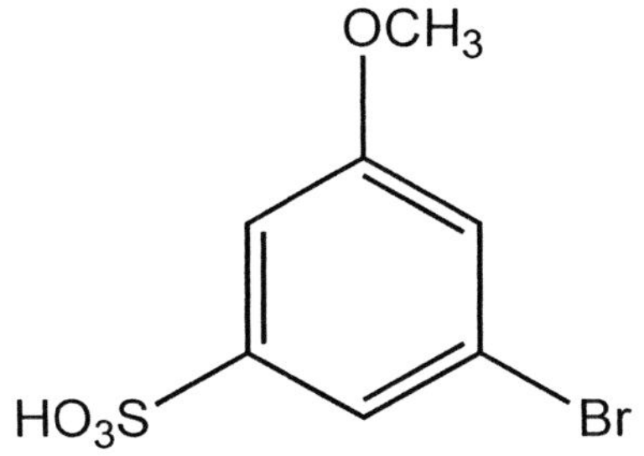

OCH$_3$

HO$_3$S

Br

Ans: C

29. What would be the **major** product from the following reaction?

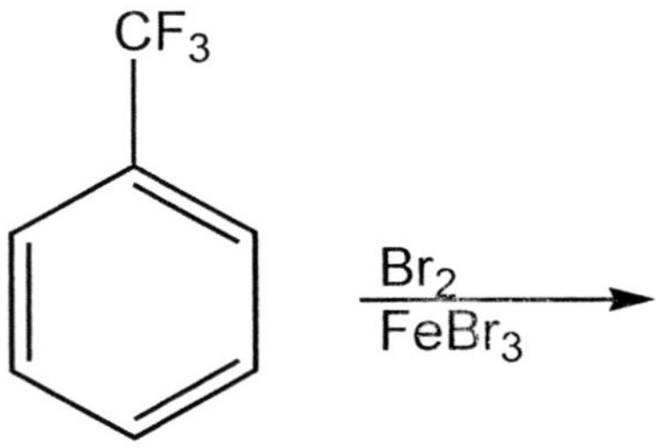

CF$_3$

$\dfrac{Br_2}{FeBr_3}$ →

A)

CF$_3$

Br

B)

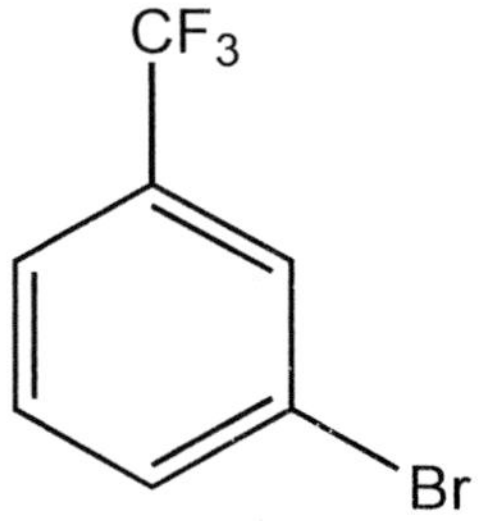

CF$_3$

Br

C)

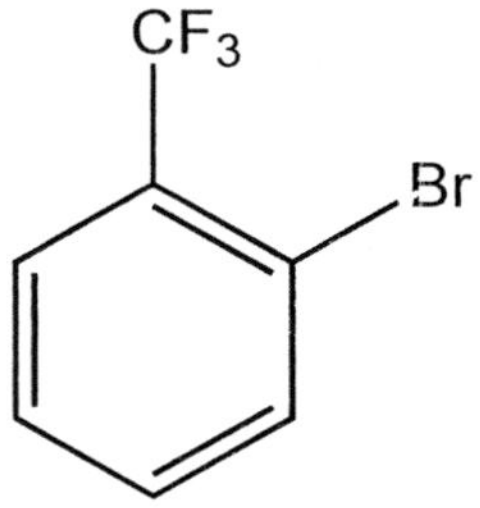

CF$_3$

Br

D)

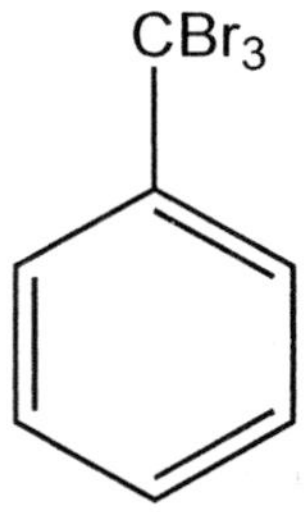

CBr$_3$

E)   both A and C

Ans: B

30. How many lines would be seen in the ^{13}C NMR spectrum of the product from the following reaction?

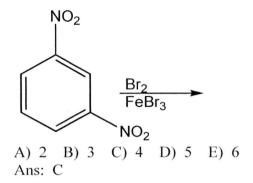

A) 2   B) 3   C) 4   D) 5   E) 6

Ans: C

Chapter 17: Aldehydes and Ketones: The Carbonyl Group

1. What would be the **major** product of the following reaction sequence?

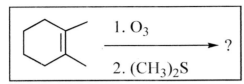

$$\xrightarrow[\text{2. }(CH_3)_2S]{\text{1. }O_3} \quad ?$$

A)

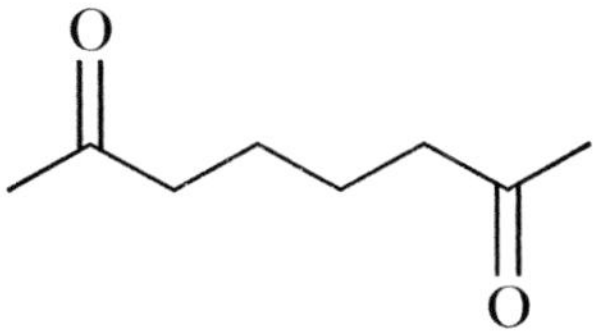

B)

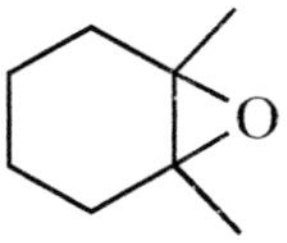

C)

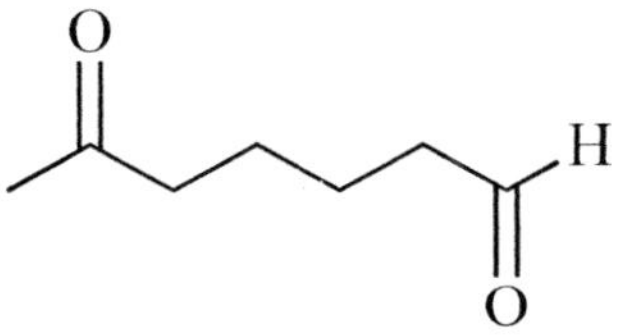

D)

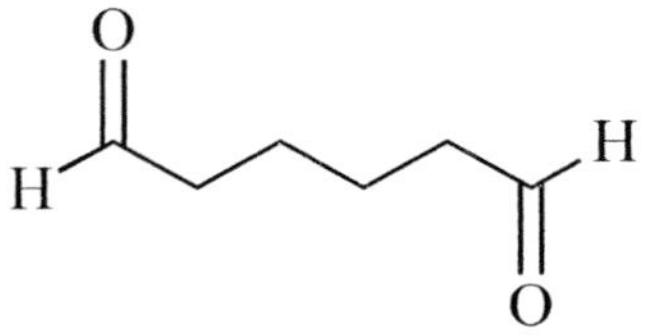

E)

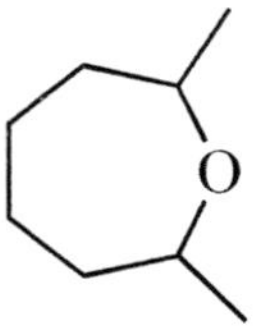

Ans: A

2. What would be the expected product of the following reaction sequence?

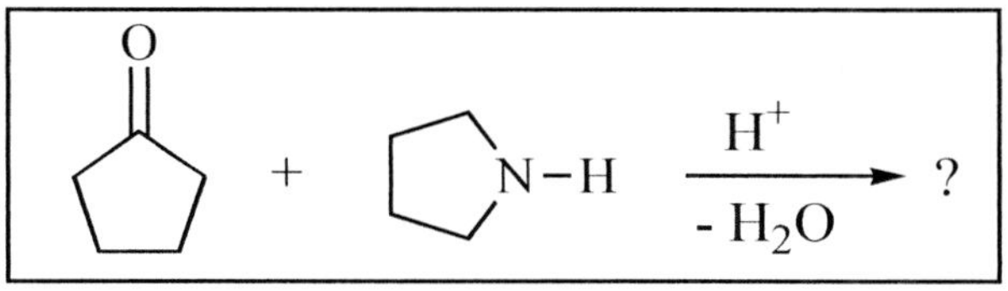

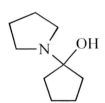

A)

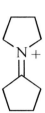

B)

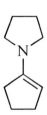

C)

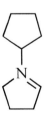

D)

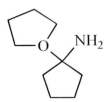

E)

Ans: C

3. Indicate to which side, if any, the following equilibrium lies:

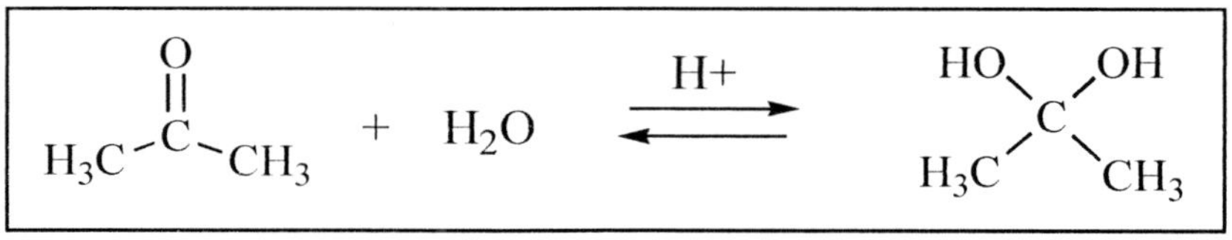

A)   To the right
B)   To the left
C)   Equally to right and left
Ans: B

D)   Reaction cannot occur
E)   A different product is formed

4. What would be the **major** product of the following reaction?

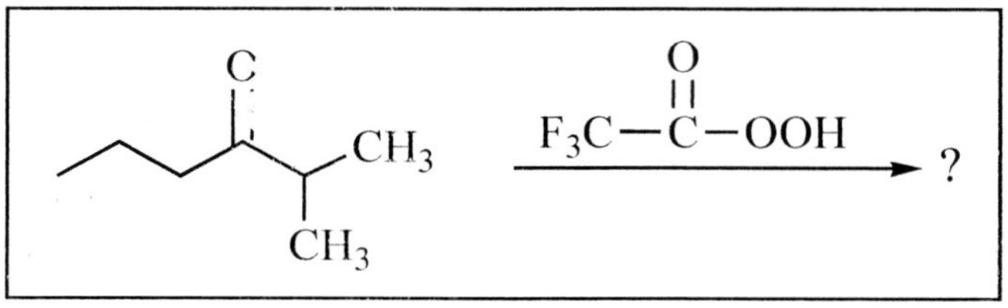

A)

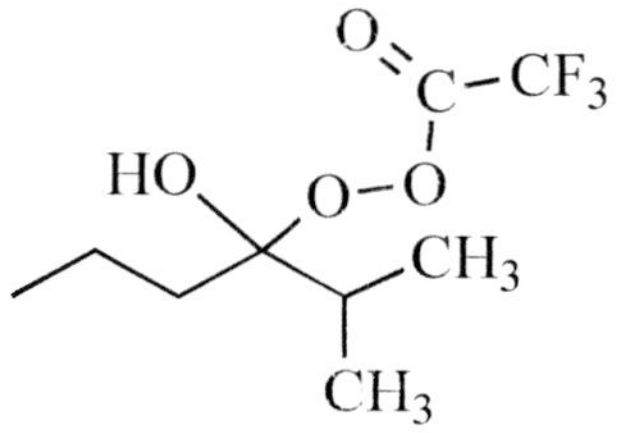

B)

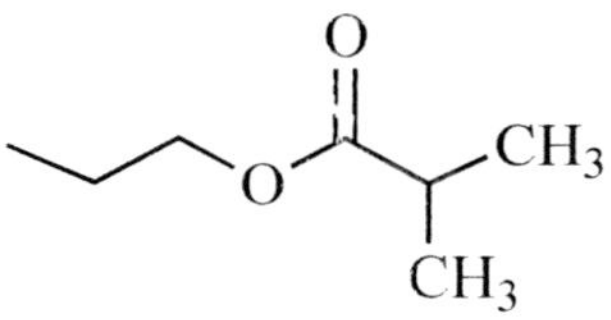

C)

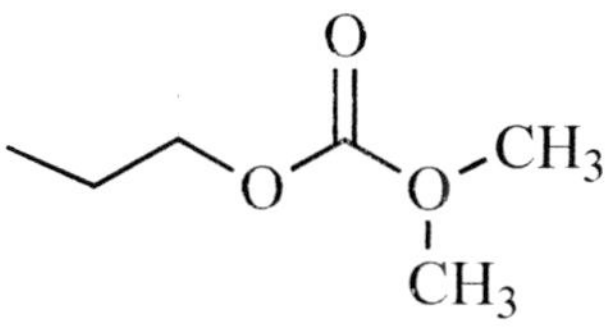

D)

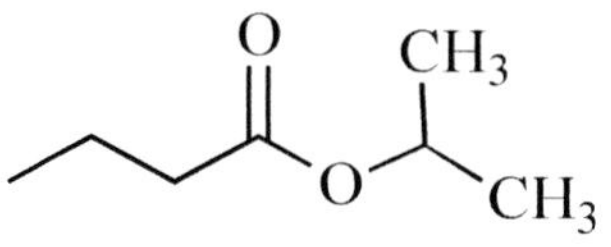

E)

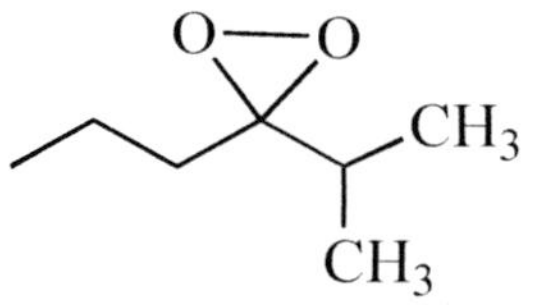

Ans: D

5. What product would you expect from the following reaction?

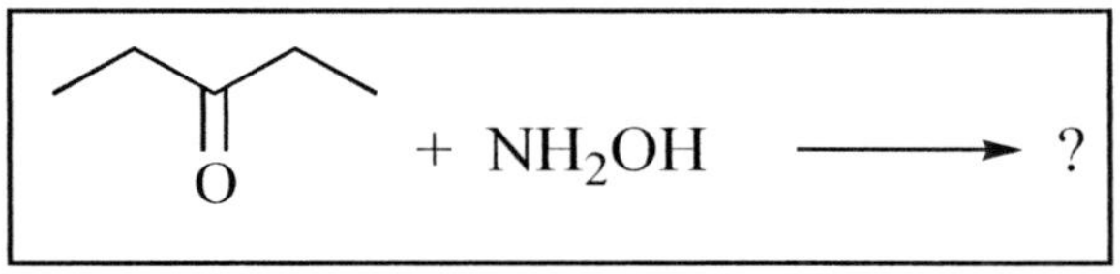

A)

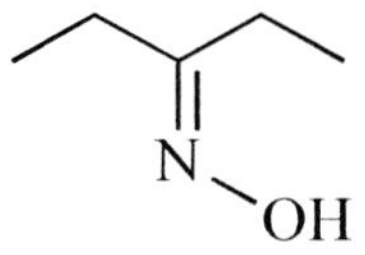

B)

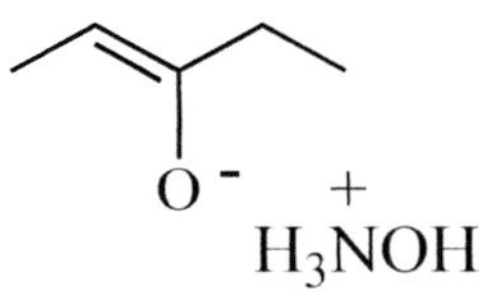

C)

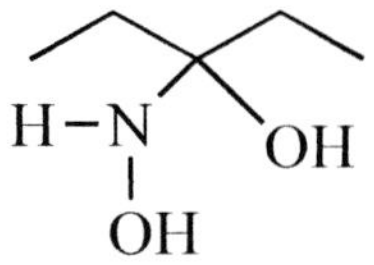

D)

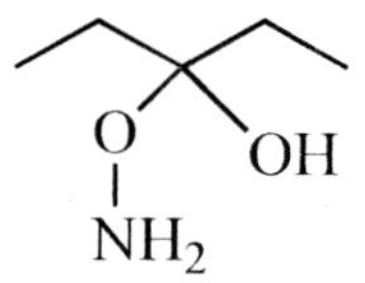

E)

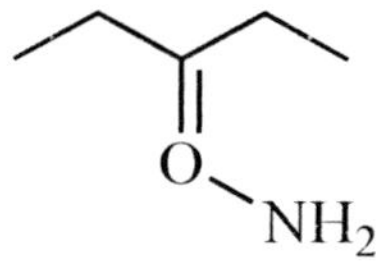

Ans: A

6. What product would you expect from the following reaction? (Hint: In what form does the reactant actually exist?)

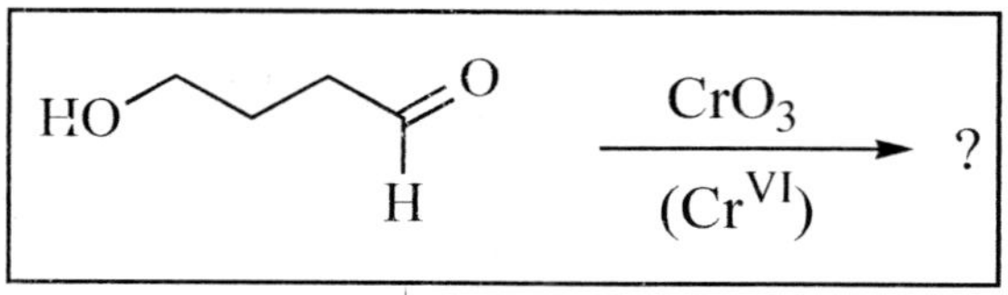

A)

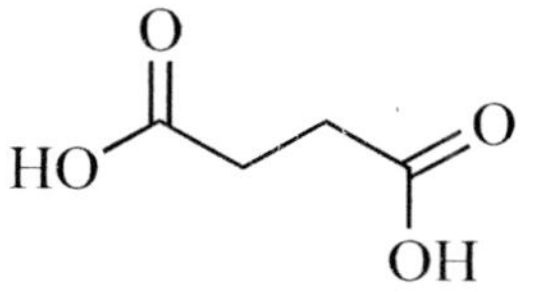

B)

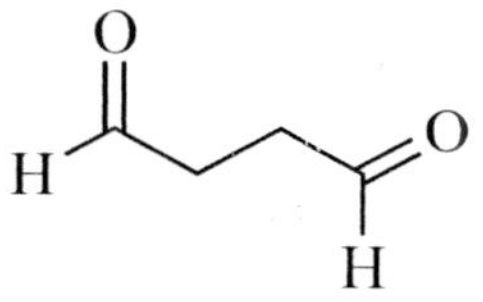

C)

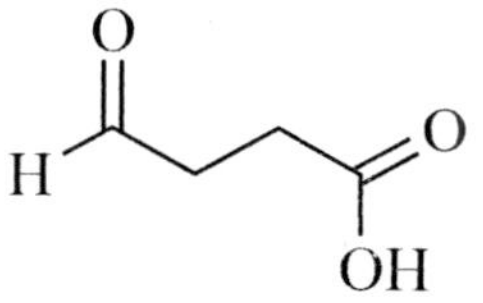

D)

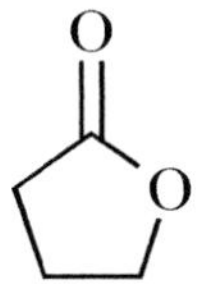

E)

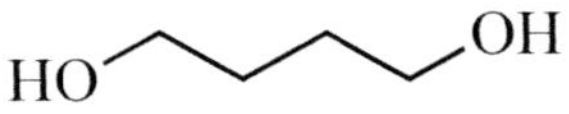

HO⟋⟍⟋OH

Ans: D

7. What would be the best name of the following compound?

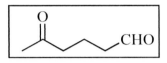

A)   6-oxo-2-hexanone   D)   1,5-dioxohexane
B)   5-oxohexanal   E)   2-oxohexanal
C)   Hexan-5-one-1-al

Ans: B

8. Which of the following would react with Ag⁺ under **basic** conditions?
   A)

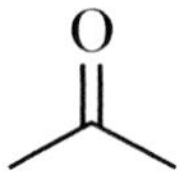

   B)

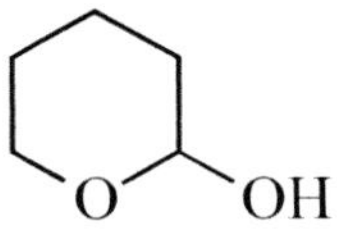

   C) $CH_3CH_2CO_2CH_2CH_3$
   D)

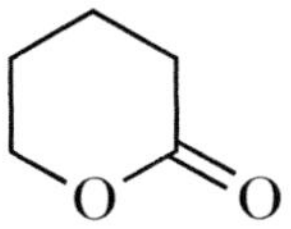

   E)

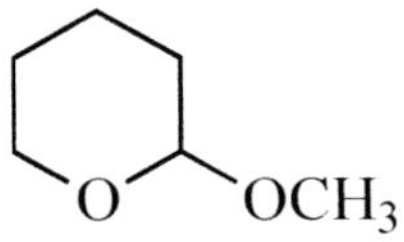

Ans: B

9. To which side (if any) would the following equilibrium lie?

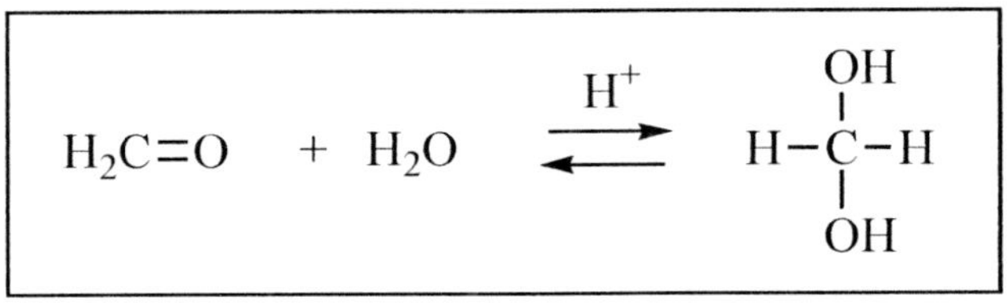

$$H_2C=O \quad + \quad H_2O \quad \xrightleftharpoons{H^+} \quad H-\underset{\underset{OH}{|}}{\overset{\overset{OH}{|}}{C}}-H$$

A) To left
B) To right

D) Reaction cannot occur at all
E) Equilibrium favors a different product.

C) Equally to the right and left

Ans: B

10. What would be the proper name of the following molecule?

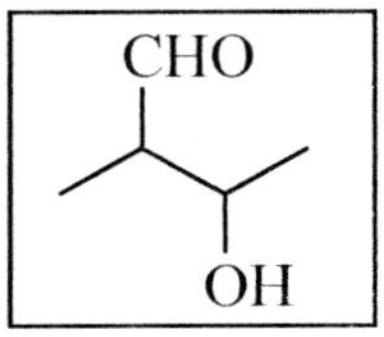

A) 3-formyl-2-butanol
B) 2-(hydroxyethyl)propanal
C) 3-hydroxy-2-methylbutanal

D) 2,3-dimethylpropan-3-ol-1-al
E) 1-methyl-3-formyl-1-propanol

Ans: C

11. What would you expect to result from the following reaction?

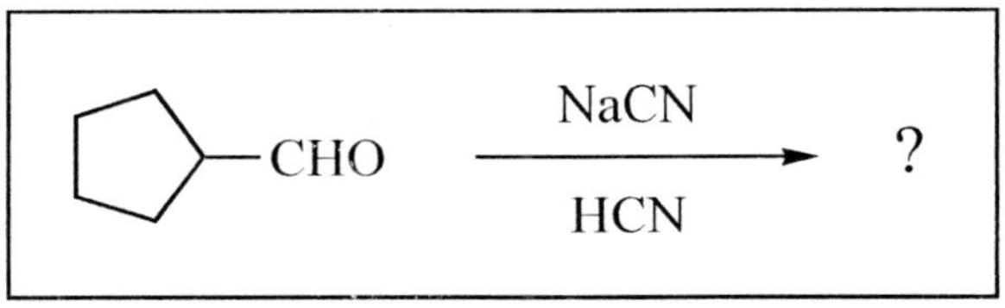

$$\text{cyclopentyl-CHO} \quad \xrightarrow[\text{HCN}]{\text{NaCN}} \quad ?$$

A)

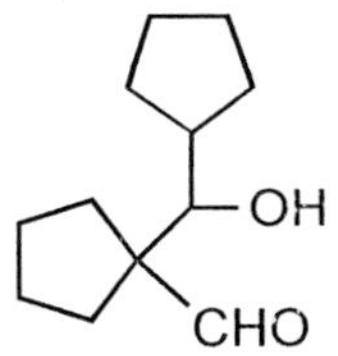

B)

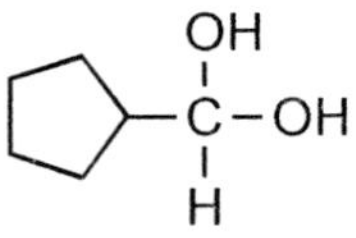

C)

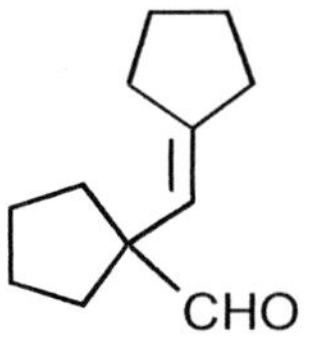
CHO

D)

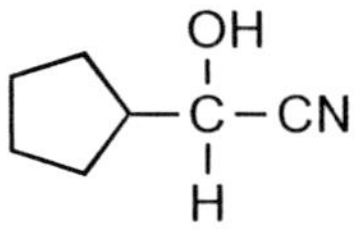
OH
C-CN
H

E)

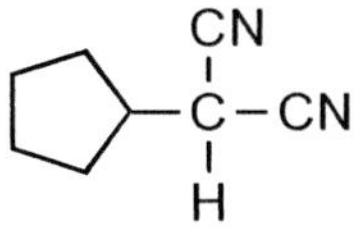
CN
C-CN
H

Ans: D

12. Indicate which side, if any, would be favored in the reaction shown below.

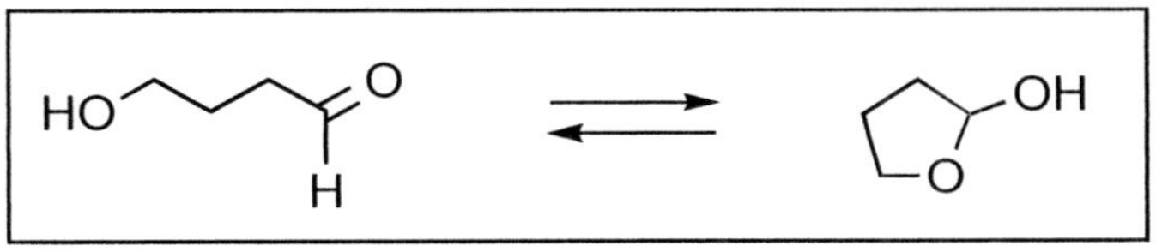
HO
O
H
OH
O

A) To the right
B) To the left
C) Equally to both sides
D) This reaction cannot occur
E) A different product would be favored.
Ans: A

13. Predict the major organic product of the following reaction sequence.

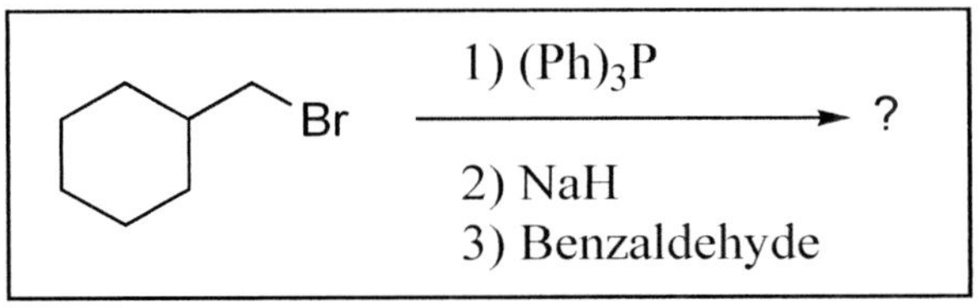
Br
1) $(Ph)_3P$
2) NaH
3) Benzaldehyde
?

A)

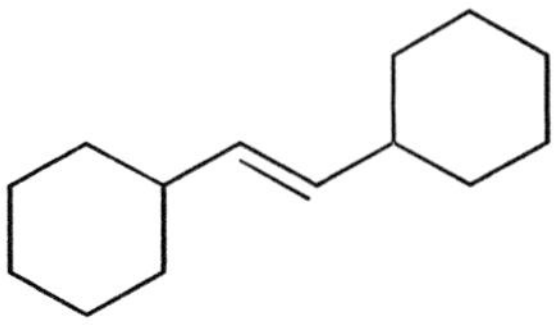

B)

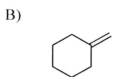

C)

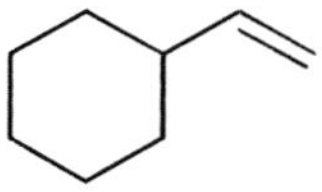

D)

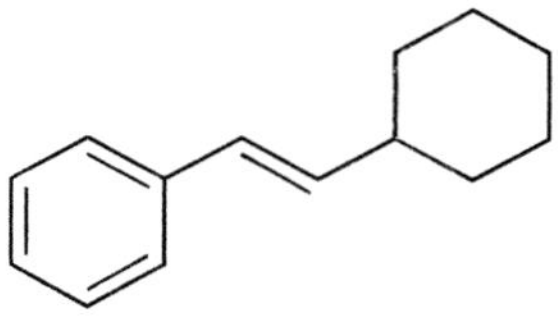

E)

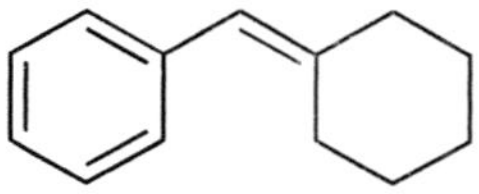

Ans: D

14. What is the **major organic** product of the reaction below?

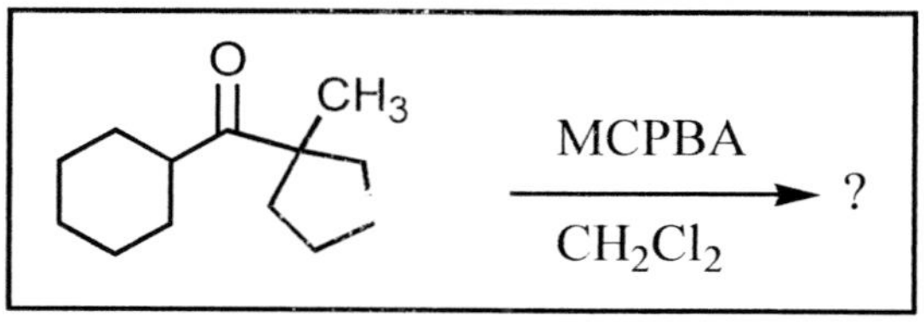

MCPBA

CH₂Cl₂

?

A)

HO OH

CH₃

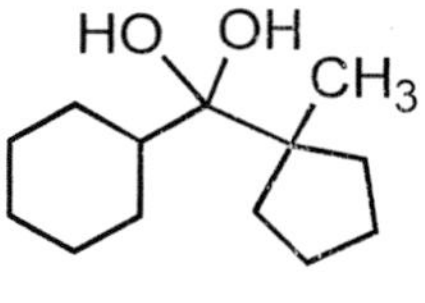

B)

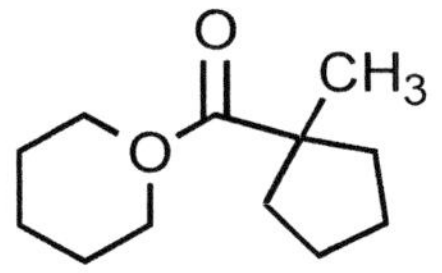

C)

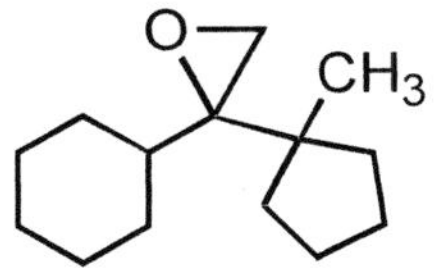

D)

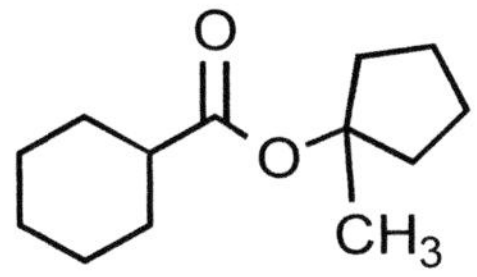

E)

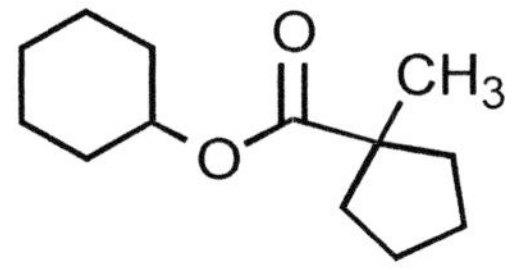

Ans: D

15. Which of the following could **not** be involved in a given Wittig reaction?

A)
$$Ph_3\overset{+}{P}-\overset{-}{C}H_2$$

B)

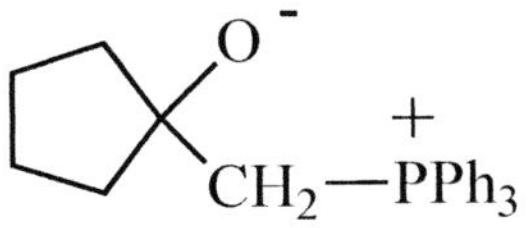

C)

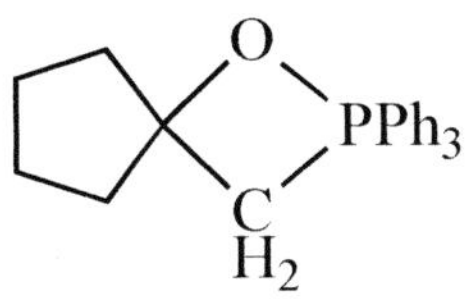

D)

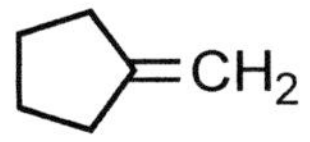

E)   All of these are involved.

Ans: E

16. Why is the reaction of the type shown below usually done?

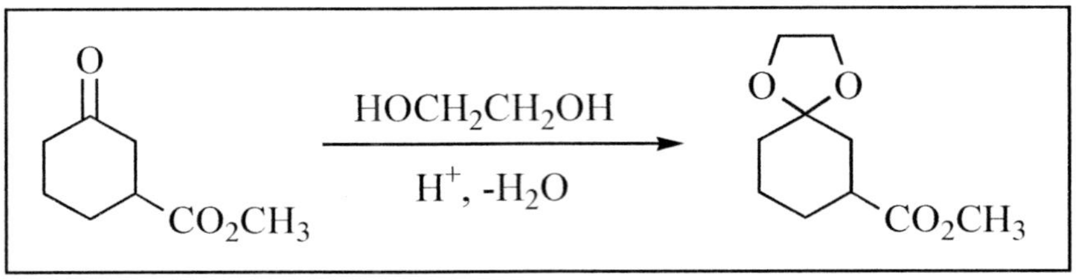

A) To make the α hydrogens more acidic
B) To protect a ketone or aldehyde carbonyl
C) To make the molecule more reactive
D) To make an aldehyde or ketone less water soluble
E) To increase the oxygen content
Ans: B

17. Suppose that a special catalyst was discovered that would allow an equilibrium to occur between the two molecules shown below. To which side, if any, would you expect the equilibrium to lie?

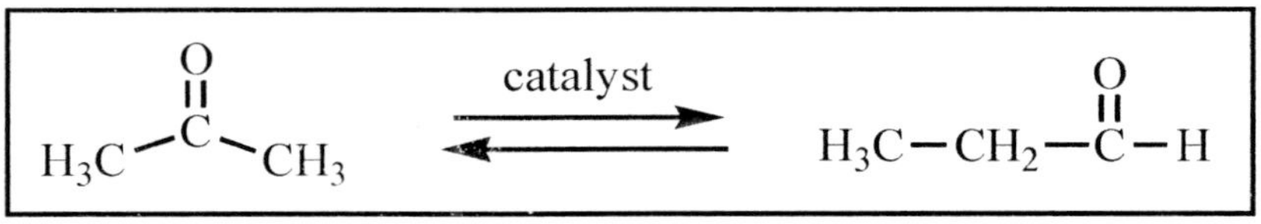

A) To the right   D) There is no way to predict this.
B) To the left   E) These molecules are not isomers.
C) Equally to the right and left
Ans: B

18. Which of the following represents an oxaphosphetane intermediate formed during a Wittig reaction?
A)

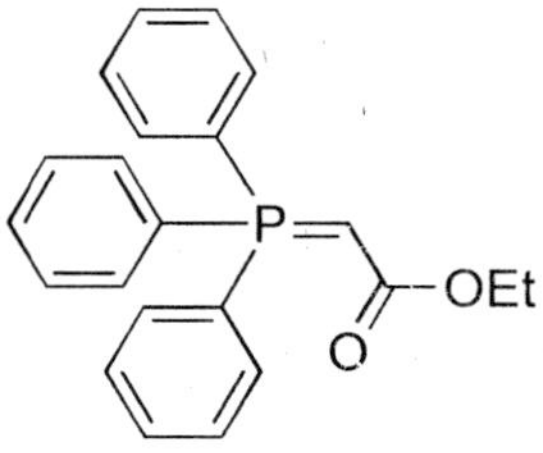

B)

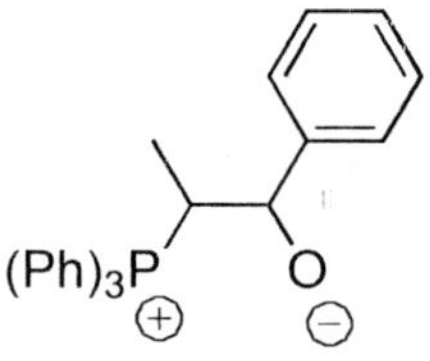

C)

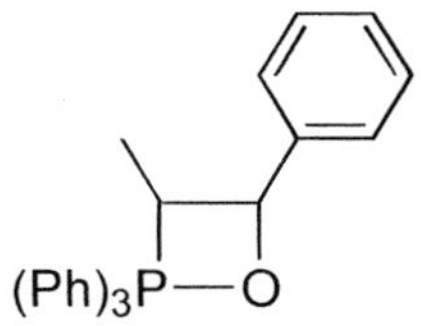

D)

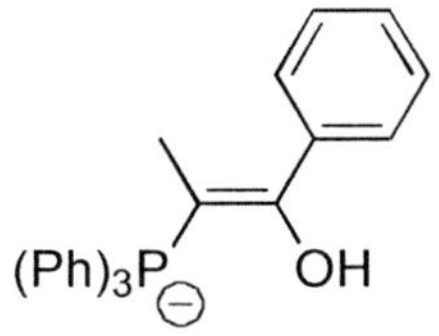

E)

Ans: C

19. Which of the following is a typical ^{13}C-NMR shift value for a carbonyl carbon?
    A) 208 ppm   B) 29.3 ppm   C) 9.8 ppm   D) 45.2 ppm   E) 1700 cm^{-1}
    Ans: A

20. What test is used to detect the presence of an aldehyde?
    A) Tollen's   B) Lucas   C) Fehling   D) A and B   E) A and C
    Ans: E

21. Predict the product of the following reaction:

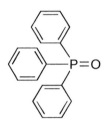

A)

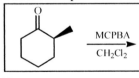

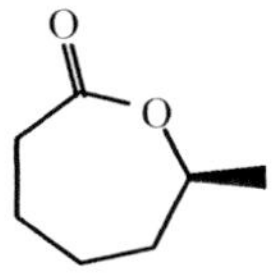

B)

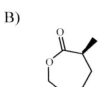

C)

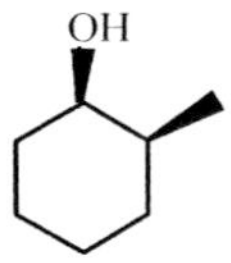

OH

D)

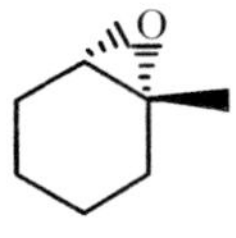

O

E)

OH

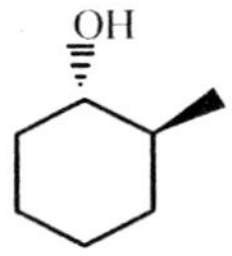

Ans: A

22. Predict the product of the following reaction:

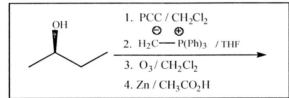

OH

1. PCC / CH₂Cl₂

2. H₂C⊖——P(Ph)₃⊕ / THF

3. O₃/ CH₂Cl₂

4. Zn / CH₃CO₂H

A)

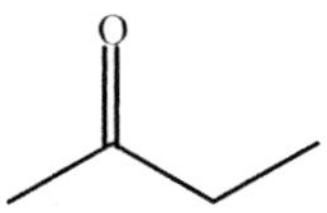

O

B)

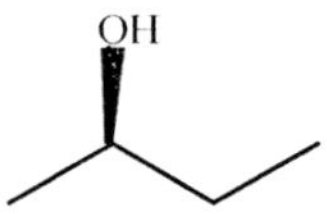

OH

C)

O
‖
C
H   H

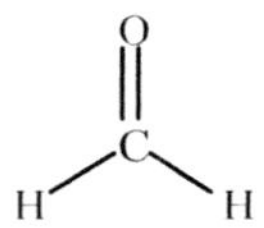

D)   CH₃OH

E)   Both A and C

Ans: E

23. Given the geometry of nitrogen (which is **not** represented properly here), the oxime shown below could exist as how many isomers?

    A)   Only one isomer is possible.
    B)   Two enantiomers are possible.
    C)   Two diastereomers are possible.
    D)   Three stereoisomers are possible.
    E)   There are no stereoisomers of this compound possible.
Ans: C

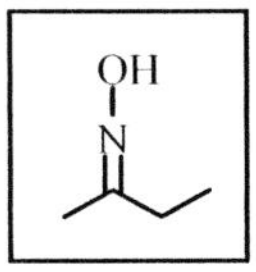

24. What reactants would be required to prepare the oxime shown below?

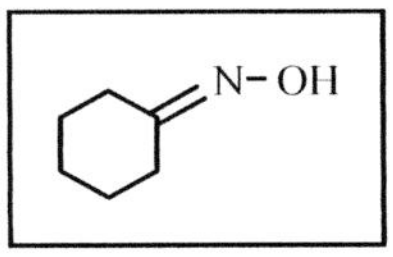

    A)

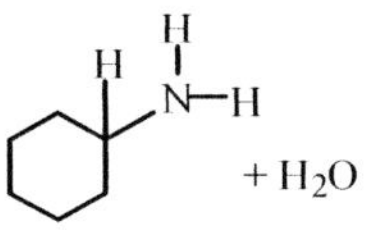

                  + H$_2$O

    B)

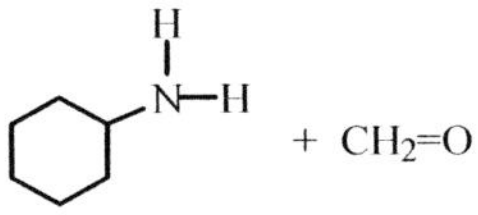

                  + CH$_2$=O

    C)

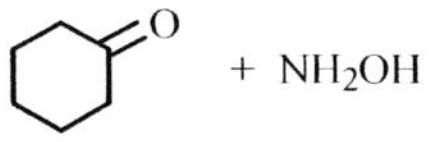

                  + NH$_2$OH

    D)

                  + N=O

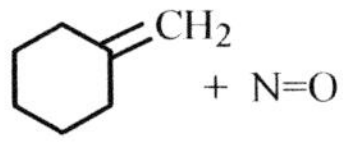

    E)   None of these would produce the desired product.
Ans: C

25. Old bottles of benzaldehyde (a liquid that smells like cherries) are often observed to have crystals on the bottom; what is the identity of this solid?

A)

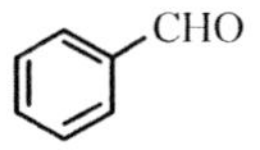

CHO

B)

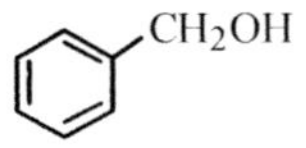

CH₂OH

C)

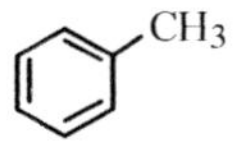

CH₃

D)

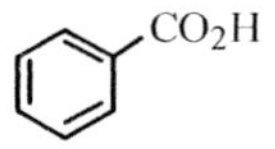

CO₂H

E)

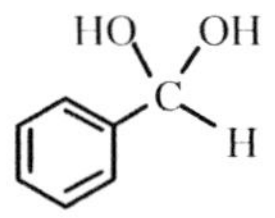

HO   OH
   C
      H

Ans: D

26. What is the name of the reaction by which aldehydes and ketones are converted directly to alkenes?
A) Friedel-Crafts   B) Williamson   C) Wittig   D) Hofmann   E) Fischer
Ans: C

27. At which atom of the following structure will a nucleophile attack?

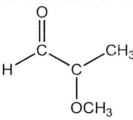

A)   At the carbonyl oxygen   D)   At the ether oxygen
B)   At the carbonyl carbon   E)   At the aldehyde hydrogen
C)   At the methyl carbon
Ans: B

28. Predict the product from the following reaction.

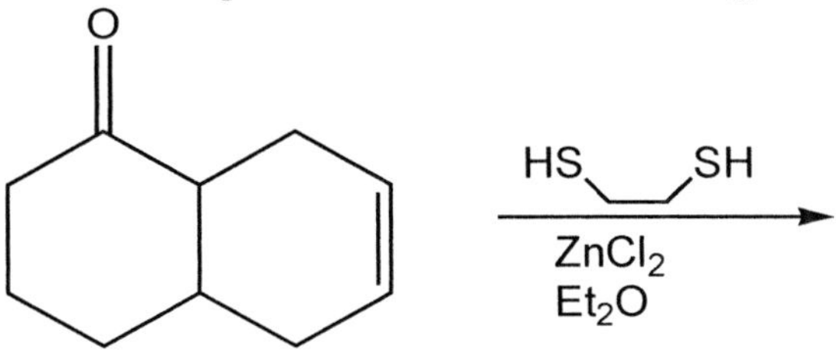

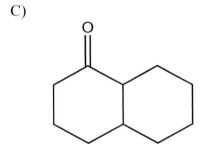

HS⌢SH

ZnCl₂
Et₂O

A)

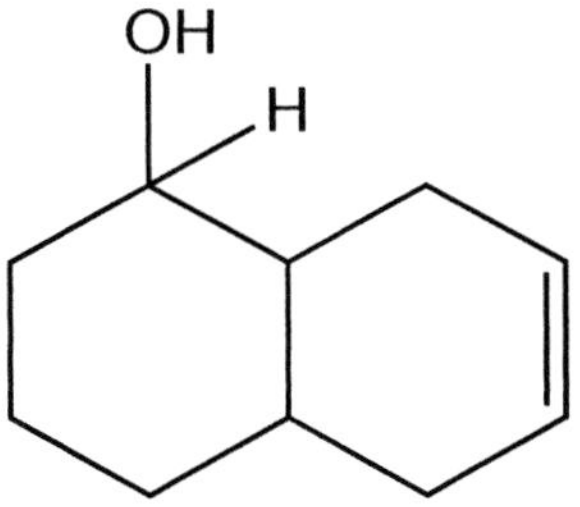

B)

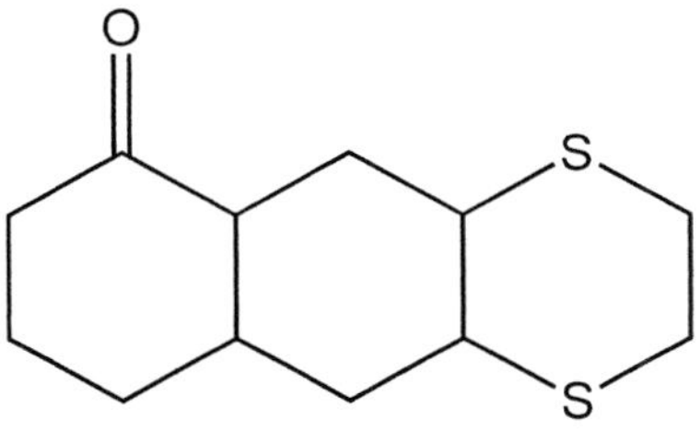

C)

D)

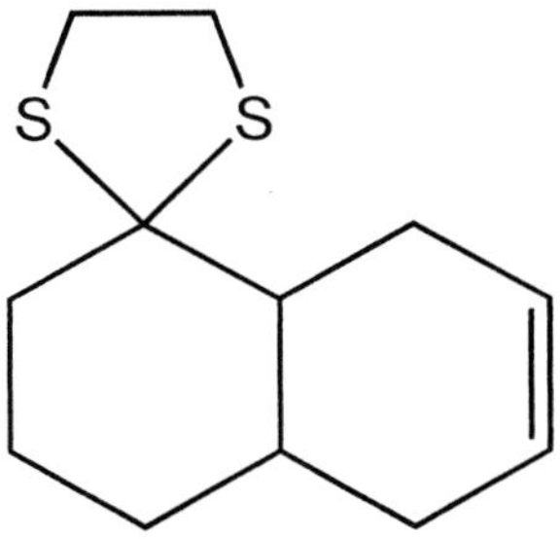

E)

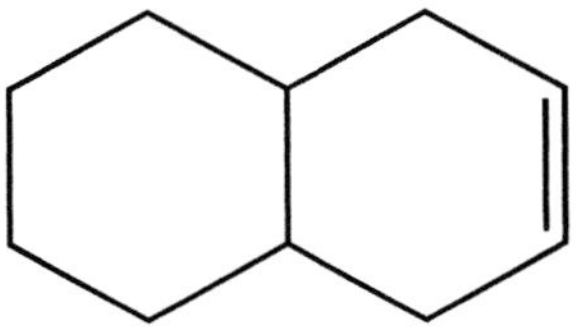

Ans: D

29. Predict the product from the following reaction sequence.

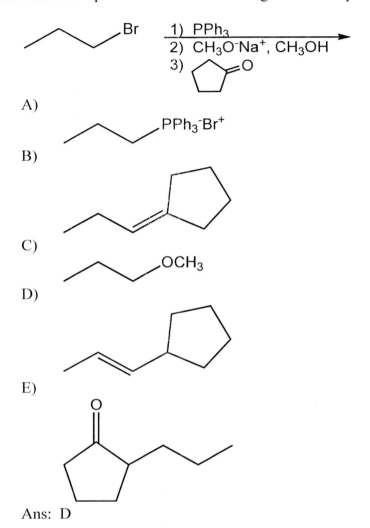

A)

B)

C)

D)

E)

Ans: D

Chapter 18: Enols, Enolates, and the Aldol Condensation: α, β-Unsaturated Aldehydes and Ketones

1. Which product would you **not** expect in the crossed aldol reaction between acetaldehyde and propionaldehyde?

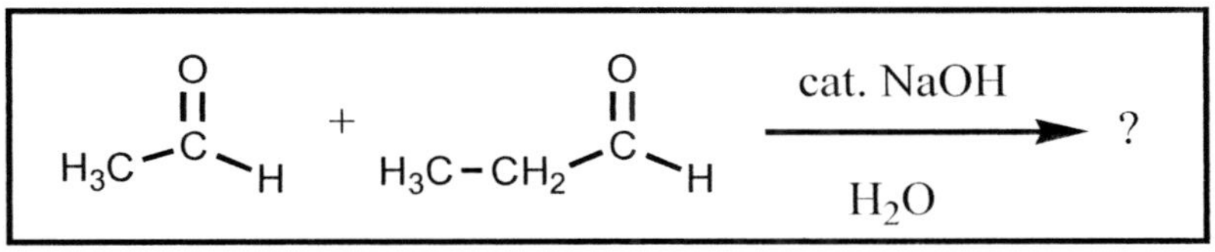

A)

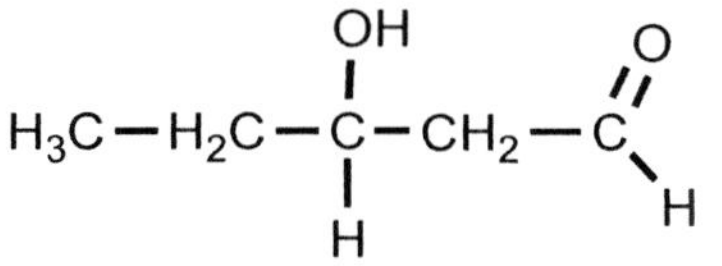

B)

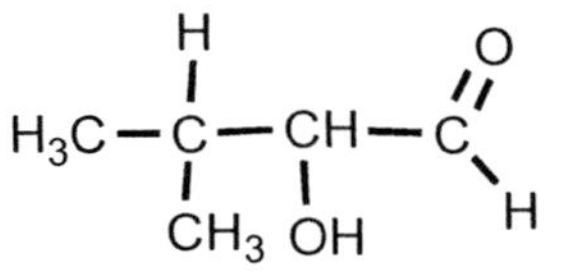

C)

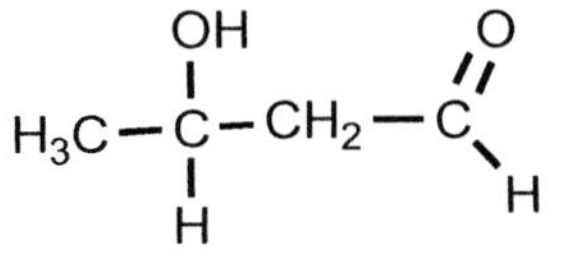

D)

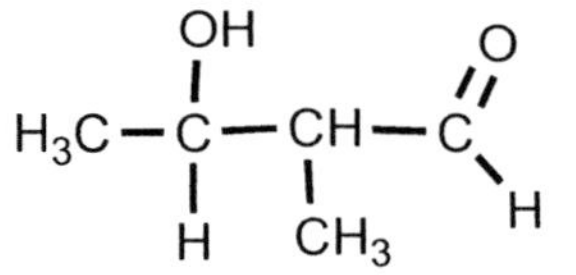

E)

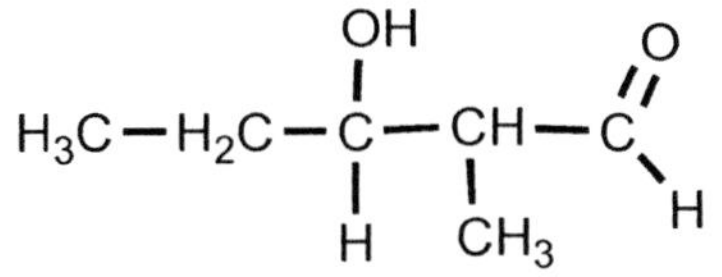

Ans: B

2. What organic molecule would you expect to be present **in significant amounts** under the following conditions?

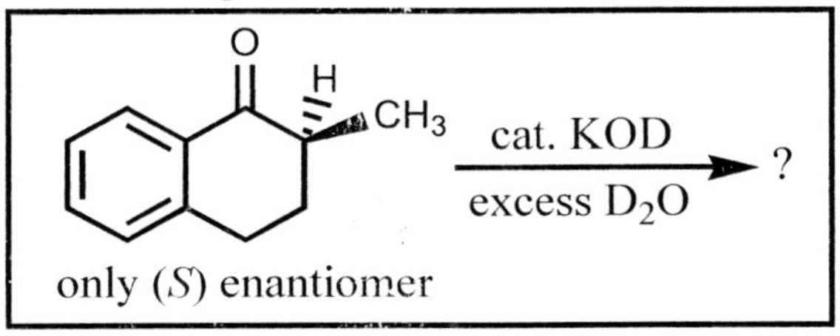

cat. KOD

excess D_2O

?

only (S) enantiomer

A)

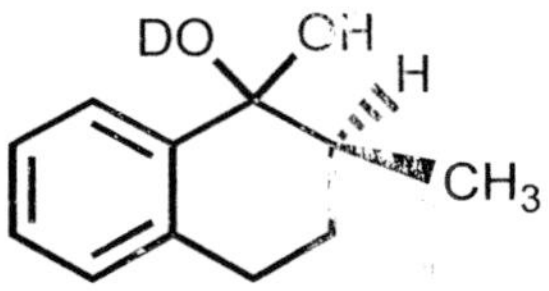

DO CH

H

CH3

B)

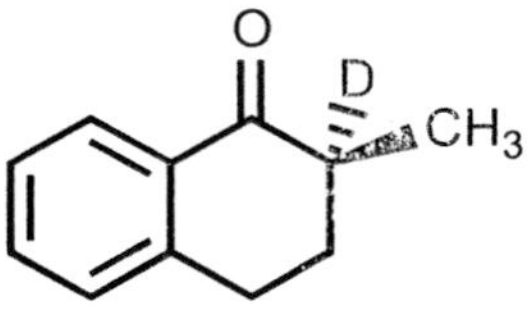

O

D

CH3

C)

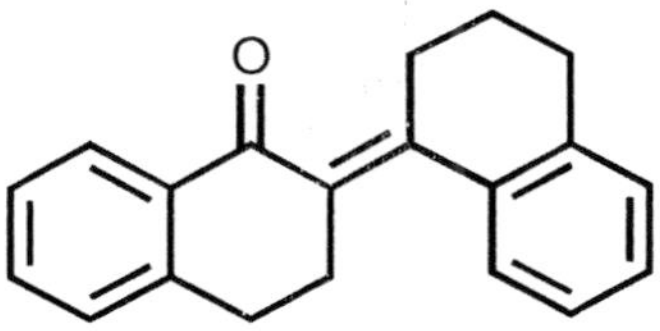

O

D)

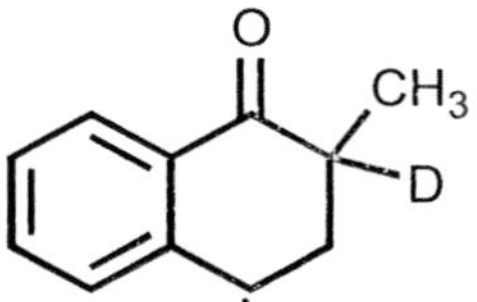

O

CH3

D

racemic

E)

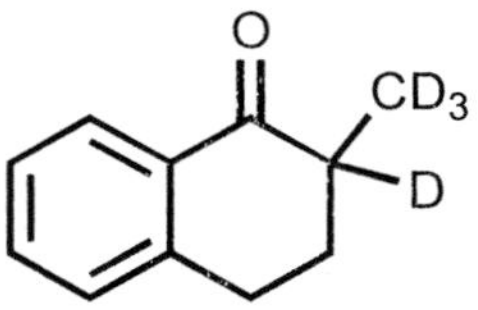

O

CD3

D

racemic

Ans: D

3. What reactants would be used to produce cinnamaldehyde?

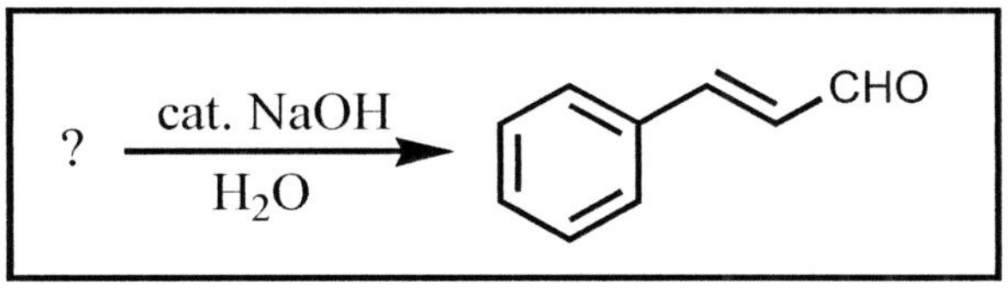

A)

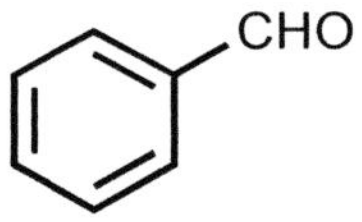

+ CH_3CHO

B)

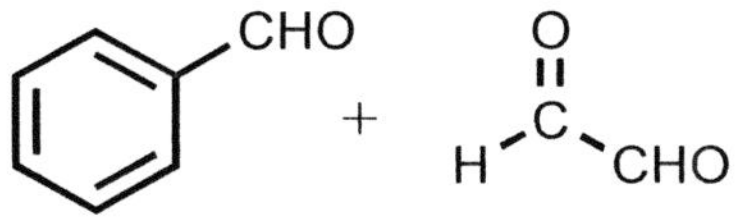

C)

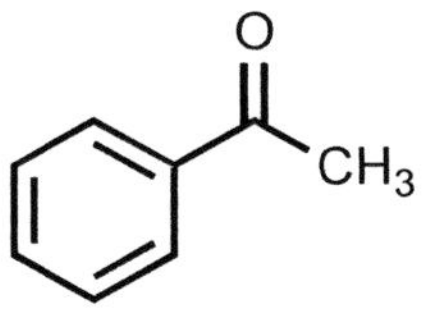

+ $CH_2=O$

D)

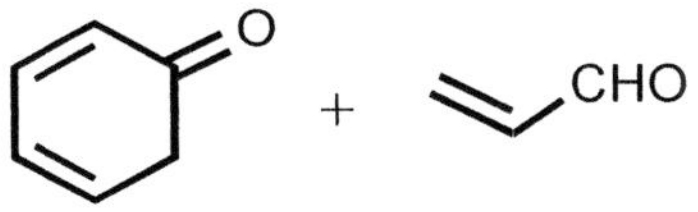

+

E)

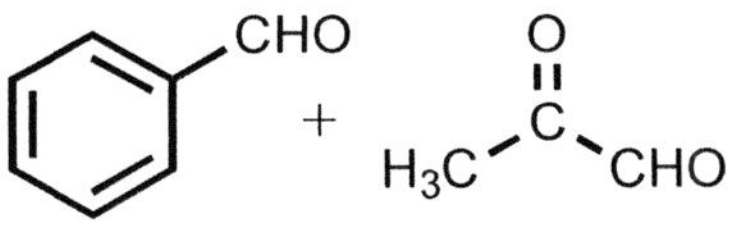

Ans: A

4. What would you expect to result from the following reaction?

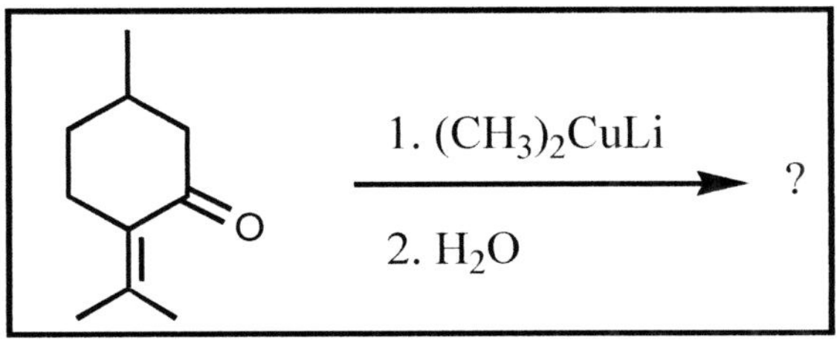

1. $(CH_3)_2CuLi$

2. H_2O

?

A)

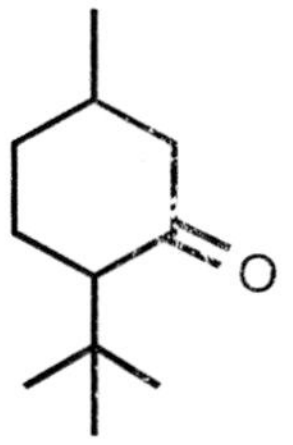

B)

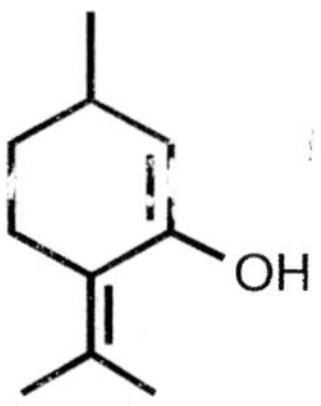

OH

C)

OH

CH$_3$

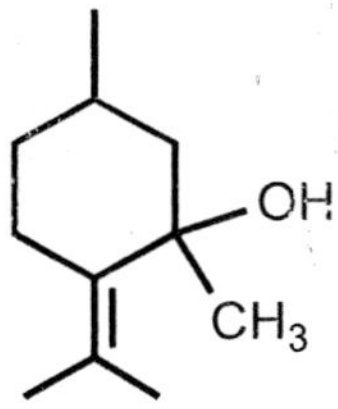

D)

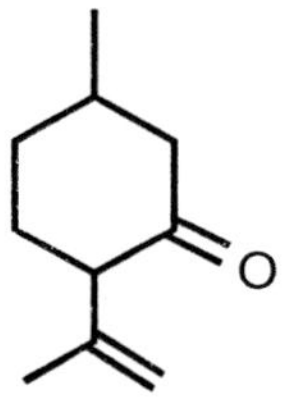

E)

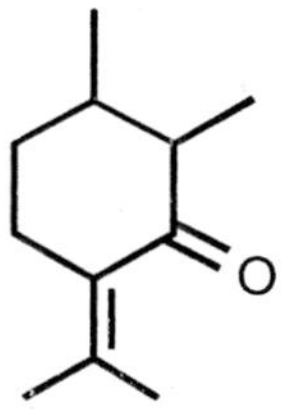

Ans: A

5. Indicate to which side, if any, the following equilibrium lies:

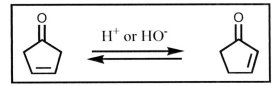

A)   To the right
B)   To the left
C)   Equally to right and left
D)   Cannot be predicted
E)   Major product is an enol or enolate ion, respectively
Ans: A

6. What would be the expected product of the following reaction?

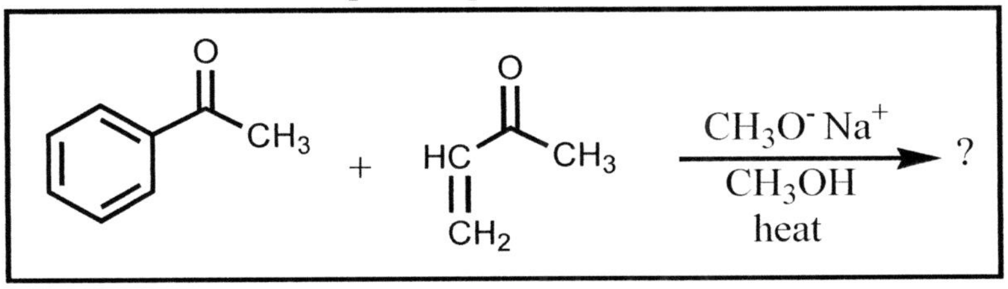

A)

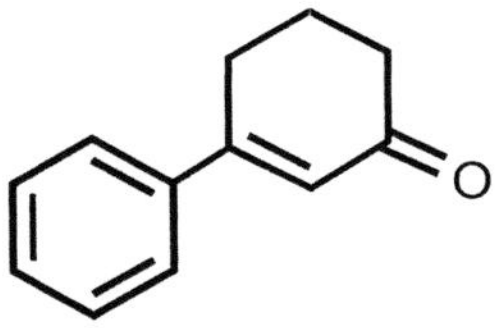

B)

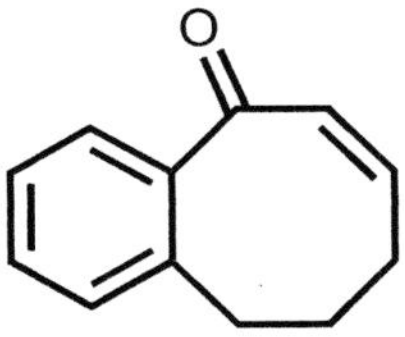

C)

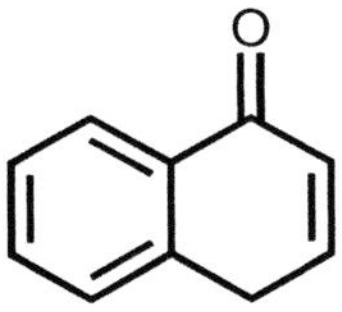

D)

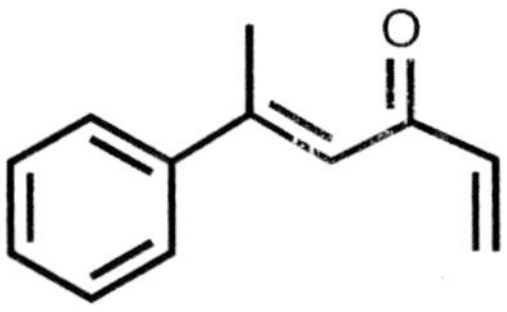

E)

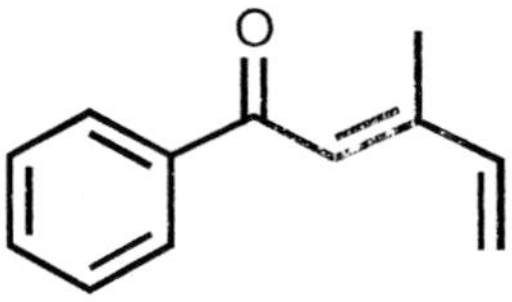

Ans: A

7. What **major** product would you expect from the following reaction?

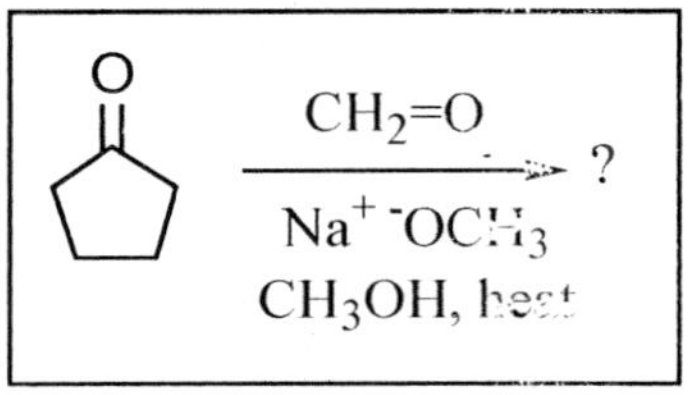

A)

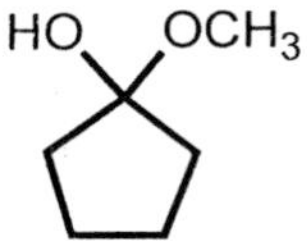

B)

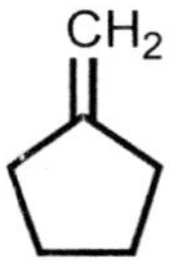

C)

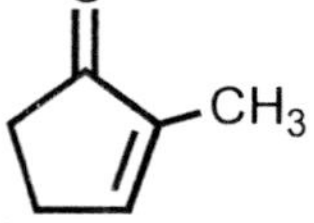

D)

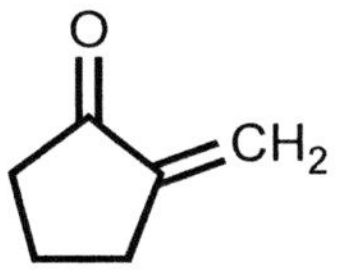

E)

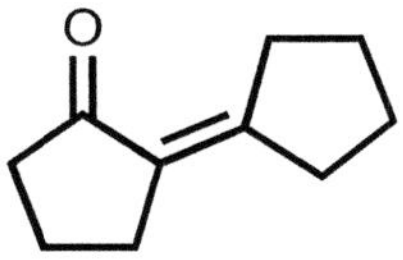

Ans: D

8. Which proton in the following molecule is the most acidic?

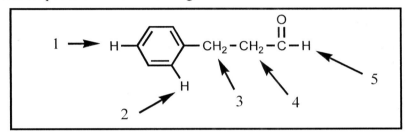

A) 1   B) 2   C) 3   D) 4   E) 5
Ans: D

9. What product is formed in the aldol condensation of propanal?

$$CH_3CH_2CHO \xrightarrow[\text{H}_2\text{O}]{\text{KOH}} ?$$

A)

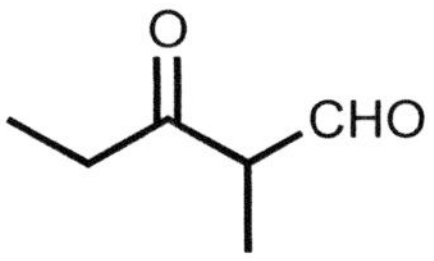

B)

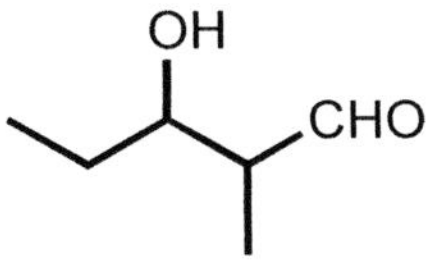

C)

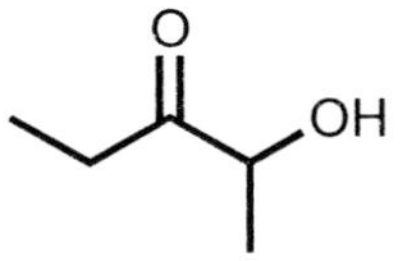

D)

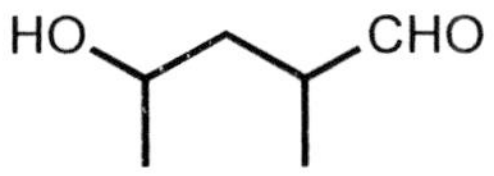

E)

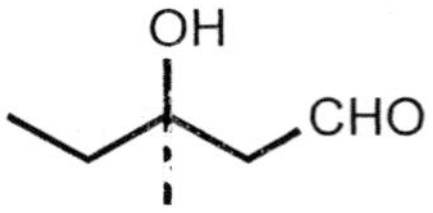

Ans: B

10. To which side, if any, would the following equilibrium lie?

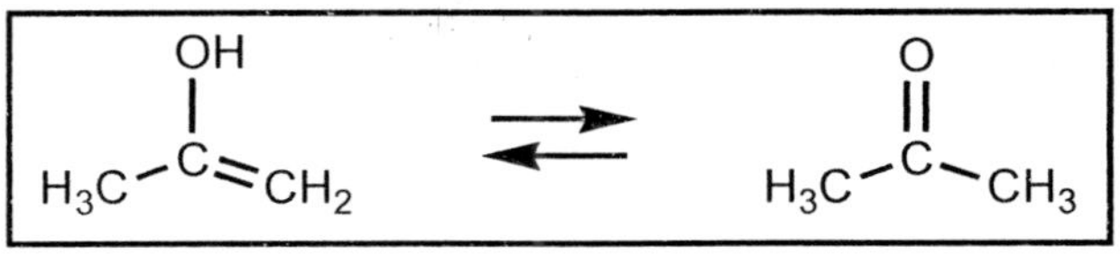

A)   To the left
B)   To the right
C)   Equally to the left and right

D)   Reaction cannot occur at all
E)   Equilibrium favors a different product.

Ans: B

11. To which side, if any, would the following equilibrium lie?

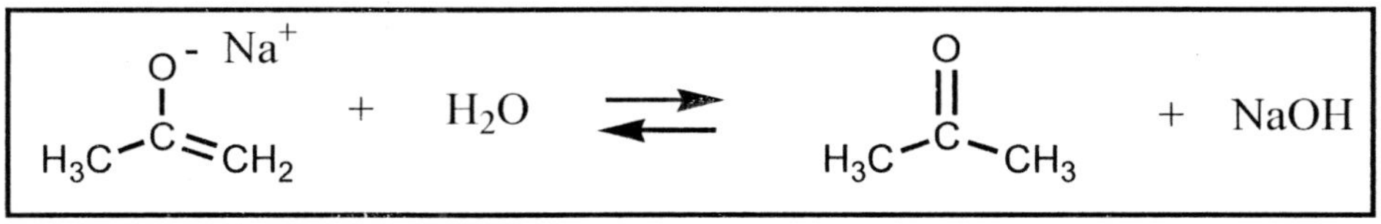

A)   To the left
B)   To the right
C)   Equally to the left and right

D)   Reaction cannot occur at all
E)   Equilibrium favors a different product.

Ans: B

12. Which **major** product would you expect when the following diketone undergoes aldol cyclization in base, followed by acid?

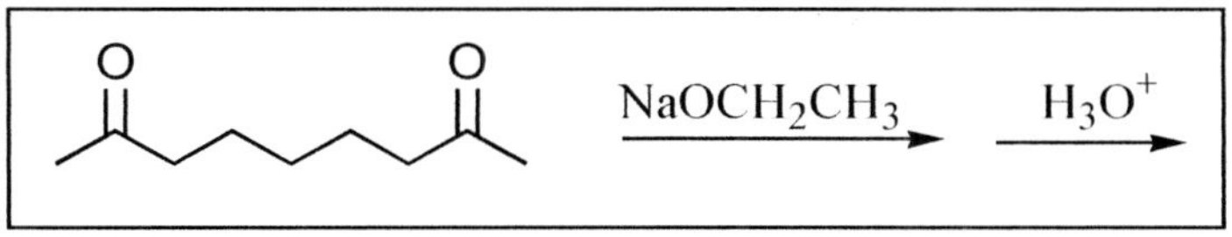

A)

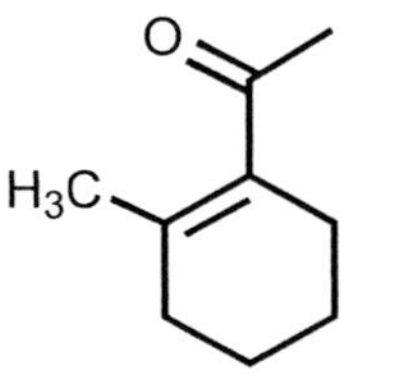

B)

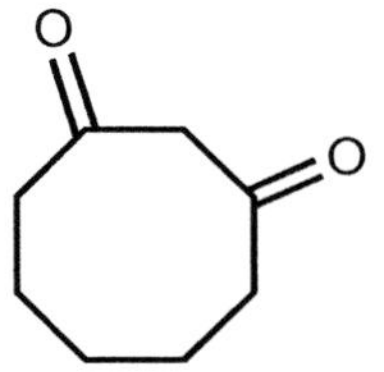

C)

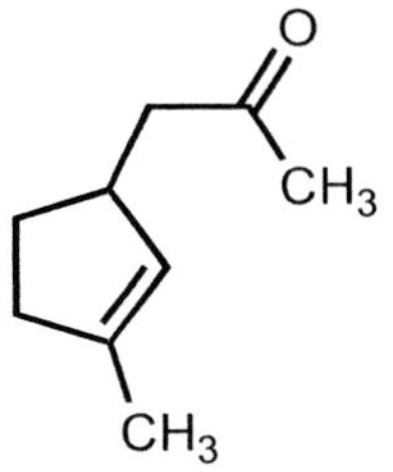

D)

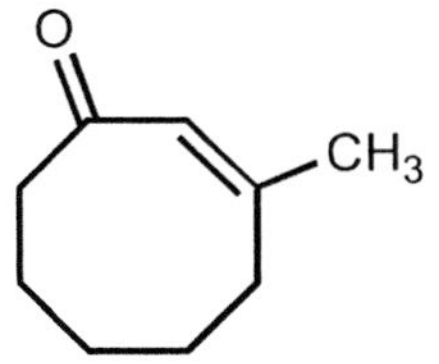

E)

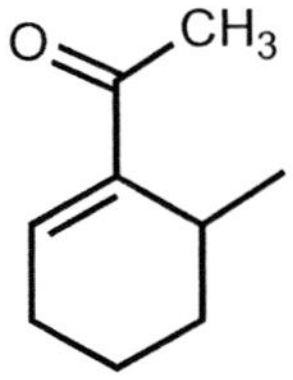

Ans: A

13. Which set of reagents would be needed for the following conversion?

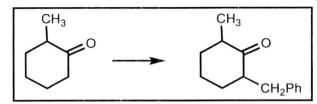

A)   NaOCH$_2$CH$_3$, CH$_3$I
B)   PhCH$_2$MgBr, then H$_3$O$^+$
C)   CH$_3$MgBr, then PhCH$_2$Br

D)   H$_3$O$^+$, then PhCH$_2$Br
E)   LDA, then PhCH$_2$Br

Ans: E

14. What product results when the following aldol product is treated with dilute acid?

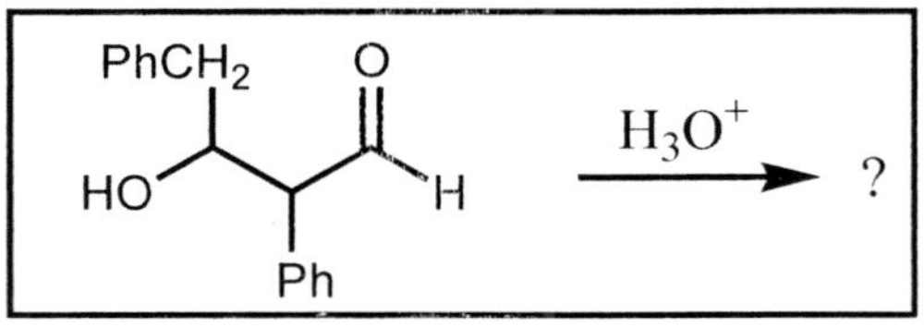

A)

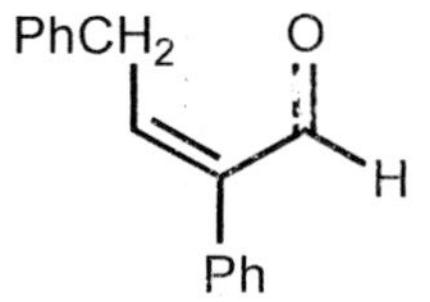

B)

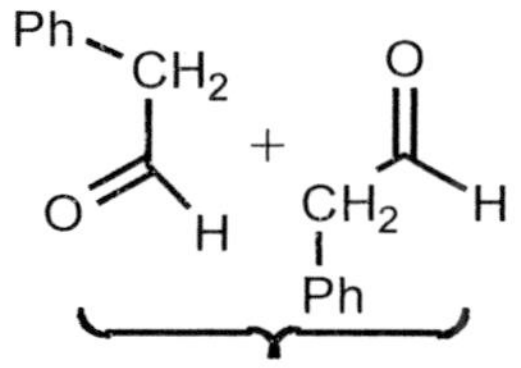

C)

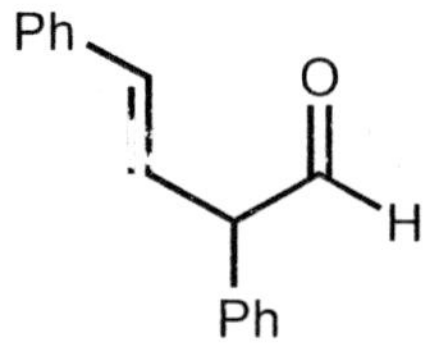

D)

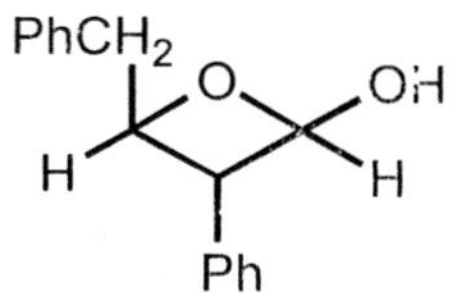

E)   None of these

Ans: A

15. Which of the following sets of reaction conditions will result in the following transformation?

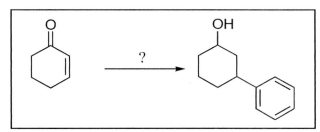

A)

$$\frac{\text{1) PhMgBr / THF}}{\text{2) H}_3\text{O}^+}$$
3) LAH / THF

B)

$$\frac{\text{1) PhMgBr / THF}}{\text{2) H}_3\text{O}^+}$$
3) LDA / THF

C)

$$\frac{\text{1) PhMgBr / THF}}{\text{2) H}_3\text{O}^+}$$
3) LAH / H$_2$O

D)

1) (Ph)$_2$CuLi
$$\frac{\text{2) H}_3\text{O}^+}{\text{3) NaBH}_4\text{ / CH}_3\text{OH}}$$

E)

$$\frac{\text{1) (Ph)}_2\text{CuLi}}{\text{2) H}_3\text{O}^+}$$
3) MCPBA

Ans: D

16. Predict the major organic product of the following reaction.

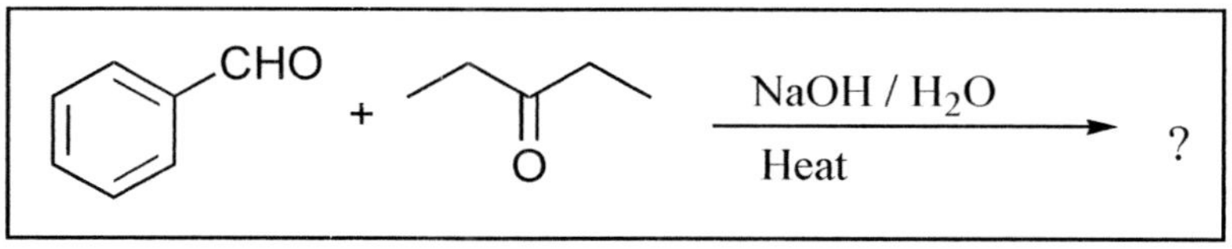

A)

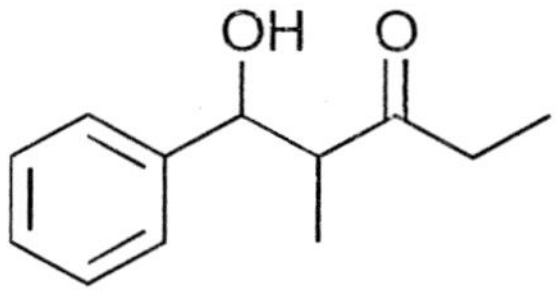

B)

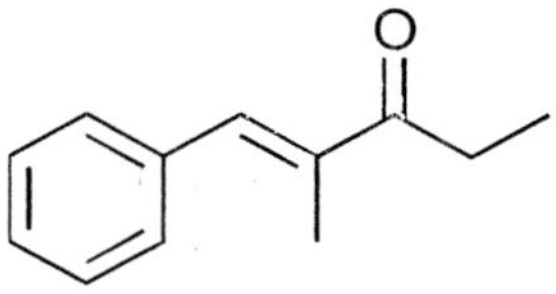

C)

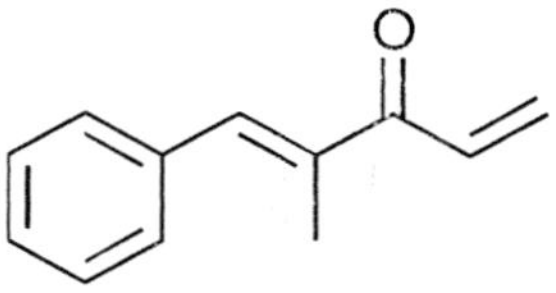

D)

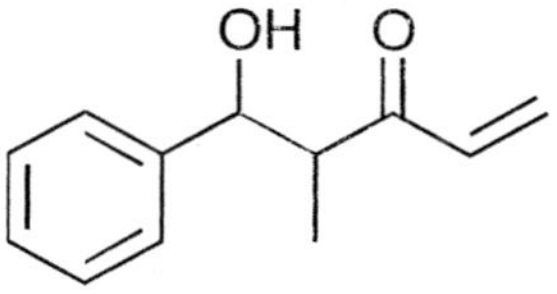

E)

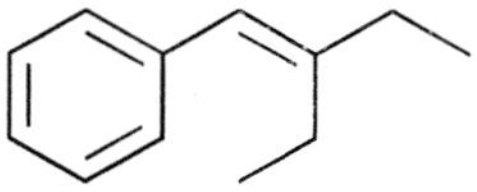

Ans: B

17. Predict the major organic product of the following reaction.

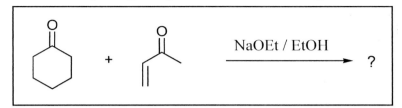

A)

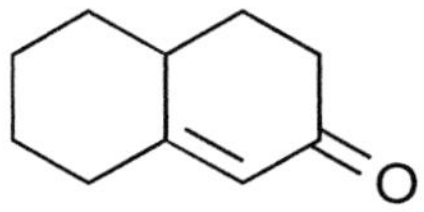

B)

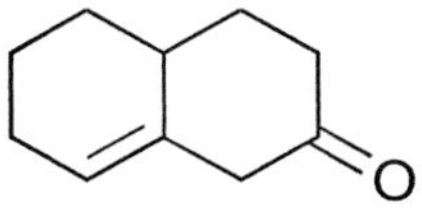

C)

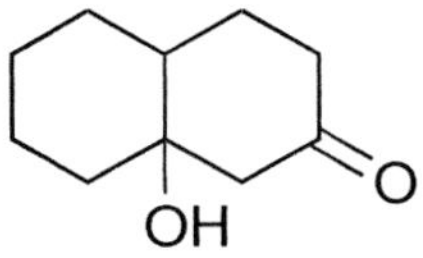

D)

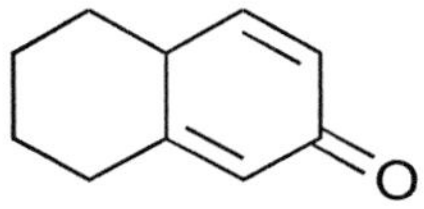

E)

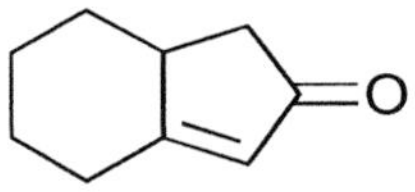

Ans: A

18. Predict the major organic product of the following reaction sequence.

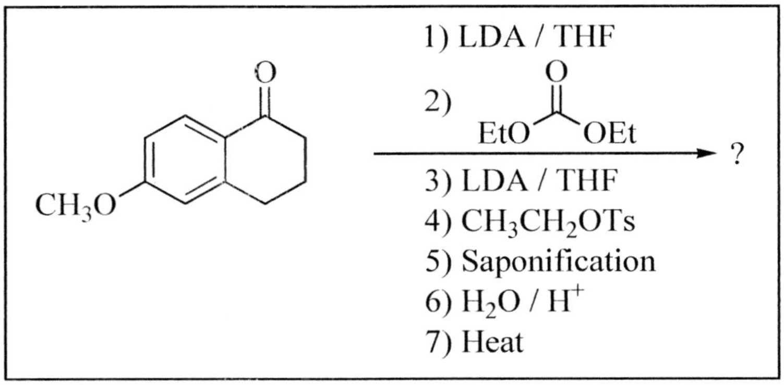

1) LDA / THF

2)

EtO—C(=O)—OEt

3) LDA / THF
4) CH₃CH₂OTs
5) Saponification
6) H₂O / H⁺
7) Heat

?

A)

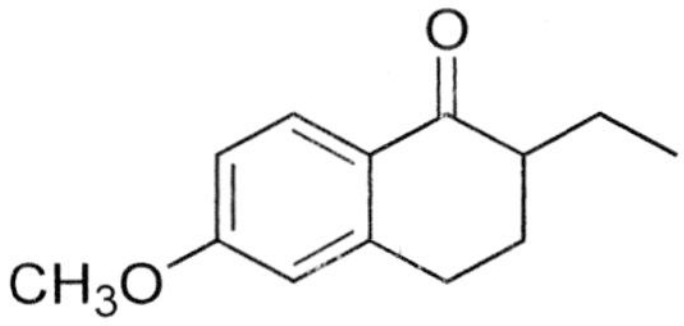

CH₃O—

B)

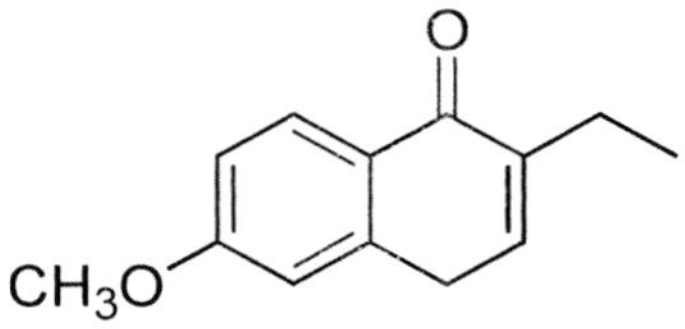

CH₃O—

C)

CH₃O—

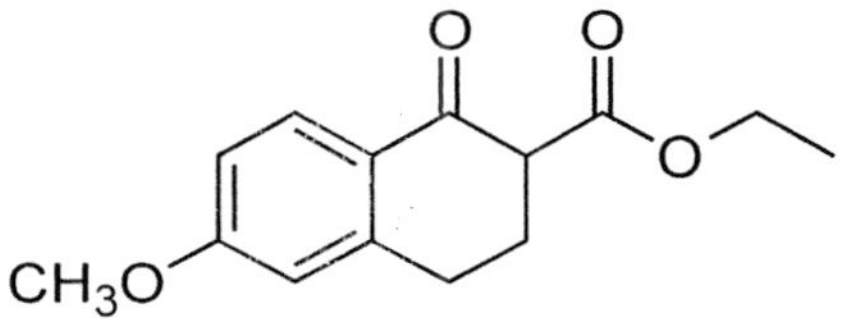

D)

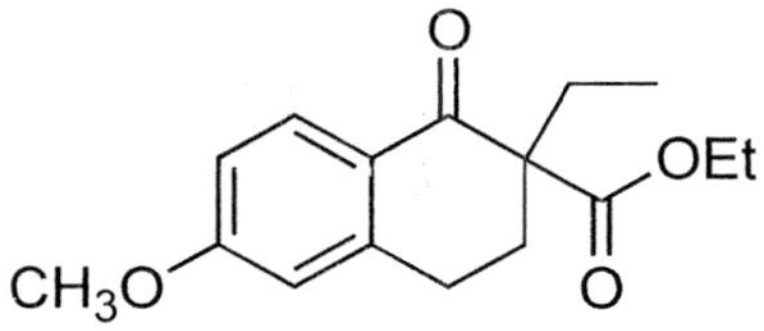

OEt

CH₃O—

E)

CH₃O—

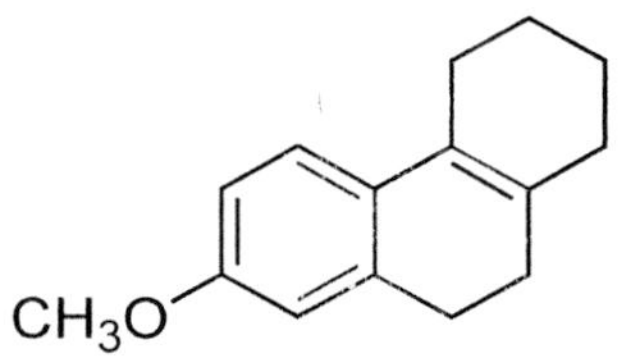

Ans: A

19. Predict the major organic product of the following reaction sequence.

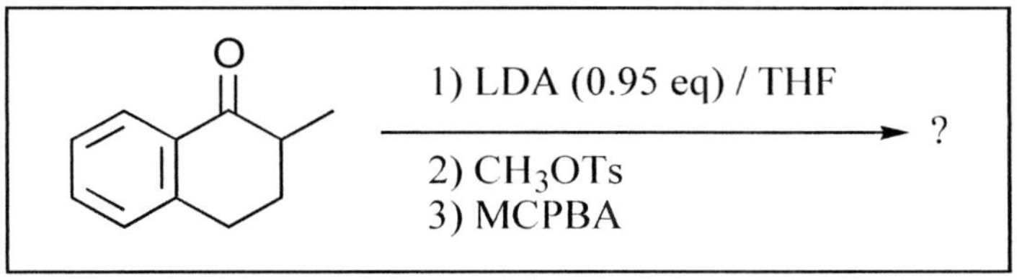

1) LDA (0.95 eq) / THF

2) CH₃OTs
3) MCPBA

?

A)

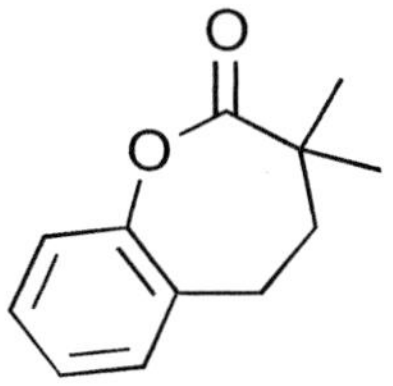

B)

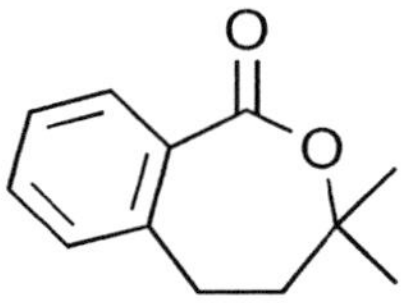

C)

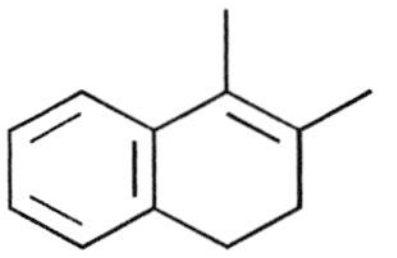

D)

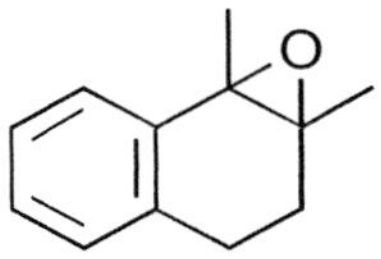

E)

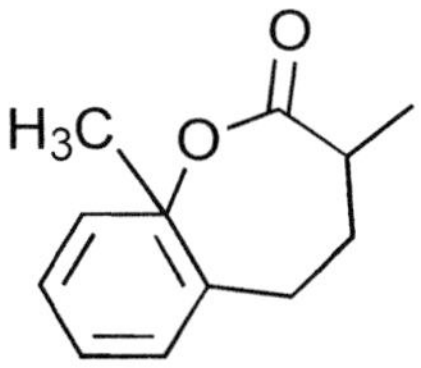

Ans: B

20. The addition of either the methyl Grignard reagent or methyllithium to camphor, followed by hydrolysis, produces a tertiary alcohol known as 2-methylisoborneol, an algal metabolite which imparts a musty odor to water at very low concentrations. However, the yield of alcohol does not exceed 50%, and large amounts of camphor are recovered from the reaction even when a large excess of the Grignard or lithium reagent are used. What would be the most plausible explanation?

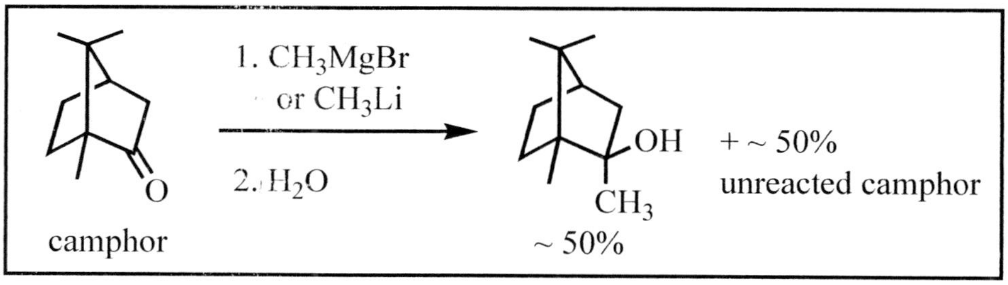

A) Ketones do not react with Grignard or lithium reagents.
B) The Grignard or lithium reagent had obviously degraded during storage.
C) The mechanism requires that, for each alcohol formed, one ketone molecule must remain unreacted.
D) With hindered ketones, the organometallic reagent could function as a base rather than as a nucleophile.
E) Alcohol formed early in the reaction could form an unreactive hemiacetal with remaining ketone.

Ans: D

21. Predict the product of the following reaction:

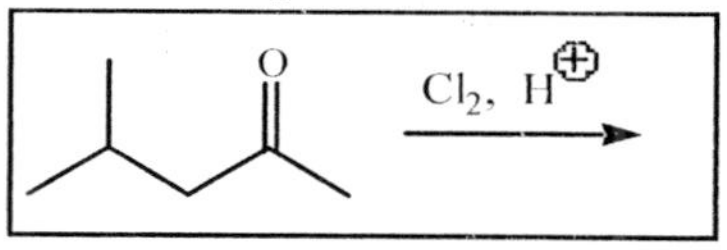

A)

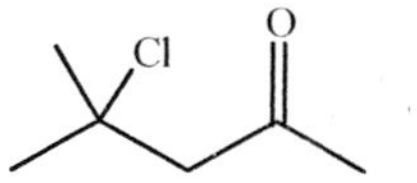

B)

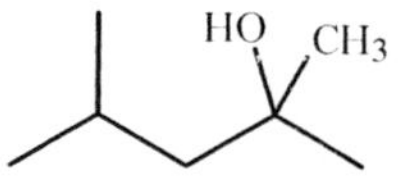

C)

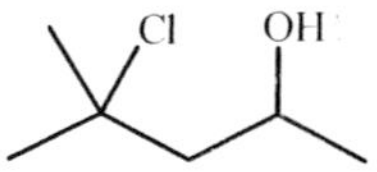

D)

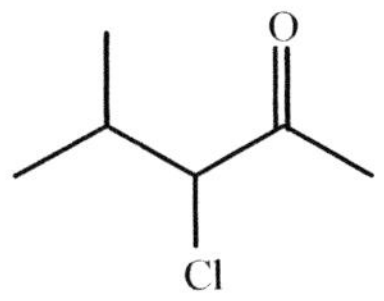

E)

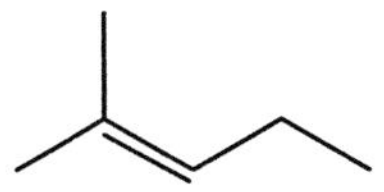

Ans: D

22. One product of the following reaction would be:

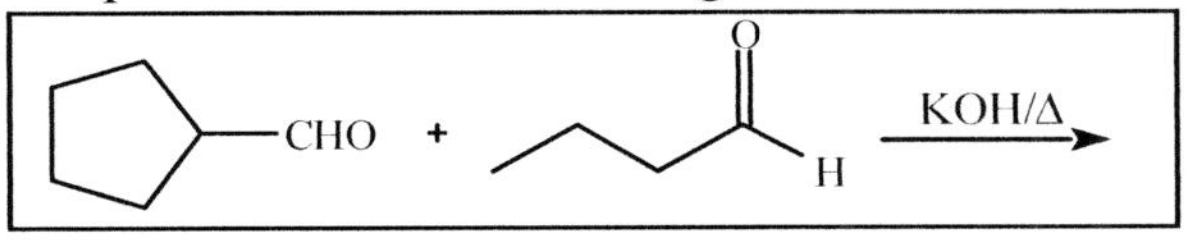

A)

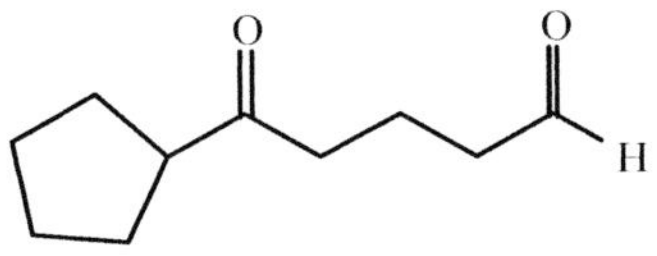

B)

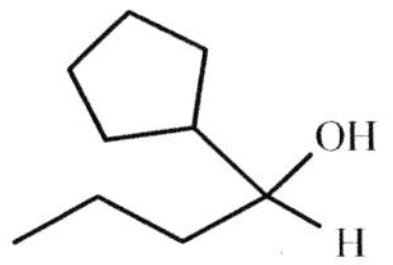

C)

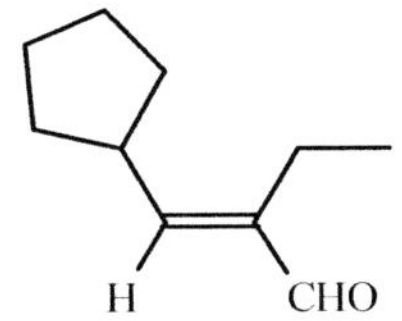

D)

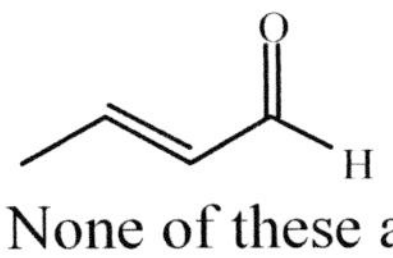

E)   None of these are correct.

Ans: C

23. Which of the following conditions will **not** successfully alkylate a ketone?
    A) 1. H_2O, H^+
        2. CH_3CH_2OH
    B) 1.

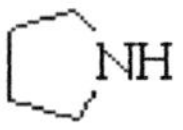

        2. CH_3CH_2Br
        3. H^+, H_2O
    C) 1. LDA, THF
        2. $BrCH_2CO_2C_2H_5$
    D) 1. LDA, THF
        2. $(CH_3)_2C=CHCH_2Br$
    E) All of these will alkylate a ketone.
    Ans: A

24. Predict the product of the following reaction:

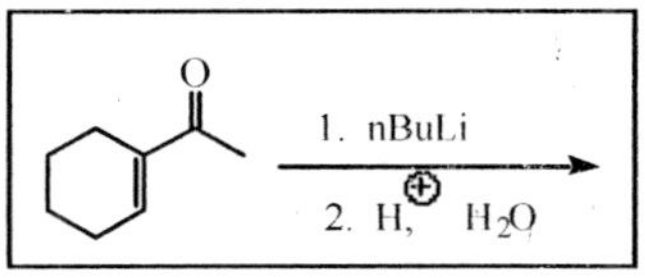

    A)

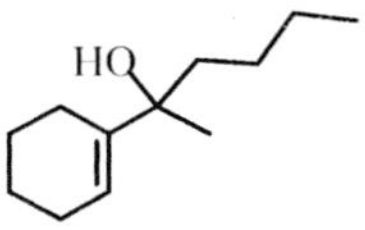

    B)

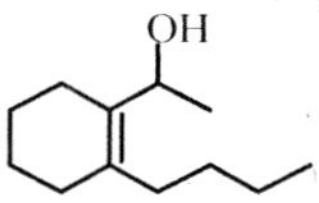

    C)

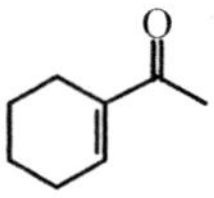

    D)

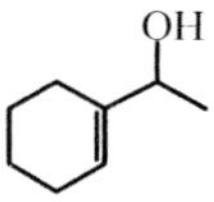

    E)

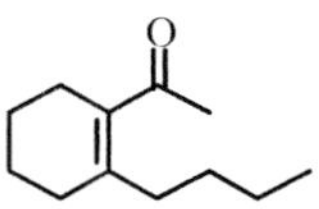

    Ans: A

25. Predict the product of the following reaction:

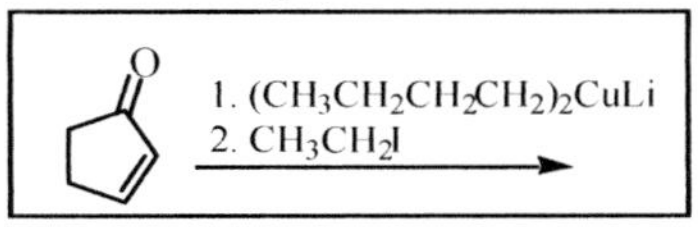

1. (CH₃CH₂CH₂CH₂)₂CuLi
2. CH₃CH₂I

A)

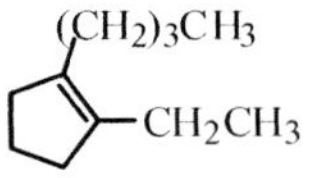

(CH₂)₃CH₃

—CH₂CH₃

B)

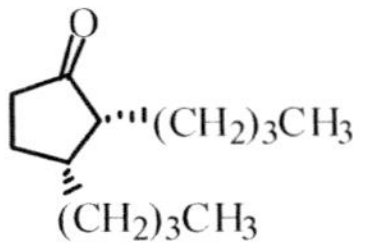

····(CH₂)₃CH₃

(CH₂)₃CH₃

C)

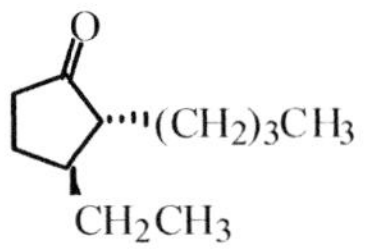

····(CH₂)₃CH₃

CH₂CH₃

D)

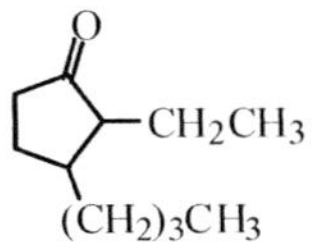

—CH₂CH₃

(CH₂)₃CH₃

E)

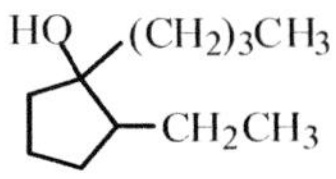

HO   (CH₂)₃CH₃

—CH₂CH₃

Ans: D

26. Predict the product of the following reaction:

1) LDA/THF

2)

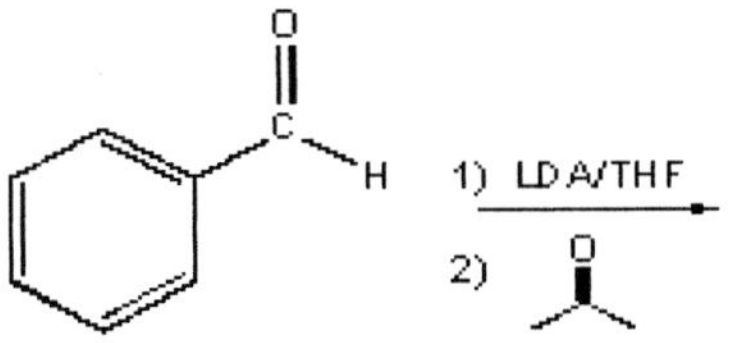

A)

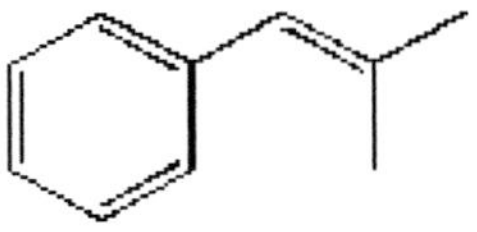

B)

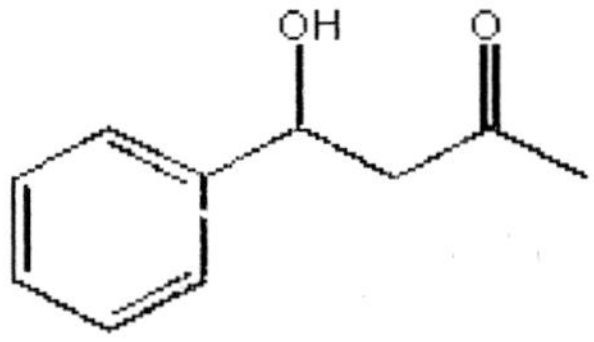

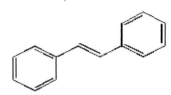

C)

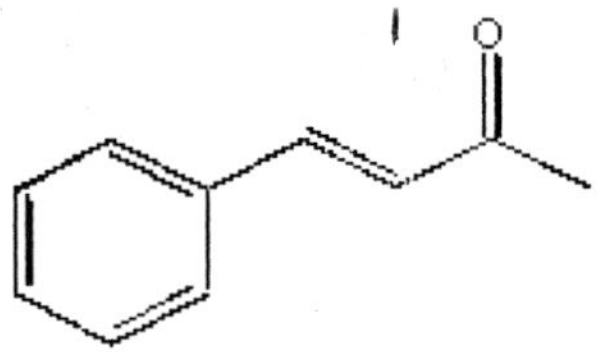

D)

E)   no reaction occurs

Ans: D

27. Predict the product of the following reaction:

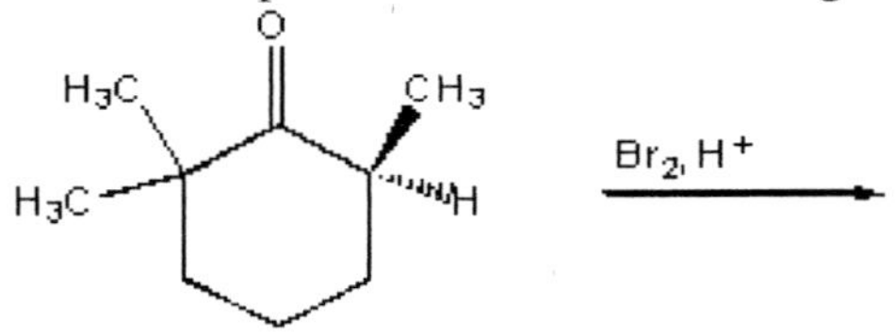

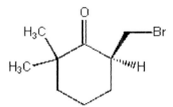

Br_2, H^+

A)

B)

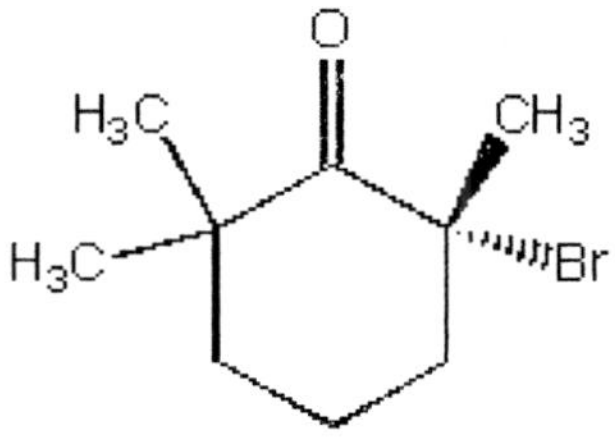

C)

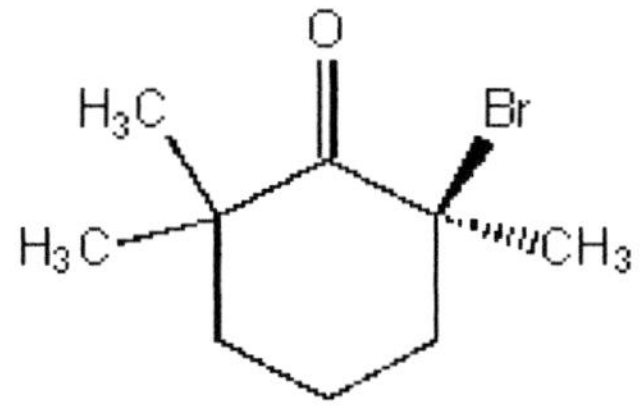

D)

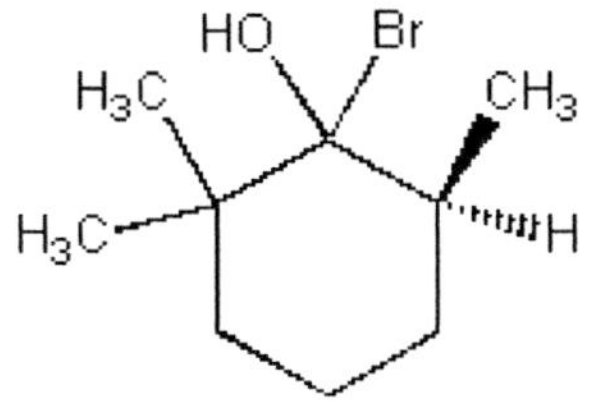

E)   both B and C
Ans: E

28. Predict the product of the following reaction:

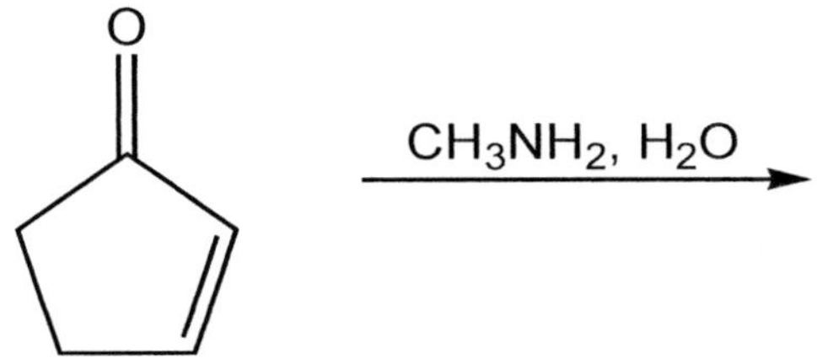

CH$_3$NH$_2$, H$_2$O

A)

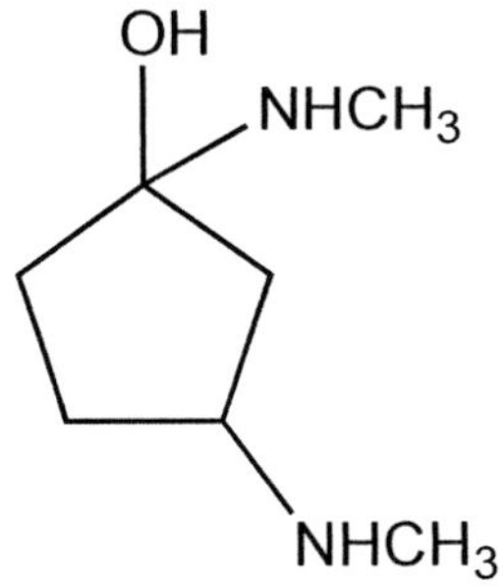

B)

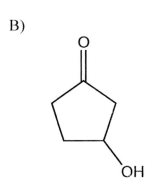

C)

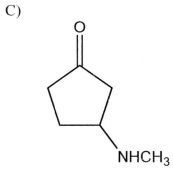

D)

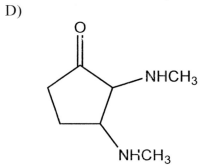

E)

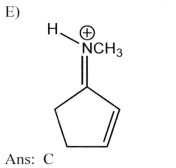

Ans: C

29. Given a large excess of D_2O, what product(s) would result from the following reaction at equilibrium?

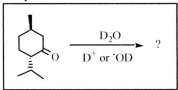

A)

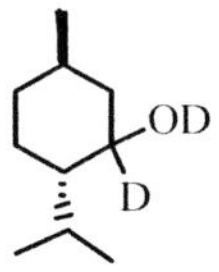

B)

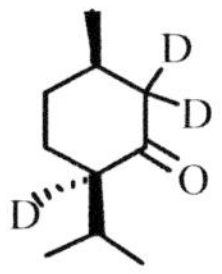

C)

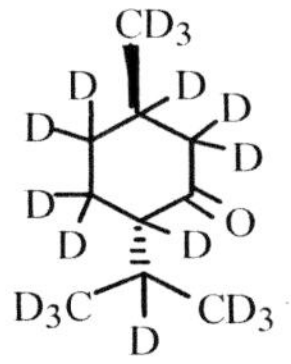

D)

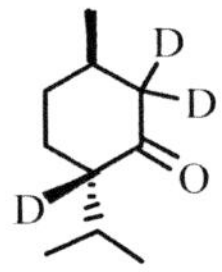

E)   both B and D would be formed
Ans: E

30. The **best** reactants to convert cyclohexanone to 2-methylcyclohexanone cleanly would be:

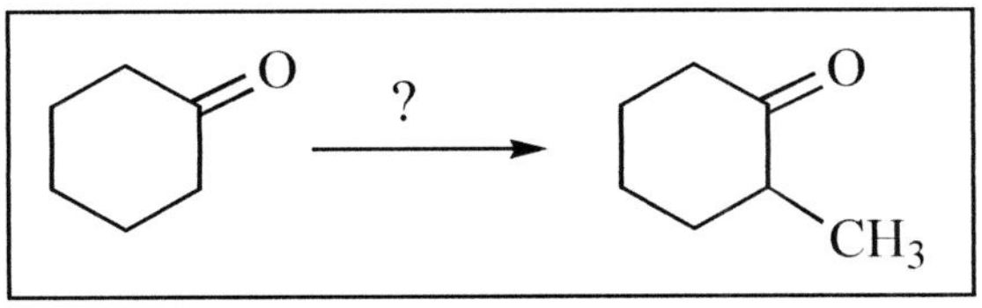

A)

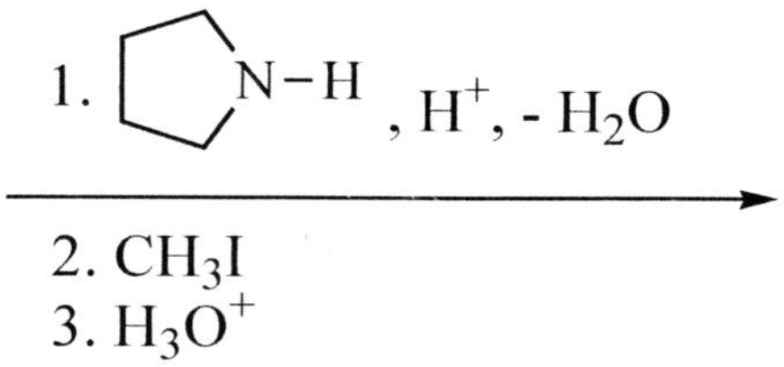

1. $\underset{\displaystyle \text{N}-\text{H}}{\bigcirc}$, H^+, - H_2O

2. CH_3I
3. H_3O^+

B)

NaOH, CH_3I

C)

1. LDA
2. CH_3I

D)

1. CH_3Li
2. H_3O^+

E)

1. NaH
2. CH_3I
3. H_3O^+

Ans: A

31. What would be the **major** product of the following reaction?

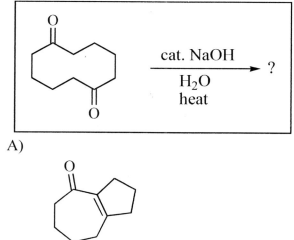

A)

B)

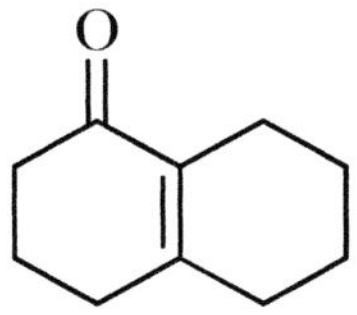

C)

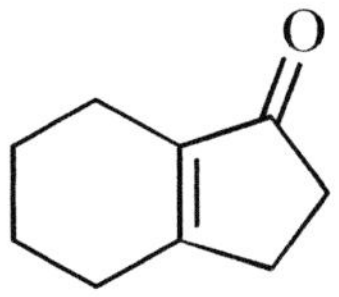

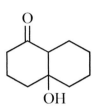

D)

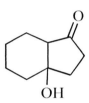

OH

E)

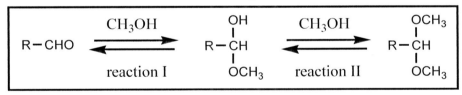

OH

Ans: A

32. Which statement is true of the following reactions?

$$R-CHO \underset{\text{reaction I}}{\overset{CH_3OH}{\rightleftarrows}} R-\underset{OCH_3}{\overset{OH}{|}}CH \underset{\text{reaction II}}{\overset{CH_3OH}{\rightleftarrows}} R-\underset{OCH_3}{\overset{OCH_3}{|}}CH$$

A)   Reactions I and II are only acid-catalyzed.
B)   Reaction I is catalyzed by either acid or base, but reaction II requires acid.
C)   Reactions I and II are both base-catalyzed.
D)   Reaction II is catalyzed by either acid or base, but reaction I requires acid.
E)   Both reactions I and II are catalyzed by either acid or base.
Ans: B

Chapter 19: Carboxylic Acids

1. Which would be the best name of the following compound?

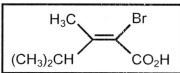

A)   2-bromo-3-isopropylbutenoic acid
B)   (*E*)-2-bromo-3,4-dimethyl-2-pentenoic acid
C)   (*E*)-2-bromo-3-methyl-2-hexenoic acid
D)   (*E*)-2-bromo-3-methyl-2-pentenoic acid
E)   (*Z*)-2-bromo-3-methyl-2-pentenoic acid
Ans: B

2. Rank the following in **decreasing** order of acidity (most acidic on left):

		Br
H₃C—CH₂—CO₂H	H₃C—CH₂—CH₂OH	H₃C—CH-CO₂H
X	**Y**	**Z**

A) X > Z > Y   B) Y > X > Z   C) Z > X > Y   D) Z > Y > X   E) X > Y > Z
Ans: C

3. What would be the **major** organic product of the following reaction?

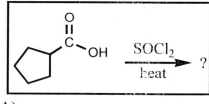

A)

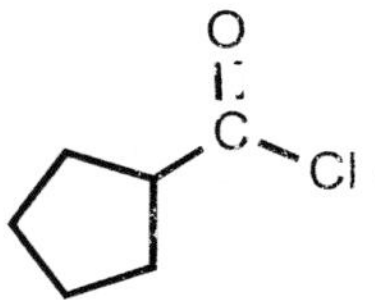

B)

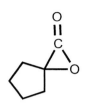

C)

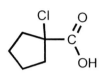

D)

E)

Ans: A

4. The reaction of propanoic acid with lithium aluminum hydride, followed by water, would result in what product?

A)

$$H_3C-CH_2-\overset{\overset{\displaystyle O}{\|}}{C}-H$$

B) $H_3C-CH_2-CO_2Li$

C) $H_3C-CH_2-CH_2Li$

D) $H_3C-CH_2-CH_2OH$

E) $H_3C-CH_2-CH_3$

Ans: D

5. What would the **common** name of the following di-acid be?

$$HO_2C-CH_2-CH_2-CO_2H$$

A)   Malonic acid
B)   Oxalic acid
C)   Succinic acid

D)   Adipic acid
E)   Glutaric acid

Ans: C

6. Which of the following sets of reagents would convert benzyl bromide to phenylethanoic acid?

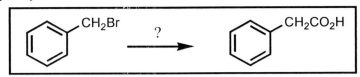

A)
$$\xrightarrow[\text{H}_2\text{O}]{\text{H}_2\text{CrO}_4}$$

B)
1. Mg, ether
$$\longrightarrow$$
2. CO$_2$
3. H$_3$O$^+$

C)
$$\xrightarrow{\text{HCO}_2^- \text{ K}^+}$$

D)
1. NaCN
$$\longrightarrow$$
2. H$^+$, H$_2$O, heat

E)   both B and D

Ans: E

7. The higher acidity of carboxylic acids compared to other functional groups is **best** explained by
A)   hydrogen bonding.   D)   resonance.
B)   electronegativity of oxygen.   E)   electronegativity of carbon.
C)   water solubility.

Ans: D

8. What would be the name of the following?

$$\boxed{\text{HO}_2\text{CCH}_2\text{CO}_2\text{H}}$$

A)   Malonic acid   D)   Succinic acid
B)   Propanoic acid   E)   Butanedioic acid
C)   Oxalic acid

Ans: A

9. What would be the organic product of the following reaction?

$$HO_2CCH_2CH_2CO_2H \xrightarrow{\text{heat}} ?$$

A) $CH_3CH_2CO_2H$ + CO_2

B)   2 CH_3CO_2H

C)

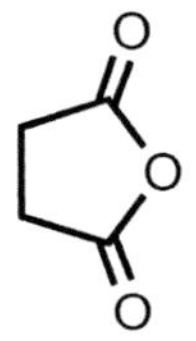

D)

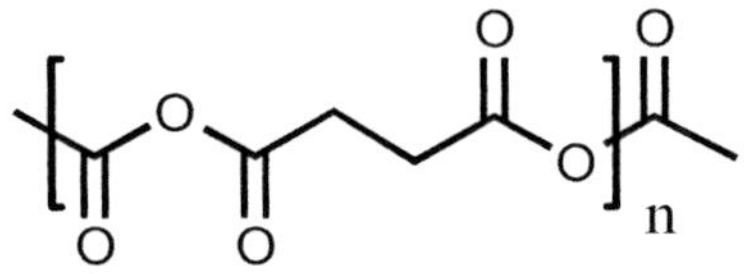

(a polymeric anhydride)

E)   none of these

Ans: C

10. What reagent(s) would accomplish the following conversion?

$$CH_3CH_2CO_2H \xrightarrow{\quad ? \quad} CH_3CHBrCO_2H$$

A) Br_2 B) PBr_3 C) Br_2/light   D) Br_2 + cat. PBr_3 E) PBr_3 + cat. Br_2

Ans: D

11. Which of the following sets of reagents would accomplish the chemical transformation shown?

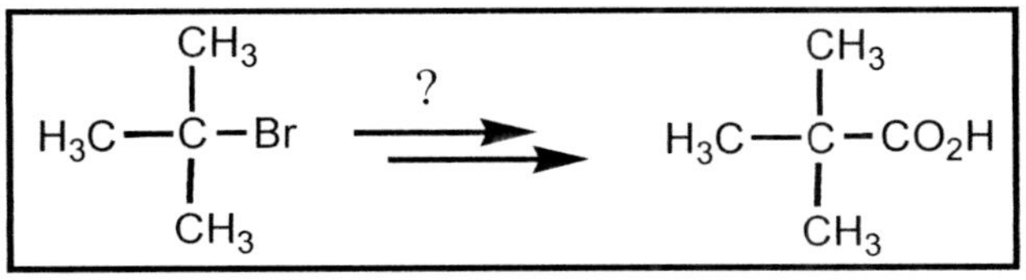

A)

   1. NaCN

   2. H_3O^+, heat

B)
> 1. Mg, ether
>
> 2. CO_2
>
> 3. H_3O^+

C)
> 1. KOH, heat
>
> 2. O_3
>
> 3. H_2O_2, H^+

D)
> 1. HCO_2H, H^+
>
> 2. $LiAlH_4$
>
> 3. H_3O^+

E)
> 1. HCN, NaCN
>
> 2. KOH, H_2O, heat
>
> 3. H_3O^+

Ans: B

12. Several 2-arylpropanoic acids are used as analgesics (painkillers). Three of these [Ibuprofen (= Advil), Naproxen (= Aleve) and Ketoprofen (= Orudis KT)] are currently available in over-the-counter form. Which of the following sets of reagents would accomplish conversion of an ethyl aromatic to a 2-arylpropanoic acid?

$$ArCH_2CH_3 \xrightarrow{\quad ? \quad} CH_3-\underset{\underset{Ar}{|}}{CH}-CO_2H \qquad (Ar = \text{aryl group})$$

A)
> 1. Br_2, light
>
> 2. NaCN
>
> 3. H_3O^+, ?

B)

    1. Br$_2$, light

    2. Mg, ether

    3. CO$_2$

    4. H$_3$O$^+$

C)

    1. Br$_2$, light

    2. KOH

    3. O$_3$

    3. H$_2$O$_2$, H$^+$

D)

    1. Br$_2$, light

    2. CH$_3$CO$_2^-$ K$^+$

    3. H$_3$O$^+$

E)   both A and B

Ans: E

13. What would be the product of the following reaction?

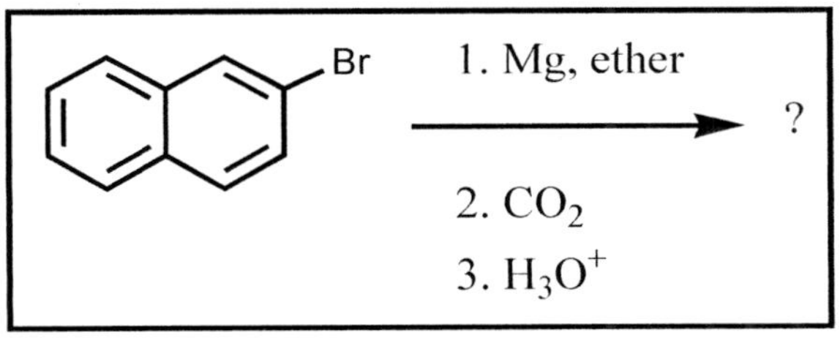

A)

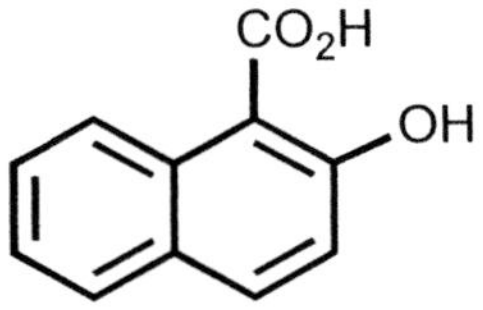

B)

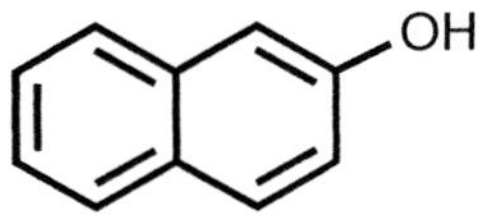

C)

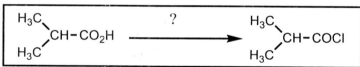

(naphthalene-2-carboxylic acid structure with CO₂H)

D)

(structure: naphthalen-2-yl acetate)

E)   none of these

Ans: C

14. Which would be the strongest acid of the following?
    A) $BrCH_2CH_2CO_2H$ D) CF_3CO_2H
    B) $ClCH_2CH_2CO_2H$ E) $CH_3CHClCOCl$
    C) $CH_3CHClCO_2H$
    Ans: D

15. What best accounts for the unusually high boiling points of carboxylic acids relative to other organic compounds of similar molecular weight?
    A)   The relatively large concentration of oxygen atoms.
    B)   The presence of intramolecular hydrogen bonding.
    C)   Carboxylic acids are mostly ionized and thus are mostly ionic compounds.
    D)   The presence of intermolecular hydrogen bonding.
    E)   Carboxylic acids do **not** have unusually high boiling points.
    Ans: D

16. What reagent is needed to complete the reaction shown?

(reaction scheme: $(CH_3)_2CH-CO_2H \xrightarrow{?} (CH_3)_2CH-COCl$)

A) CH_3Cl B) PCl_3 C) Cl_2 D) $LiAlH_4$ E) none of these
Ans: B

17. What **major** product would result from the following reaction?

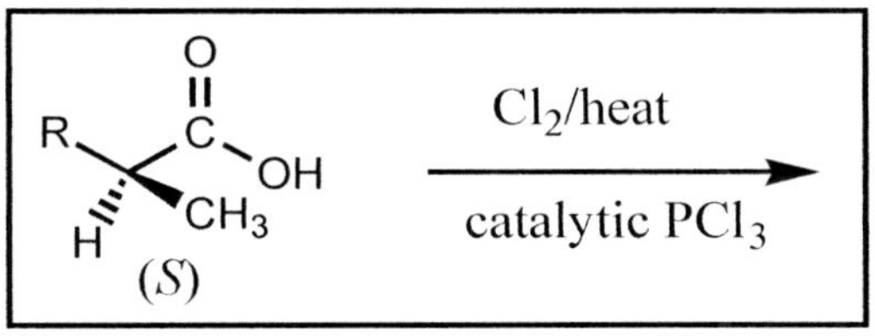

R—C(H)(CH₃)—COOH (S) $\xrightarrow[\text{catalytic PCl}_3]{\text{Cl}_2/\text{heat}}$

A)

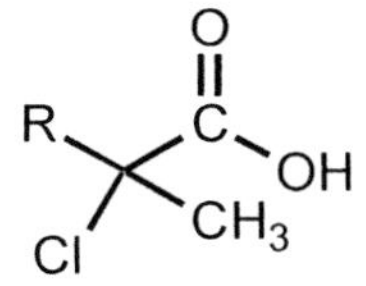

racemic

B)

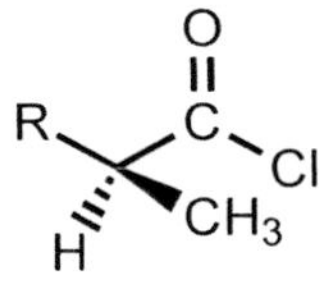

(S)

C)

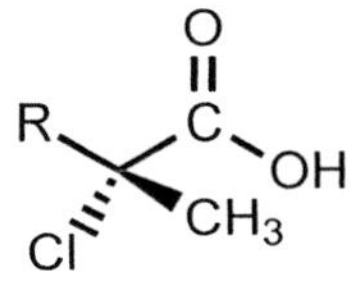

(R)

D)

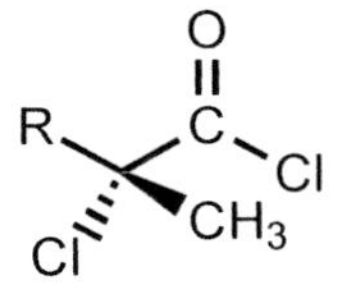

(R)

E)

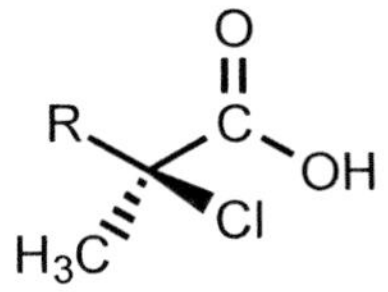

(S)

Ans: A

18. What reagent(s) is (are) needed to complete the reaction shown?

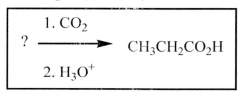

A) CH_3CH_2Br D) CH_3Li
B) $KMnO_4/ ^-OH$ E) CH_3COCl
C) CH_3CH_2MgBr
Ans: C

19. Which, if any, of the reactions below would produce 2-methylpropanoic acid?

A)
$\rangle-MgBr + CO_2$ followed by H_3O^+

B)
$\rangle-Br + KCN$ followed by H_3O^+ and heat

C)
$\rangle-CH_2OH + H_2CrO_4$

D) All of these reactions would produce the desired product.
E) None of these reactions would produce the desired product.
Ans: D

20. Which, if any, functional group in the molecule below would undergo basic hydrolysis most easily?

A) A   B) B   C) C   D) D   E) None of these groups would react.
Ans: C

21. What reagent(s) would accomplish the following?

$R-\overset{O}{\overset{||}{C}}-OH \longrightarrow R-\overset{O}{\overset{||}{C}}-Cl$

A) Cl_2, light   B) Cl_2, H_2O C) $SOCL_2$ D) $MgCl_2$ E) aqueous HCl
Ans: C

22. Which functional group has the lowest IR absorption frequency?

A) $R-\overset{O}{\overset{||}{C}}-H$ B) $R-\overset{O}{\overset{||}{C}}-R$ C) $R-\overset{O}{\overset{||}{C}}-OR$ D) $R-\overset{O}{\overset{||}{C}}-NR_2$ E) $R-C\equiv N$
Ans: D

23. Rank the following in order of decreasing acidity (more acidic > less acidic):

ROH	RCO$_2$H	RNH$_2$	$R-\overset{\overset{O}{\parallel}}{\underset{\underset{O}{\parallel}}{S}}-OH$	R$_3$C-H
I	II	III	IV	V

A)   II > III > I > IV > V
B)   IV > II > I > III > V
C)   II > IV > I > III > V

D)   V > III > I > II > IV
E)   II > IV > I > V > III

Ans: B

24. Rank the following benzoic acids in order of decreasing acidity:

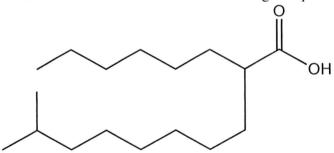

A) III > I > II   B) I > III > II   C) II > I > III   D) I > II > III   E) III > II > I
Ans: C

25. Carboxylic acids have unusually high boiling points because:
A)   they are significantly heavier than organic molecules with the same molecular weight.
B)   they repel each other in the gas phase.
C)   they strongly attract each other in the liquid phase.
D)   they are usually solids, and solids are not volatile.
E)   they exist mostly as ions (RCO$_2$- + H$^+$) and ionic materials are not volatile.
Ans: C

26. What is the IUPAC name of the following compound?

A)   2-hexyl-9-methyldecanoic acid
B)   2-isononyloctanoic acid
C)   1-methyl-9-carboxypentadecane

D)   2-hexyldecanoic acid
E)   14-methyl-7-carboxypentadecane

Ans: A

27. In the carboxylic acid dimer (below), which bond(s) has a strength of about 6-8 kcal/mol?

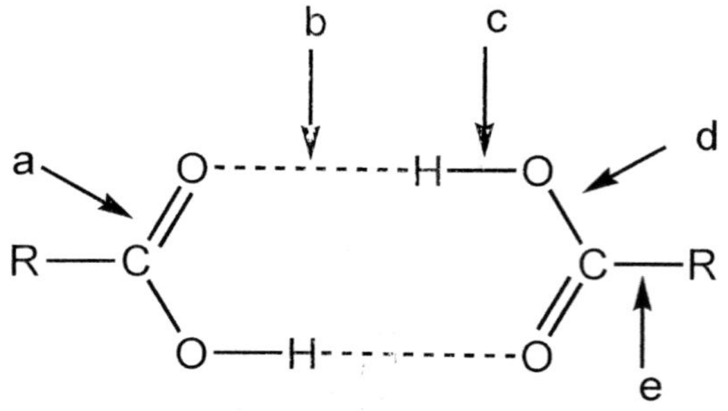

A) Bond a   B) Bond b   C) Bond c   D) Bond d   E) Bond e
Ans: B

28. Which compound best fits the following spectroscopic data?
^{1}H NMR δ = 1.00 (t, J=7.4 Hz, 3H); 1.65 (sextet, J=7.5 Hz, 2H); 2.31 (t, J=7.4 Hz, 2H); and 11.68 (s, 1H) ppm. ^{13}C NMR δ = 13.4, 18.5, 36.3, 179.6 ppm.

A)

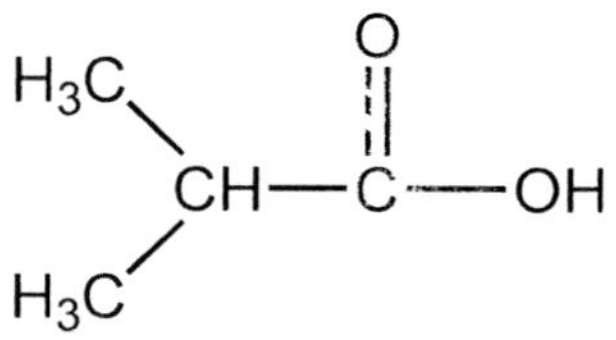

B)

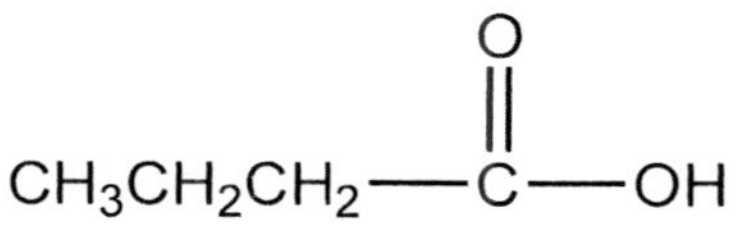

C)

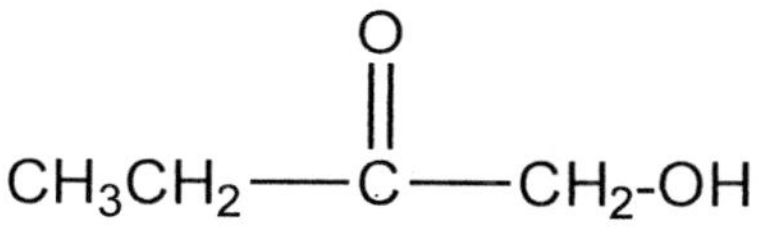

D)

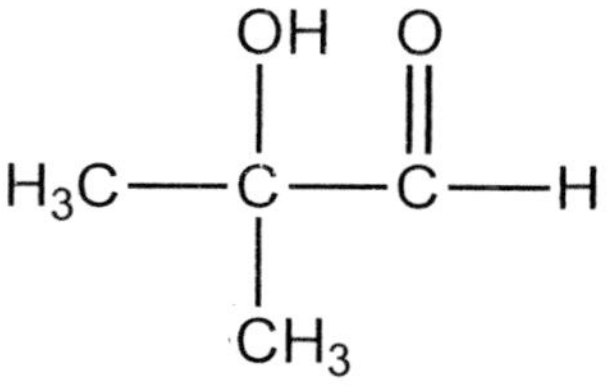

E)   none of the above
Ans: B

29. Which of the following intermediates are not involved in the acid catalyzed esterification reaction of a carboxylic acid?

A)

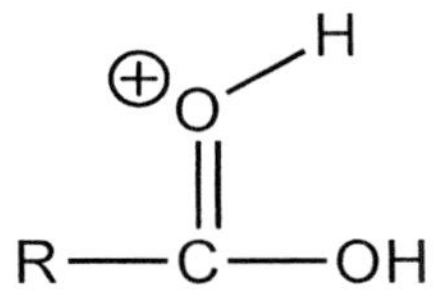

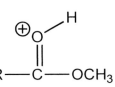

B)

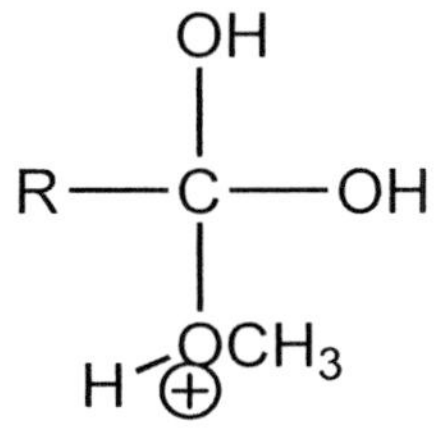

C)

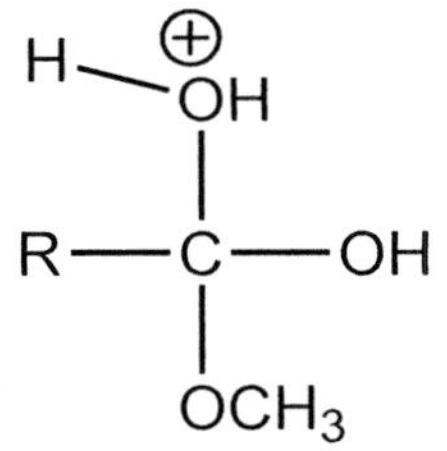

D)

E)   All of the above are intermediates.

Ans: E

Chapter 20: Carboxylic Acid Derivatives

1. Rank the following carboxylic acid derivatives in order of **decreasing** reactivity toward hydrolysis (most reactive on left):

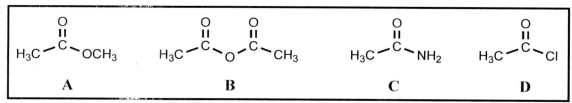

A   B   C   D

A)   D > B > A > C   D)   A > B > D > C
B)   C > A > B > D   E)   D > B > C > A
C)   B > D > A > C

Ans: A

2. Which of the following is **not** an intermediate in the Hofmann rearrangement of ethanamide to methylamine?

$$H_3C-\overset{\overset{\displaystyle O}{\|}}{C}-NH_2 \quad \xrightarrow[\substack{NaOH \\ H_2O}]{Br_2} \quad CH_3-NH_2$$

A)

$$H_3C-\overset{\overset{\displaystyle O}{\|}}{C}-\overset{\ominus}{NH}$$

B) $H_3C-N=C=O$

C)

$$\overset{\ominus}{H_2C}-\overset{\overset{\displaystyle O}{\|}}{C}-NH_2$$

D)

$$\underset{H}{\overset{H_3C}{\diagdown}}N-\overset{\overset{\displaystyle O}{\|}}{C}-OH$$

E)

$$H_3C-\overset{\overset{\displaystyle O}{\|}}{C}-NHBr$$

Ans: C

3. In the reaction shown below, which product(s) would be formed?

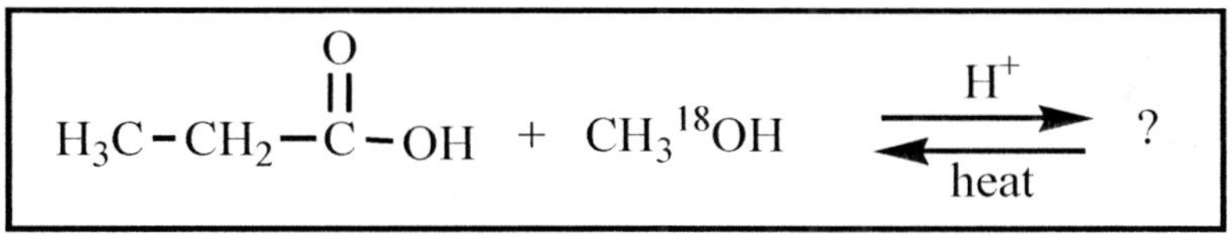

$$H_3C-CH_2-\overset{\overset{\text{O}}{\|}}{C}-OH \quad + \quad CH_3{}^{18}OH \quad \underset{\text{heat}}{\overset{H^+}{\rightleftharpoons}} \quad ?$$

A)

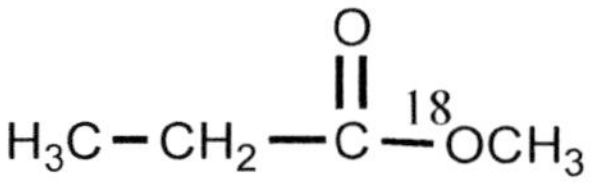

$$H_3C-CH_2-\overset{\overset{\text{O}}{\|}}{C}\overset{18}{-}OCH_3$$

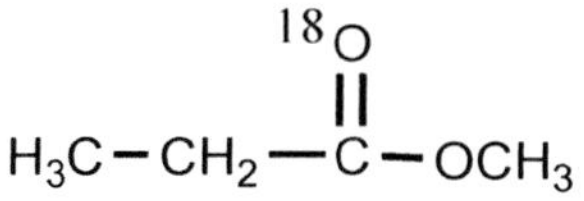

B)

$$H_3C-CH_2-\overset{\overset{{}^{18}\text{O}}{\|}}{C}-OCH_3$$

C)

$$H_3C-CH_2-\overset{\overset{{}^{18}\text{O}}{\|}}{C}\overset{18}{-}OCH_3$$

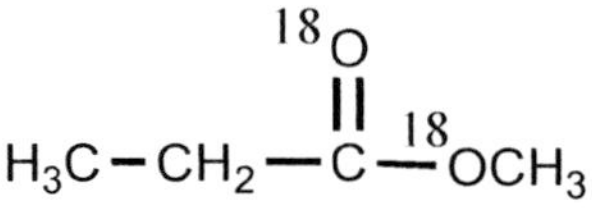

D)

$$H_3C-CH_2-\overset{\overset{{}^{16}\text{O}}{\|}}{C}\overset{16}{-}OH$$

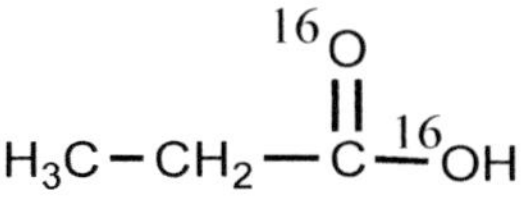

E)   both A and B

Ans: A

4. Which of the following would be properly named as 2-chloroethyl benzoate?

A)

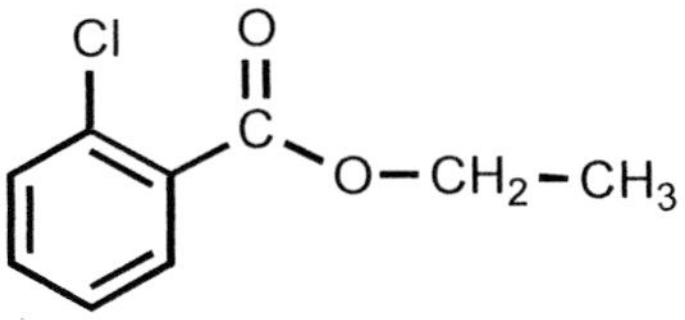

B)

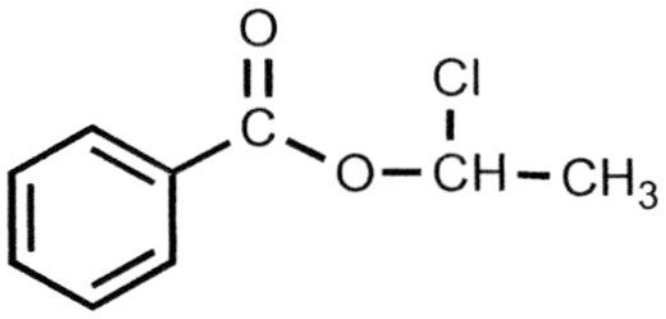

C)

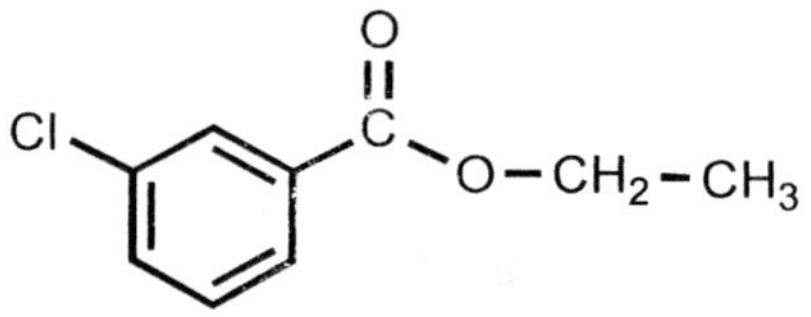

D)

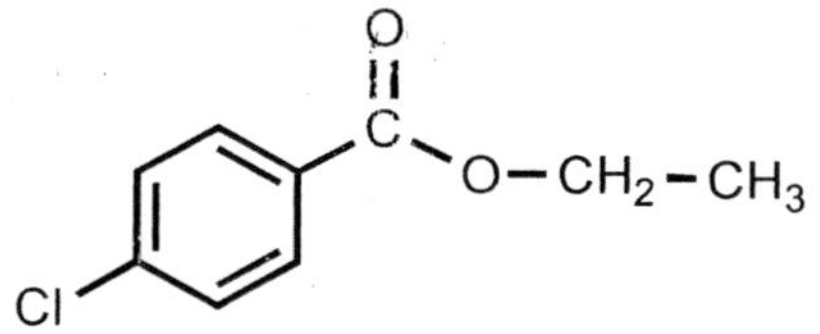

E)

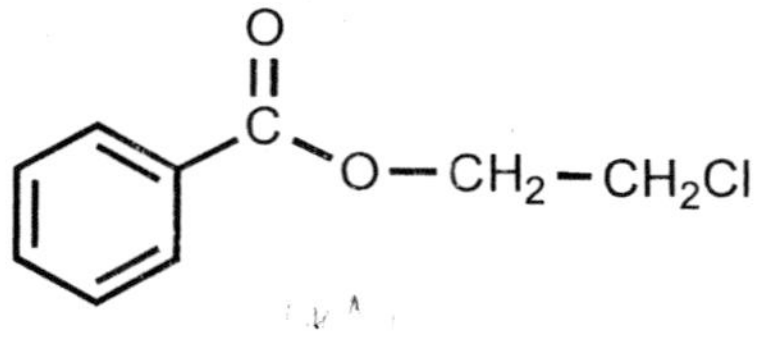

Ans: E

5. Which reagent(s) would accomplish the following transformation?

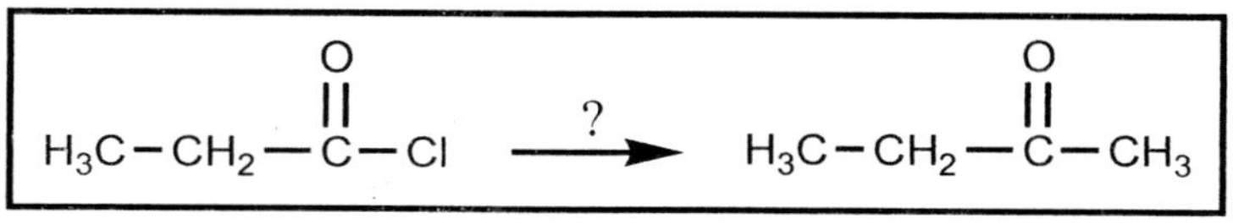

A) CH_3Li B) CH_3I, NaOH   C) CH_3MgBr D) $(CH_3)_2CuLi$ E) either A or C
Ans: D

6. How many different CH_3 signals would you expect in the room-temperature proton NMR spectrum of the molecule below?

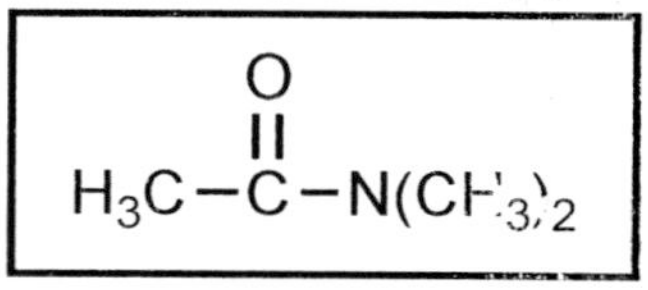

A) One   B) Two   C) Three   D) Four   E) Five
Ans: C

7. What would be the name of the following cyclic ester?

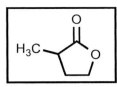

A) γ-valerolactone
B) β-butyrolactone
C) 2-methyl-γ-butyrolactone

D) 2-methyl-β-butyrolactone
E) 2-methyl-γ-valerolactone

Ans: C

8. What would account for the fact that the molecule below racemizes easily, despite having three chiral centers?

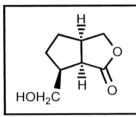

A) Lactones are configurationally unstable
B) Molecule loses CO_2 easily
C) Enolization occurs easily
D) Intramolecular transesterification occurs easily
E) This molecule is not chiral.

Ans: D

9. What would be the major organic product of the following reaction?

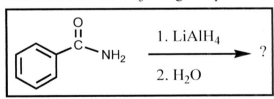

A)

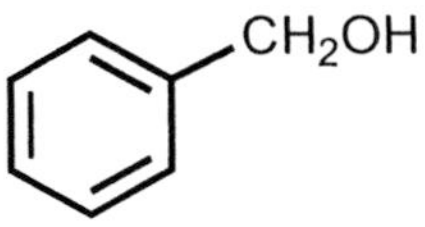

CH₂OH

B)

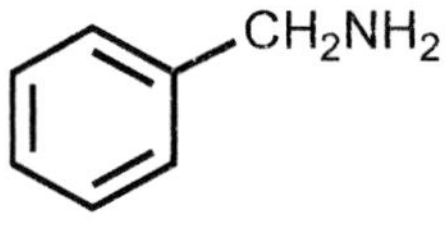

CH₂NH₂

C)

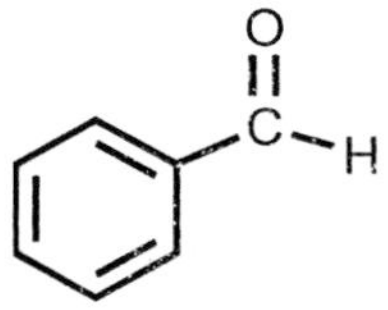

O
‖
C–H

D)

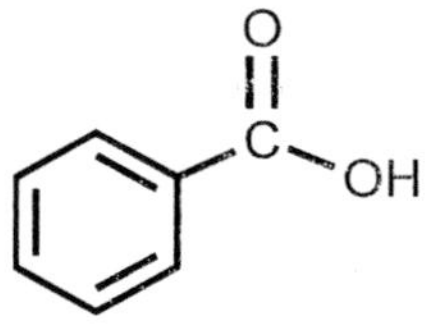

O
‖
C–OH

E)

CH₃

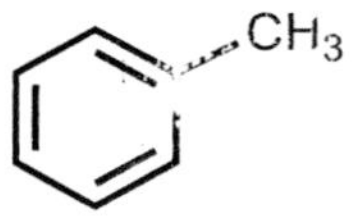

Ans: B

10. What type of functional group do the natural products known as **waxes** have?
    A) Ester   B) Amide   C) Carboxylic acid   D) Alcohol   E) Amine
    Ans: A

11. What would be the **major** organic product expected from the following reaction?

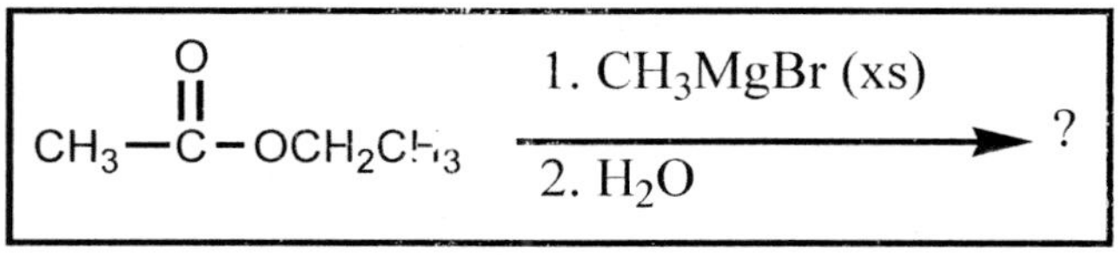

$$CH_3-\overset{O}{\underset{\|}{C}}-OCH_2CH_3 \xrightarrow[\text{2. } H_2O]{\text{1. } CH_3MgBr \text{ (xs)}} ?$$

A)

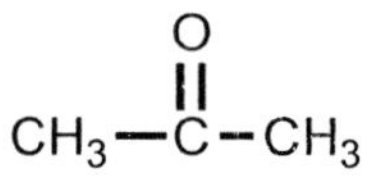

$$CH_3-\overset{O}{\underset{\|}{C}}-CH_3$$

B)

$$CH_3-\overset{OH}{\underset{\underset{CH_3}{|}}{C}}-CH_2CH_3$$

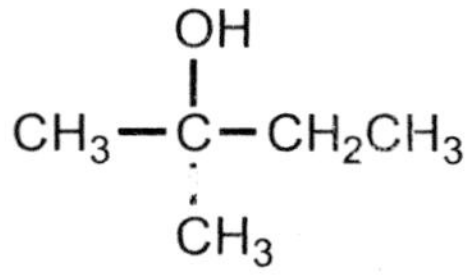

C)

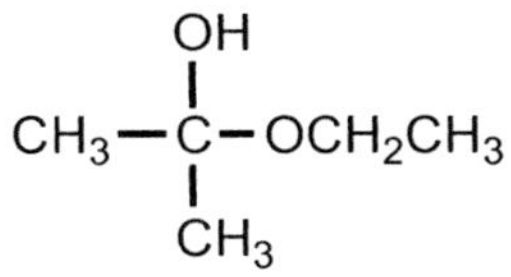

OH
|
CH₃—C—OCH₂CH₃
|
CH₃

D)

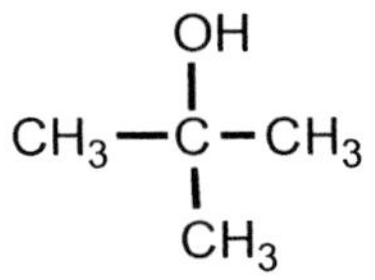

OH
|
CH₃—C—CH₃
|
CH₃

E)

OH
|
CH₃—C—CH₂CH₃
|
CH₂CH₃

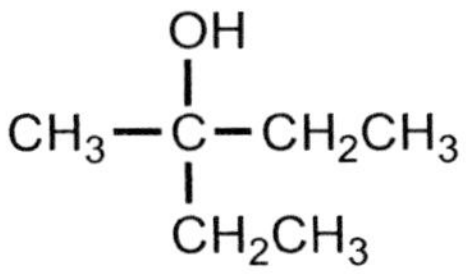

Ans: D

12. What would be the product of the following reaction?

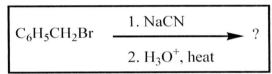

A) $C_6H_5CO_2H$ D) $C_6H_5CH_2CH_2NH_2$
B) $C_6H_5CH_2CO_2H$ E) $C_6H_5CH_3$
C) $C_6H_5CH_2OH$
Ans: B

13. What would be the proper name of the following?

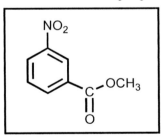

A)   3-nitro-methylbenzoate   D)   5-nitro-methylbenzoate
B)   methyl 3-nitrobenzoate   E)   3-nitrocarboxymethylbenzene
C)   3-nitro-methoxybenzoate
Ans: B

14. What would be the organic product of the following reaction?

$$(CH_3)_2CHCOCl \quad + \quad (CH_3)_2CuLi \quad \longrightarrow \quad \xrightarrow{H_2O} \quad ?$$

A)

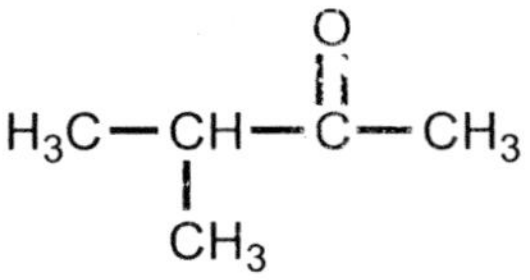

H₃C—CH—C—CH₃ with O double bond on C and CH₃ below CH

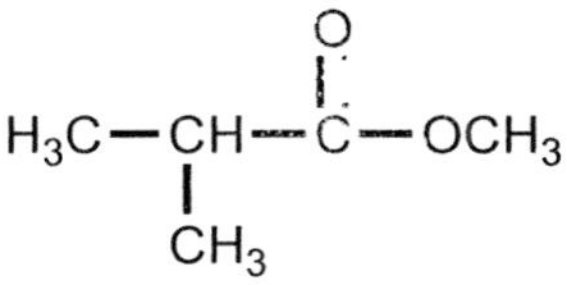

$$H_3C-CH(CH_3)-\overset{\overset{\displaystyle O}{\|}}{C}-CH_3$$

B)

$$H_3C-CH(CH_3)-\overset{\overset{\displaystyle O}{\|}}{C}-OCH_3$$

C)

$$H_3C-CH(CH_3)-\overset{\overset{\displaystyle OH}{|}}{\underset{\underset{\displaystyle CH_3}{|}}{C}}-CH_3$$

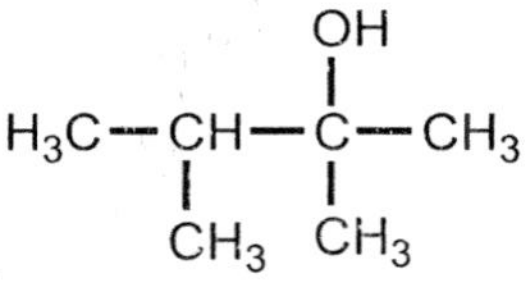

D)

$$H_3C-CH(CH_3)-\overset{\overset{\displaystyle OCH_3}{|}}{\underset{\underset{\displaystyle CH_3}{|}}{C}}-CH_3$$

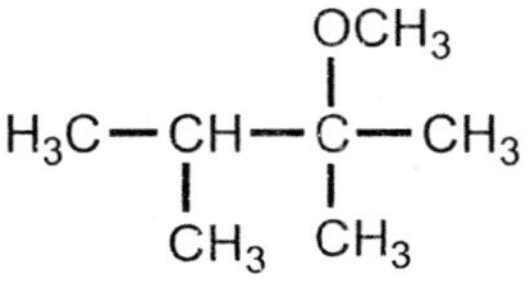

E)   none of these

Ans: A

15. Lactones are:
    A)   Cyclic amides
    B)   Cyclic anhydrides
    C)   Cyclic esters
    D)   Cyclic acids
    E)   Cyclic ketones

Ans: C

16. What would be the organic product of the following reaction? (^{18}O is a rare oxygen isotope.)

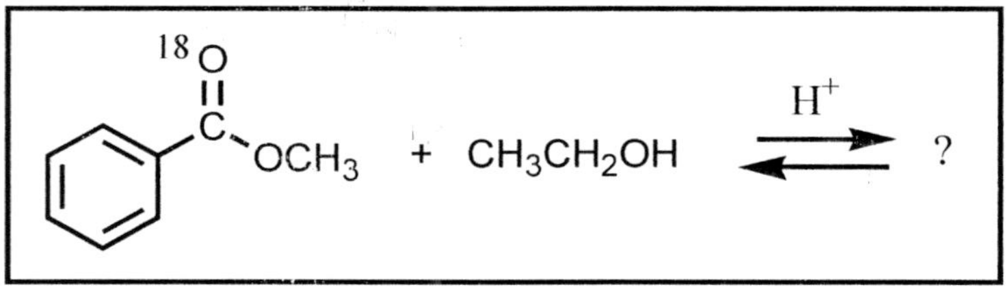

$$\text{Ph}-\overset{\overset{\displaystyle ^{18}O}{\|}}{C}-OCH_3 \quad + \quad CH_3CH_2OH \quad \underset{\longleftarrow}{\overset{H^+}{\longrightarrow}} \quad ?$$

A)

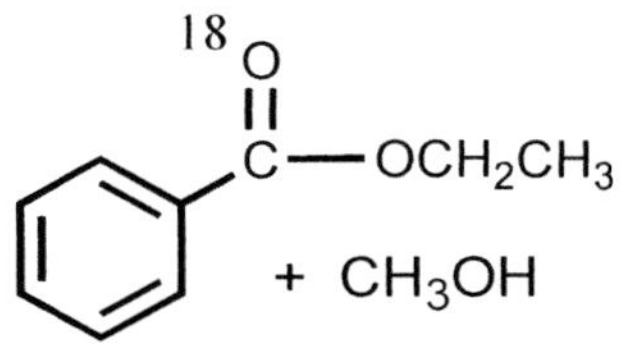

18 O
‖
C—OCH₂CH₃

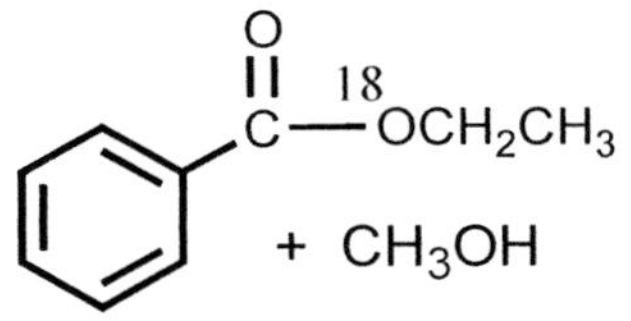

+ CH₃OH

B)

O
‖   18
C—OCH₂CH₃

+ CH₃OH

C)

O
‖
C—OCH₂CH₃

            18
+ CH₃—OH

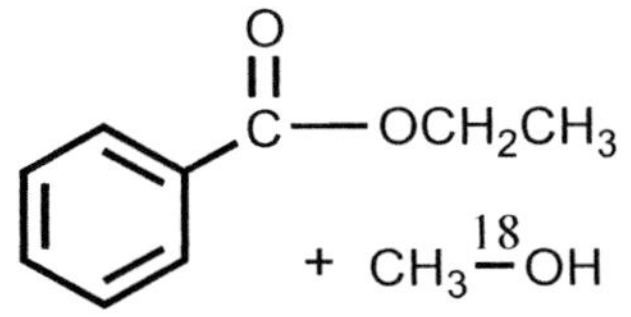

D)   more than one of these
E)   none of these
Ans: A

17. What would be the organic product of the following reaction?

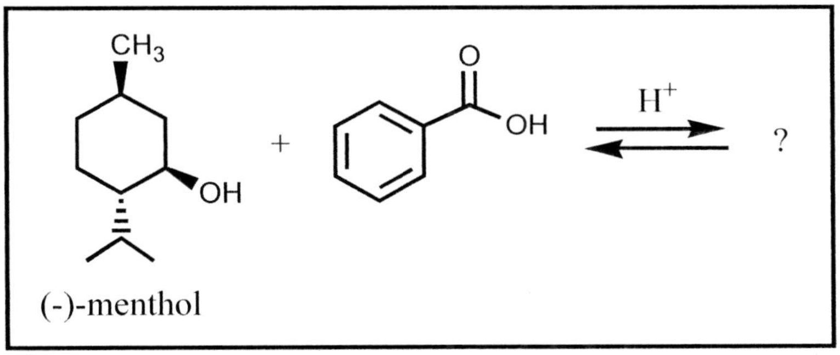

CH₃ ... OH (–)-menthol + benzoic acid (with C=O and OH) $\xrightarrow{H^+}$?

(–)-menthol

A)

CH₃ ... (menthyl benzoate structure)

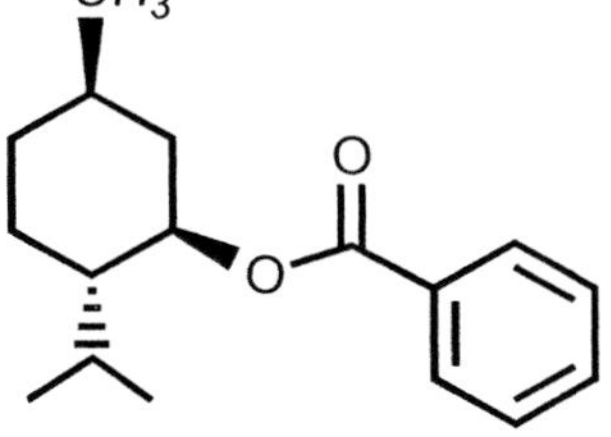

B)

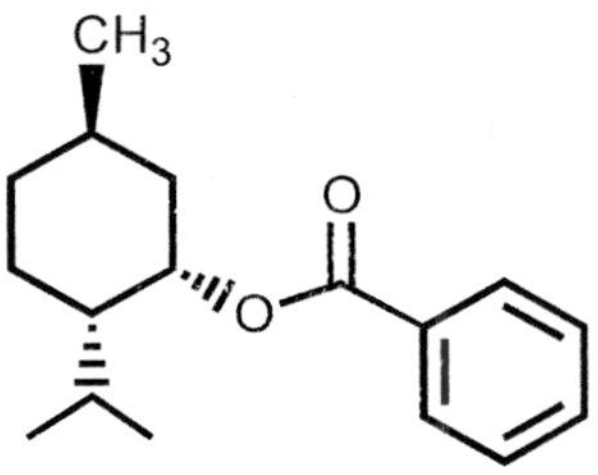

C)   mixture of A and B
D)   none of these
E)   no reaction occurs
Ans: A

18. Which of the reactions listed below would produce benzyl acetate (= benzyl ethanoate)?
    A)

$$C_6H_5CH_2OH \xrightarrow[\text{(CH}_3\text{CO)}_2\text{O}]{\text{pyridine}}$$

    B)

$$C_6H_5CH_2OH \xrightarrow[\text{H}^+, -\text{H}_2\text{O}]{\text{CH}_3\text{CO}_2\text{H}}$$

    C)

$$C_6H_5CH_2OH \xrightarrow[\text{pyridine}]{\text{CH}_3\text{COCl}}$$

    D)   two of these
    E)   all of these
    Ans: E

19. The product of the following reaction would be:

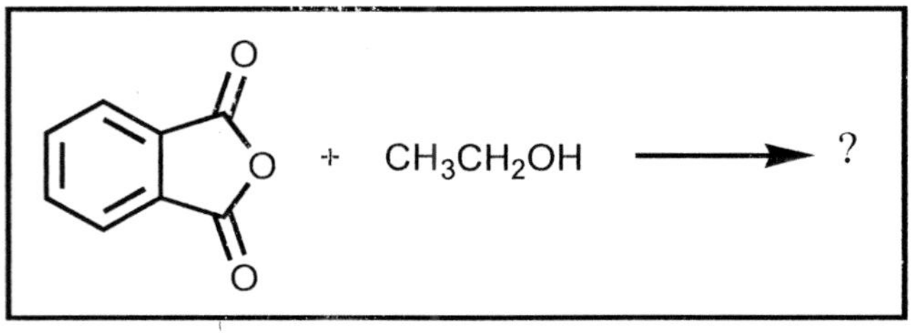

A)

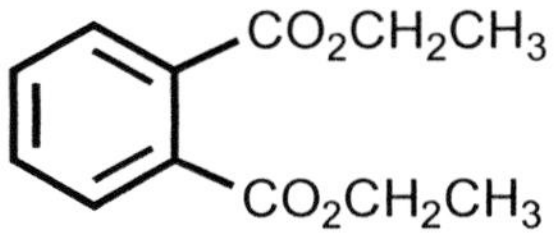

B)

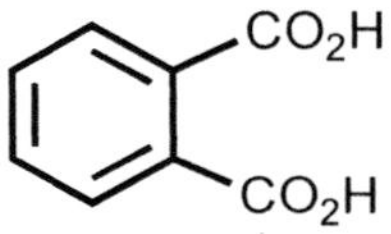

C)

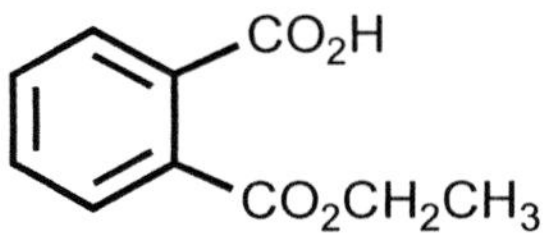

D)

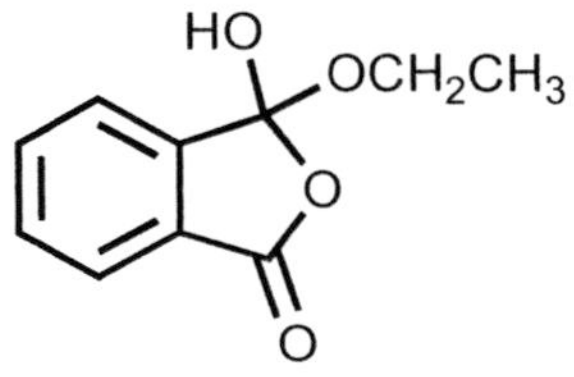

E)

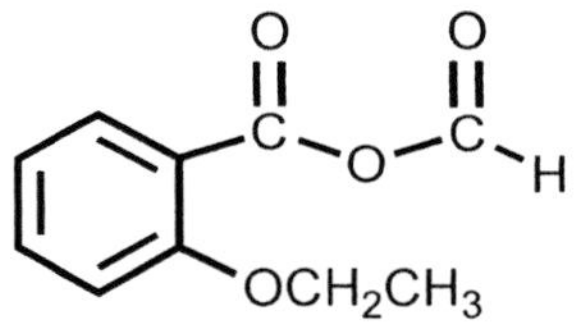

Ans: C

20. What would be the **major** expected product from the reaction shown below?

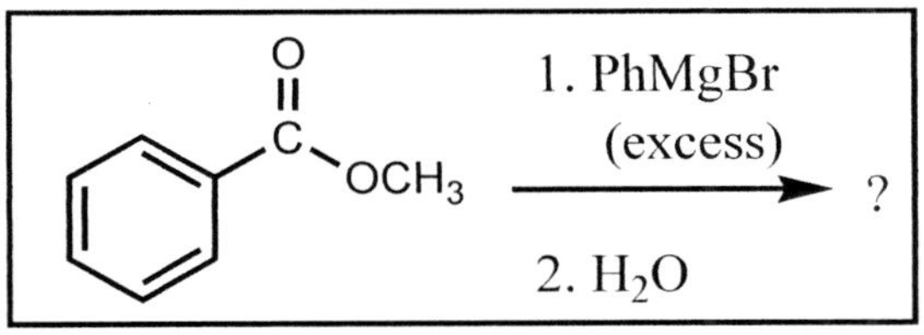

A)

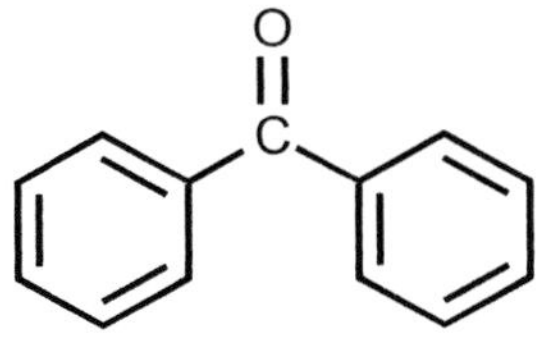

B)

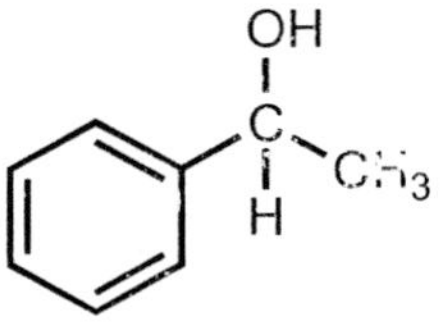

C)

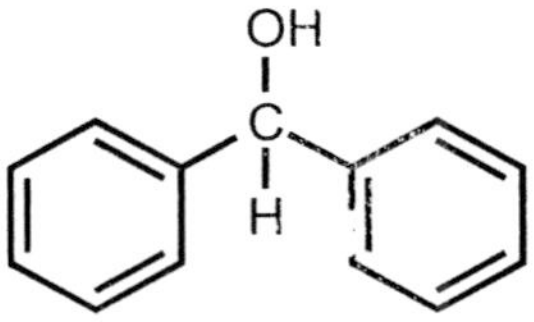

D)

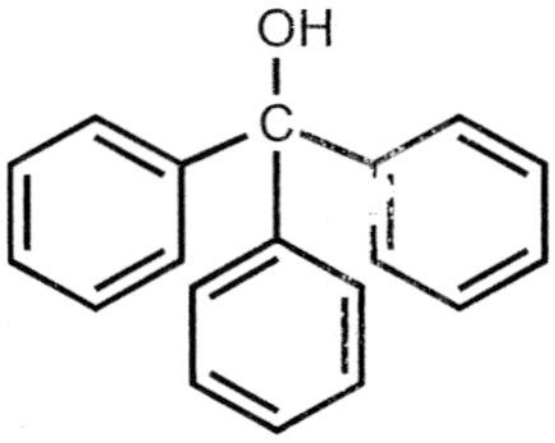

E)

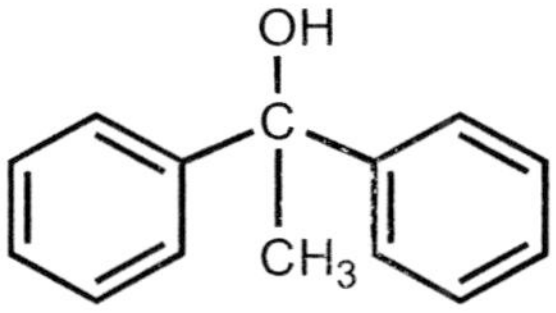

Ans: D

21. Substitutions at sp^2 carbons do not occur by an S_N2 mechanism, but rather by way of a "tetrahedral intermediate." The tetrahedral intermediate shown could occur in which reaction?

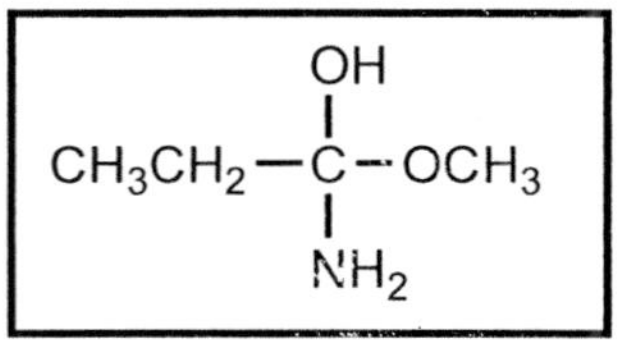

A)   methyl propanoate + ammonia   D)   propanamide + ethanol
B)   propanamide + hydroxide   E)   none of these
C)   propanoic acid + methanol
Ans: A

22. What would be the product of the following reaction?

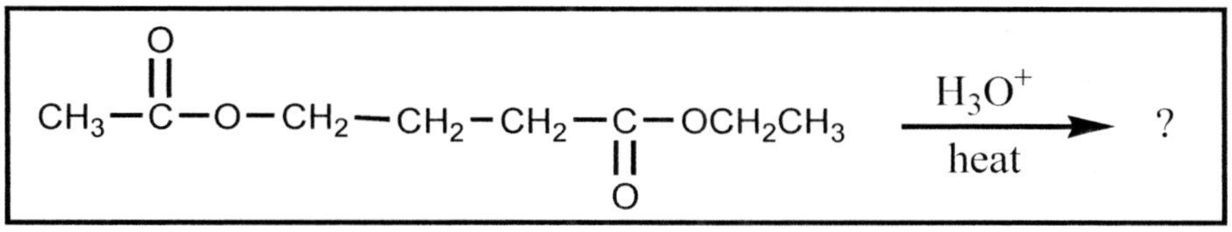

A)

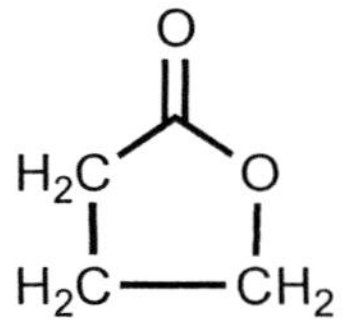

$+ \ CH_3CO_2H \ + \ CH_3CH_2OH$

B)

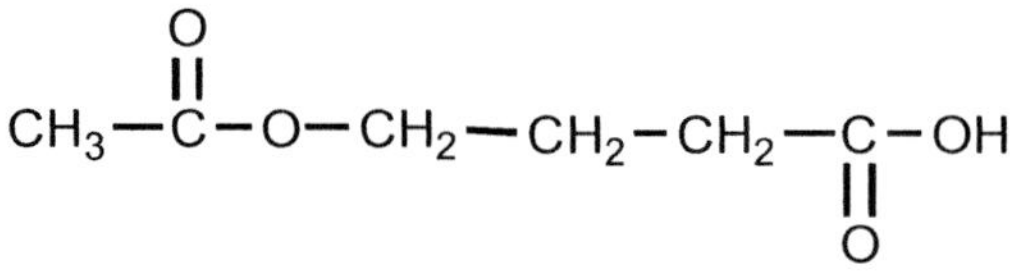

$+ \ CH_3CH_2OH$

C)

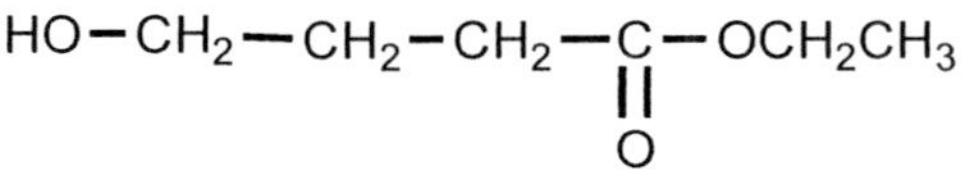

$+ \ CH_3CO_2H$

D)

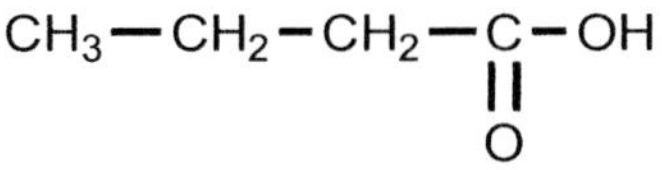

$+ \ CH_3CO_2H \ + \ CH_3CH_2OH$

E)   none of these

Ans: A

23. A multistep preparation of propylpropanoate from **only** 1-propanol would require the use of how many of the reagents below (i.e., what reagents would you need to use if you only had 1-propanol to start with)?

$$CH_3CH_2CO_2CH_2CH_2CH_3$$

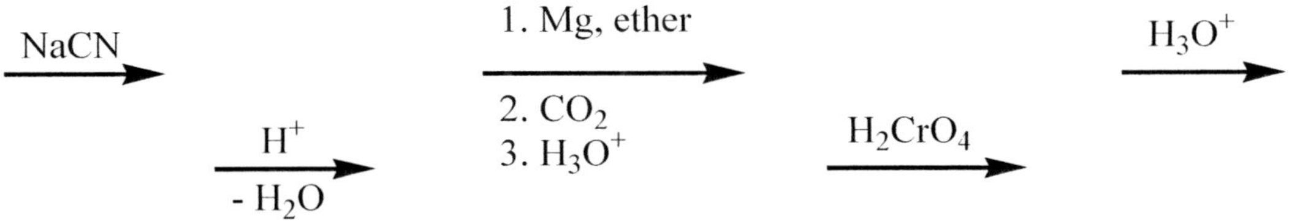

A)   two of the above
B)   three of the above
C)   four of the above
D)   all of the above
E)   cannot be done with only these reagents

Ans: A

24. What would be the products of the following reaction?

$$CH_3CH_2CH_2CO_2CH_3 + CH_3NH_2 \rightleftharpoons \quad ?$$

   A) $CH_3CH_2CH_2CH_2NH(CH_3) + H_2O$
   B) $CH_3NHC(=O)CH_2CH_2CH_3 + CH_3OH$
   C) $CH_3CH_2CH_2CONH_2 + CH_3CH_2OH$
   D) $CH_3OH + CH_3CH_2CH_2OC(=O)NHCH_3$
   E) $CH_3CH_2CH_2NH(CH_3)COCH_3 + H_2O$
   Ans: B

25. How can the importance of the following resonance be evaluated?

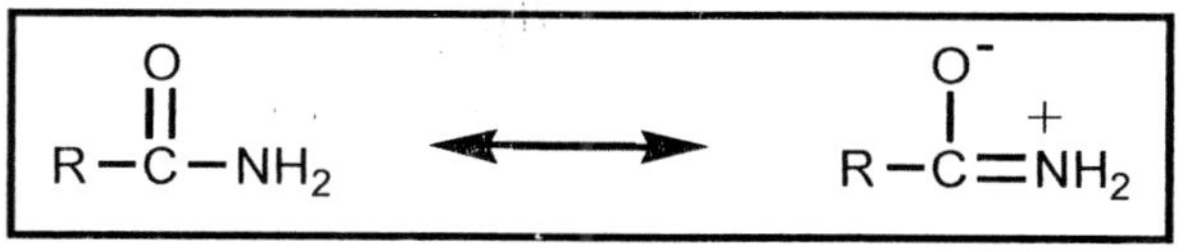

   A)   Charged resonance structures are always more important.
   B)   The C=O IR stretch for amides is significantly different than for other C=O groups.
   C)   The water solubility of amides implicates charged structures.
   D)   The C-N rotational barrier can be determined by NMR.
   E)   More than one of the above are correct.
   Ans: E

26. What is the relative reactivity of carboxylic acid derivatives toward hydrolysis (left = least reactive)?
   A)   ester < amide < acid chloride < anhydride
   B)   amide < ester < acid chloride < anhydride
   C)   ester < amide < anhydride < acid chloride
   D)   amide < ester < anhydride < acid chloride
   E)   The relative reactivities really cannot be compared.
   Ans: D

27. When compound X is heated with aqueous acid, acetic acid and acetaldehyde (ethanal) are formed. The proton NMR spectrum of X is shown below. What is the structure of X?

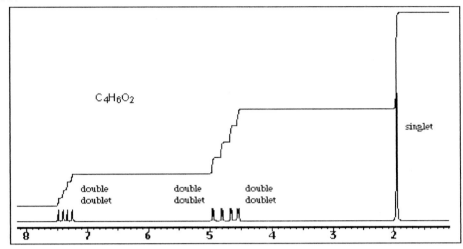

C$_4$H$_6$O$_2$

singlet

double doublet   double doublet   double doublet

A)   CH$_2$=CHO$_2$CCH$_3$ D)   CH$_3$CH=CHO$_2$CH
B)   CH$_2$=CHOCH$_2$CH$_3$ E)   CH$_2$=CHCH$_2$CO$_2$H
C)   CH$_2$=C(CH$_3$)O$_2$CH

Ans: A

28. What would be the other product of the following reaction?

$$C_6H_5CO_2CH_2CH_3 \quad \xrightarrow[\text{2. } H_3O^+]{\text{1. } CH_3MgBr} \quad ? \quad + \quad HOCH_2CH_3$$

A)

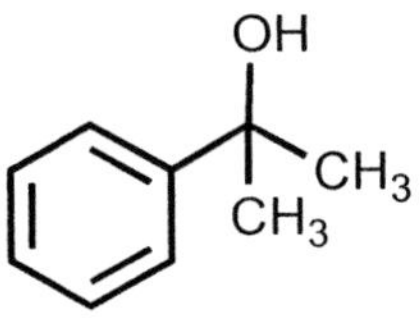

    OH
    |
Ph—C—CH$_3$
    |
   CH$_3$

B)

    O
    ‖
Ph—C—CH$_3$

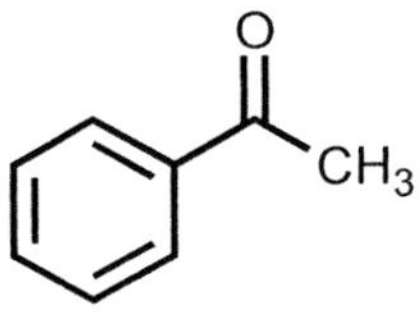

C)

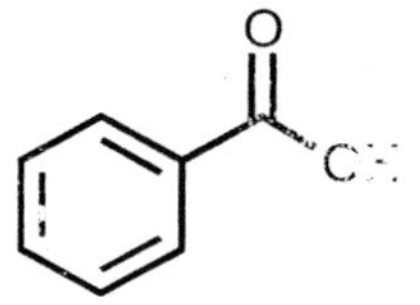

D)

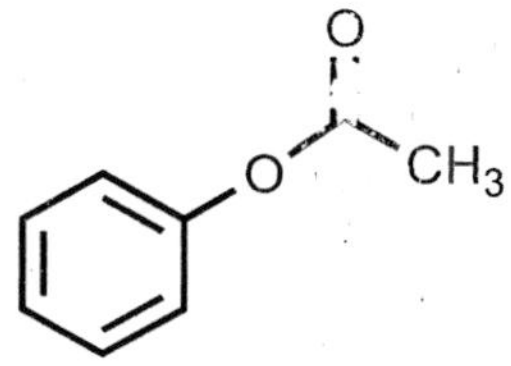

E)

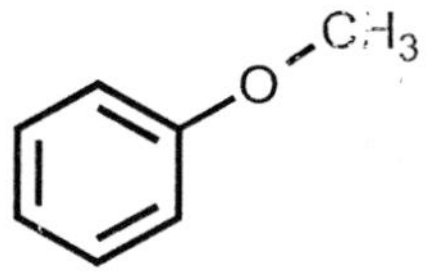

Ans: A

29. Which of the following has the **highest** IR absorption frequency for the C=O group?

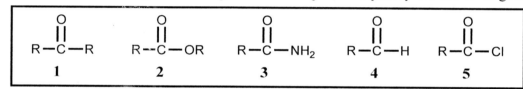

A) 1   B) 2   C) 3   D) 4   E) 5
Ans: E

30. 4-Hydroxybutanoic acid spontaneously cyclizes to give what compound?
A)

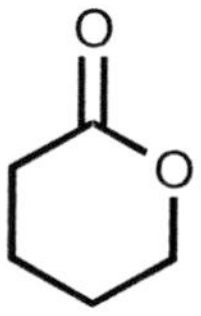

B)

C)

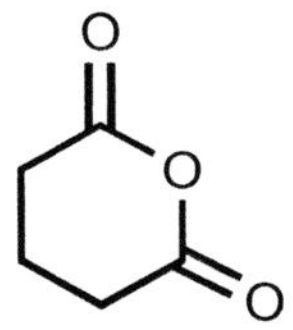

D)

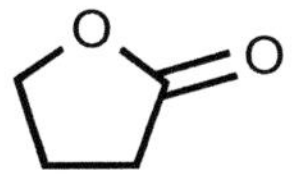

E)

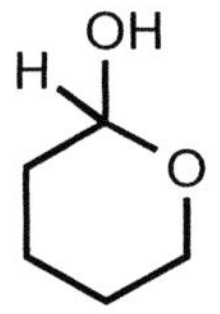

Ans: D

31. Reduction of which of the following esters with lithium aluminum hydride would yield **two** molecules of the **same** alcohol?

A)

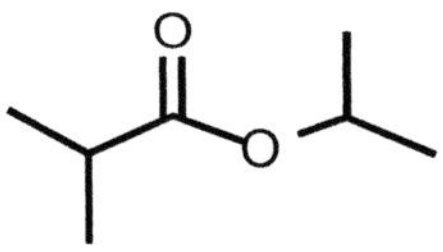

B)

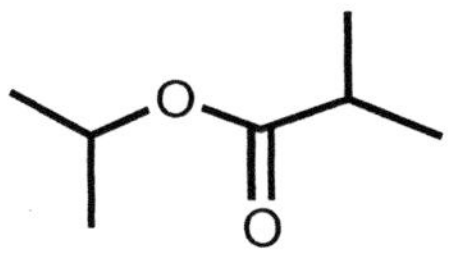

C)

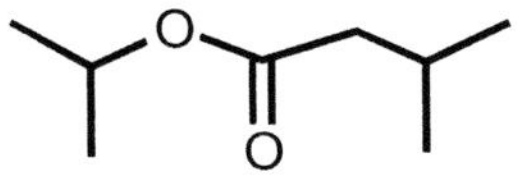

D)

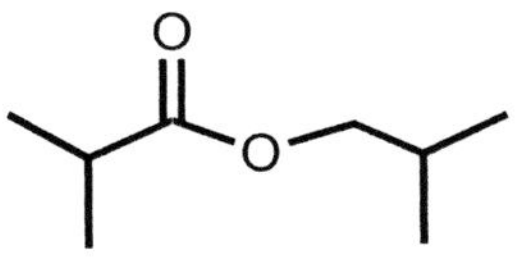

E)   none of these

Ans: D

32. What reagent(s) would be required to achieve the following conversion?

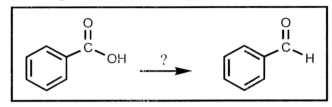

A)
> 1. SOCl$_2$, ?
> 2. LiAl(O^{t}Bu)$_3$H

B)
> 1. NaBH$_4$
> 2. H$_2$CrO$_4$

C)
> 1. LiAlH$_4$
> 2. H$_2$O
> 3. PCC

D)
> 1. Br$_2$, cat. P
> 2. H$_2$O

E)   both A and C

Ans: E

33. Which of the following would be most likely to result from saponification of a natural triglyceride?

triglyceride $\xrightarrow[\text{H}_2\text{O}]{\text{NaOH}}$?

A)

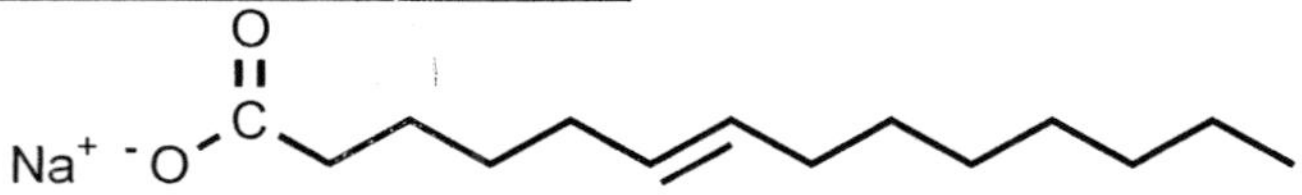

Na$^+$ $^-$O

B)

Na$^+$ $^-$O

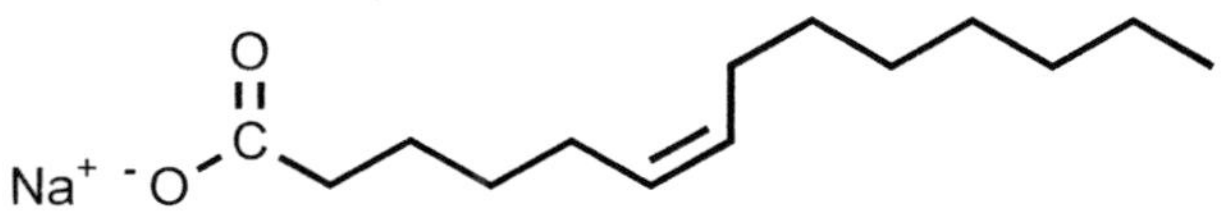

C)

D)

E)

Ans: B

34. What is the major reason that vegetable oils are partially hydrogenated commercially?
    A)   To increase their melting point and shelf life
    B)   To decrease their flammability in deep-frying situations
    C)   To improve the flavor and color
    D)   To make them more digestible and healthy
    E)   To improve their odor
    Ans: A

35. Place the following compounds in order of increasing rate of hydrolysis:

    A)   I, III, IV, II
    B)   IV, II, III, I
    C)   III, I, II, IV
    D)   I, II, IV, III
    E)   All carboxylic derivatives exhibit similar reactivies with H_2O.
    Ans: B

36. What is the product of combining pentanoic acid with thionyl chloride, followed by propanol and base?
    A)   pentanol   D)   1-tosyl pentanol
    B)   pentyl propanoate   E)   1-chloropentanol
    C)   propyl pentanoate
    Ans: C

37. Predict the product of the following reaction:

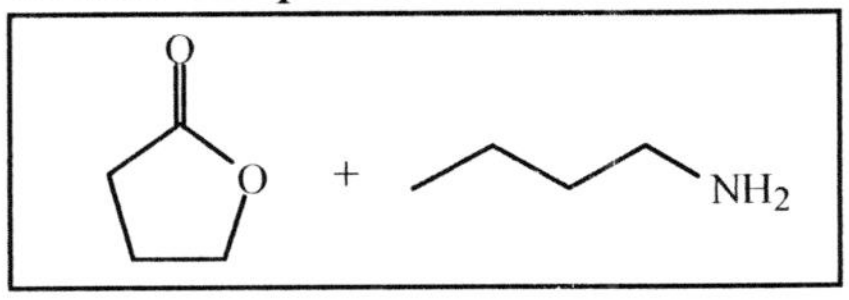

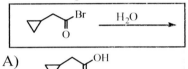

A)

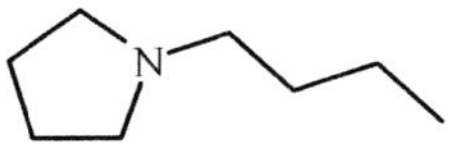

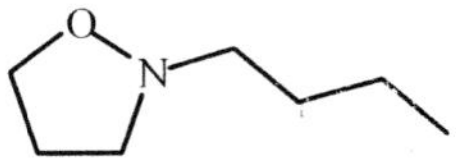

D)

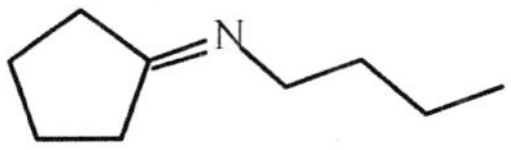

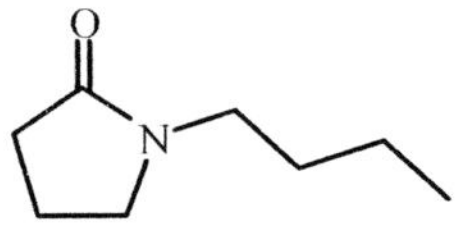

B)

E)   none of these

C)

Ans: E

38. Predict the product of the following reaction:

A)

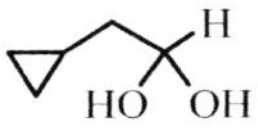

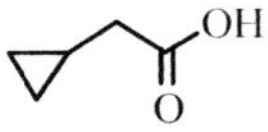

D)

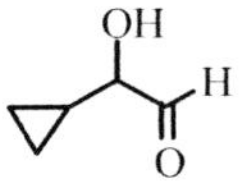

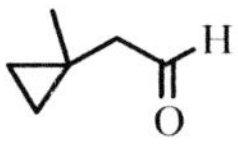

B)

E)   no reaction occurs

C)

Ans: A

39. Which of the following is a lactam?
A)

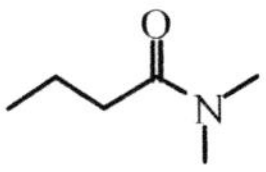

B)

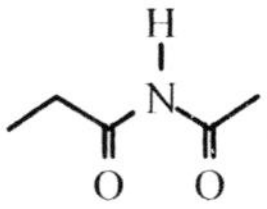

C)

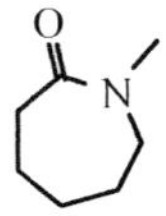

D)

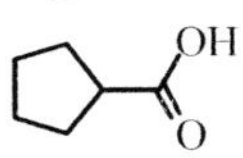

E)   Two of these can be considered lactams.
Ans: C

40. Predict the product of the following reaction:

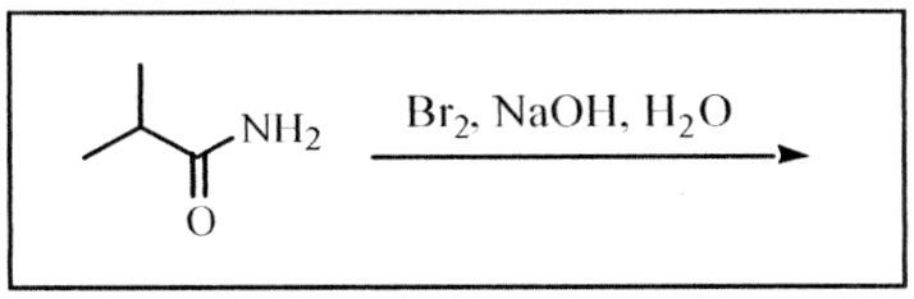

A)

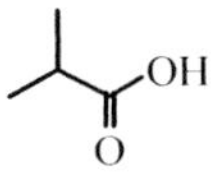

B)

C)

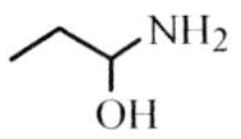

D)

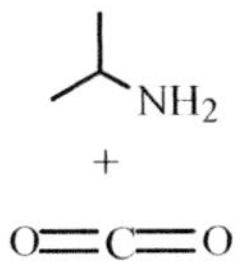

+

$O=C=O$

E)

Ans: D

41. What structure is **not** an intermediate in the following reaction?

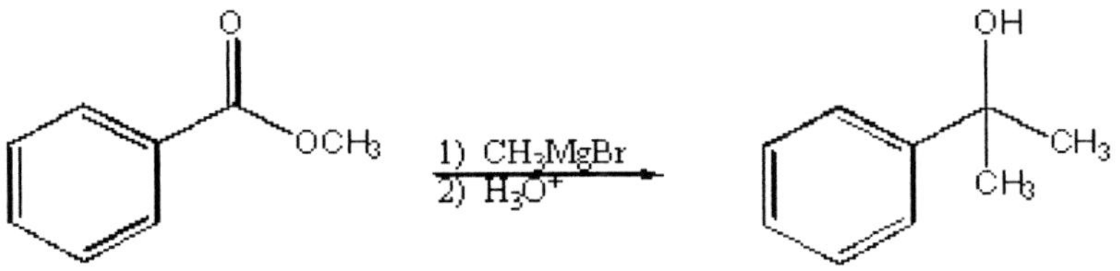

A)

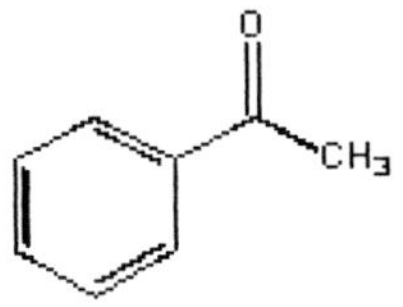

B)

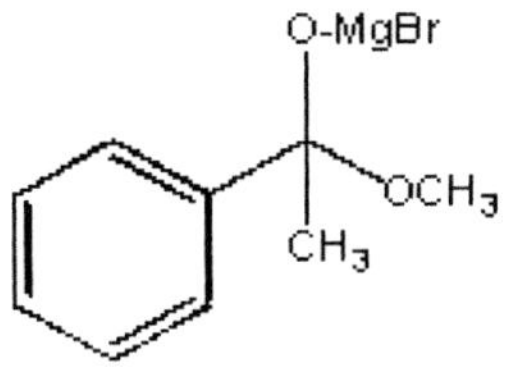

C)

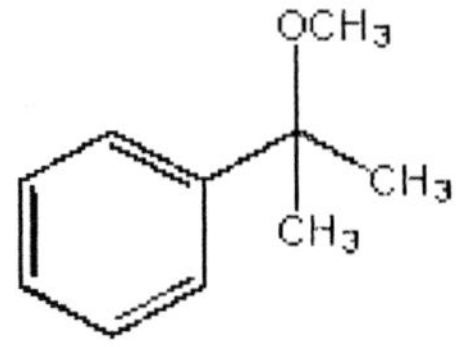

D)

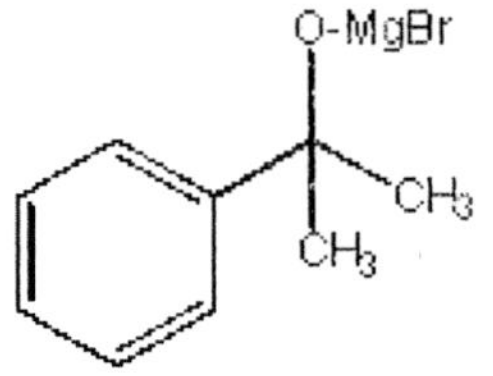

E)   none of the above
Ans: C

42. Which of the following reactions will produce N-methyl benzamide?
    A)

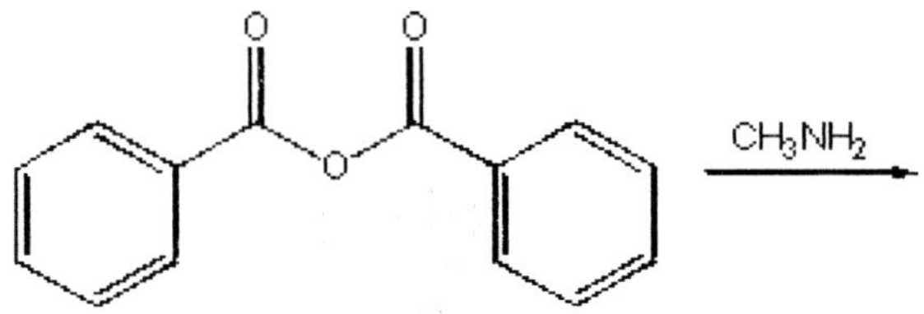

    B)

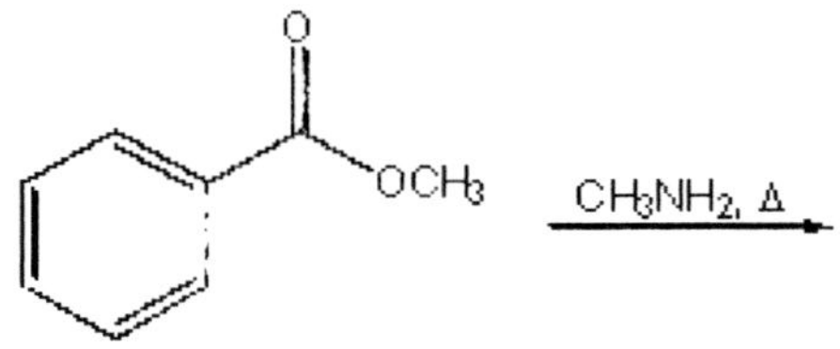

    C)

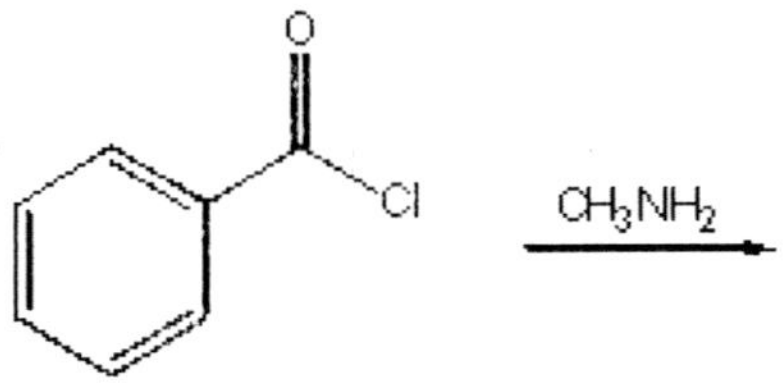

    D)   both A and C
    E)   all of the above
    Ans: E

43. Which of the following reactions will **not** give a carboxylic acid as a product?

A)

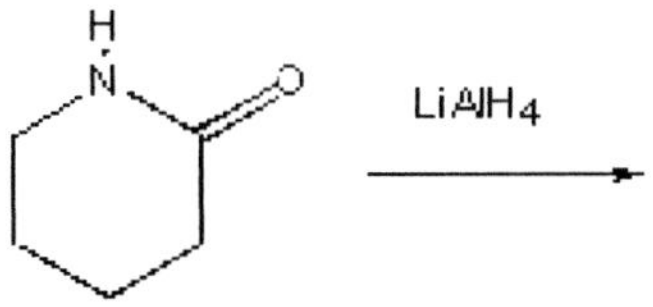
LiAlH4

B)

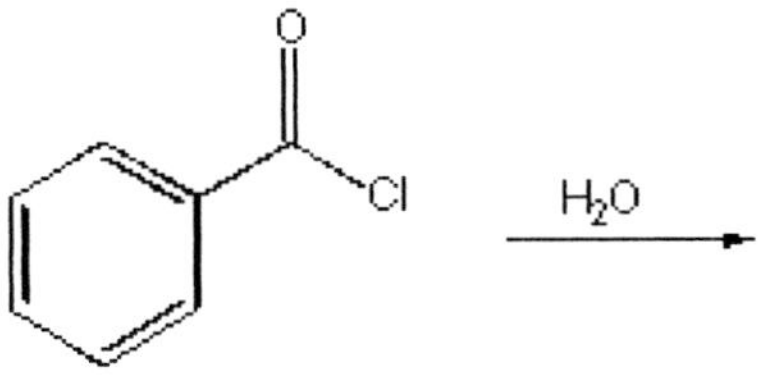
Cl
H2O

C)

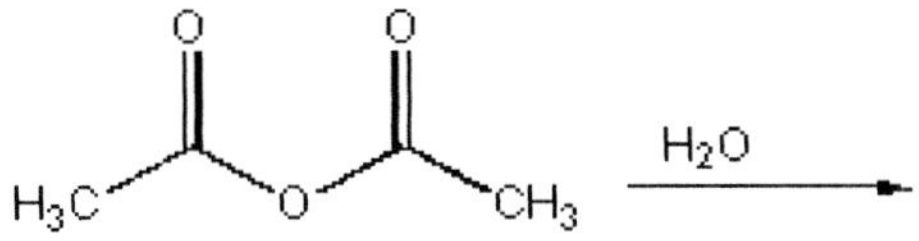
H3C
CH3
H2O

D)

$CH_3\text{-}CN \xrightarrow{H^+,\ H_2O}$

E)

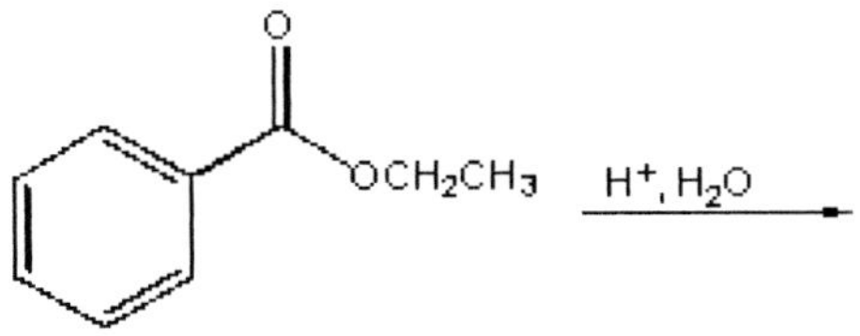
OCH2CH3
H+, H2O

Ans: A

44. What is the product from the following reaction?

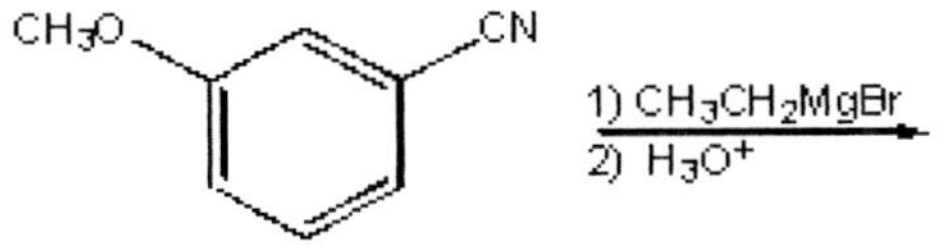
CH3O
CN
1) CH3CH2MgBr
2) H3O+

A)

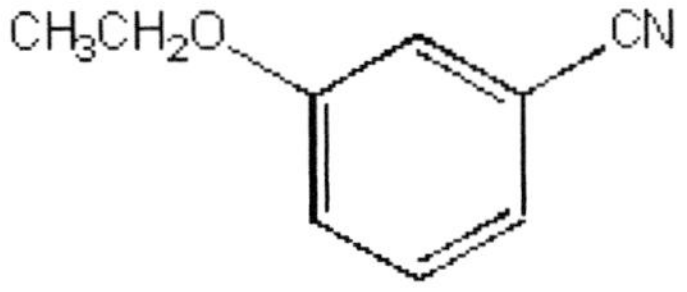
CH3CH2O
CN

B)

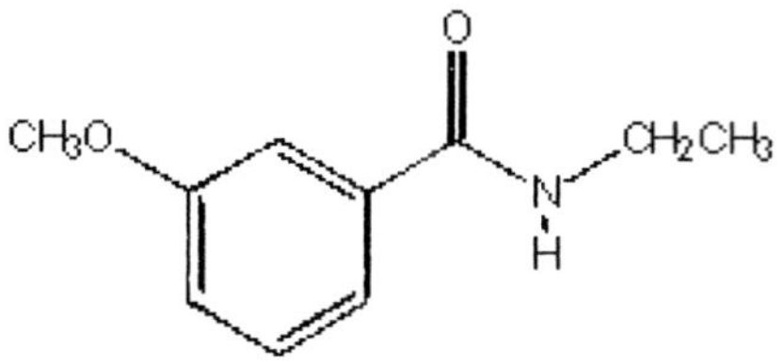

C)

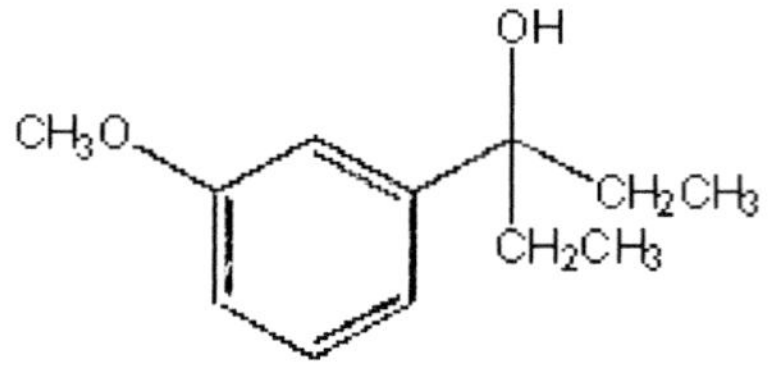

D)

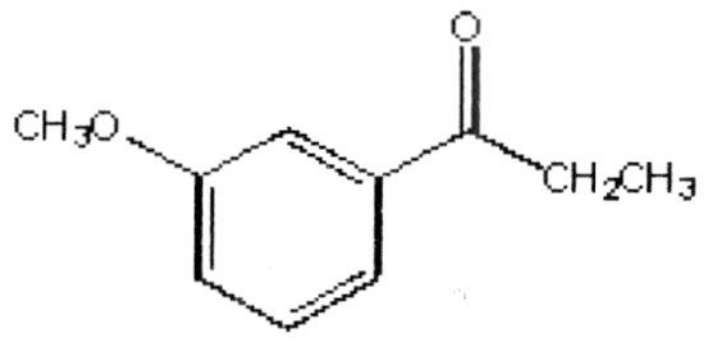

E)

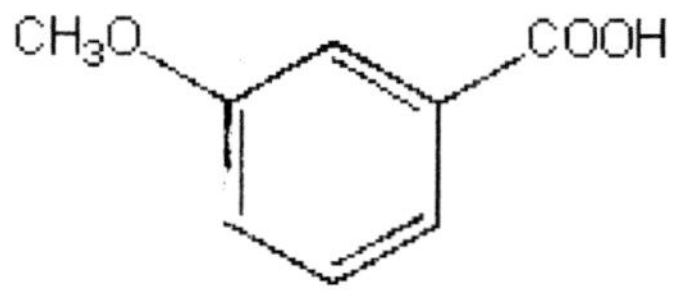

Ans: D

45. What reagent is needed to complete the reaction shown?

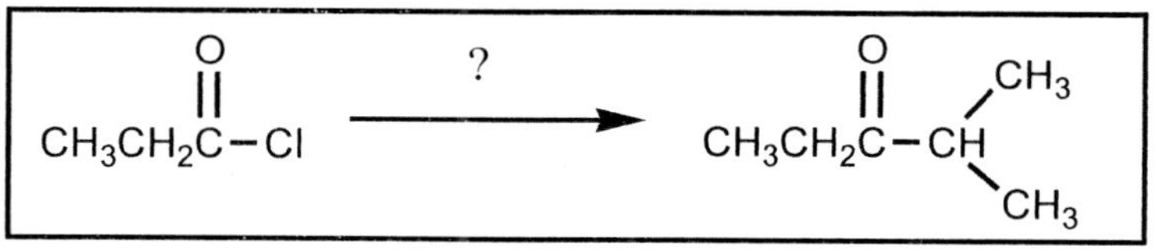

A) $((CH_3)_2CH)_2CuLi$ D) $BrMgCH(CH_3)_2$
B)   KCN/NaOH   E) $(CH_3)_2CHLi$
C) $HOCH(CH_3)_2$
Ans: A

Chapter 21: Amines and Their Derivatives: Functional Groups Containing Nitrogen

1. Rank the following in order of **decreasing** basicity (most basic on left):

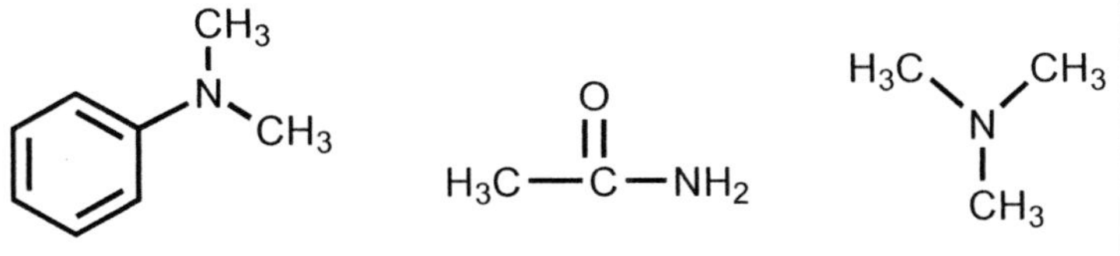

X   Y   Z

A) Z > X > Y   B) Y > X > Z   C) Z > Y > X   D) X > Z > Y   E) X > Y > Z
Ans: A

2. Which of the following sets of reagents would accomplish the reaction shown below?

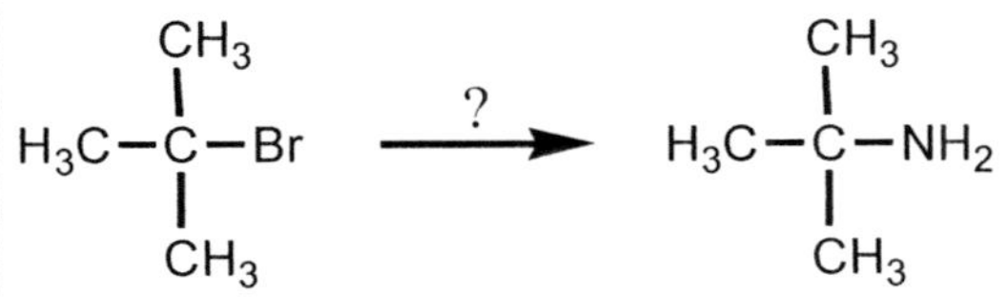

A)

     1. $Na^+ N_3^-$
     2. $LiAlH_4$
     3. H_2O

B)

     1. $Na^+ {}^-CN$
     2. $LiAlH_4$
     3. H_2O

C)

     NH_3

D)

1. Mg, ether
2. CO_2
3. H_3O^+

$\longrightarrow$

4. $SOCl_2$, ?
5. NH_3
6. Br_2, NaOH

E)

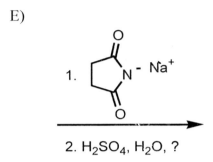

1.
N
Na+
O
O
2. H2SO4, H2O, ?

Ans: D

3. Which of the following products would you expect to result from the following reactions?

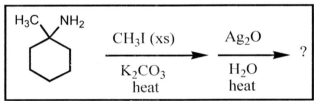

H3C
NH2
CH3I (xs)
K2CO3
heat
Ag2O
H2O
heat
?

A)

H3C
NH(CH3)

B)

H3C
N(CH3)2

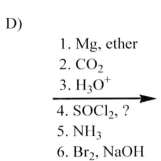

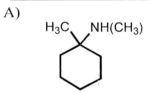

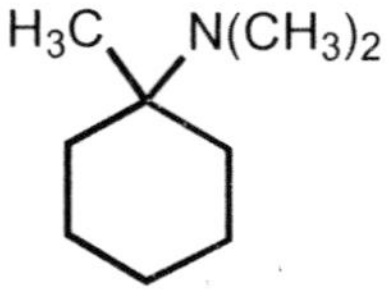

C)

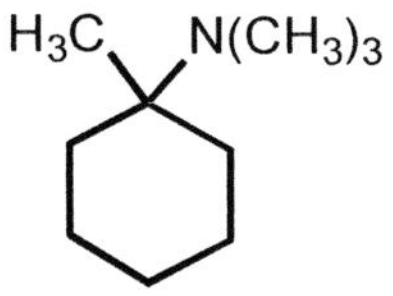

H3C   N(CH3)3

D)

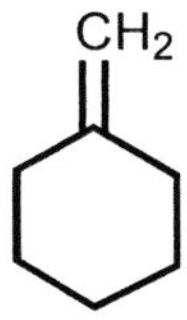

CH2

E)

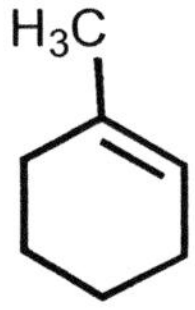

H3C

Ans: D

4. What product would result from the following reaction?

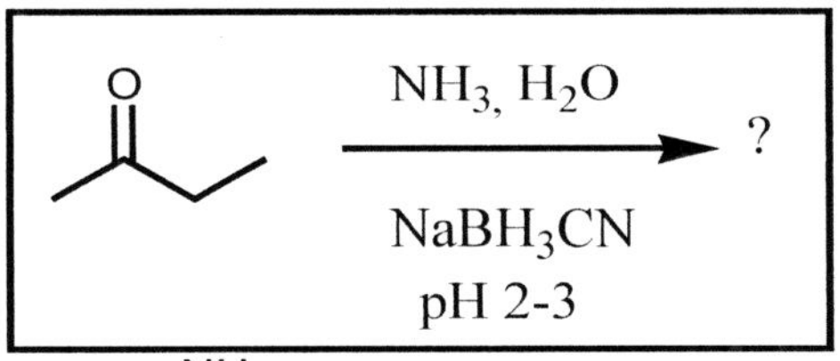

O
‖   NH3, H2O
                ————————→   ?
                NaBH3CN
                pH 2-3

A)   NH
     ‖

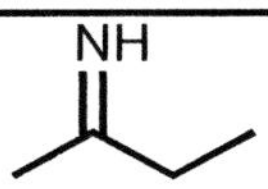

B)   OH

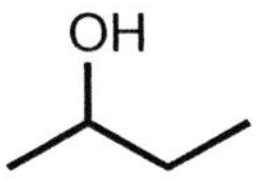

C)   HO   CN

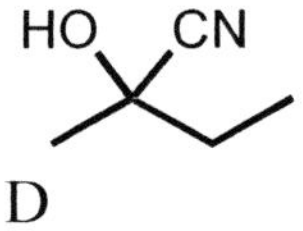

D)   NH2

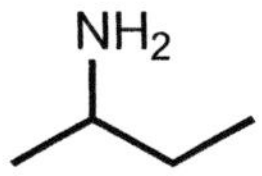

E)   NH2

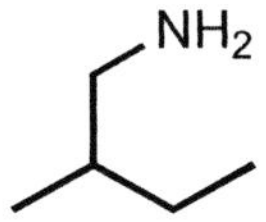

Ans: D

5. Which of the following represents N-ethyl-2-phenylethylamine?
    A)

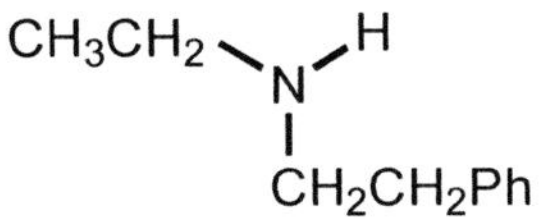

    CH3CH2 ~ N ~ H
              |
         CH2CH2Ph

B)

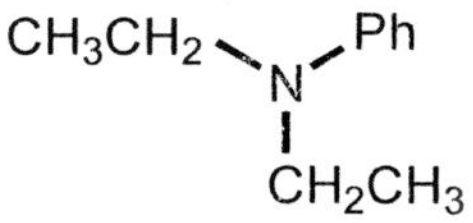

$$CH_3CH_2 \diagdown N \diagup Ph$$
$$| \quad CH_2CH_3$$

C)

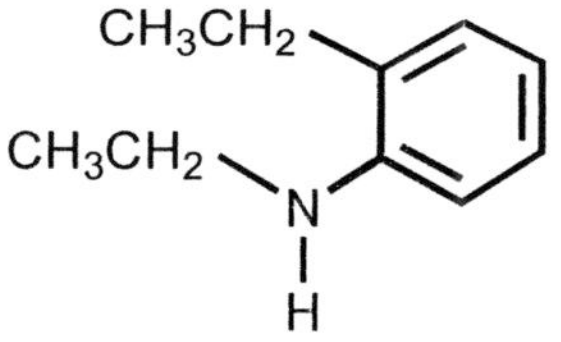

$$CH_3CH_2 \diagdown$$
$$CH_3CH_2 \diagdown N \diagup$$
$$| \quad H$$

D)

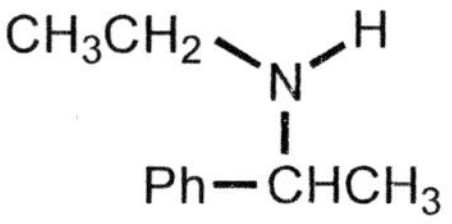

$$CH_3CH_2 \diagdown N \diagup H$$
$$| \quad Ph—CHCH_3$$

E)

$$NH_2$$
$$CH_2CH_3$$

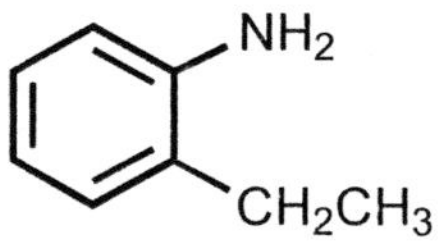

Ans: A

6. What would be formed in the following reaction?

$$NH_3 \quad + \quad CH_3I \quad \longrightarrow \quad ?$$
1 mole   1 mole

A) CH_3NH_2 B) $(CH_3)_2NH$ C) $(CH_3)_3N$ D) none of these   E) all of these
Ans: E

7. N-nitrosoamines (called nitrosamines) have what outstanding characteristic?
   A)   An intense fishy odor   D)   Easily rearrange
   B)   Tend to be carcinogenic   E)   Have acidic N-H hydrogens
   C)   Ammonia-like odor
   Ans: B

8. What is the result of the reaction shown?

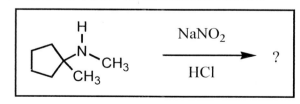

A)

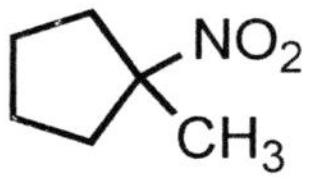

$$NO_2$$
$$CH_3$$

B)

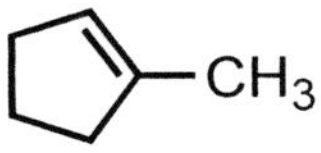

C)

D)

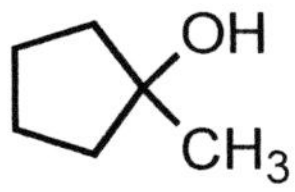

E)

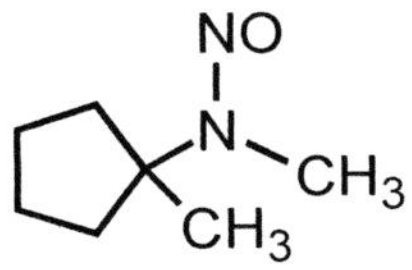

Ans: E

9. Predict the **major** organic product of the following reaction.

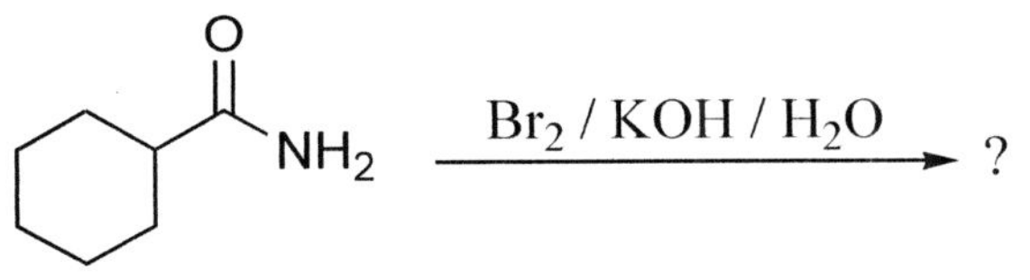

A)

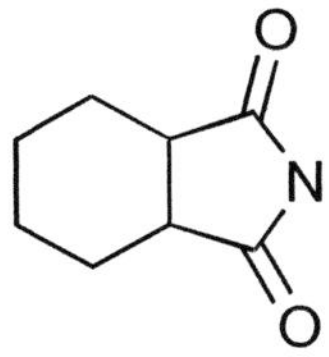

B)

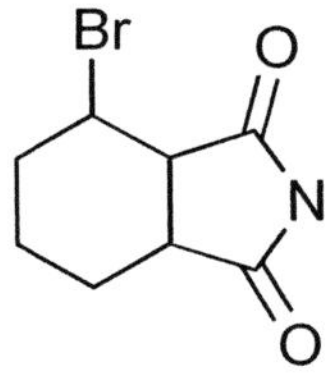

C)

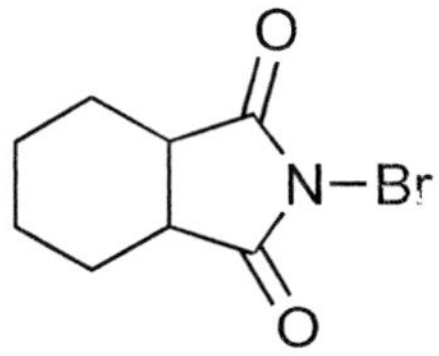

D)

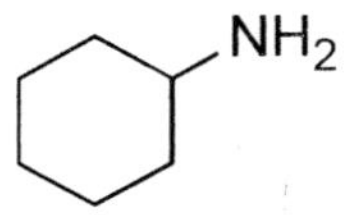

E)

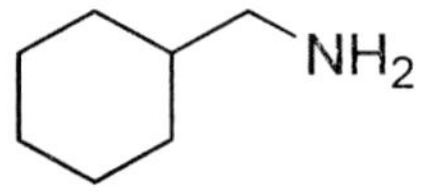

Ans: D

10. What by-product(s) would you expect to contaminate methyl amine prepared by the following reaction?

$$2\ NH_3\ +\ CH_3I\ \longrightarrow\ CH_3NH_2\ +\ NH_4^+\ I^-$$

A) $(CH_3)_2NH$ D)   all of the above
B) $(CH_3)_3N$ E)   none of the above
C) $(CH_3)_4N^+\ I^-$
Ans: D

11. Which of the following is **not** limited to the synthesis of primary amines ($R-NH_2$ or $Ar-NH_2$) (i.e., which, if any, can be used to make 2° or 3° amines)?
A)   Gabriel synthesis
B)   Reduction of amides with LAH
C)   Hofmann rearrangement
D)   Reduction of nitriles with LAH
E)   Reduction of nitro groups with Fe/HCl
Ans: B

12. What product would result from the Hofmann elimination of the following quaternary ammonium hydroxide?

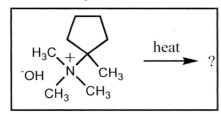

A)

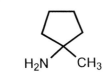

B)

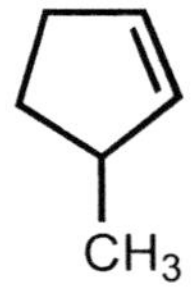

C)

D)

E)

Ans: D

13. What is the structure of lithium diisopropylamide (LDA)?

A)

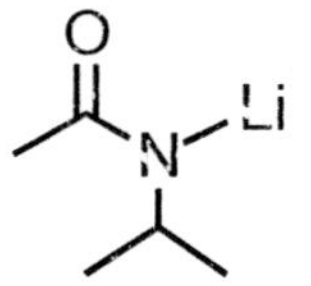

B)

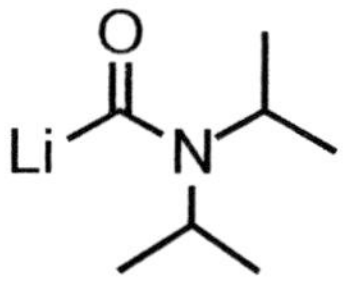

C)

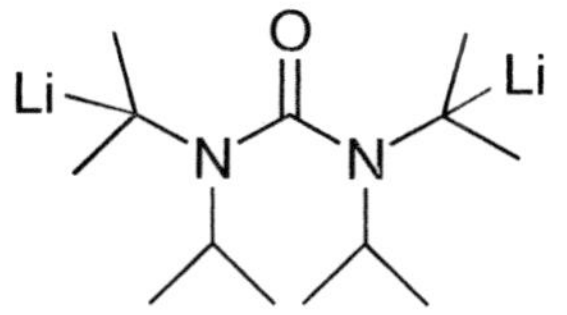

D)

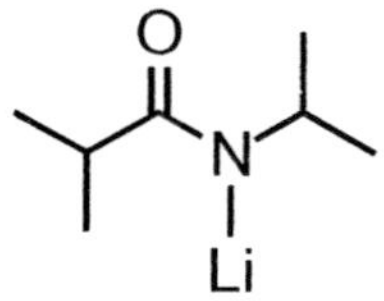

E)

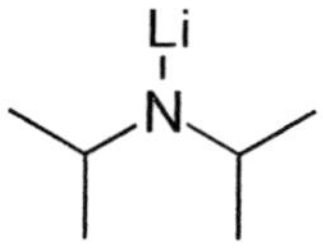

Ans: E

14. Which of the following is **not** formed as either an intermediate along the reaction pathway or as a final product for the Mannich reaction shown below?

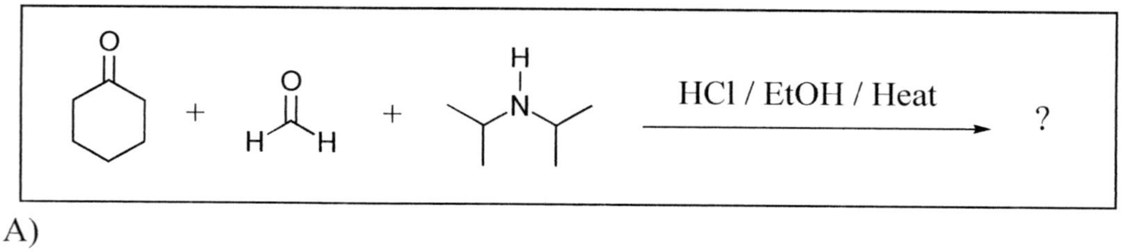

A)

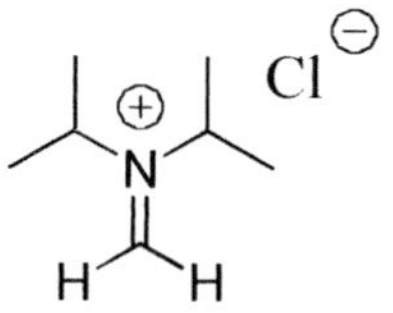

B)

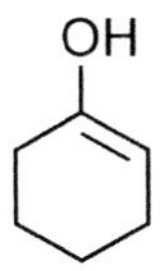

C)

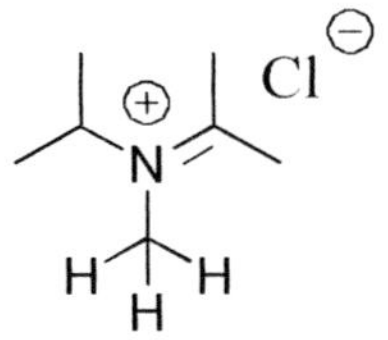

D)

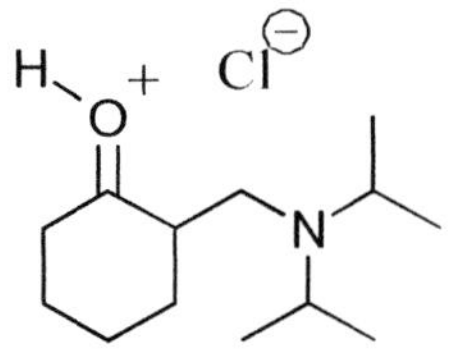

E)

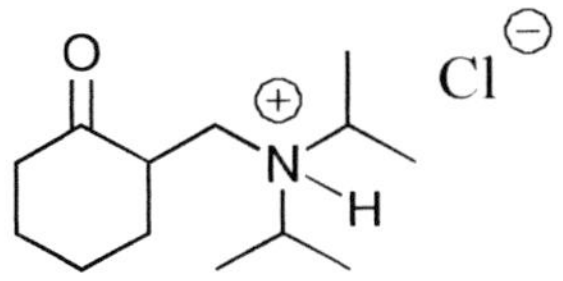

Ans: C

15. What process accomplishes the following transformation?

$$R-\overset{O}{\overset{\|}{C}}-NH_2 \xrightarrow{?} R-NH_2$$

A) Gabriel synthesis
B) Hofmann rearrangement
C) Reductive amination
D) Mannich reaction
E) Hofmann elimination

Ans: B

16. What reagent(s) would accomplish the following?

$$R-\overset{O}{\overset{\|}{C}}-NH_2 \xrightarrow{?} R-CH_2-NH_2$$

A) Br_2, NaOH, H_2O
B) 1. $LiAlH_4$ 2. H_2O
C) 1. CH_3I, heat 2. Ag_2O, heat
D) P_2O_5
E) excess NH_3

Ans: B

17. What **major** product would you expect from the reaction shown?

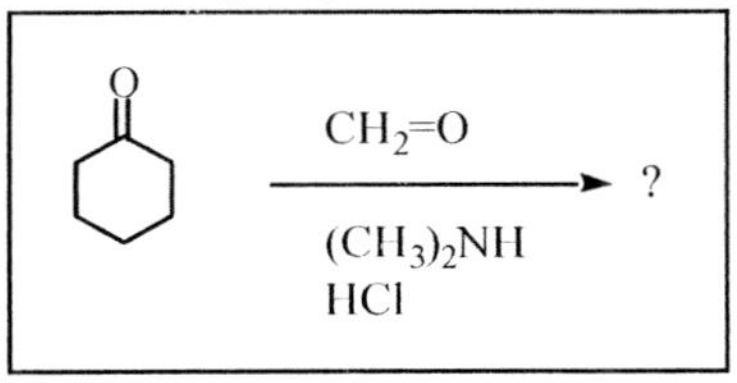

A)

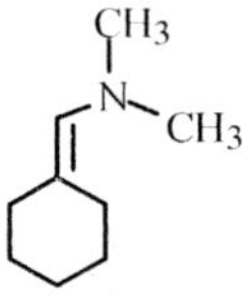

B)

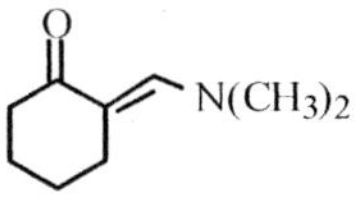

C)

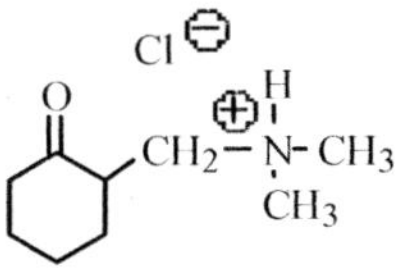

D)

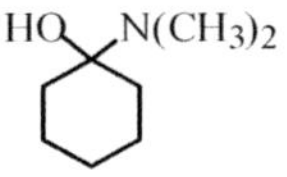

E)

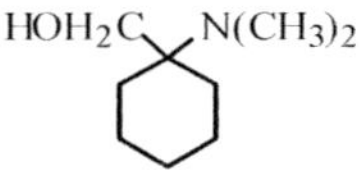

Ans: C

18. Which of the molecules below is the strongest base?

A) $(CH_3)_2NH$ B) $CH_3O^{\ominus}$ C) $(CH_2)_2N^{\ominus}$ D) $Cl^{\ominus}$ E) $HO^{\ominus}$

Ans: C

19. Which of the following structures is a secondary amine?

A)

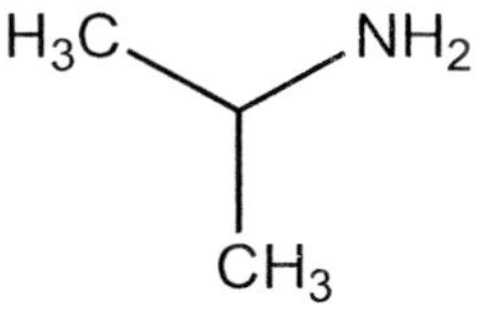

B)

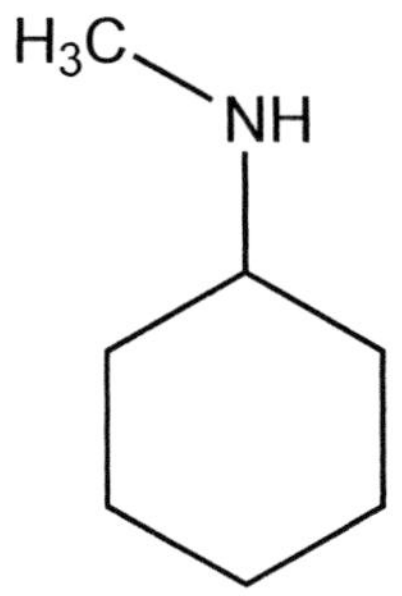

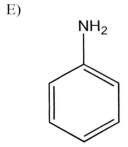

C)

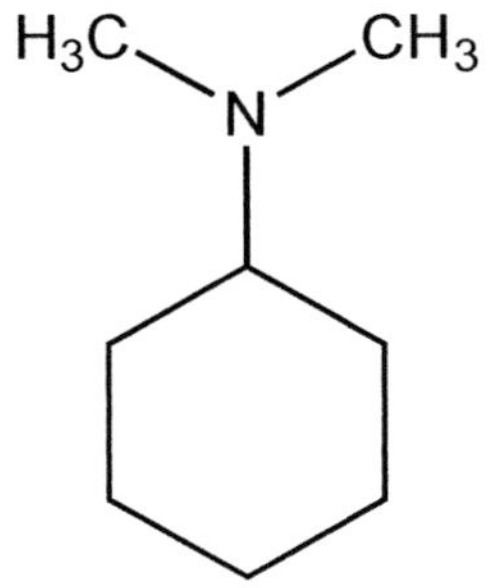

D)

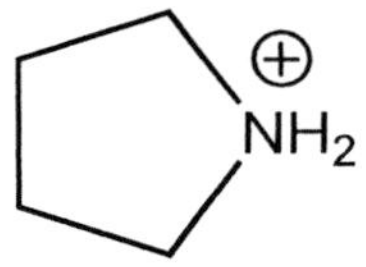

E)

Ans: C

20. Absorptions at 3358 cm⁻¹ and 3283 cm⁻¹ in the IR spectrum would suggest which of the following compounds?

   A)

B)

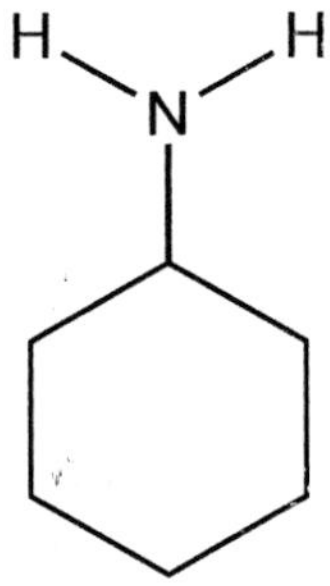

C)

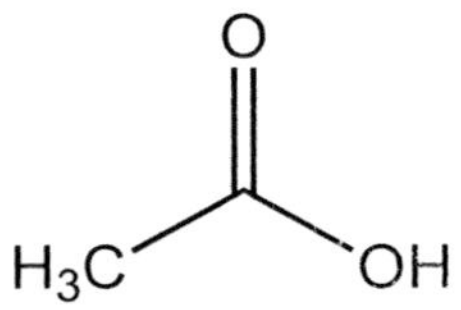

D)

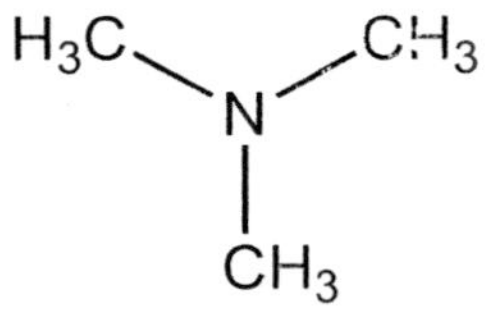

E)   cannot tell from the absorption data

Ans: B

21. Which of the following reactions can be used to prepare ethylamine?

A)

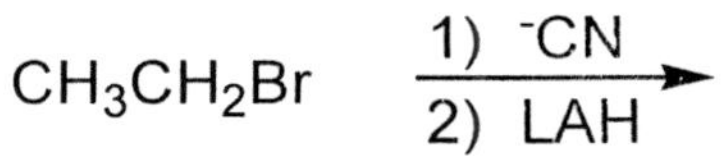

$$CH_3CH_2Br \quad \xrightarrow[\text{2) LAH}]{\text{1) }^-CN}$$

B)

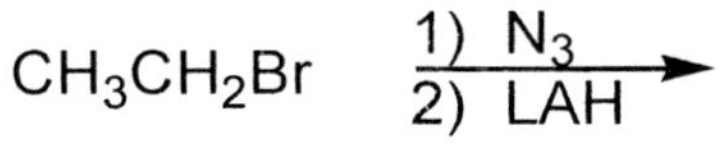

$$CH_3CH_2Br \quad \xrightarrow[\text{2) LAH}]{\text{1) N}_3}$$

C)

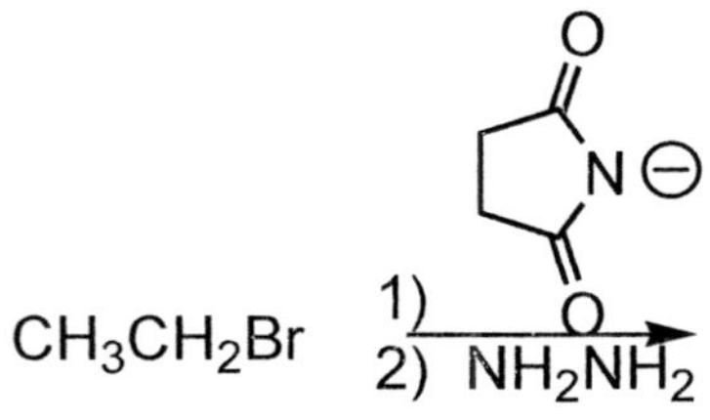

$$CH_3CH_2Br \quad \xrightarrow[\text{2) NH}_2\text{NH}_2]{\text{1)}}$$

D)

$$CH_2\text{-C-NH}_2 \quad \xrightarrow{\text{LAH}}$$

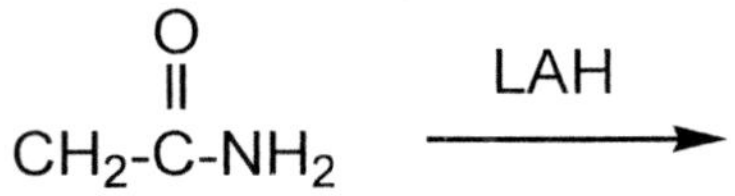

E)   all of the above

Ans: E

Chapter 22: Chemistry of Benzene Substituents:
Alkylbenzenes, Phenols, and Benzenamines

1. Which ion would be **most** stabilized by resonance?
   A)

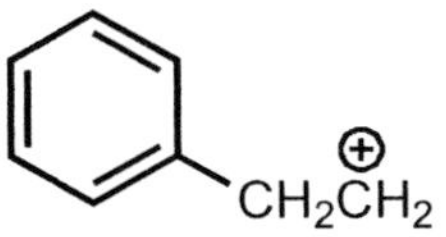

   CH₂C⁺H₂

   B)

   C⁺HCH₃

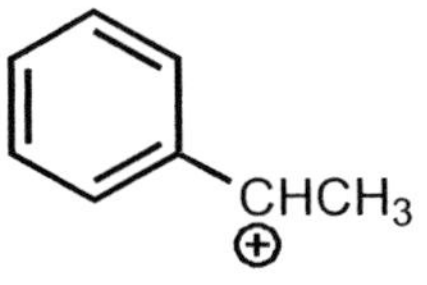

   C)

   CH₂CH₃

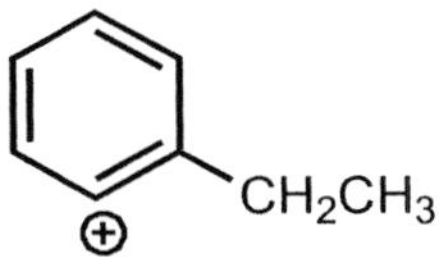

   D)

   CH₂CH₃

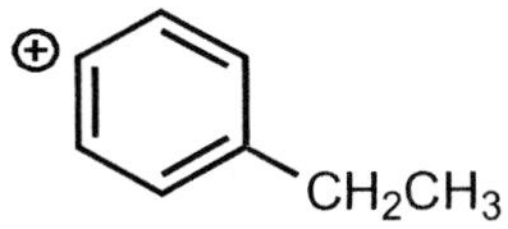

   E)   all are equally stabilized
   Ans: B

2. Which of the following resonance structures of the phenoxide anion would be the major contributor to the real structure?
   A)

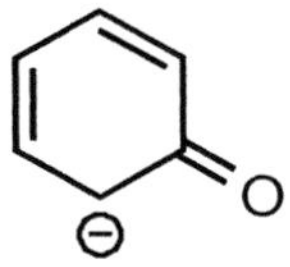

   B)

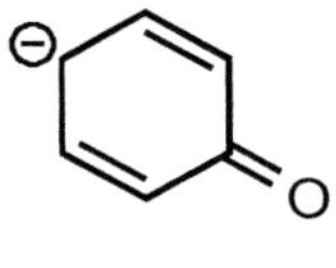

C)

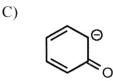

D)

E)   all are equally important

Ans: D

3. What is the main use of azo compounds in general?

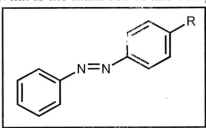

A)   Antibiotic properties   D)   Herbicides and/or pesticides
B)   Fragrances and flavorings   E)   Dyes and coloring agents
C)   Chemotherapy agents

Ans: E

4. To which side (if any) would the following equilibrium lie?

$$C_6H_5O^- \; + \; HOH \;\rightleftharpoons\; C_6H_5OH \; + \; {}^-OH$$

A)   To the left   D)   Reaction cannot occur at all
B)   To the right   E)   Equilibrium favors a different
                                              product.

C)   Equally to the left and right

Ans: A

5. Why does the substitution of ortho or para <u>nitro groups</u> onto chlorobenzene greatly
   increase the tendency of the chlorine to be displaced by nucleophiles?
   A) NO_2 groups stabilize the S_N1 transition state by resonance.
   B)   The NO_2 groups facilitate removal of a hydrogen α to chlorine.
   C) NO_2 groups stabilize the S_N2 transition state.
   D) NO_2 groups stabilize negative charge resulting from addition of a nucleophile.
   E)   The NO_2 groups exert a general inductive effect which is independent of
         substitution position.

Ans: D

6. By which of the following can the N₂ group of a benzenediazonium salt **not** be substituted?

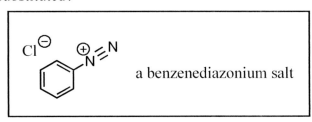

a benzenediazonium salt

A) CN   B) CH₃   C) H   D) F   E) OH
Ans: B

7. What material is produced easily by means of the Kolbe reaction? (sodium phenoxide + CO_2 + heat/pressure, then H_3O^+)
   A)   Phenol   D)   Cinnamic acid
   B)   Benzaldehyde   E)   Salicylic acid
   C)   Succinic acid
   Ans: E

8. What product would result from the following reaction?

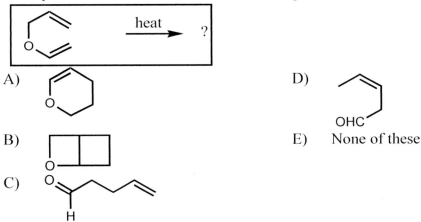

   A)

   B)

   C)

   D)

   E)   None of these

   OHC

   Ans: C

9. What happens when a **secondary** amine is treated with nitrous acid?
   A)   A diazonium salt is formed.
   B)   It immediately loses nitrogen to form a carbocation.
   C)   A simple acid-base reaction occurs to give an alkyl ammonium nitrite salt.
   D)   An N-nitroso amine is formed.
   E)   A dealkylation occurs to give a primary amine.
   Ans: D

10. What major product would you expect from the following reaction?

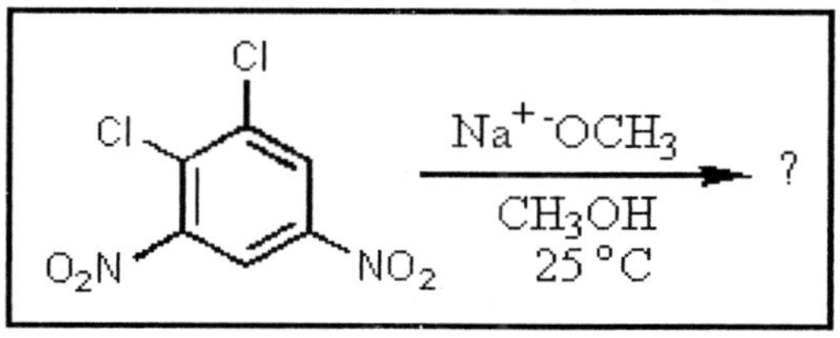

A)

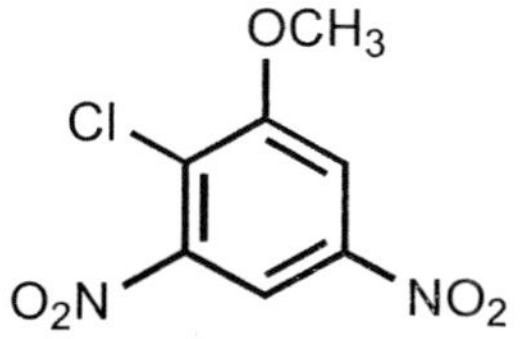

B)

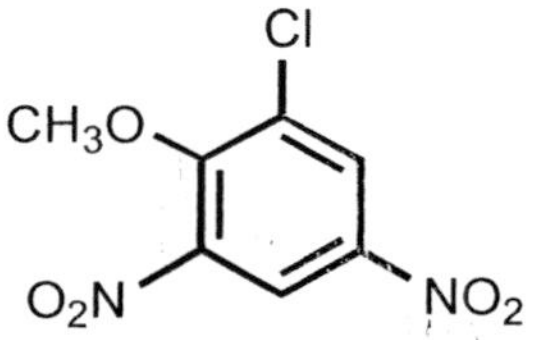

C)

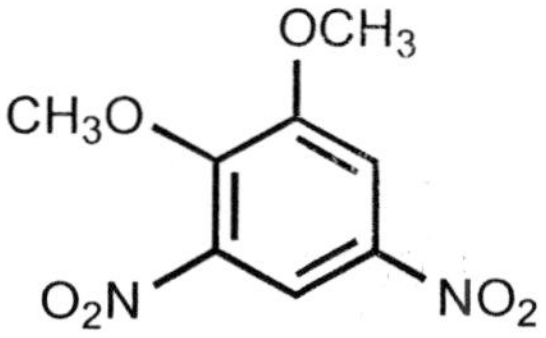

D)

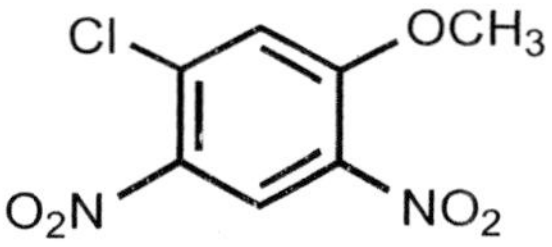

E)   both A and D
Ans: B

11. How would you rank the following in decreasing order of reactivity toward nucleophilic aromatic substitution (most reactive on left)?

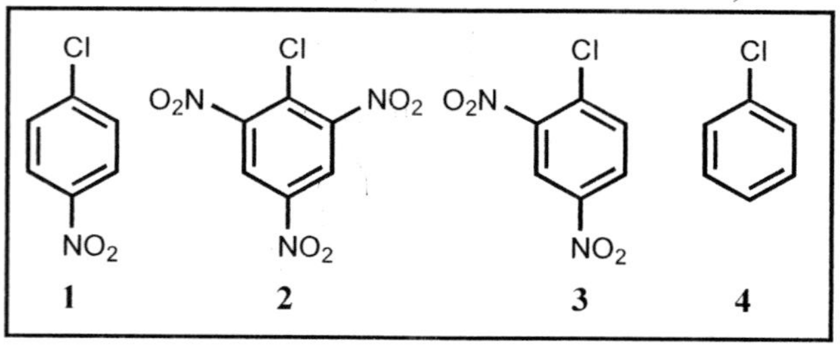

A) $4 > 1 > 3 > 2$ D) $1 > 3 > 2 > 4$
B) $2 > 3 > 1 > 4$ E)   impossible to predict
C) $3 > 2 > 4 > 1$
Ans: B

12. What would be the result of the following?

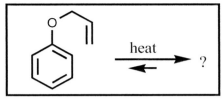

A)

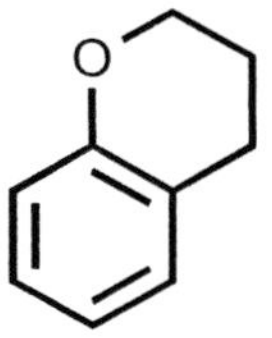

B)

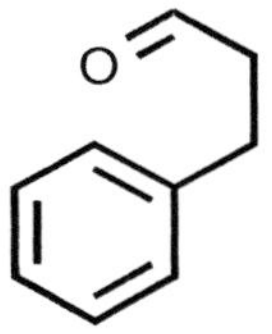

C)

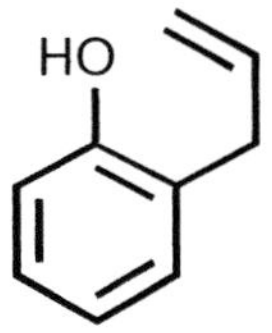

D)

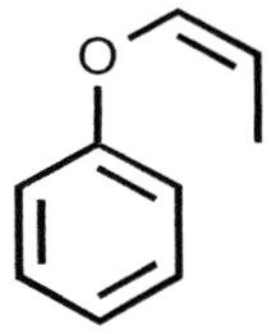

E)   no reaction
Ans: C

13. What would be the expected product of the following reaction?

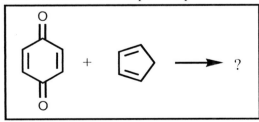

A)

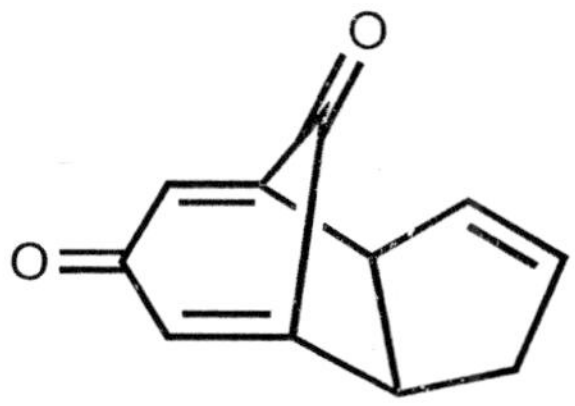

B)

C)

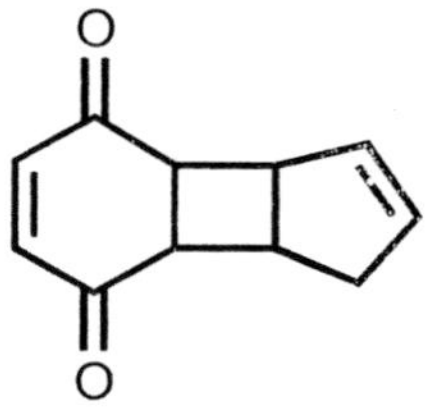

D)

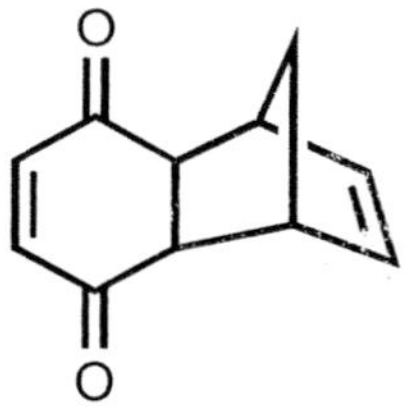

E)

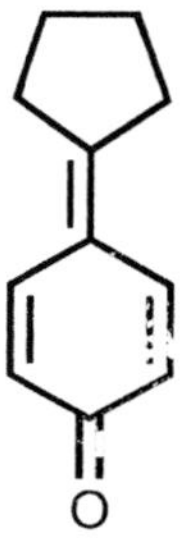

Ans: D

14. What product would you expect from the following reaction?

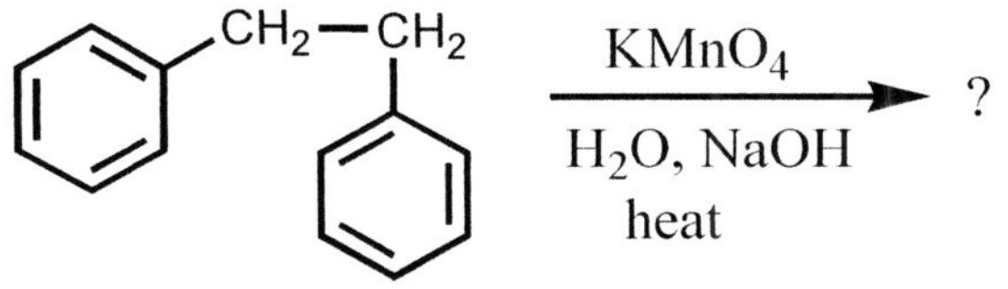

A)

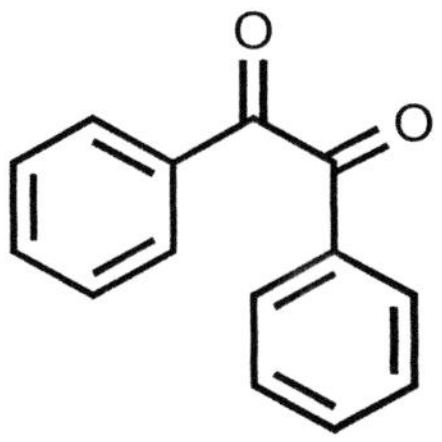

B)

2 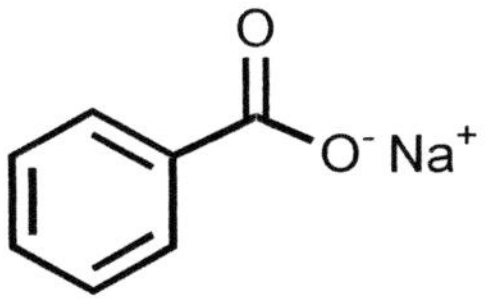

C)

2 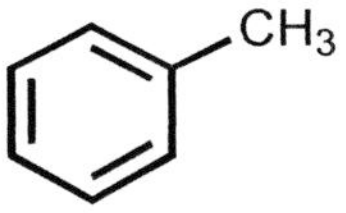

D)

2 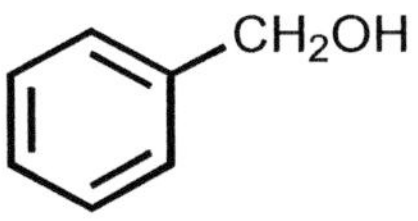

E)

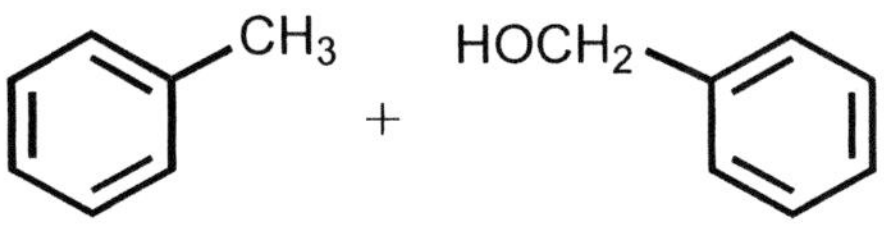

Ans: B

15. From what starting materials would the following be made?

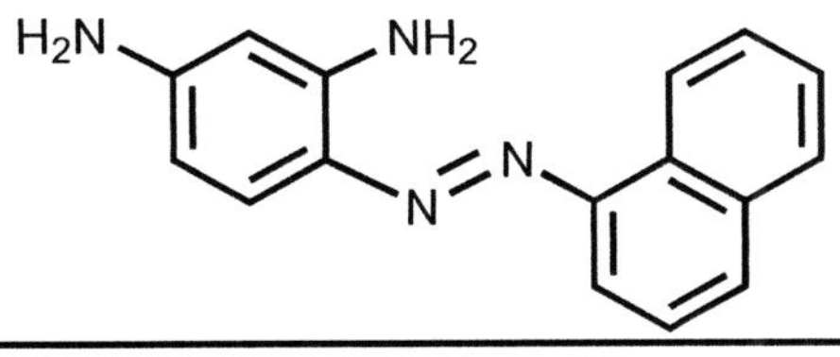

A)

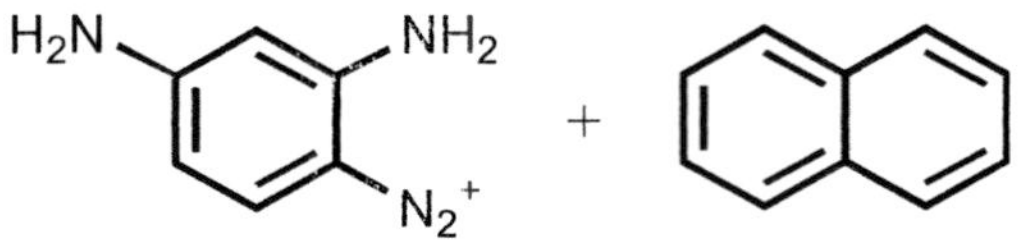

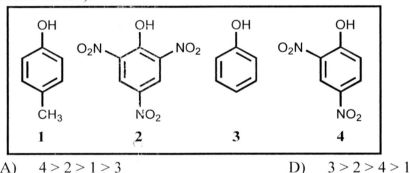

B)

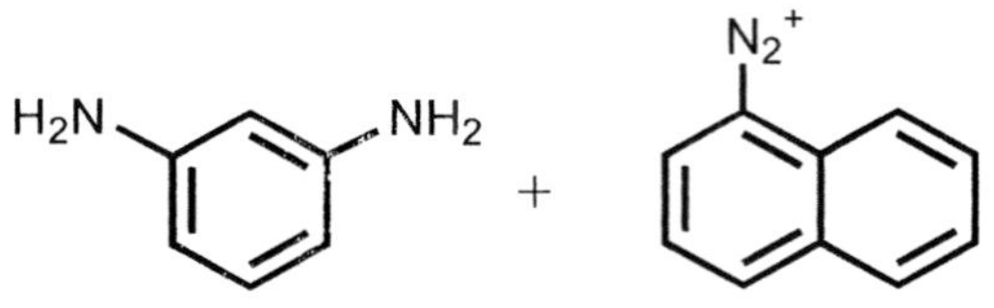

C)   Either A or B
D)   Neither A nor B
E)   The compound shown is too unstable to isolate
Ans: B

16. What would be the proper ranking of the following in order of **decreasing** acidity(most acidic on left)?

A)   4 > 2 > 1 > 3   D)   3 > 2 > 4 > 1
B)   3 > 1 > 4 > 2   E)   2 > 4 > 3 > 1
C)   2 > 4 > 1 > 3
Ans: E

17. What reagent(s) would be required to accomplish the following reaction?

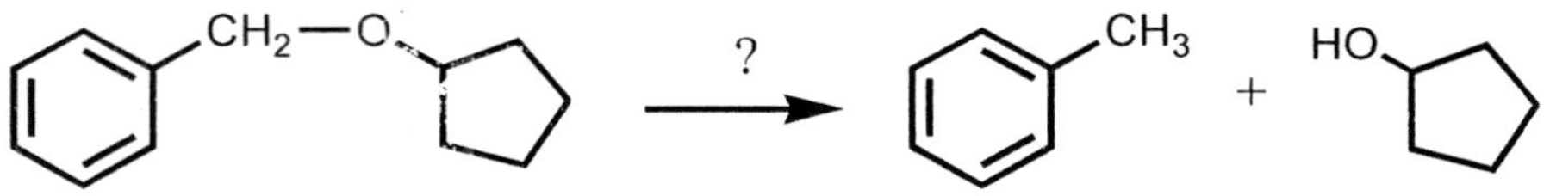

A) H_2SO_4/H_2O
B)   1. $LiAlH_4$
      2. H_2O
C) H_2, Pd
D)   HBr, heat
E) $NaBH_4$, CH_3OH
Ans: C

18. What would be the expected product of the following reaction?

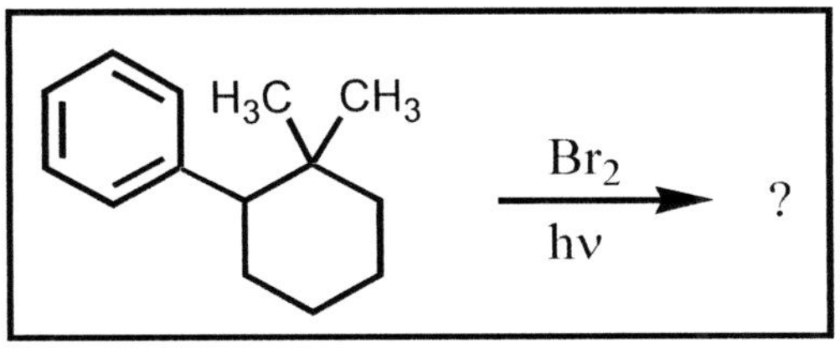

A)

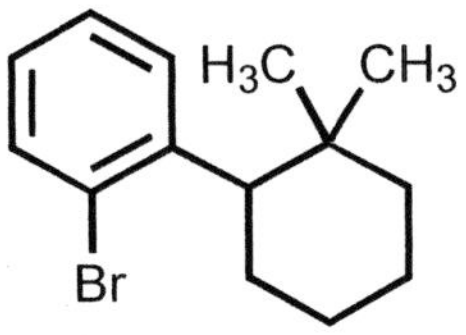

B)

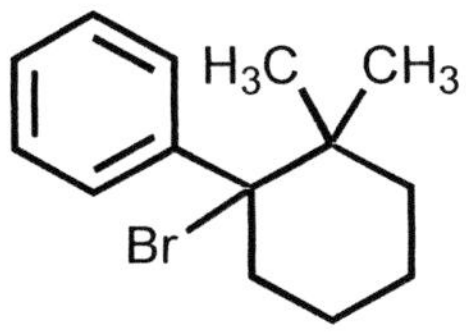

C)

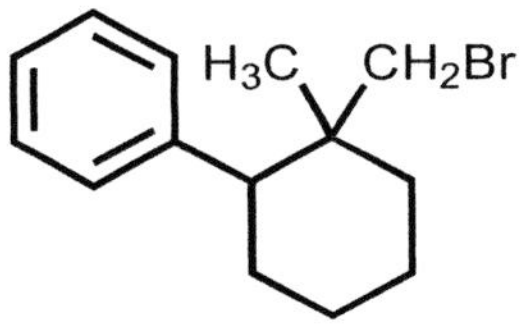

D)

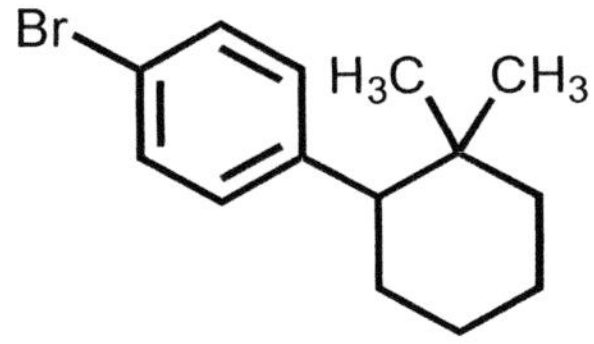

E)   both A and D

Ans: B

19. What would be the expected product(s) from the following reaction?

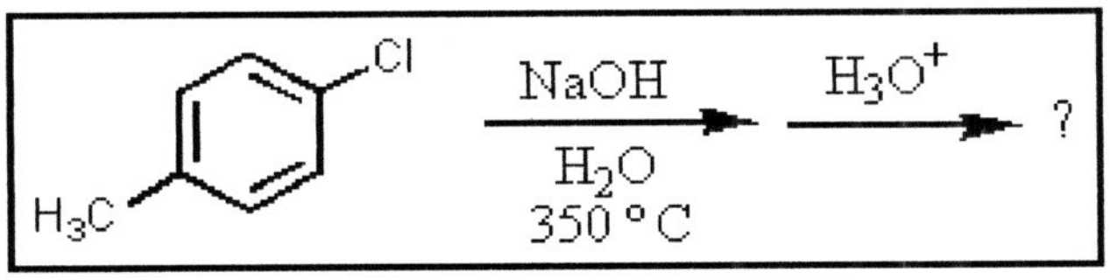

A)

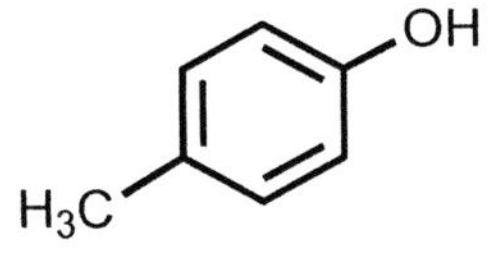

B)

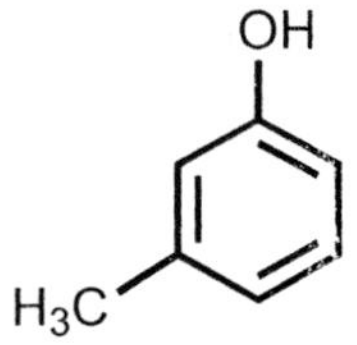

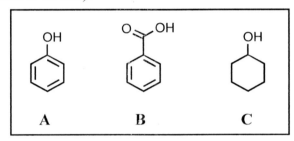

C)

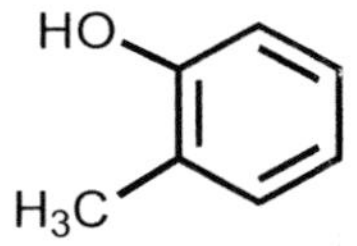

D)   both A and B
E)   all of the above
Ans: D

20. What would be the proper ranking of the following in order of **decreasing** acidity (most acidic on left)?

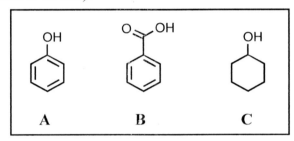

A) A > B > C   B) B > C > A   C) A > C > B   D) B > A > C   E) C > B > A
Ans: D

21. Which of the following is **not** a valid resonance contributor to the benzyl radical?
A)

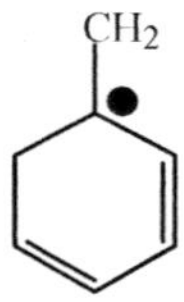

B)

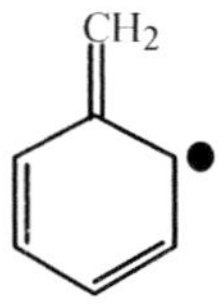

C)

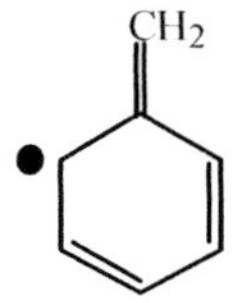

D)

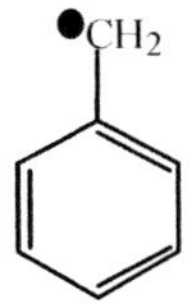

E)

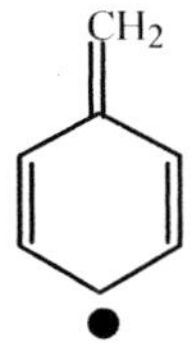

Ans: A

22. Predict the **major** product of the following solvolysis reaction:

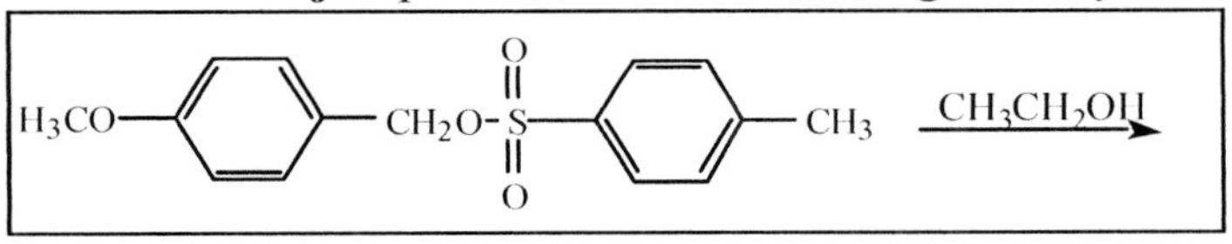

A)

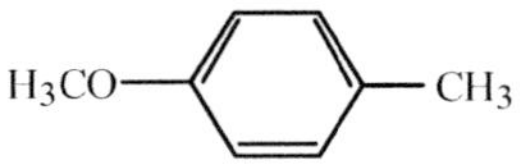

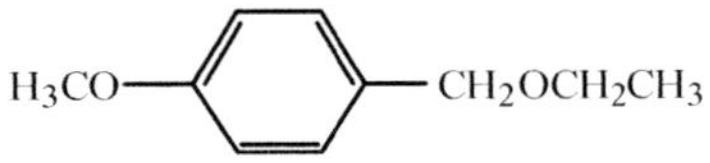

D)

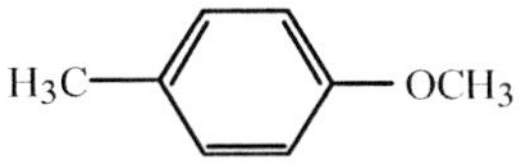

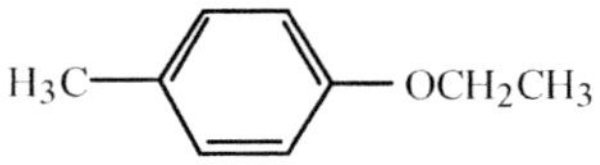

B)

E) none of the above

C)

Ans: C

23. The following reaction most likely proceeds by what mechanism:

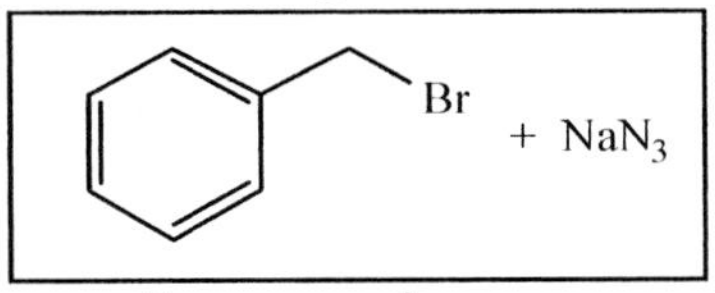

A) S_N^2 B) S_N^1 C) E2   D) EI   E) Free radical halogenation
Ans: A

24. Which of the following represents a hydrogenolysis reaction?
    A)

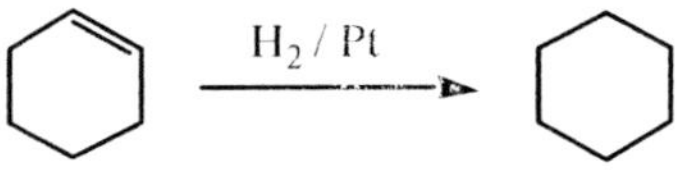

    B)

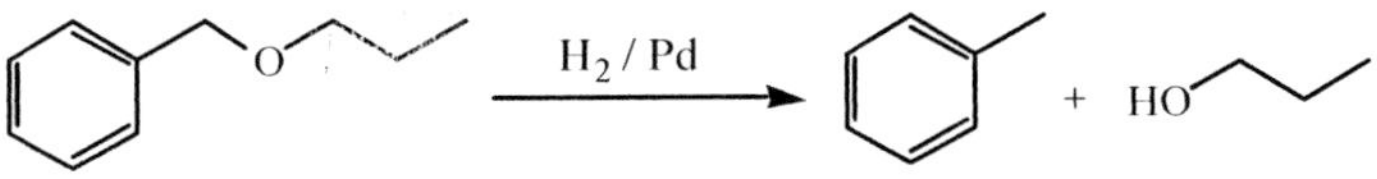

    C)

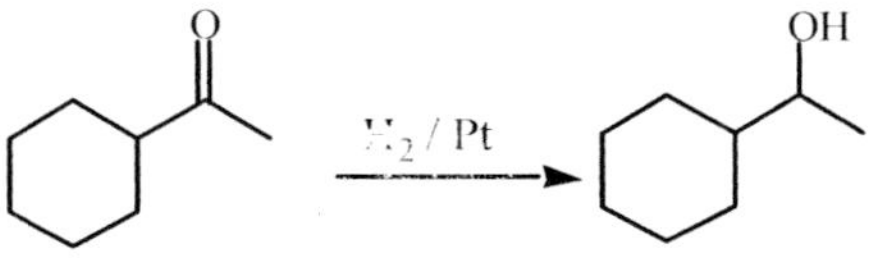

    D)

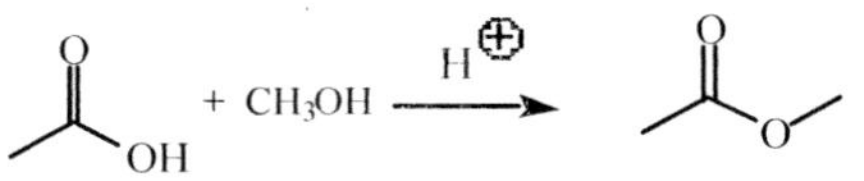

    E)   Two or more of these are correct.
    Ans: B

25. Considering the mechanism for the following reaction, which of the following is most likely the rate determining step (RDS)?

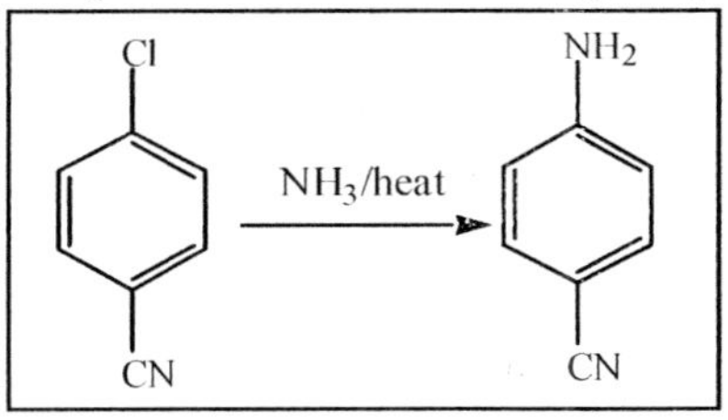

    A)

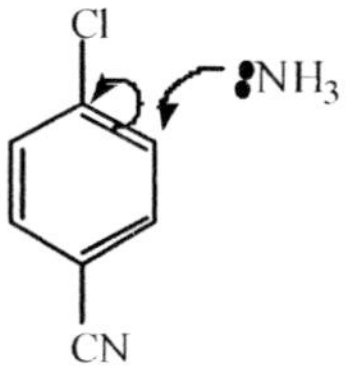

    B)

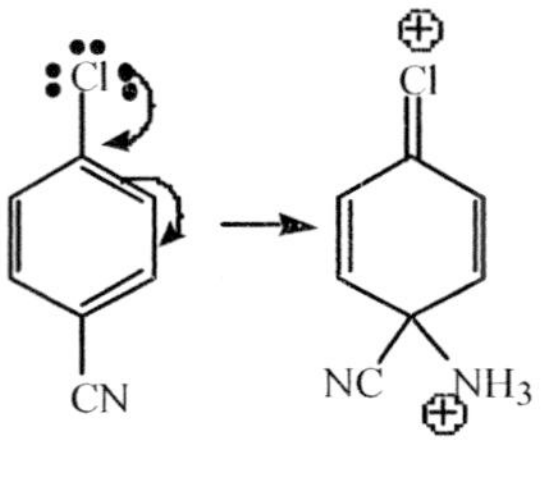

C)

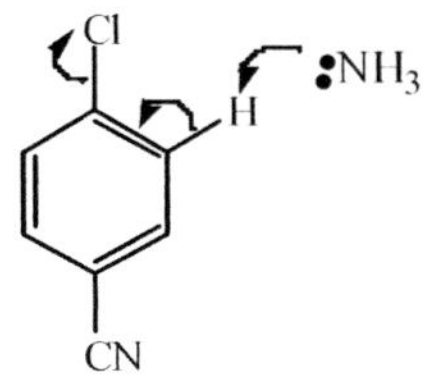

D)

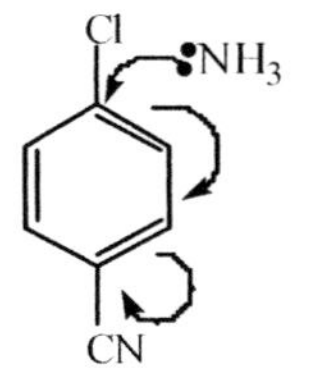

E)

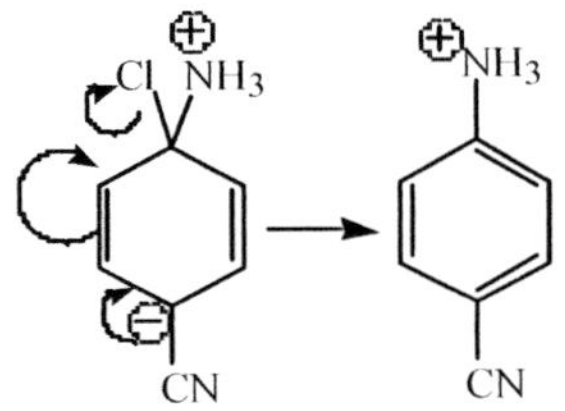

Ans: D

26. When considering the mechanism of the reaction shown below, which of the following is most likely an intermediate along the reaction pathway?

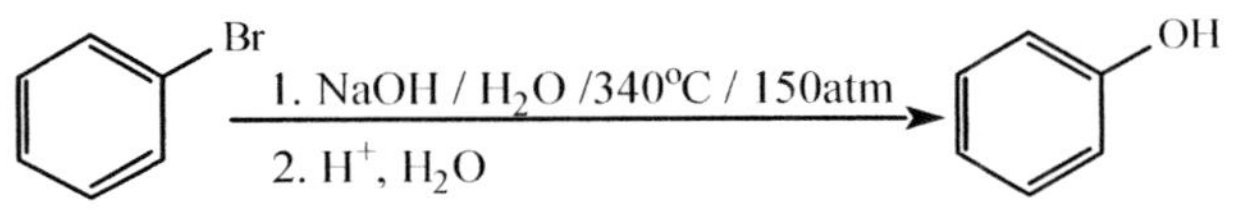

A)

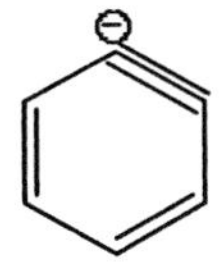

B)

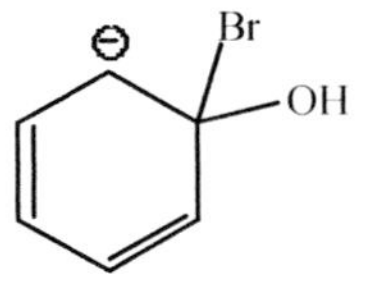

C)

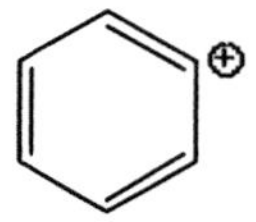

D)

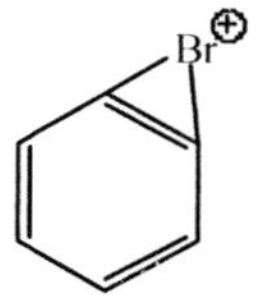

E)

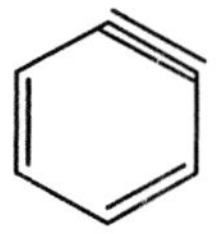

Ans: E

27. Predict the major product of the following reaction:

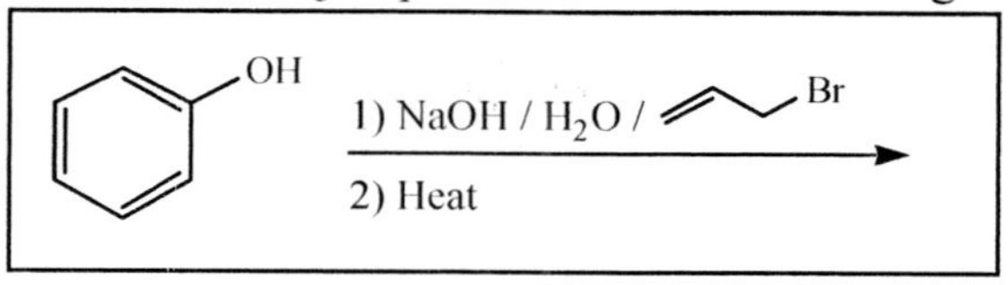

A)

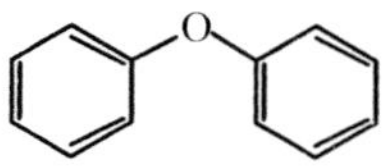

B)

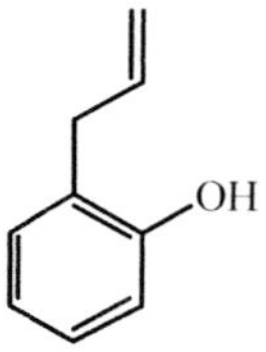

C)

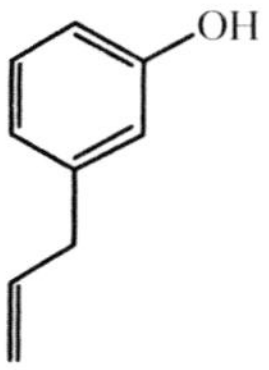

D)

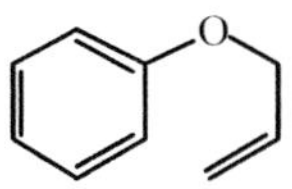

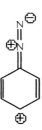

E)

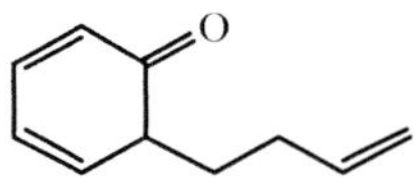

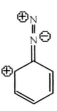

Ans: B

28. Which of the following is **not** a valid resonance contributor in the benzenediazonium cation?

A)

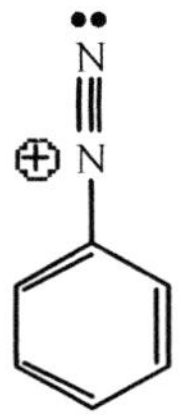

B)

C)

D)

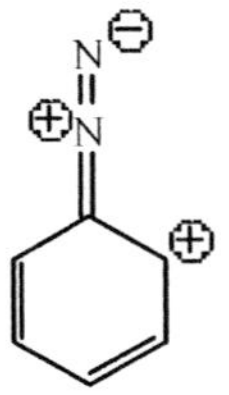

E)   All of the above are valid resonance structures.

Ans: C

29. Predict the major product of the following Sandmeyer reaction:

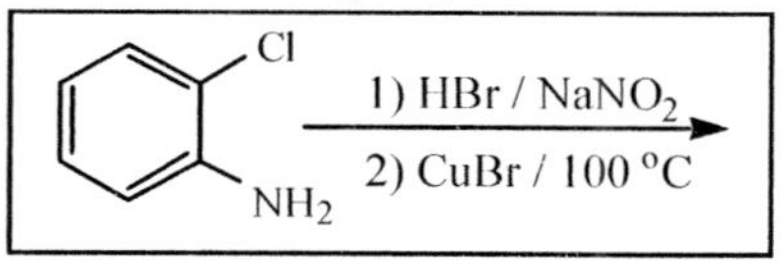

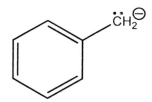

1) HBr / NaNO₂
2) CuBr / 100 °C

A)

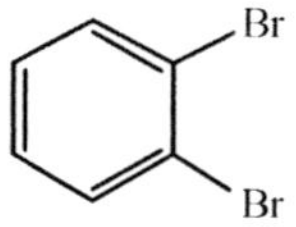

Br
Br

B)

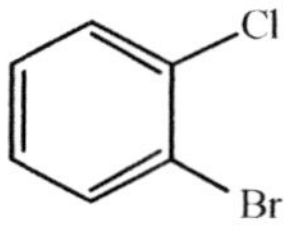

Cl
Br

C)

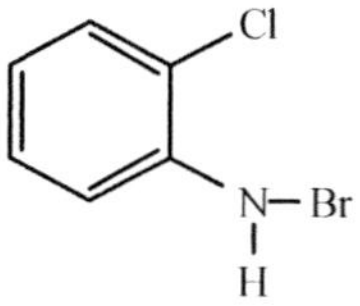

Cl
N—Br
H

D)

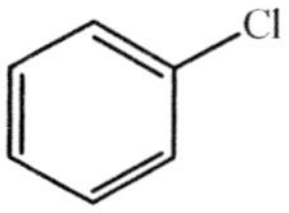

Cl

E)

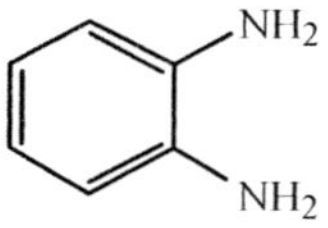

NH₂
NH₂

Ans: B

30. Which of the following is **not** a valid resonance contributor in the benzylic anion?

A)

CH₂⊖

B)

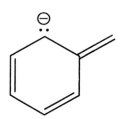

C)

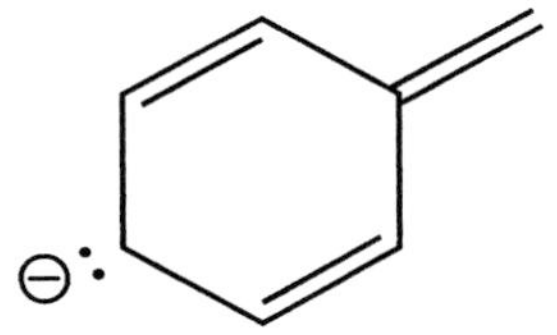

D)

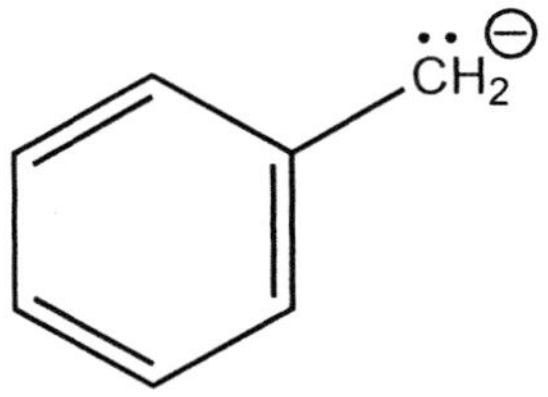

E)   All of these are valid resonance structures.
Ans: E

31. Arrange the following structures according to **decreasing** acidity?

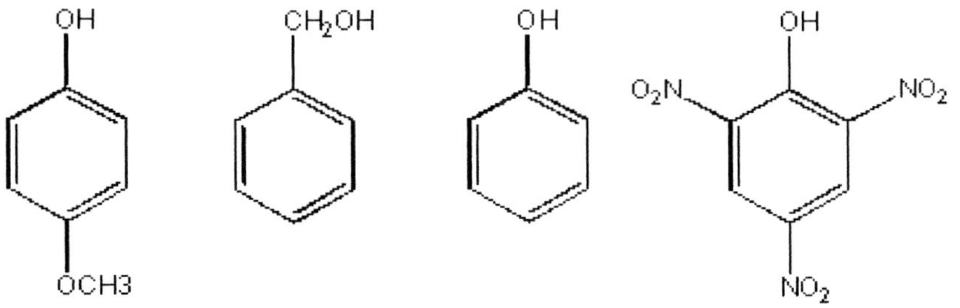

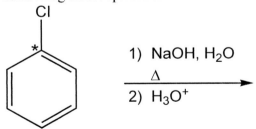

| | | | |
| 1 | 2 | 3 | 4 |

A)   1 > 3 > 4 > 2   D)   3 > 2 > 1 > 4
B)   2 > 4 > 3 > 1   E)   4 > 1 > 3 > 2
C)   4 > 3 > 1 > 2
Ans: C

32. Starting with the labeled chlorobenzene (label indicated by *), what is the product of the following nucleophilic aromatic substitution reaction?

1) NaOH, H₂O
Δ
2) H₃O⁺

A)

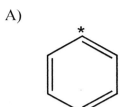

B)

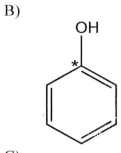

C)

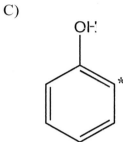

D)

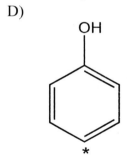

E)   structures B and C

Ans: E

Chapter 23: Ester Enolates and the Claisen Condensation

1. What would be the organic product of the following reaction?

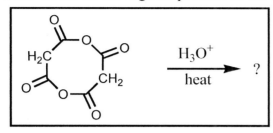

A)   2 HO₂CCH₂CO₂H
B)   2 CH₃C(=O)CH₃
C)   2 CH₃CO₂H
D)   HO₂CCH₂C(=O)O₂CCH₂C(=O)O₂CCH₂CO₂H
E)   No reaction occurs

Ans: C

2. What product would result from the following reaction sequence?

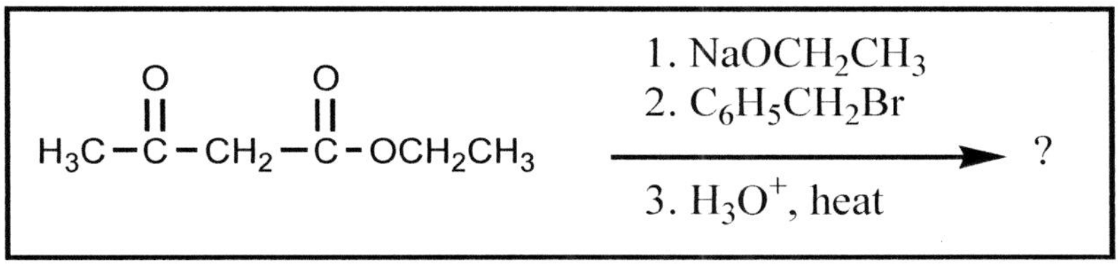

$$H_3C-\overset{O}{\underset{\|}{C}}-CH_2-\overset{O}{\underset{\|}{C}}-OCH_2CH_3 \quad \xrightarrow[\text{3. } H_3O^+, \text{ heat}]{\substack{\text{1. NaOCH}_2\text{CH}_3 \\ \text{2. C}_6\text{H}_5\text{CH}_2\text{Br}}} \quad ?$$

A)

$$H_3C-\overset{O}{\underset{\|}{C}}-CH_2-C_6H_5$$

B)

$$HO-\overset{O}{\underset{\|}{C}}-CH_2-CH_2C_6H_5$$

C)

$$HO-\overset{O}{\underset{\|}{C}}-CH_2-C_6H_5$$

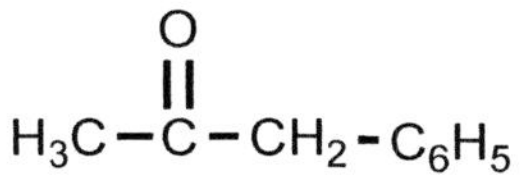

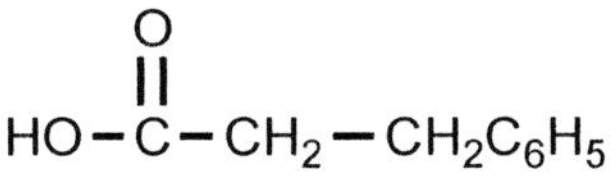

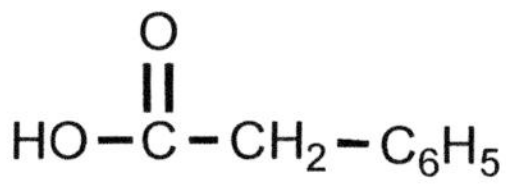

D)

$$H_3C-\overset{\overset{\displaystyle O}{\|}}{C}--CH_2-CH_2C_6H_5$$

E)

$$H_3C-\overset{\overset{\displaystyle O}{\|}}{C}-\underset{\underset{\displaystyle CH_2C_6H_5}{|}}{CH}-\overset{\overset{\displaystyle O}{\|}}{C}-OCH_2CH_3$$

Ans: D

3. To which side, if any, would the following equilibrium lie?

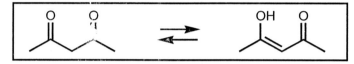

A) To the left   D) Reaction cannot occur at all
B) To the right   E) Equilibrium favors a different
                                             product.

C) Equally to the left and right
Ans: B

4. Which of the following would be the most acidic?
A)

B) CH₃CH₂CO₂CH₃
C)

D)

E)

Ans: D

5. Predict the products of the following reaction.

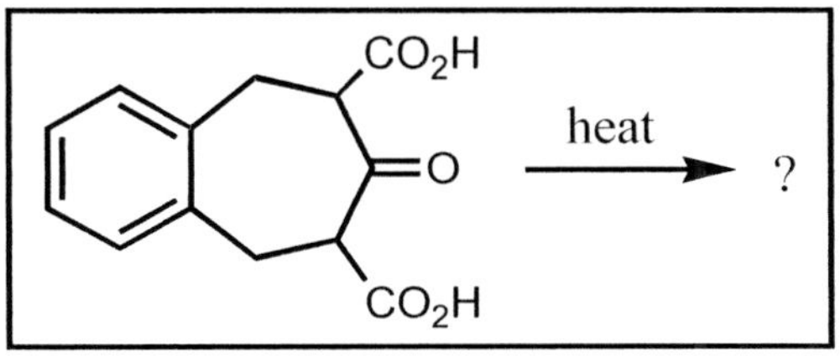

A)

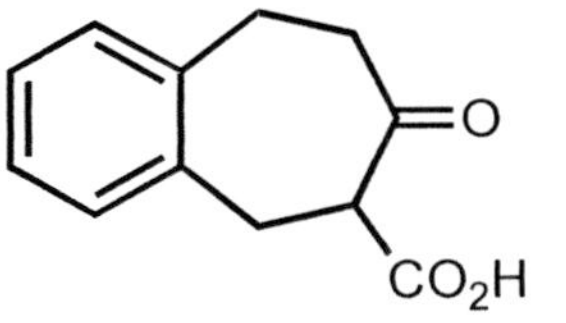

B)

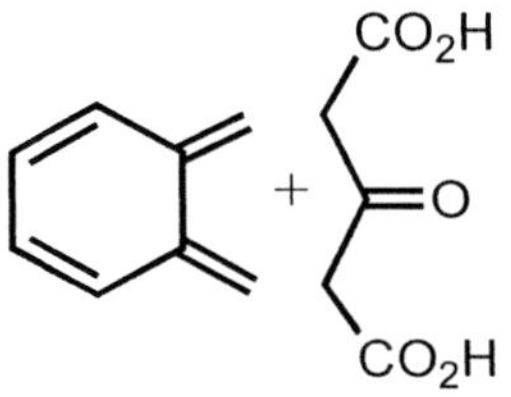

C)

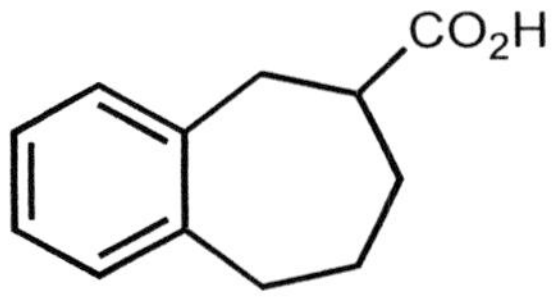

D)

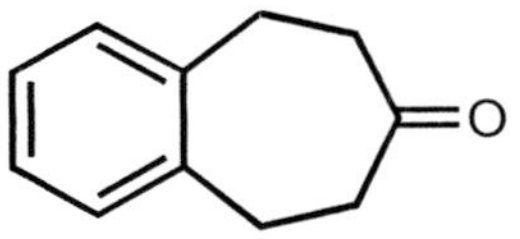

E)   none of these

Ans: D

6. What would be the expected product of the following reaction sequence?

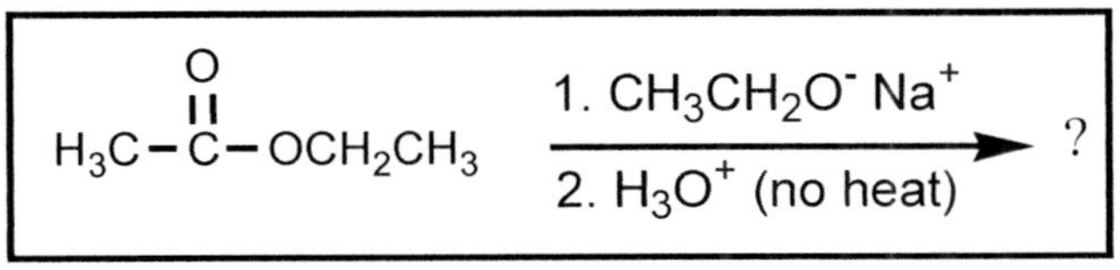

A)

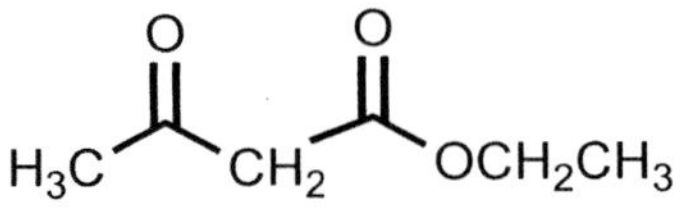

B)

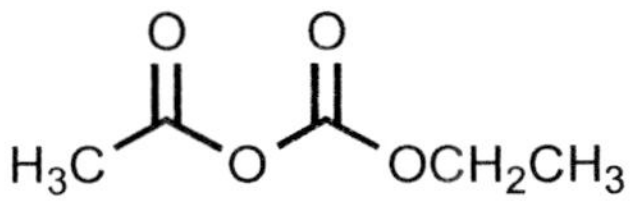

$$H_3C - \overset{\overset{O}{\|}}{C} - O - \overset{\overset{O}{\|}}{C} - OCH_2CH_3$$

C)

$$H_3C - \overset{\overset{OH}{|}}{\underset{\underset{H}{|}}{C}} - CH_2 - \overset{\overset{O}{\|}}{C} - OCH_2CH_3$$

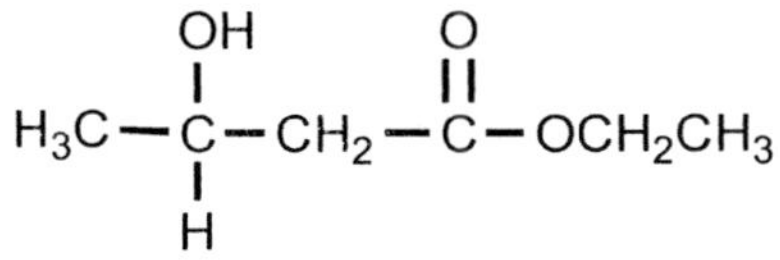

D)

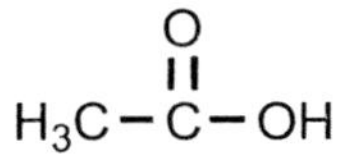

$$H_3C - \overset{\overset{O}{\|}}{C} - OH$$

E)

$$CH_3CH_2O - \overset{\overset{O}{\|}}{C} - \overset{\overset{O}{\|}}{C} - OCH_2CH_3$$

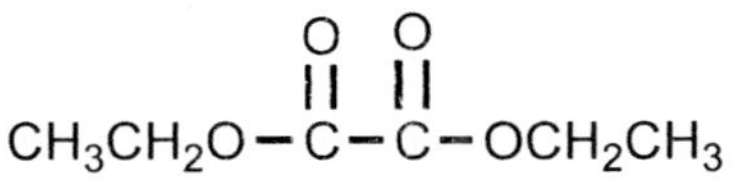

Ans: A

7. What factors contribute to the stability of the following structure?

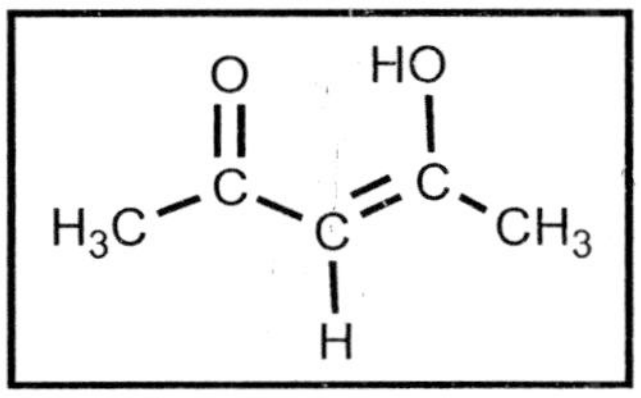

$$H_3C - \overset{\overset{O}{\|}}{C} - \overset{\overset{}{\underset{\underset{H}{|}}{C}}}{=} \overset{\overset{HO}{|}}{C} - CH_3$$

A)   structure has a 6π electron aromatic system.
B)   stabilized by conjugation between C=C and C=O.
C)   C=C is generally more stable than C=O.
D)   structure has intramolecular hydrogen bonding.
E)   more than one of the above are true.
Ans: E

8. The Dieckmann reaction is best described by which of the following statements?
A)   Intermolecular Aldol Condensation
B)   Intramolecular Aldol Condensation
C)   Intermolecular Claisen Condensation
D)   Intramolecular Claisen Condensation
E)   Michael Addition followed by intramolecular Aldol
Ans: D

9. **Why** is the following reaction typically done?

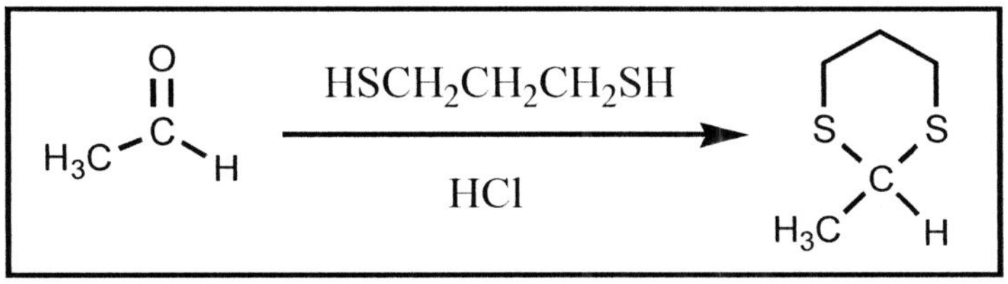

A)   To protect the aldehyde against oxidation
B)   To render the molecule inert to organometallic reagents
C)   To make the aldehyde CH more acidic
D)   To render the molecule more fragrant
E)   To protect the aldehyde against reduction
Ans: C

10. Predict the major organic product of the following reaction.

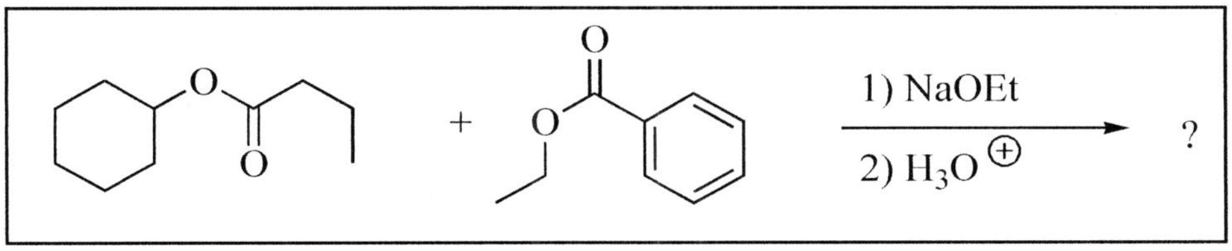

A)

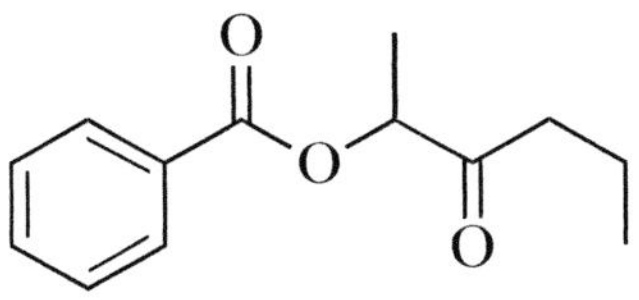

B)

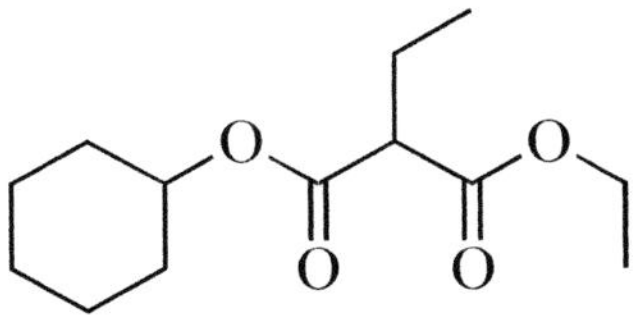

C)

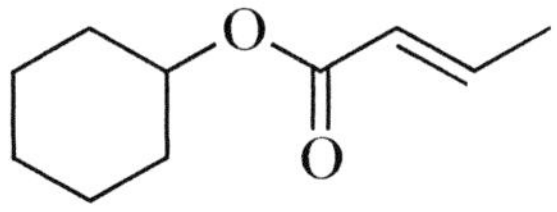

D)

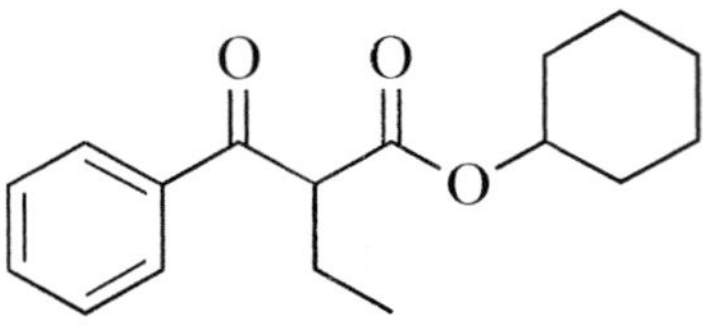

E)   reaction does not occur

Ans: D

11. What product results from treatment of the 1,2-diketone below with hydroxide?

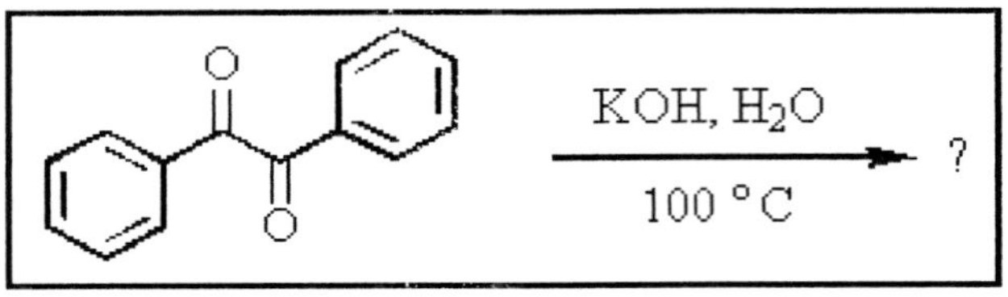

KOH, H₂O

100 °C

?

A)

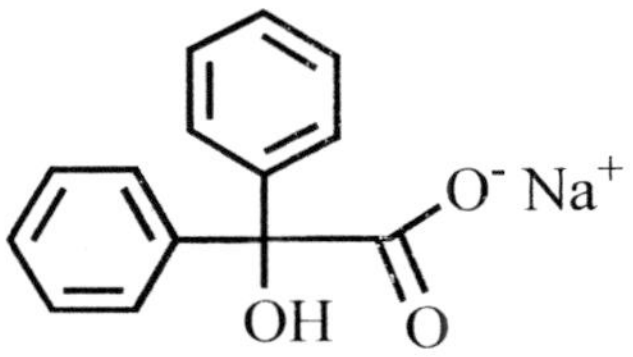

B)

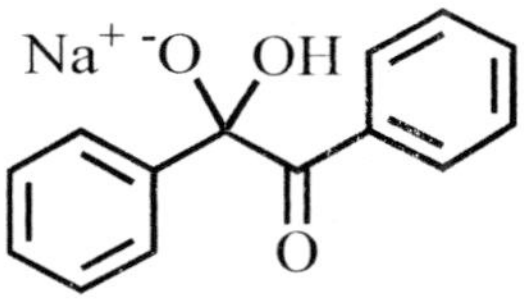

C)

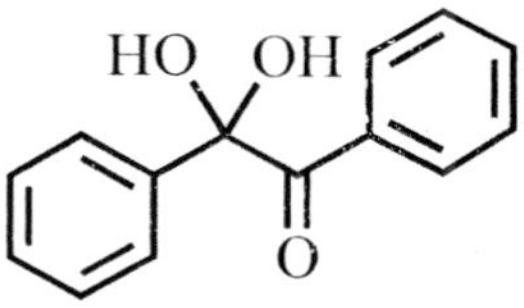

D)

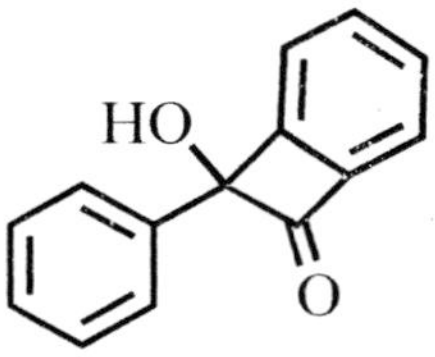

E)

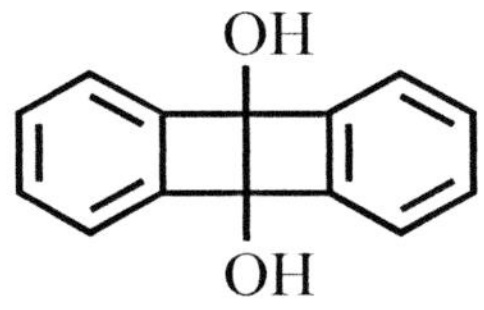

OH

OH

Ans: A

12. What product would be expected to result from the reaction sequence shown?

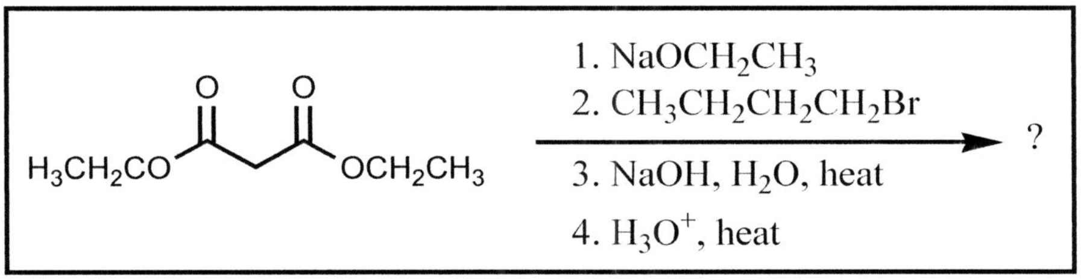

H₃CH₂CO

O O

OCH₂CH₃

1. NaOCH₂CH₃
2. CH₃CH₂CH₂CH₂Br

3. NaOH, H₂O, heat
4. H₃O⁺, heat

?

A)

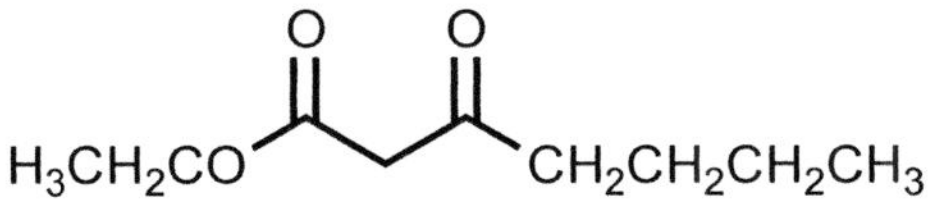

H₃CH₂CO

O O

CH₂CH₂CH₂CH₃

B)

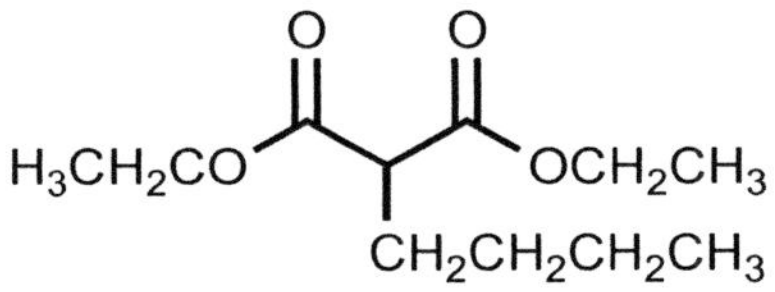

H₃CH₂CO

O O

OCH₂CH₃

CH₂CH₂CH₂CH₃

C)

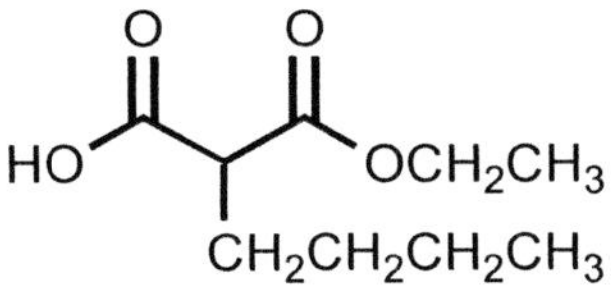

HO

O O

OCH₂CH₃

CH₂CH₂CH₂CH₃

D)

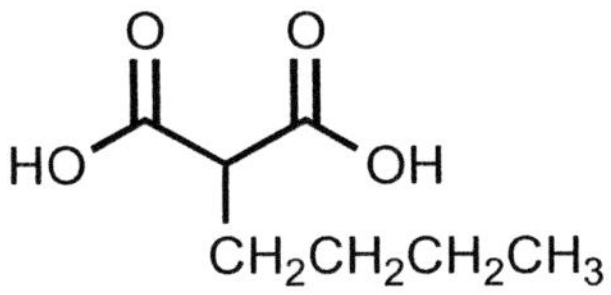

HO

O O

OH

CH₂CH₂CH₂CH₃

E)   HO₂C-CH₂CH₂CH₂CH₂CH₃

Ans: E

13. Which of the following reaction sequences will affect the following transformation?

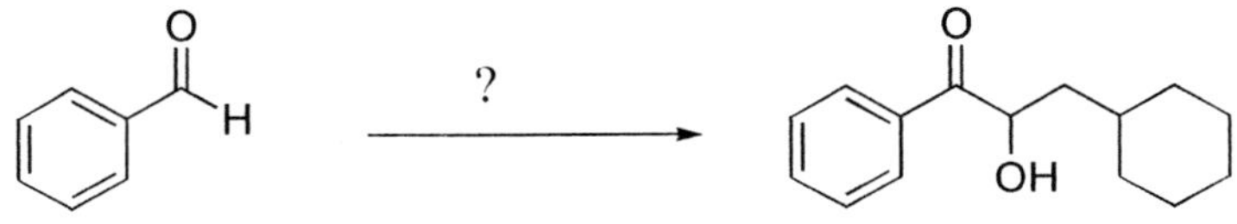

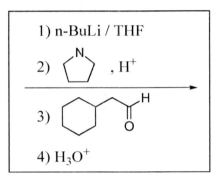

A)

1) n-BuLi / THF

2)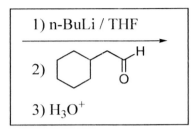

3) H_3O^+

B)

1) n-BuLi / THF

2) [pyrrolidine] , H^+

3)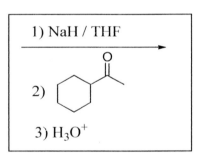

4) H_3O^+

C)

1) NaH / THF

2)

3) H_3O^+

D)

1) $HSCH_2CH_2CH_2SH$ /$ZnCl_2$

2) n-BuLi / THF

3)

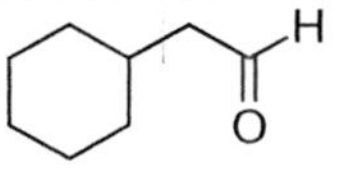

4) H_3O^+

5) $HgCl_2$ / H_2O / $CaCO_3$ / CH_3CN

E)

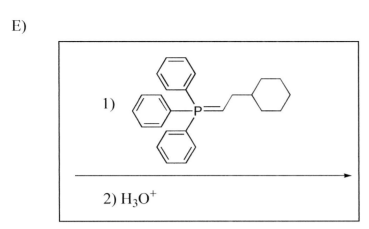

Ans: D

14. Predict the **major** product of the following reaction?

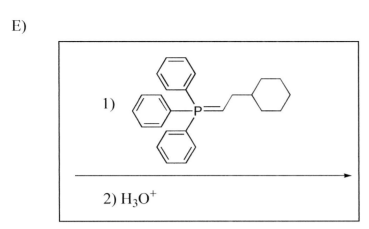

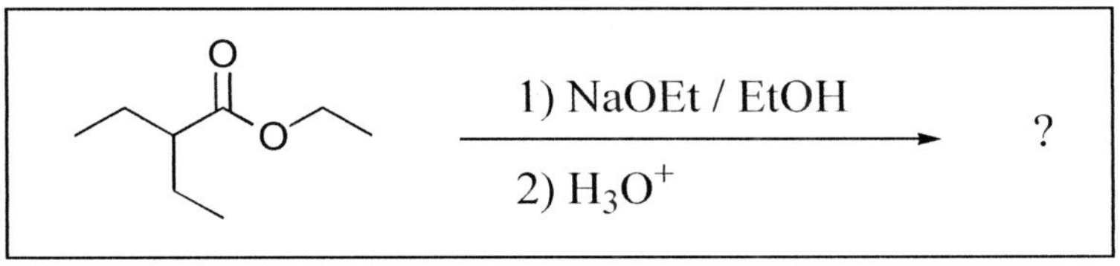

A)

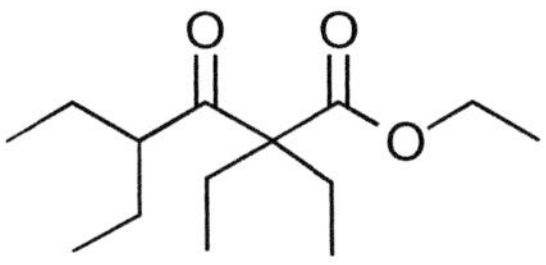

B)

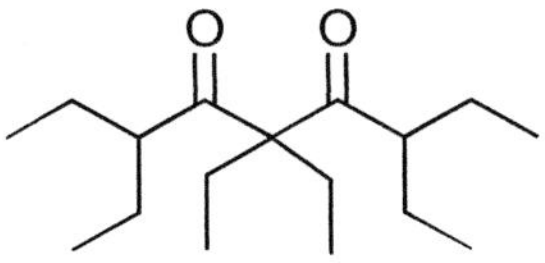

C)

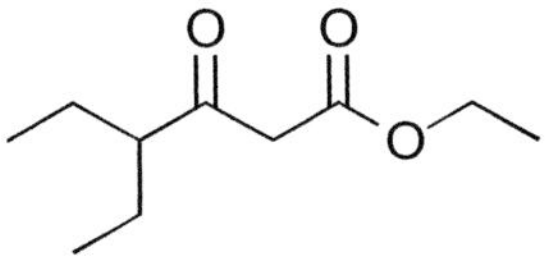

D)

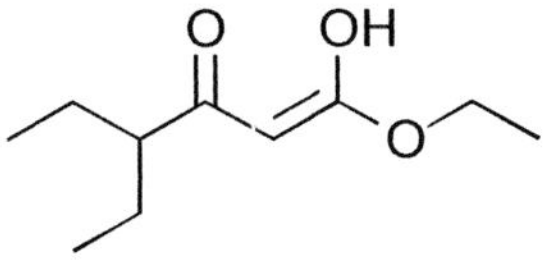

E)   no significant reaction occurs
Ans: E

15. Predict the **major** organic product of the following reaction.

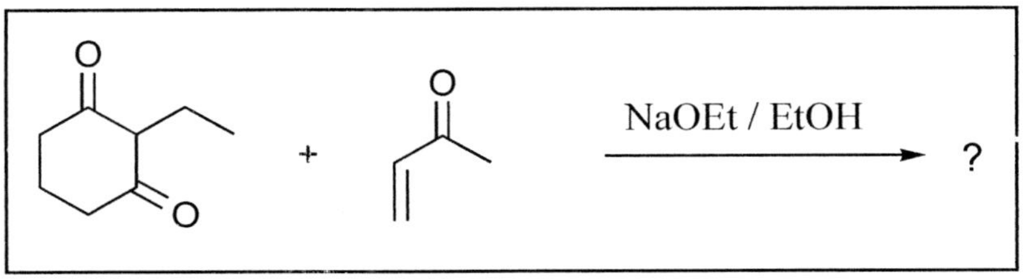

A)

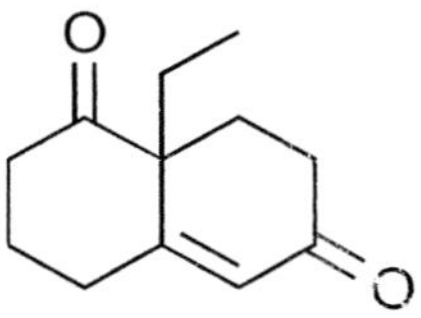

B)

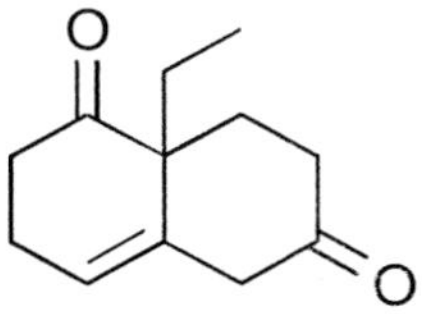

C)

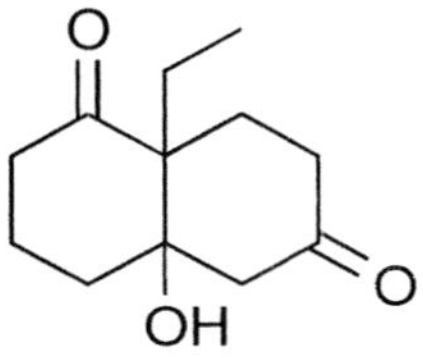

D)

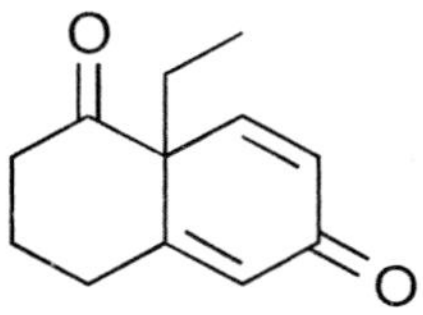

E)

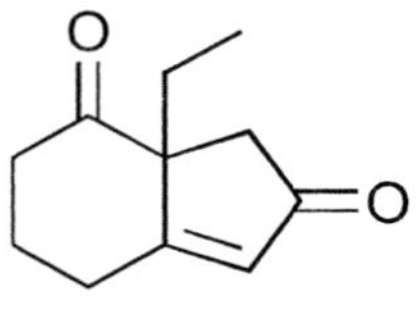

Ans: A

16. What would result from the reaction shown below?

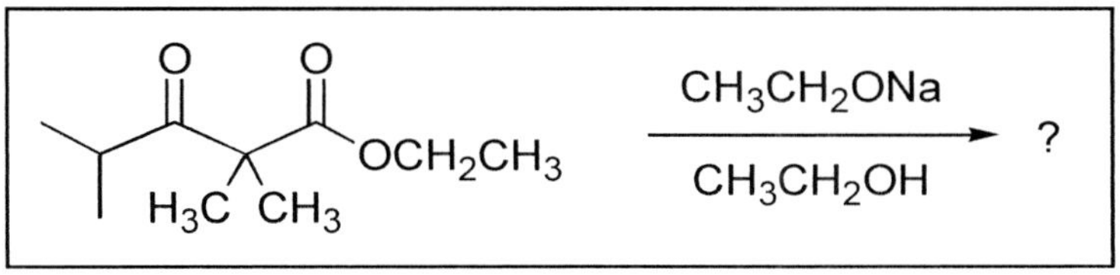

A)

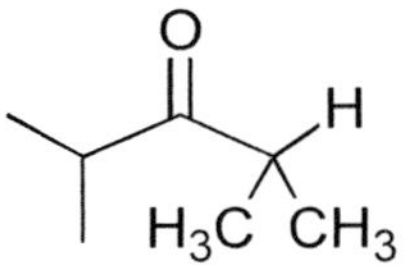

B)

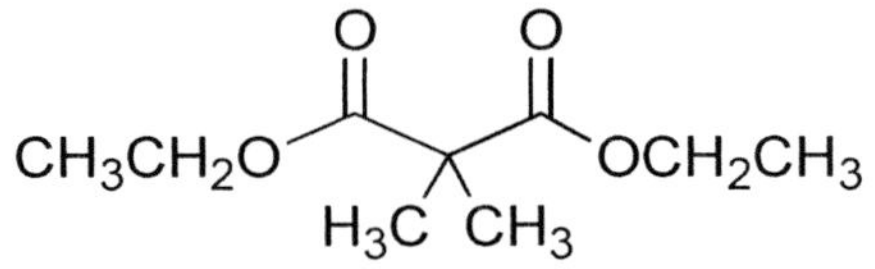

C)

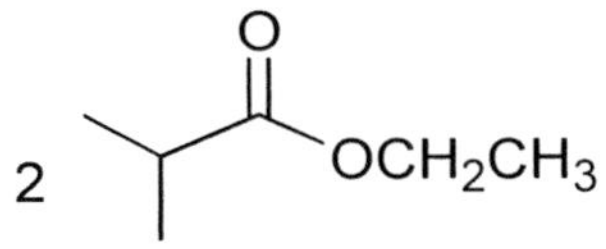

D)

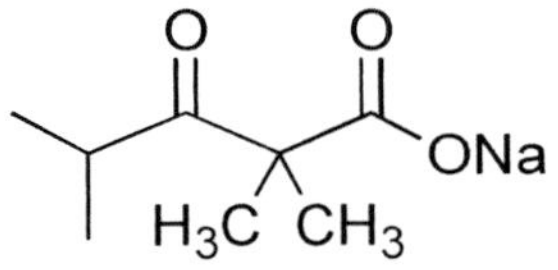

E)

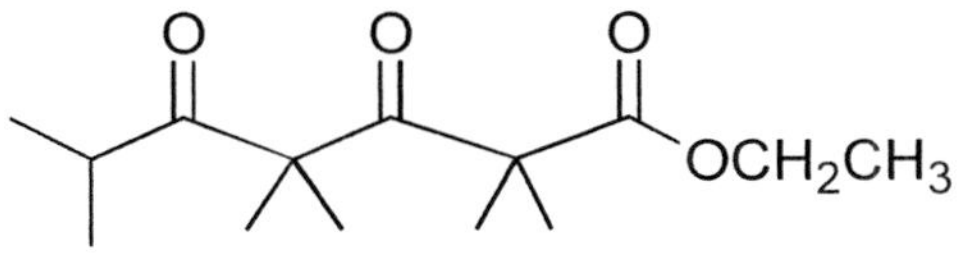

Ans: C

17. What missing reactant would be required to provide the product shown?

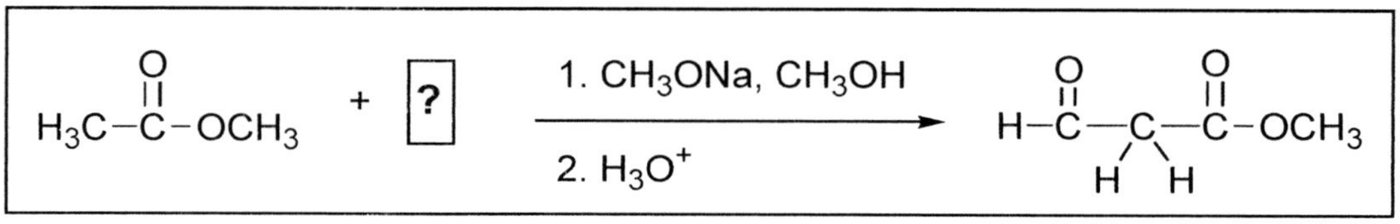

$$H_3C-\overset{\overset{\displaystyle O}{\|}}{C}-OCH_3 \quad + \quad \boxed{?} \quad \xrightarrow[\text{2. } H_3O^+]{\text{1. } CH_3ONa, CH_3OH} \quad H-\overset{\overset{\displaystyle O}{\|}}{C}-\underset{\underset{\displaystyle H \quad H}{\diagup \backslash}}{C}-\overset{\overset{\displaystyle O}{\|}}{C}-OCH_3$$

A)

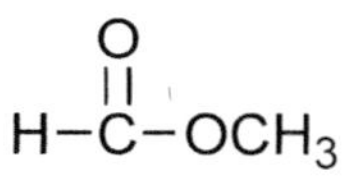

$$H-\overset{\overset{\displaystyle O}{\|}}{C}-OCH_3$$

B)

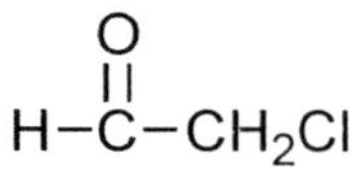

$$H-\overset{\overset{\displaystyle O}{\|}}{C}-CH_2Cl$$

C) $H_2C=O$

D)

$$CH_3O-\overset{\overset{\displaystyle O}{\|}}{C}-OCH_3$$

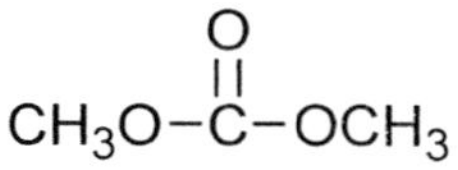

E)   None of these would work.

Ans: A

18. What problem is encountered in the synthesis of ethyl acetoacetate (shown below) if sodium methoxide is used rather than sodium ethoxide?

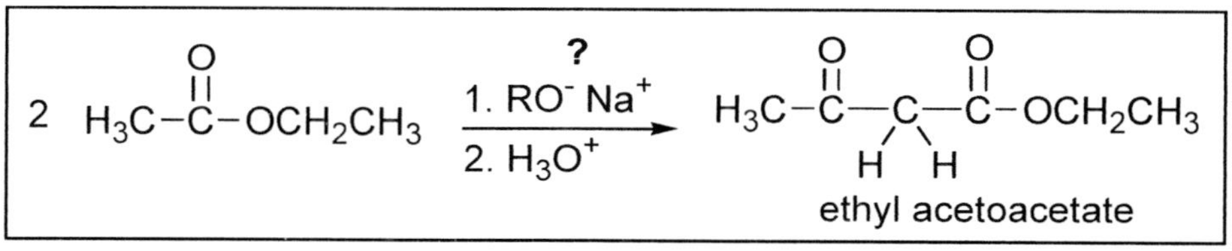

$$2 \;\; H_3C-\overset{\overset{\displaystyle O}{\|}}{C}-OCH_2CH_3 \quad \xrightarrow[\text{2. } H_3O^+]{\overset{\displaystyle ?}{\text{1. } RO^-\, Na^+}} \quad H_3C-\overset{\overset{\displaystyle O}{\|}}{C}-\underset{\underset{\displaystyle H \quad H}{\diagup \backslash}}{C}-\overset{\overset{\displaystyle O}{\|}}{C}-OCH_2CH_3$$

ethyl acetoacetate

A)   Sodium methoxide is too weak a base to cause this reaction to occur.
B)   The condensation proceeds further to give tri-carbonyl products.
C)   The reaction would produce some of both the methyl ester and the ethyl ester.
D)   Sodium methoxide is too insoluble in methanol to promote the reaction.
E)   Sodium methoxide is not basic enough to drive the reaction to completion.

Ans: C

19. Predict the **major** product of the following reaction.

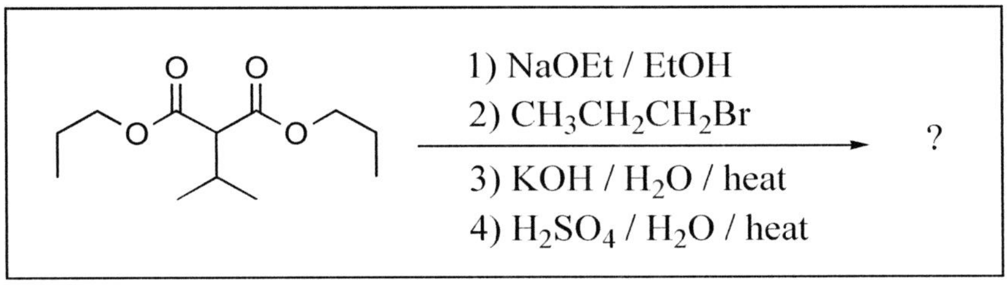

1) NaOEt / EtOH
2) $CH_3CH_2CH_2Br$
3) KOH / H_2O / heat
4) H_2SO_4 / H_2O / heat

?

A)

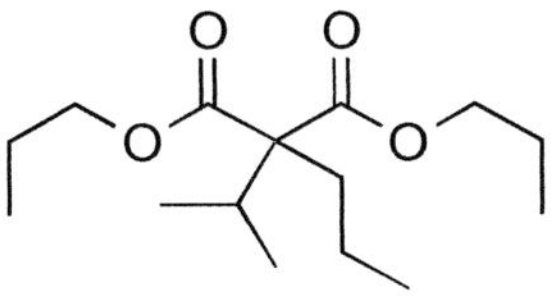

B)

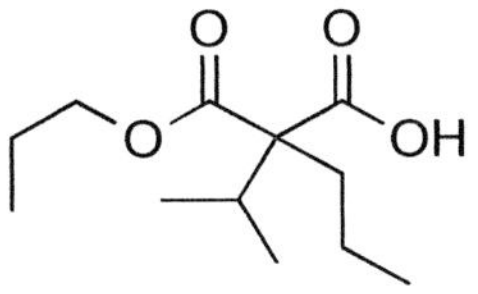

C)

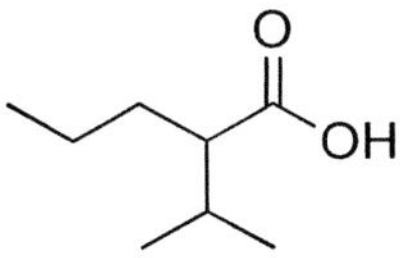

D)

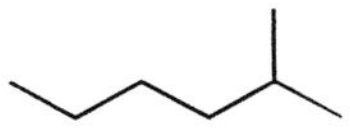

E)

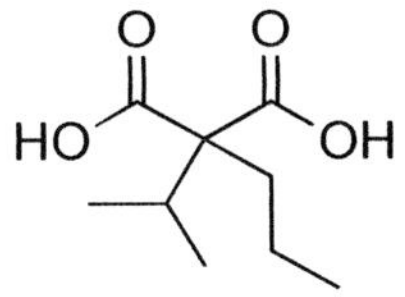

Ans: C

20. Which of the following compounds will **not** readily undergo decarboxylation (loss of CO_2) upon heating in an appropriate solvent?

A)

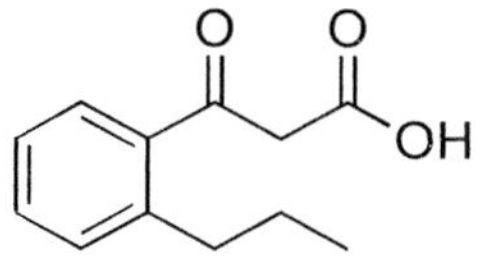

B)

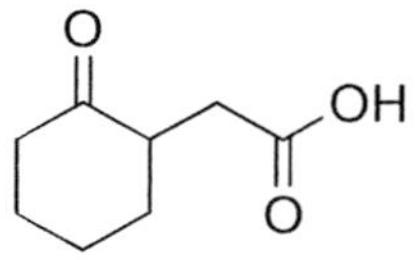

C)

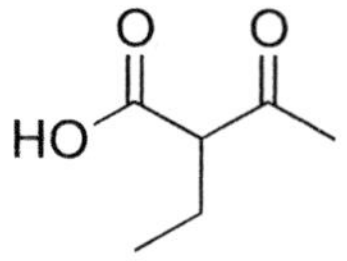

D)

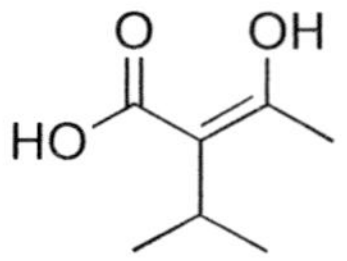

E)

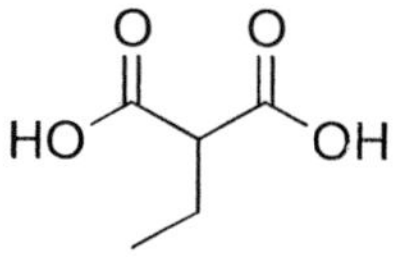

Ans: B

21. Predict the **major** product of the following reaction.

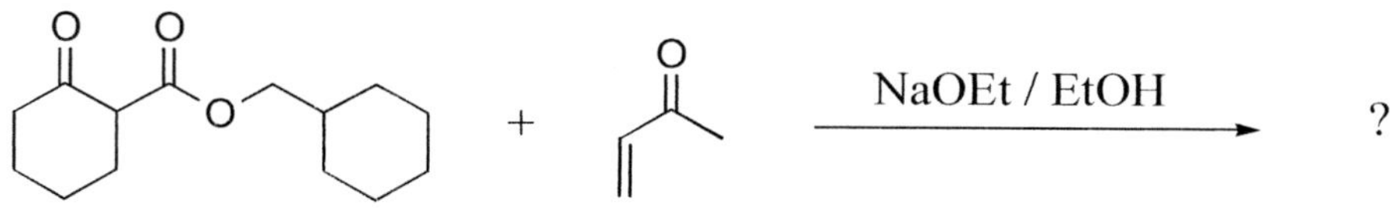

$$+ \quad \xrightarrow{\text{NaOEt / EtOH}} \quad ?$$

A)

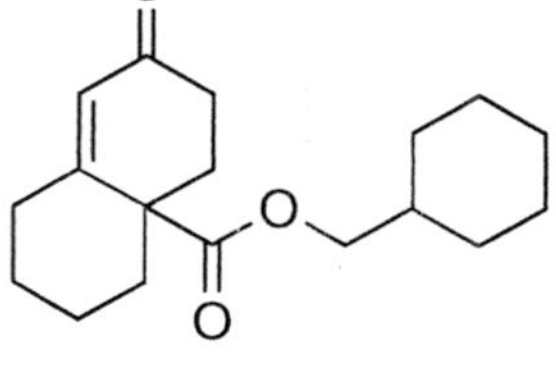

B)

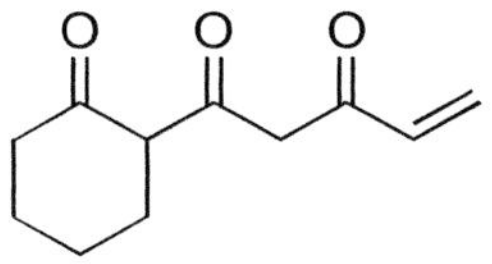

C)

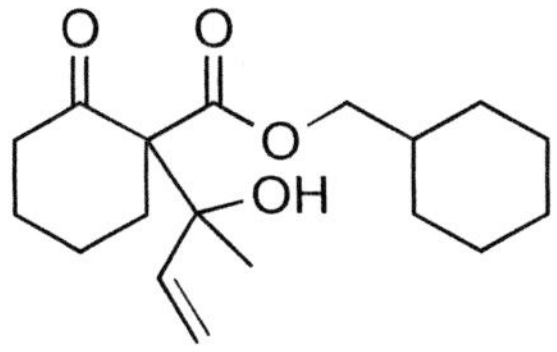

D)

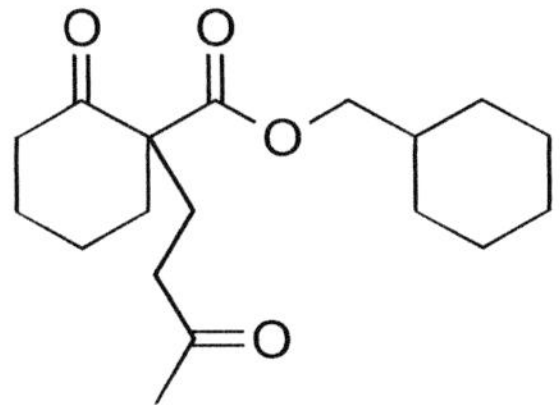

E)

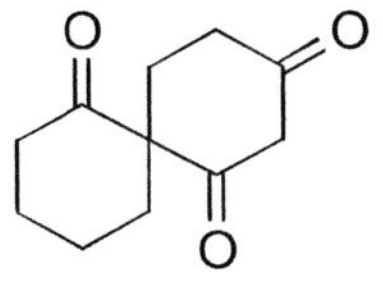

Ans: A

22. What would be the expected product of the following reaction sequence?

$$H_3C-\overset{O}{\overset{\|}{C}}-OCH_2CH_3 \quad \xrightarrow[\text{2. } H_3O^+ \text{ and heat}]{\text{1. } CH_3CH_2O^- \text{ Na}^+} \quad ?$$

A)

$$H_3C-\overset{O}{\overset{\|}{C}}-CH_2-\overset{O}{\overset{\|}{C}}-OCH_2CH_3$$

B)

$$H_3C-\overset{O}{\overset{\|}{C}}-CH_2-\overset{O}{\overset{\|}{C}}-OH$$

C)

$$H_3C-\overset{OH}{\underset{H}{\overset{|}{C}}}-CH_2-\overset{O}{\overset{\|}{C}}-OEt$$

D)

$$H_3C-\overset{O}{\overset{\|}{C}}-CH_3$$

E)

$$H_3C-\overset{O}{\overset{\|}{C}}-OH$$

Ans: D

23. Which of the following processes involves loss of one carbon as carbon dioxide?
    A)   Claisen condensation
    B)   Michael addition
    C)   Malonic ester synthesis
    D)   None involve loss of CO_2
    E)   All involve loss of CO_2
    Ans: C

24. Which would be the most acidic proton in the molecule below?

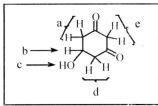

    A) Protons a   B) Proton b   C) Proton c   D) Protons d   E) Protons e
    Ans: E

25. After treatment with aqueous base + heat, followed by acidification to pH 2 followed by heating, which carbon in the molecule below would be lost as carbon dioxide?

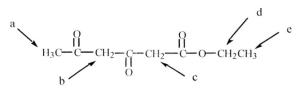

    A) Carbon a   B) Carbon b   C) Carbon c   D) Carbon d   E) Carbon e
    Ans: A

26. Which of the indicated hydrogens would be the most acidic?

    A)   Hydrogens a
    B)   Hydrogens b
    C)   Hydrogens c
    D)   Hydrogens d
    E)   Hydrogens e
    Ans: B

27. What product do you expect from the following reaction?

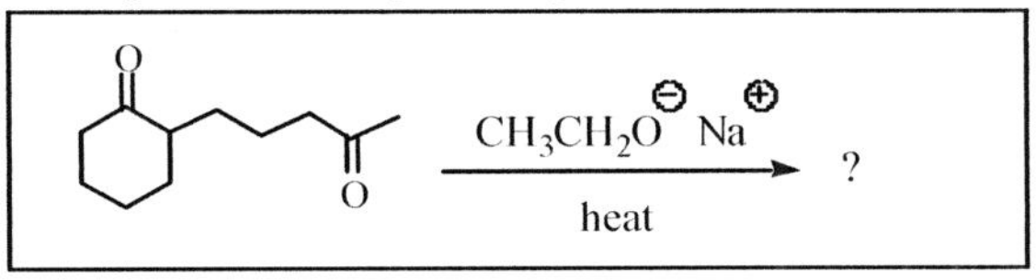

A)

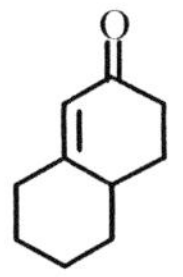

B)

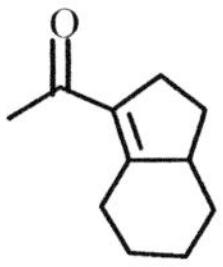

C)

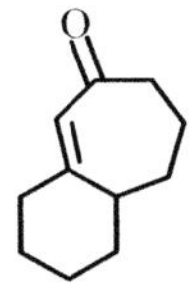

D)   some of these would be formed
E)   none of these would be formed

Ans: B

28. What product do you expect from the following reaction?

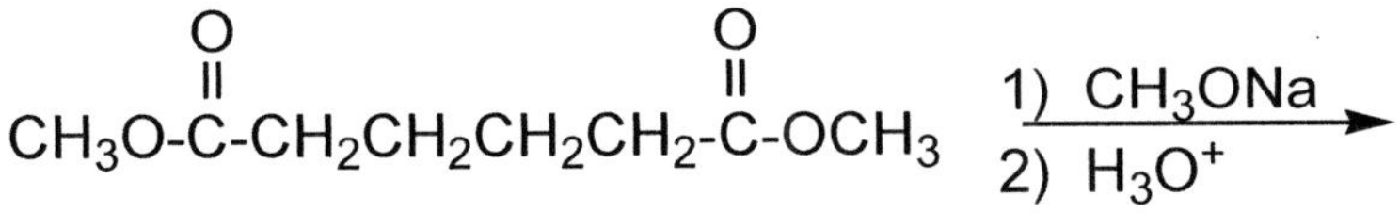

A)

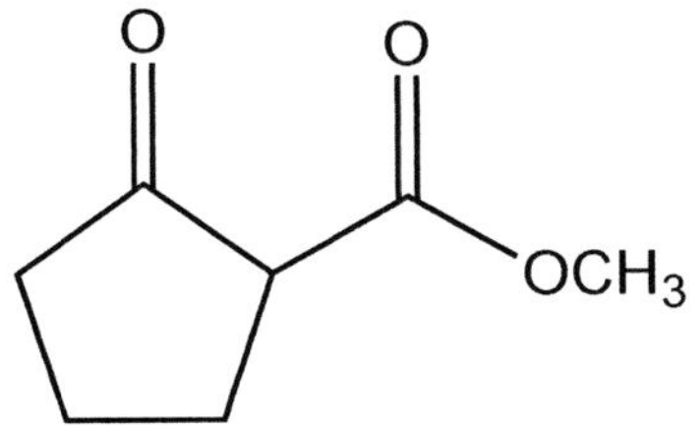

B)

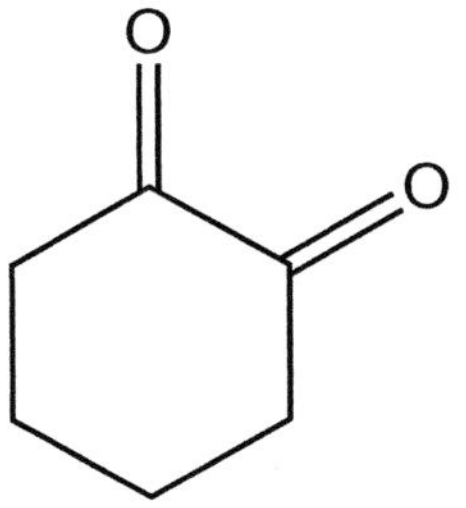

C)

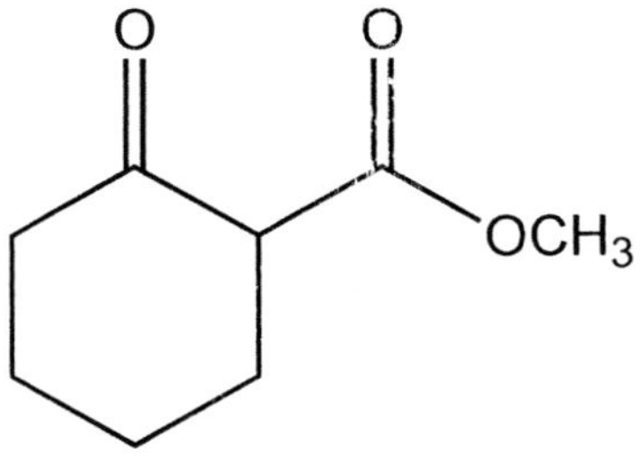

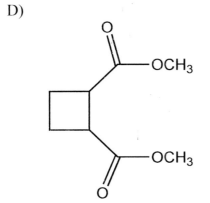

D)

E)

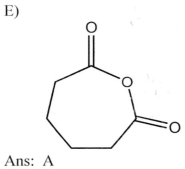

Ans: A

29. What product do you expect from the following reaction?

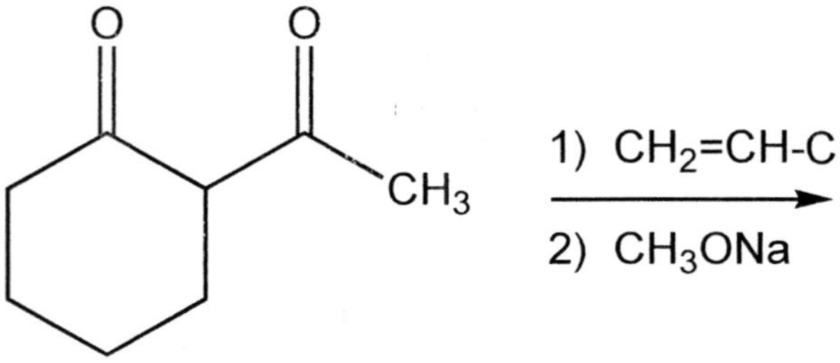

1) $CH_2=CH-C\equiv N$

2) CH_3ONa

A)

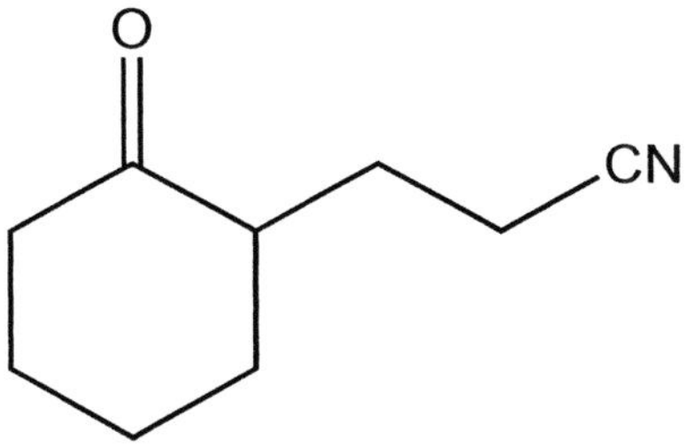

B)

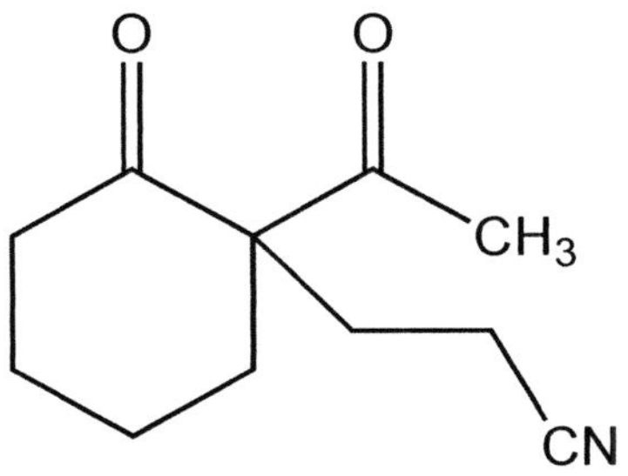

C)

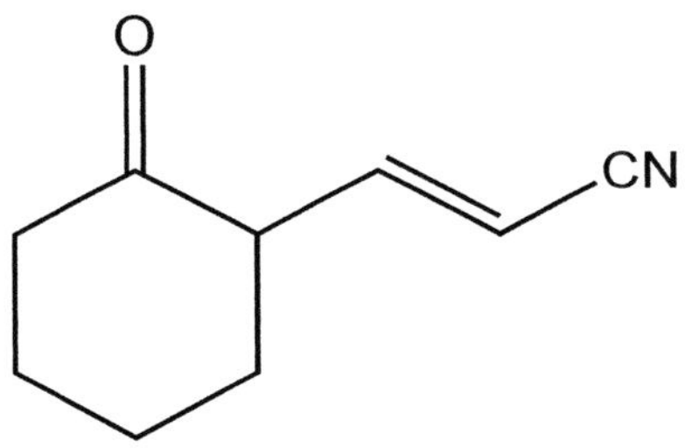

D)

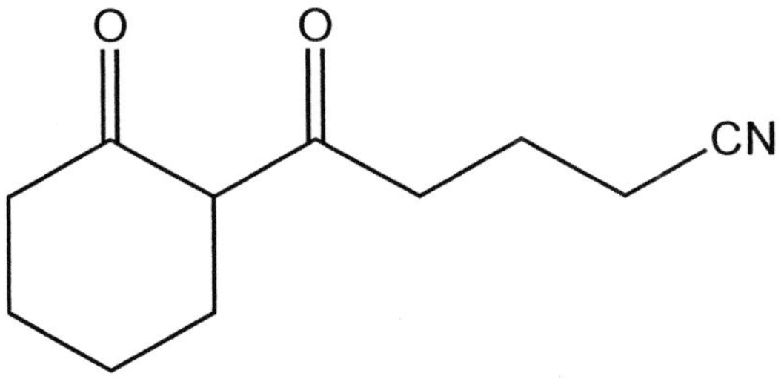

E)

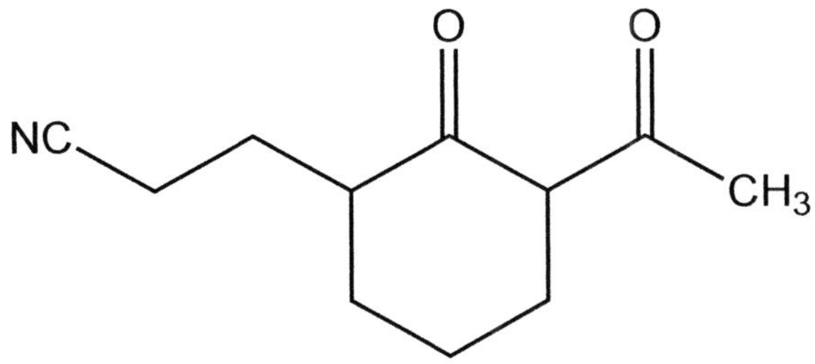

Ans: B

30. What product do you expect from the following reaction?

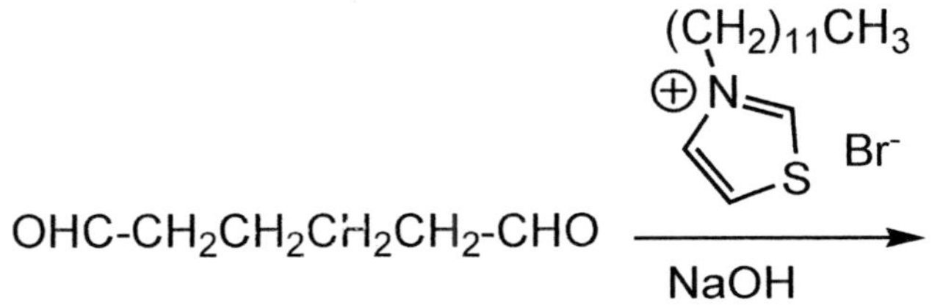
(CH2)11CH3
N
S
Br-
OHC-CH2CH2CH2CH2-CHO
NaOH

A)

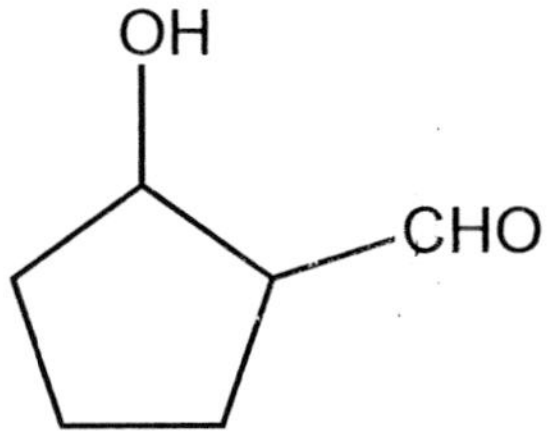
OH
CHO

B)

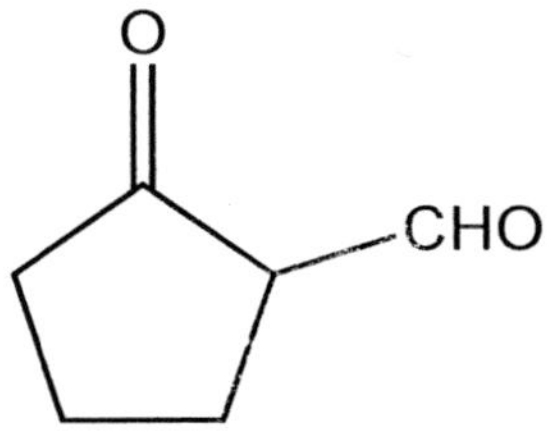
O
CHO

C)

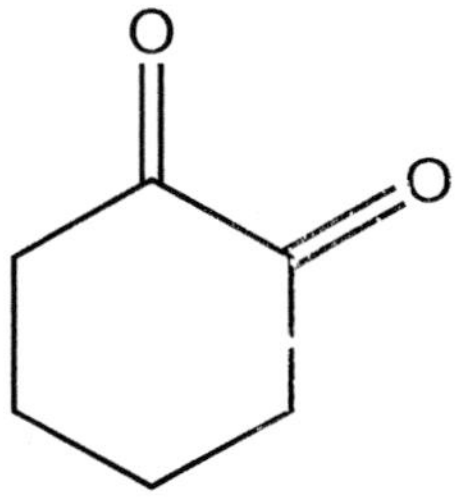
O
O

D)

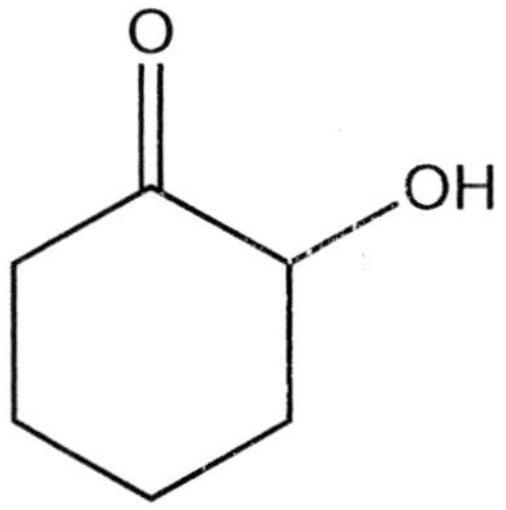
O
OH

E) no reaction

Ans: D

Chapter 24: Carbohydrates: Polyfunctional Compounds in Nature

1. What would be the name of the following sugar?

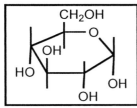

A)   β-D-glucopyranose
B)   α-D-galactopyranose
C)   α-D-glucopyranose

D)   β-D-galactopyranose
E)   β-D-glucofuranose

Ans: C

2. Which compound would result from the following reaction?

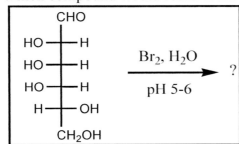

A)

B)

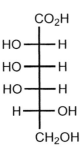

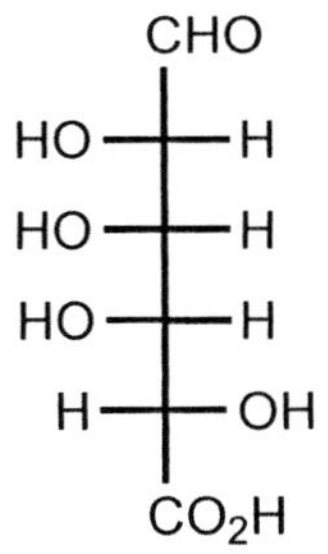

C)

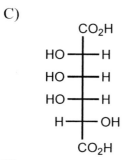

D)

E)

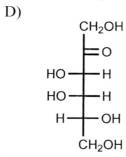

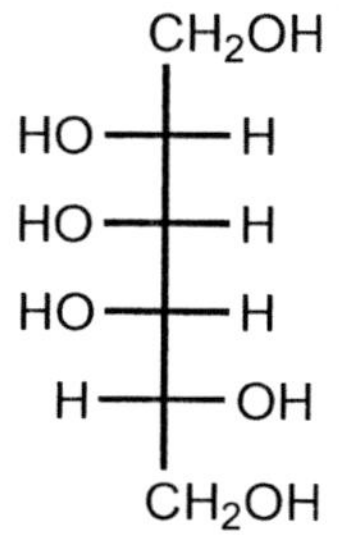

Ans: A

3. Which one of the following could **not** rotate plane polarized light?
A)

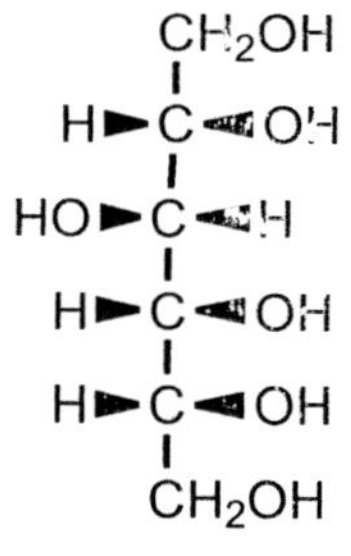

CH_2OH
H—C—OH
HO—C—H
H—C—OH
H—C—OH
CH_2OH

B)

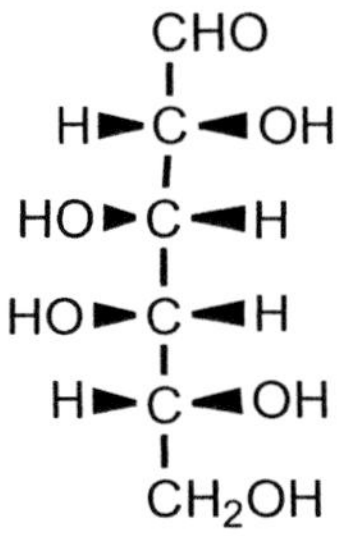

```
            CHO
             |
      H►C◄OH
             |
    HO►C◄H
             |
    HO►C◄H
             |
      H►C◄OH
             |
           CH2OH
```

C)

```
            CO2H
             |
      H►C◄OH
             |
    HO►C◄H
             |
      H►C◄OH
             |
      H►C◄OH
             |
           CH2OH
```

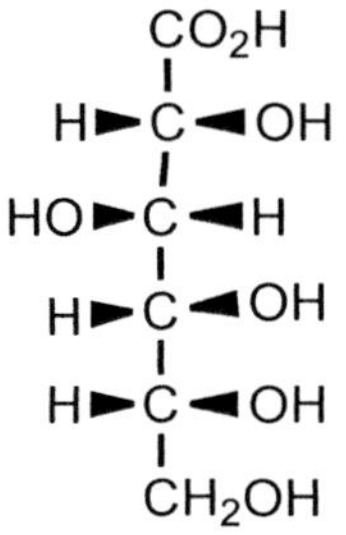

D)

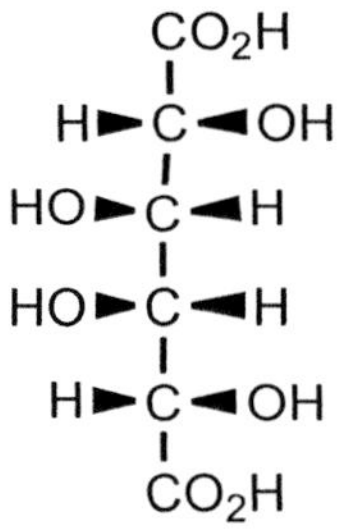

```
            CO2H
             |
      H►C◄OH
             |
    HO►C◄H
             |
    HO►C◄H
             |
      H►C◄OH
             |
           CO2H
```

E)

```
            CHO
             |
      H►C◄OH
             |
      H►C◄OH
             |
      H►C◄OH
             |
           CH2OH
```

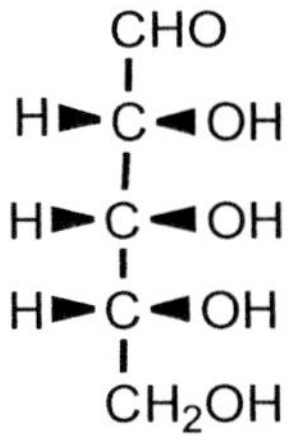

Ans: D

4. Bromine is a dense, deep red-brown liquid obtained by the oxidation of bromide ion in seawater. Bromine is very toxic. Which of the following reactions of bromine with organic materials would be **least** likely in a biological system (would **not** occur)?
   A) Addition to non-aromatic carbon-carbon double bonds (e.g., in fatty acids)
   B) Electrophillic aromatic substitution of very activated aromatic rings (e.g., in tyrosine, a phenol)
   C) Oxidation of aldoses to aldonic acids (e.g., CHO to CO_2H)
   D) α-bromination of fatty acids (e.g., $RCH_2CO_2H \rightarrow ?RCHBrCO_2H$)
   E) None of these reactions could occur in living systems
   Ans: D

5. Which of the reactions listed below would be catalyzed by a *glycosidase* enzyme?
   A)   glucose 6-phosphate ⟶ fructose 6-phosphate

   B)   sucrose ⟶ invert sugar

   C)   cellulose ⟶ glucose

   D)   amylose ⟶ glucose

   E)   glucose 6-phosphate ⟶ glucose + phosphate ion

   Ans: B

6. What would be the name of the following sugar structure?

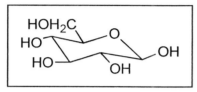

   A)   α-D-galactopyranose   D)   α-D-glucopyranose
   B)   β-D-glucopyranose   E)   β-D-galactofuranose
   C)   β-D-galactopyranose
   Ans: B

7. What would be the name of the following sugar?

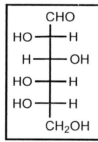

   A) D-glucose   B) L-glucose   C) L-galactose   D) L-mannose   E) D-mannose
   Ans: B

8. What would result from the following series of reactions?

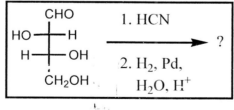

A)

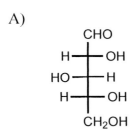

B)

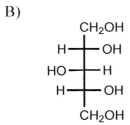

C)

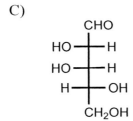

D)

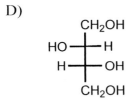

E)   both A and C

Ans: E

9. Which of the following would be a reducing sugar (i.e., react with Ag+)?
    A)

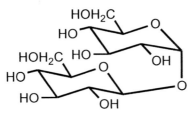

B)

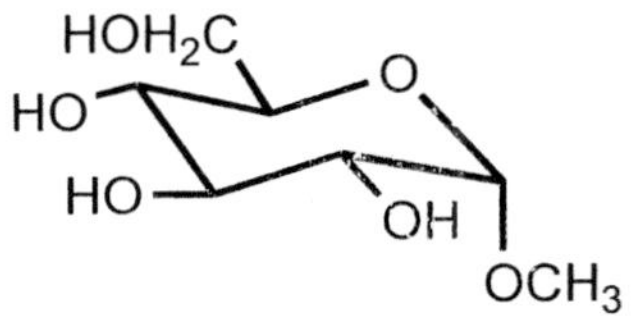

C)

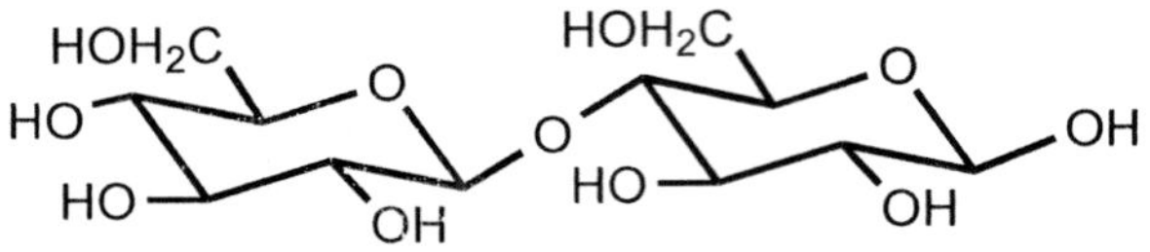

D)

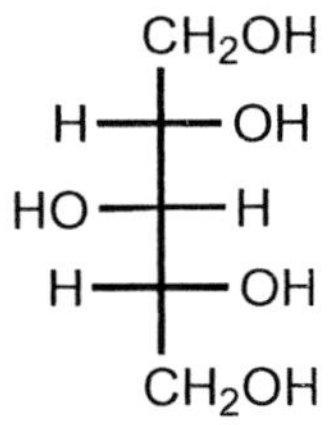

CH$_2$OH
H——OH
HO——H
H——OH
CH$_2$OH

E)

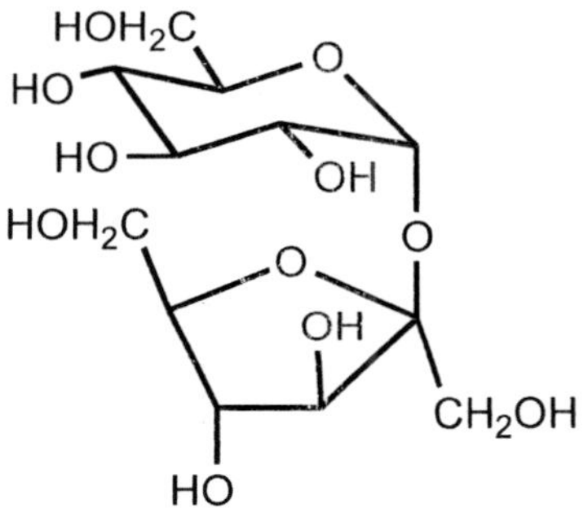

Ans: C

10. Qualitatively (not quantitatively), what products would be formed from the following reaction?

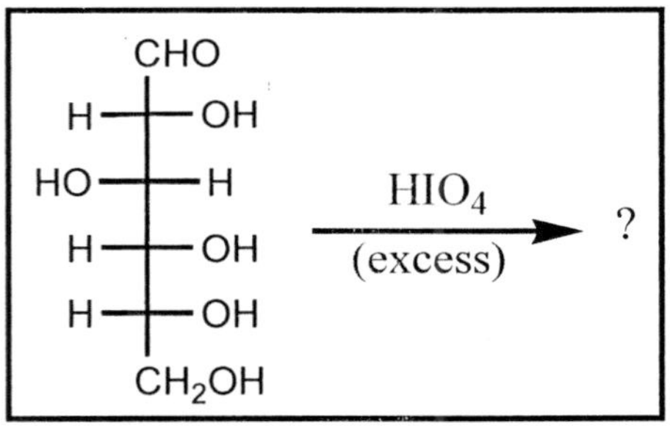

CHO
H——OH
HO——H   HIO$_4$?
H——OH   (excess)
H——OH
CH$_2$OH

A) CO_2

B) CH_2O

C)

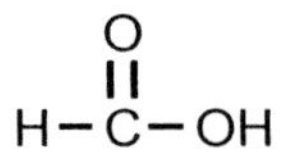

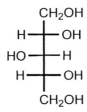

D) both B and C

E) A, B and C

Ans: D

11. Which of the following would you expect to exhibit **mutarotation**?

A)

B)

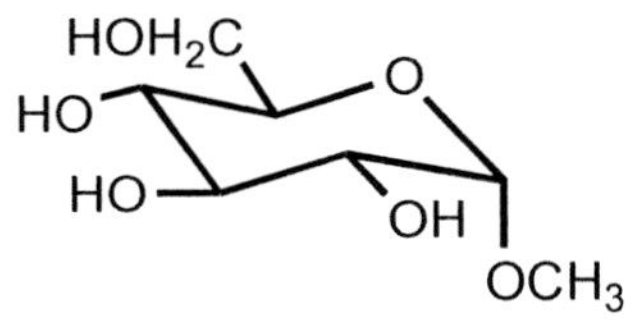

C)

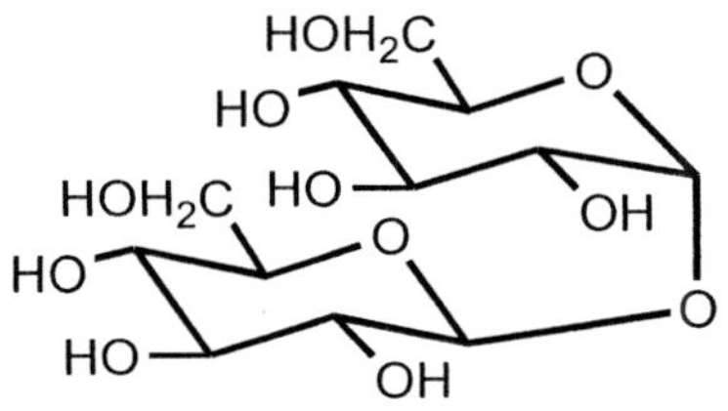

D)

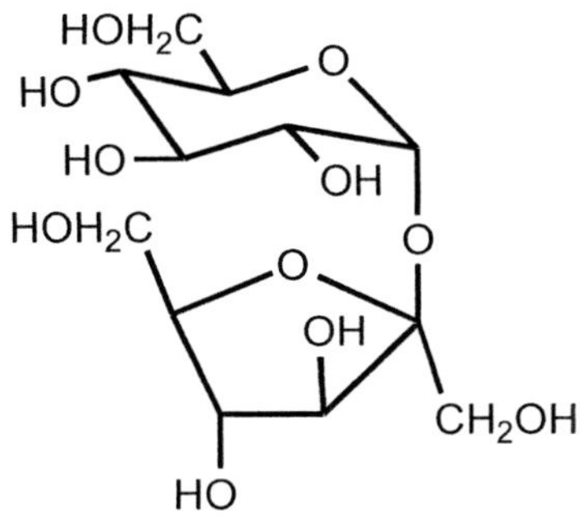

E)

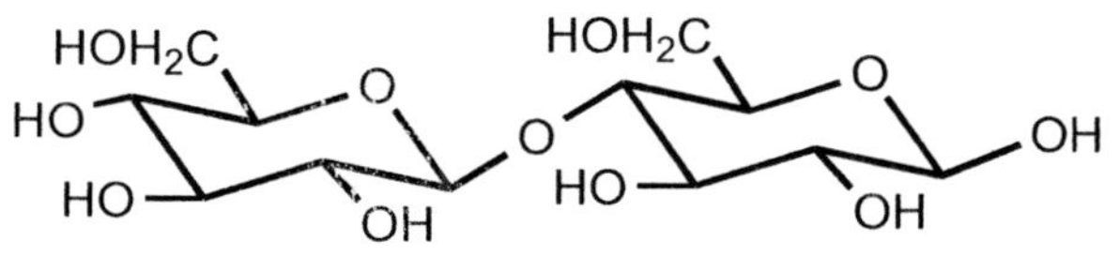

Ans: E

12. In which of the following is a **typical** (most common) disaccharide linkage present (i.e., in what way does nature link most di- and poly-saccharides: 1,1' vs 1,2' vs 1,3' vs 1,4' vs 1,6')?

A)

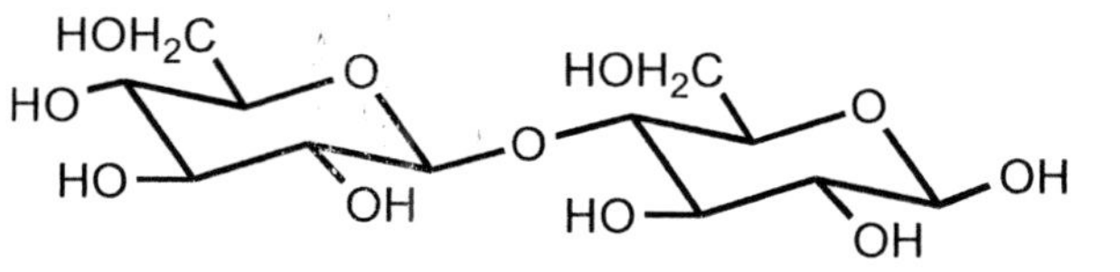

B)

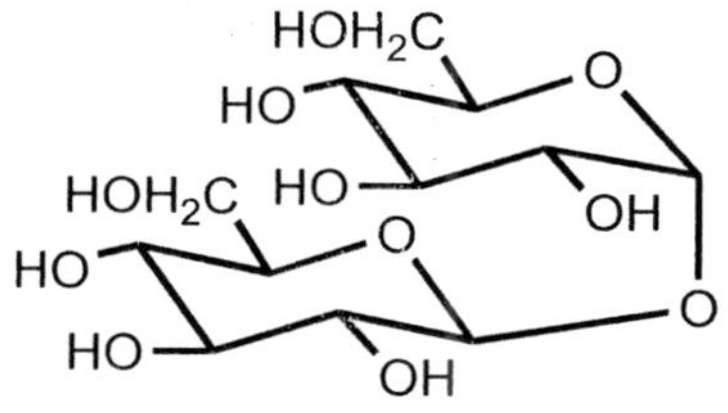

C)

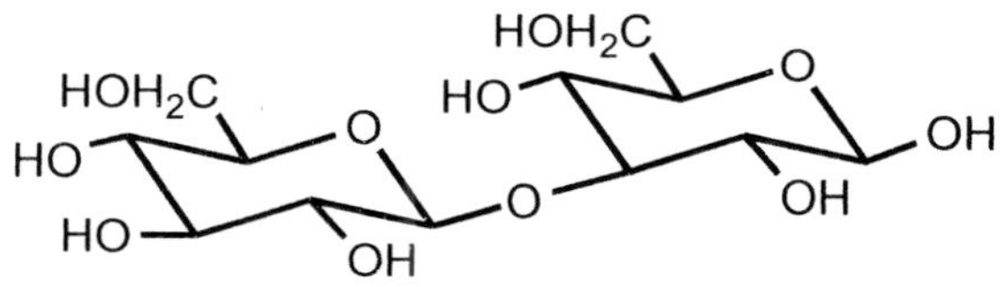

D)

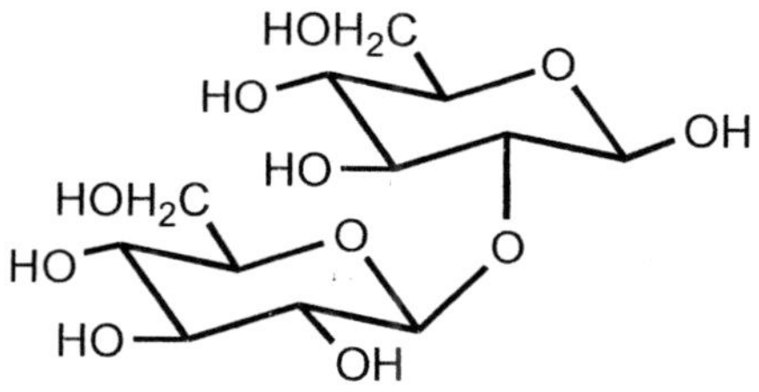

E)

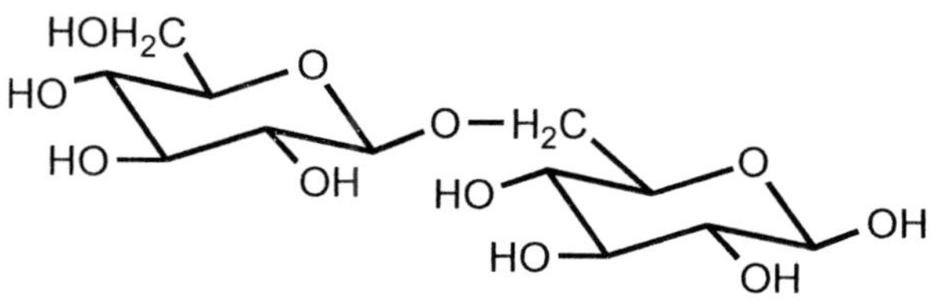

Ans: A

13. What would result from the reactions shown below?

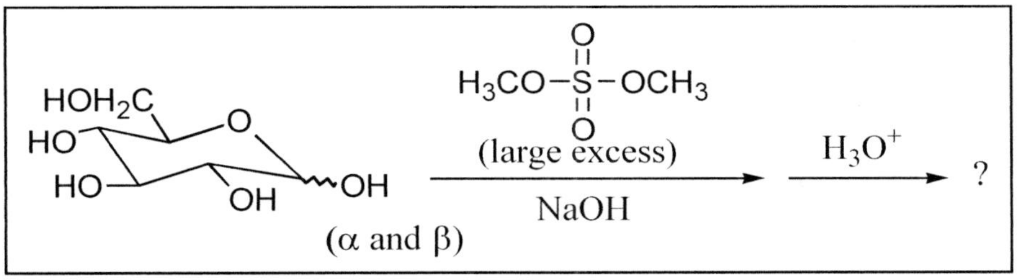

A)

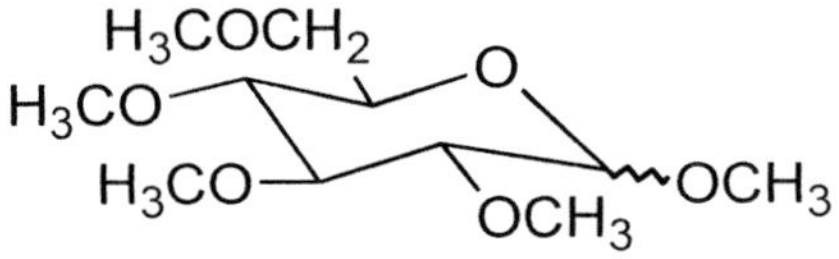

B)

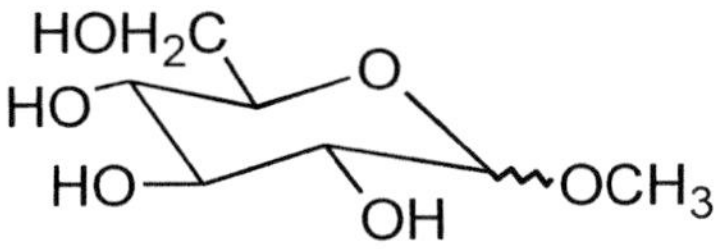

C)

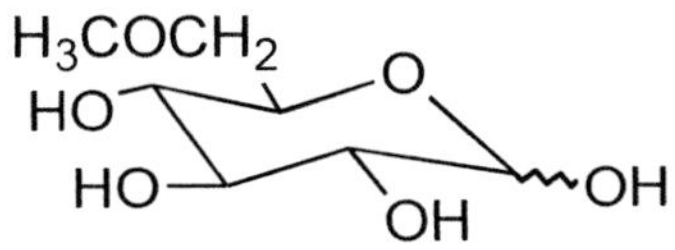

D)

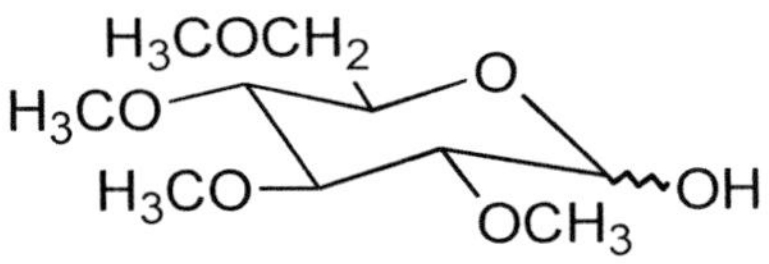

E)

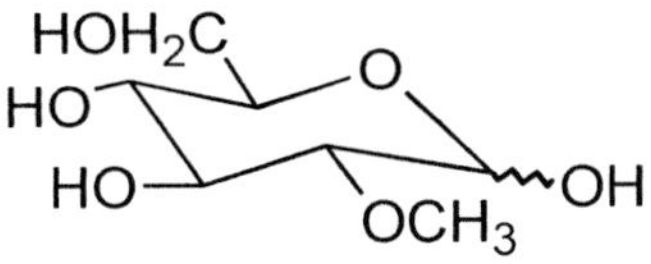

Ans: D

14. What would result from the reaction shown below?

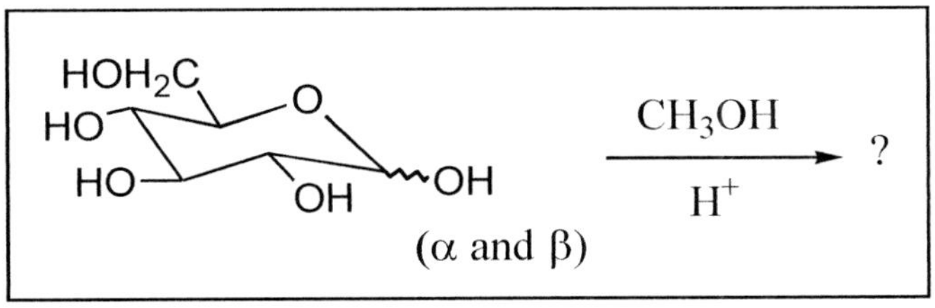

A)

B)

C)

D)

E)

Ans: B

15. Which disaccharide possesses a 1,1' linkage?
    A) Cellobiose B) Maltose C) Lactose D) Sucrose E) Glubose
    Ans: D

16. The main difference between the two forms of starch, amylose and amylopectin, is what?
    A) Amylose is more soluble in water than is amylopectin.
    B) Amylose is a linear polymer while amylopectin is branched.
    C) Amylopectin has a lower molecular weight than amylose.
    D) Amylose is metabolized in mammals, while amylopectin is not.
    E) Amylopectin is metabolized in mammals, while amylose is not.
    Ans: B

17. Which of the following is referred to as the **anomeric carbon**?

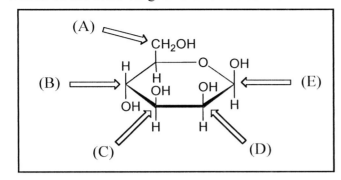

A) A   B) B   C) C   D) D   E) E

Ans: E

18. Predict the major product of the following reaction.

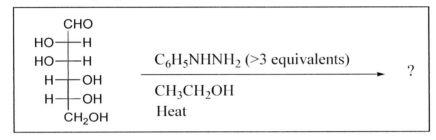

A)

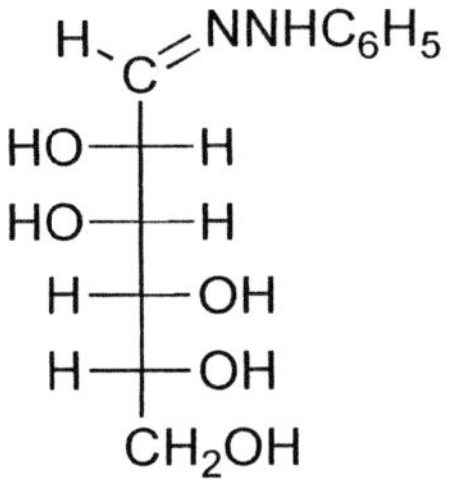

H-C=NNHC₆H₅ structure

B)

H-C=NNHC₆H₅ structure

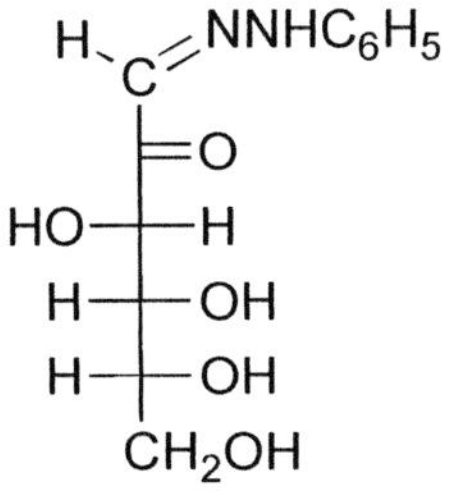

C)

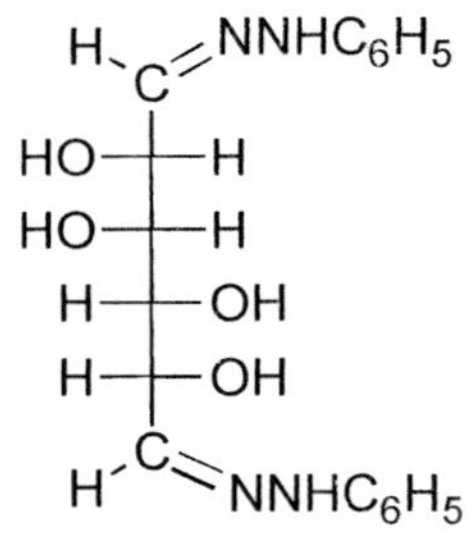

D)

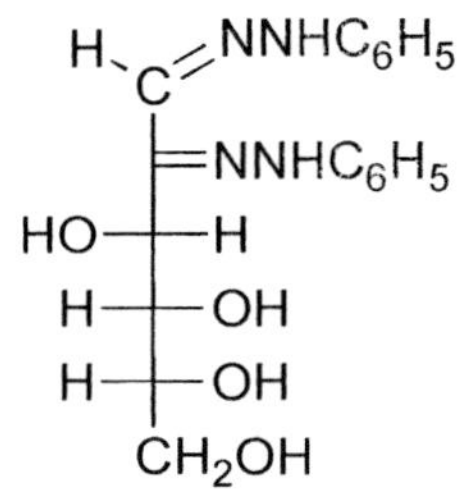

E)

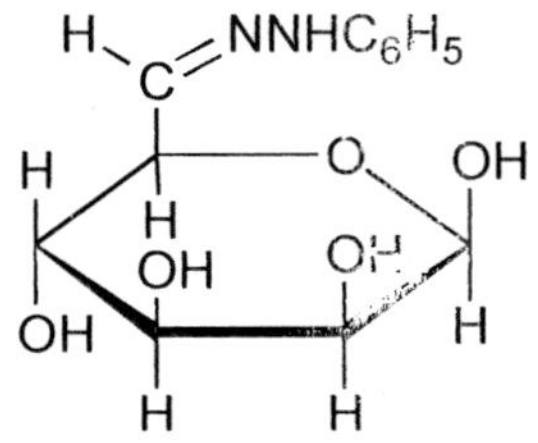

Ans: D

19. The chair conformation for α-D-Glucopyranose (shown below) may also be correctly represented by which of the following Haworth projections?

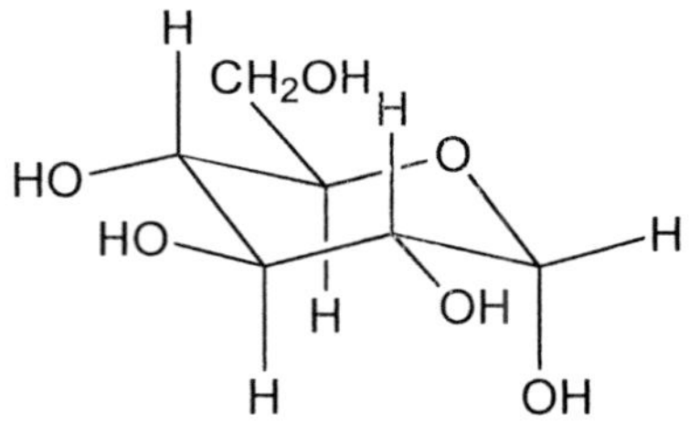

A)

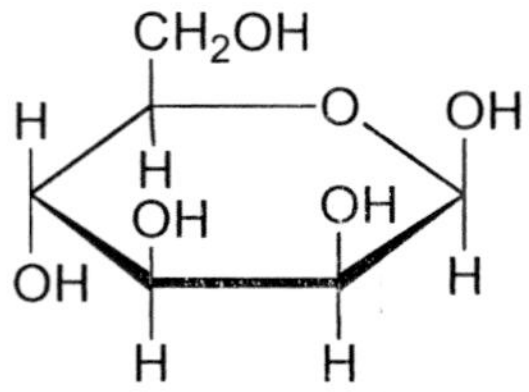

B)

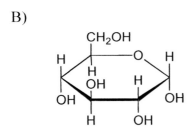

C)

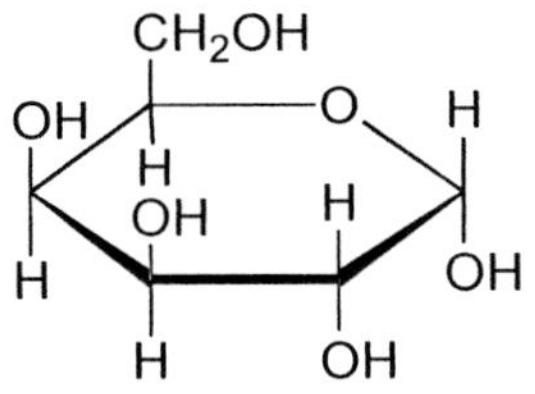

D)

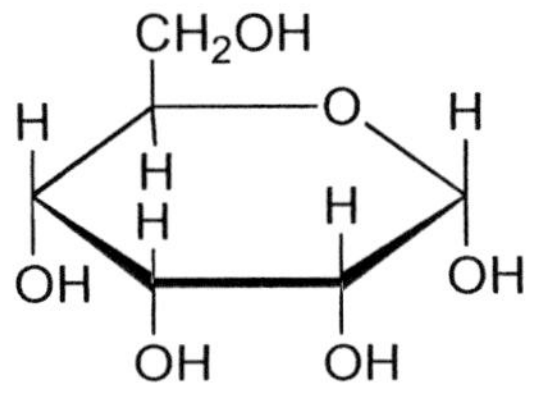

E)

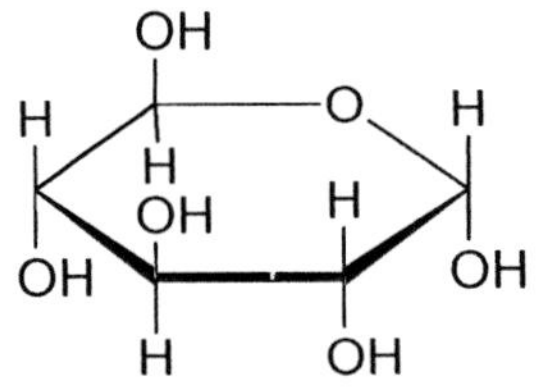

Ans: B

20. D-(+)-Glucose and D-(+)-Mannose have the same molecular formula ($C_6H_{12}O_6$). Which of the following describes the relationship between these two sugars?

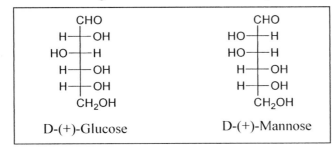

A) Constitutional isomers   D) Anomers
B) Diastereomers   E) no correct answer
C) Enantiomers

Ans: B

21. The term "epimer" is best defined as:
    A)   Molecules which are enantiomers of each other
    B)   Meso compounds
    C)   Any pair of diastereomers
    D)   Two diastereomers that differ in configuration at only one stereocenter
    E)   Racemic mixture
    Ans: D

22. Which of the following represents an L sugar?
    A)
```
          CHO
    H ——— OH
   HO ——— H
    H ——— OH
    H ——— OH
         CH2OH
```
    B)
```
          CHO
    H ——— OH
    H ——— OH
         CH2OH
```
    C)
```
          CHO
   HO ——— H
    H ——— OH
   HO ——— H
   HO ——— H
         CH2OH
```
    D)
```
          CHO
   HO ——— H
   HO ——— H
    H ——— OH
         CH2OH
```
    E)
```
          CHO
   HO ——— H
   HO ——— H
   HO ——— H
    H ——— OH
         CH2OH
```
    Ans: C

23. Which of the following arrows correctly points to the anomeric carbon?

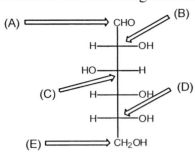

A) Arrow A   B) Arrow B   C) Arrow C   D) Arrow D   E) Arrow E
Ans: A

24. Which of the following "dash-wedge" (zig-zag) structures correclty depicts D-Glucose?

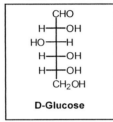

A)

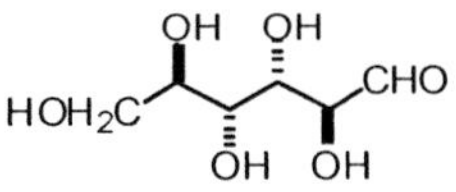

OH OH
HOH₂C   CHO
      OH OH

B)

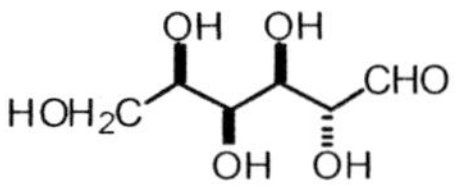

OH OH
HOH₂C   CHO
      OH OH

C)

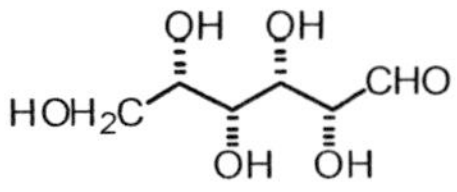

OH OH
HOH₂C   CHO
      OH OH

D)

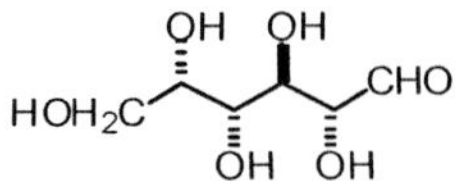

OH OH
HOH₂C   CHO
      OH OH

E)

OH OH
HOH₂C   CHO
      OH OH

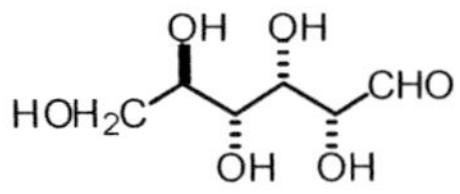

Ans: E

25. Which of the following conformations correctly depicts the structure of: α-D-(+)-Glucopyranose?

A)

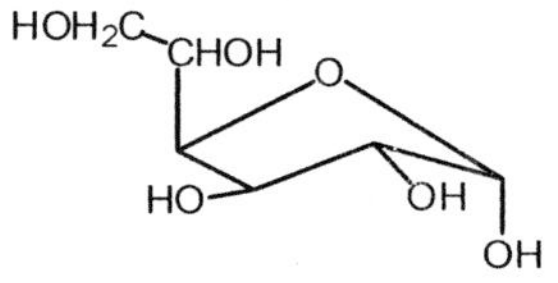

B)

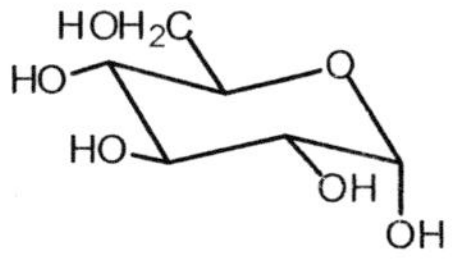

C)

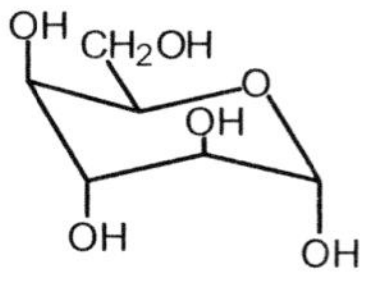

D)

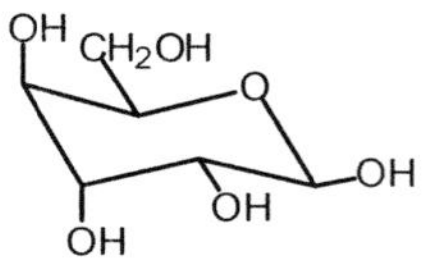

E)

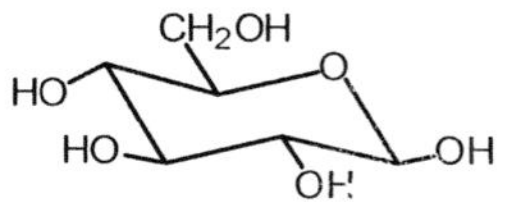

Ans: B

26. Which polysaccharide has β-1,4 glycosidic bonds?
A) Cellulose B) Glycogen C) Amylose D) Amylpectin E) B, C, and D
Ans: A

27. The carbohydrate structures below are related as

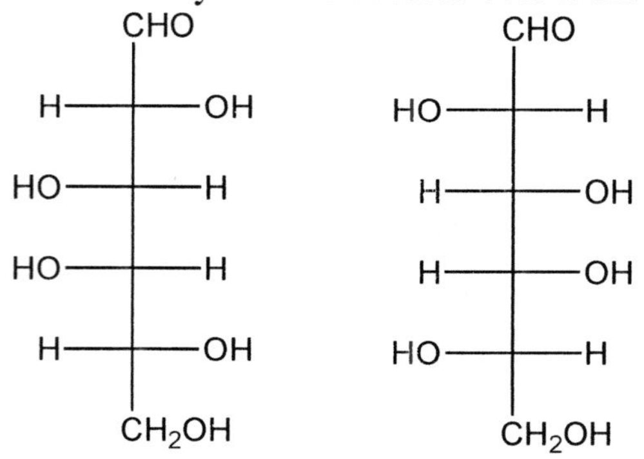

A)   Anomers
B)   Enantiomers
C)   Diastereomers

D)   D and L stereoisomers
E)   both B and D

Ans: E

28. Periodic acid degradation of the following carbohydrate will yield (quantitatively) what products?

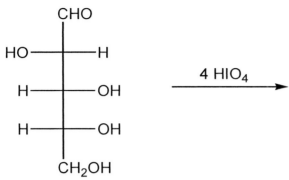

4 HIO$_4$

A)   4 HCO$_2$H + 1 CO$_2$ D)   5 HCHO
B)   3 HCO$_2$H + 1 HCHO + 1 CO$_2$ E)   4 HCHO + 1 CO$_2$
C)   4 HCO$_2$H + 1 HCHO
Ans: C

Chapter 25: Heterocycles: Heteroatoms in Cyclic Organic Compounds

1. Which nitrogen, if either, is the more basic in nicotine?

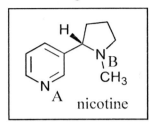

 A) Nitrogen A is more basic.
 B) Nitrogen B is more basic.
 C) The nitrogens are equally basic.
 D) Neither nitrogen is basic.
 E) There is no basis on which to predict this.
 Ans: B

2. Which of the following shows the structure of protonated pyrrole?

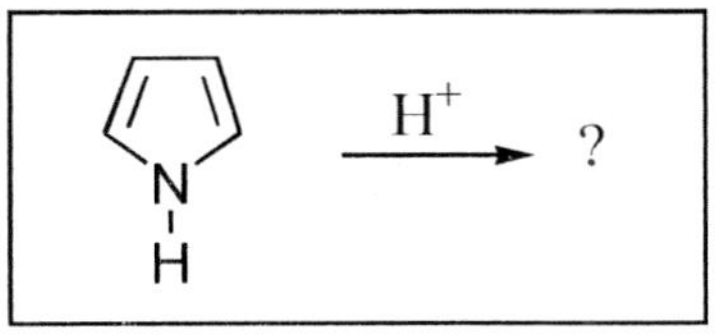

 A)

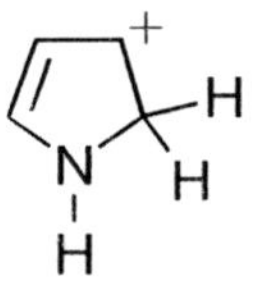

 B)

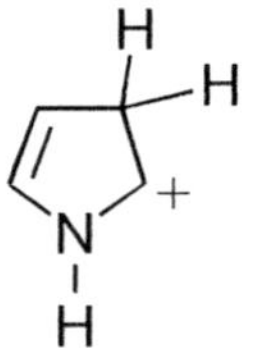

C)

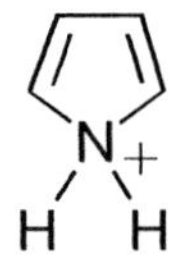

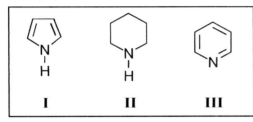

D)

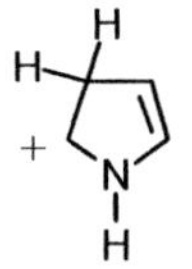

E)   All of the above are important.
Ans: A

3. How would the heterocyclic amines shown here be ranked in order of decreasing basicity (more basic > less basic)?

```
   I          II         III
```

A) III > I > II   B) I > II > III   C) II > III > I   D) I > III > II   E) II > I > III
Ans: C

4. What product do you expect from the reaction shown below?

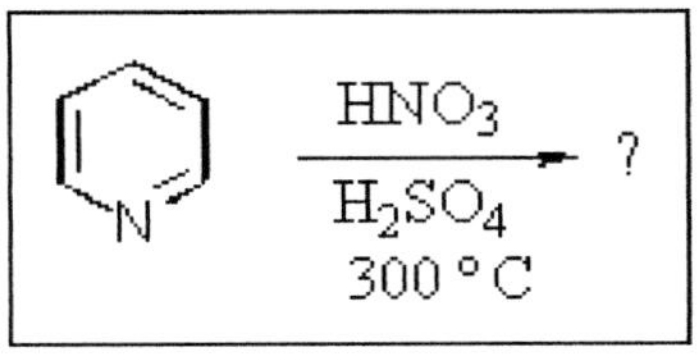

$$\xrightarrow[\substack{H_2SO_4 \\ 300\,^\circ C}]{HNO_3} \quad ?$$

A)

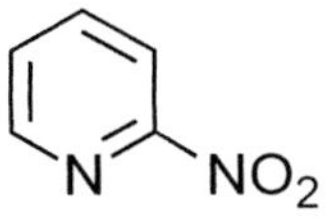

NO_2

B)

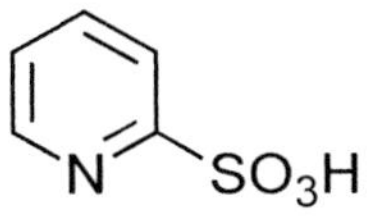

SO_3H

C)

NO_2

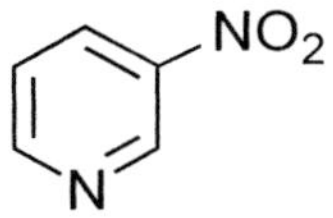

D)

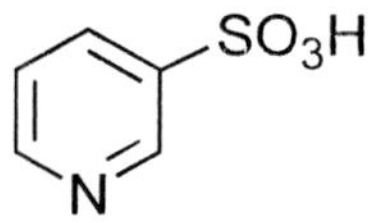

SO$_3$H

E)

NO$_2$

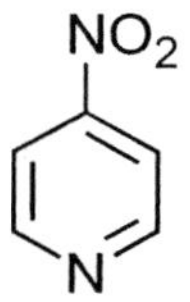

Ans: C

5. In a **formal sense**, what must be included to balance the reaction whereby NADH becomes aromatic?

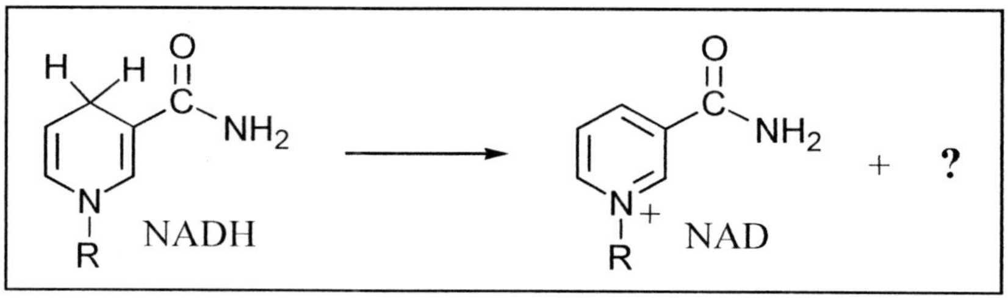

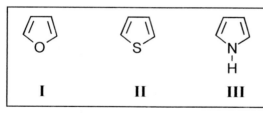

NADH → NAD + ?

A) H$^+$ B) Hï   C) H$^\tilde{n}$ D) H$_2$ E) H$_2$O
Ans: C

6. Rank the following heterocycles in decreasing order of reactivity in electrophilic aromatic substitution:

I   II   III

A) I > II > III   B) II > I > III   C) III > I >> II   D) III > II > I   E) I > III > II
Ans: C

7. Which atom in the following heterocycle would be the most basic?

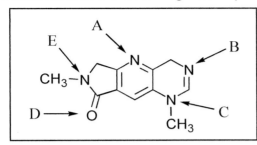

A) A   B) B   C) C   D) D   E) E
Ans: B

8. The best way to prepare a 2-alkylpyridine from pyridine would be what?

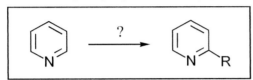

A)   Electrophilic substitution   D)   An S_N2 reaction
B)   Free-radical substitution   E)   None of the above are correct.
C)   Nucleophilic substitution
Ans: C

9. Which of the chloroquinolines shown below would be most reactive toward sodium methoxide?
A)

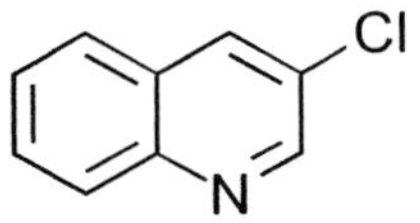

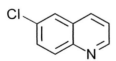

B)

C)

D)

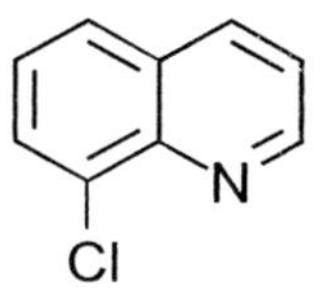

CI

E)   These are expected to be equally reactive.
Ans: C

10. Which of the following would be the most reactive diene in a Diels-Alder reaction?
     A)

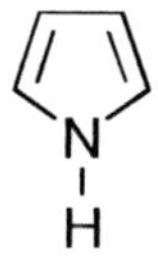

     N
     |
     H

     B)

     C)

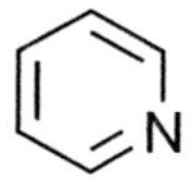

     D)   These are equally reactive.
     E)   None of these undergo Diels-Alder reactions.
     Ans: B

11. What product would be formed in the reaction below?

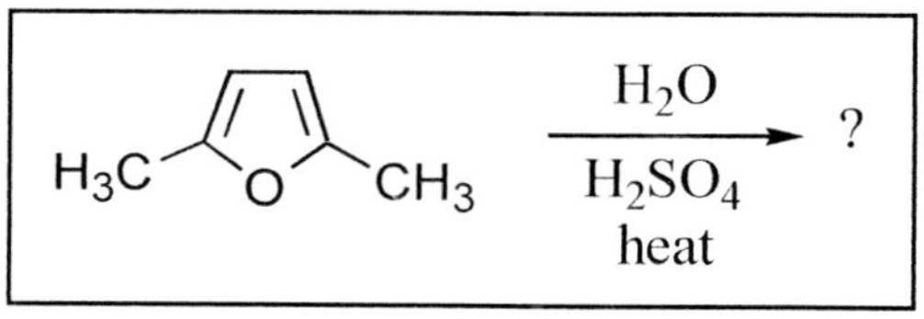

     A)

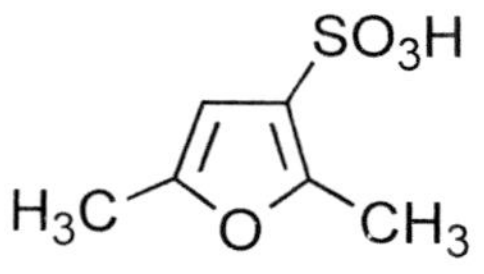

     B)

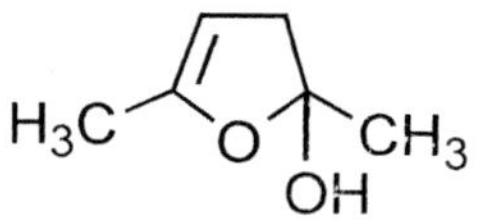

C)

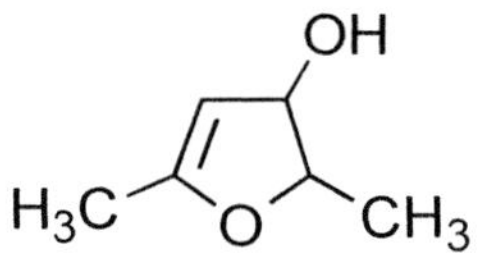

D)

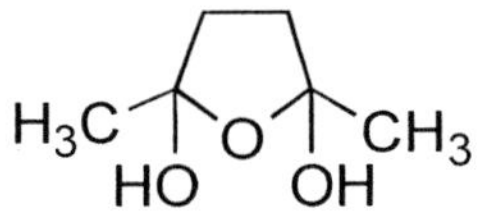

E)

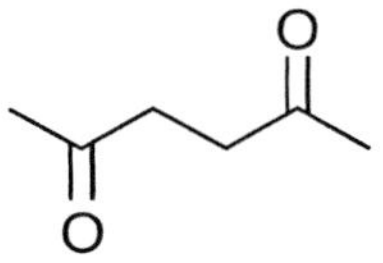

Ans: E

12. What product(s) would you obtain from the reaction below?

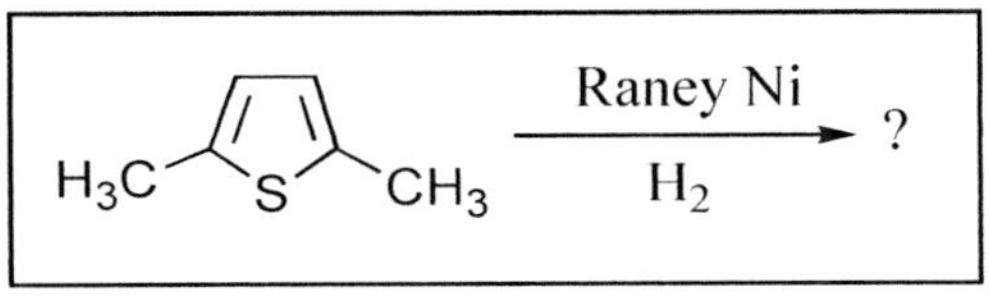

A)

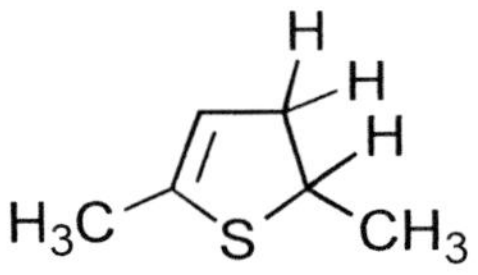

B)

C)

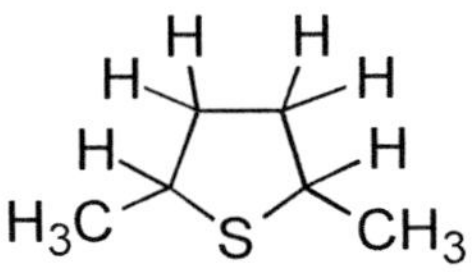

D)

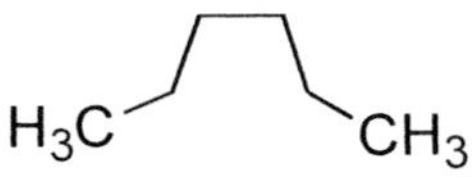

E)

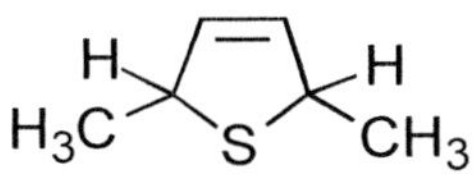

Ans: D

13. What is the name of the following amine?

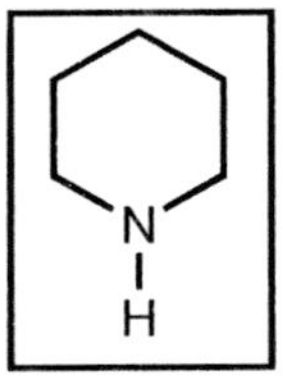

A) Piperidine   B) Pyrrolidine   C) Morpholine   D) Piperazine   E) Pyridine
Ans: A

14. Which of the following would be the most basic?

A)

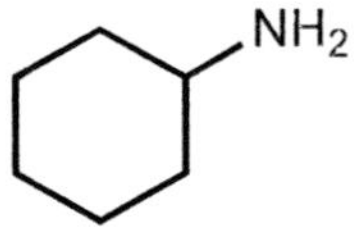

B)

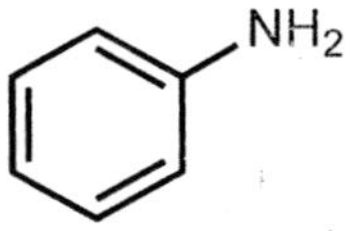

C)

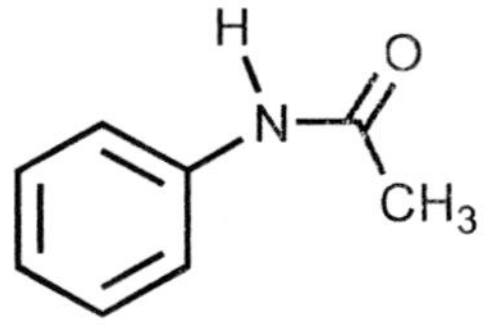

D)

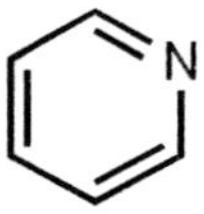

E)

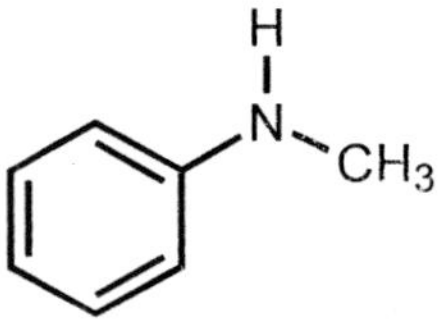

Ans: A

15. Which of the following structures represents a quinoline derivative?

A)

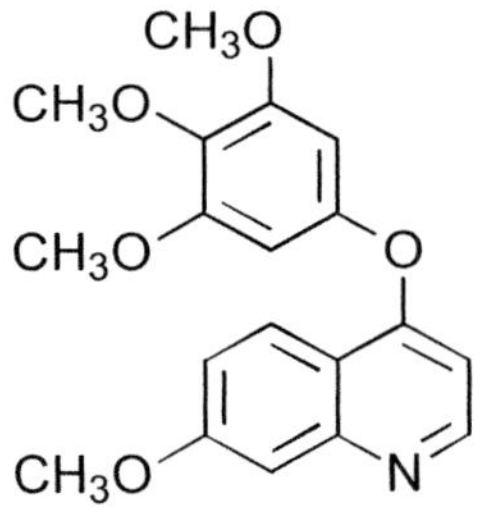

B)

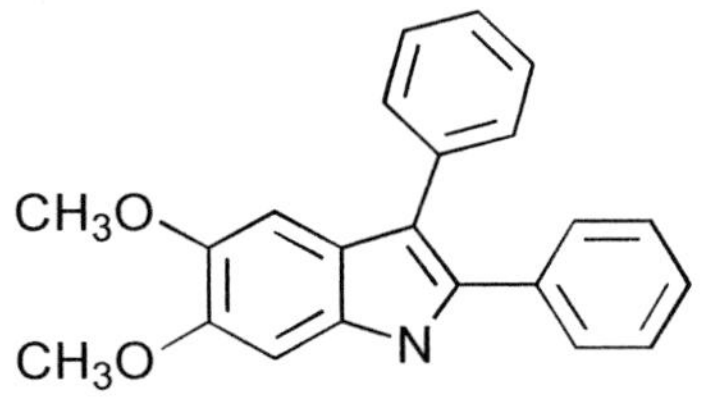

C)

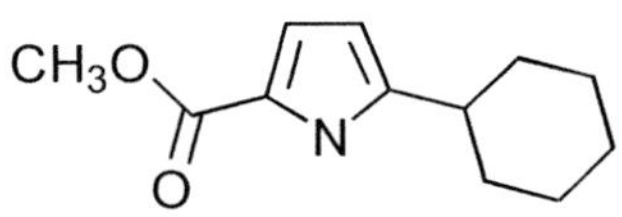

D)

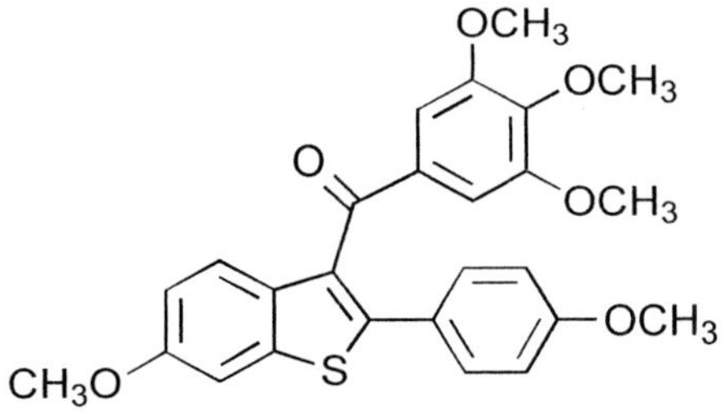

E)

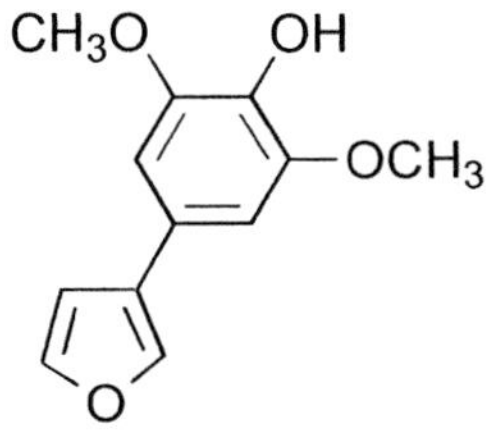

Ans: A

16. Which of the following is **not** formed as either an intermediate along the reaction pathway or as a final product for the Chichibabin reaction shown below?

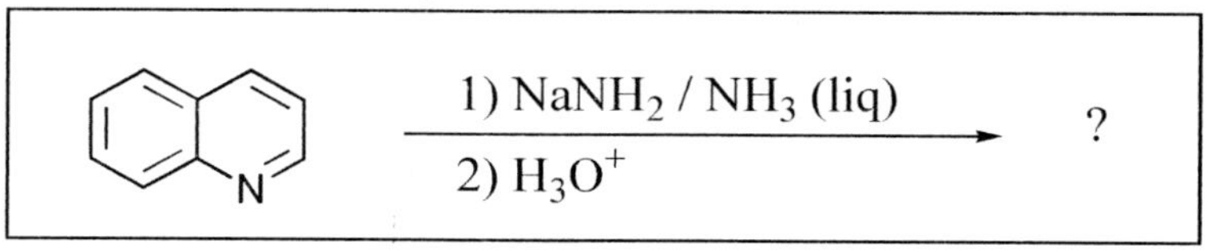

$$\text{1) NaNH}_2 \text{ / NH}_3 \text{ (liq)}$$
$$\text{2) H}_3\text{O}^+$$

?

A)

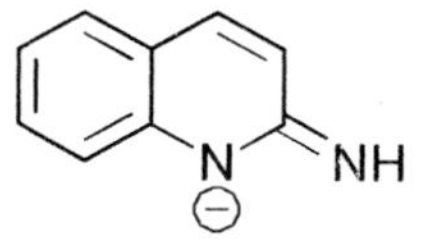

B)

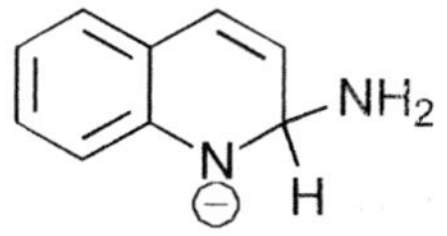

C)

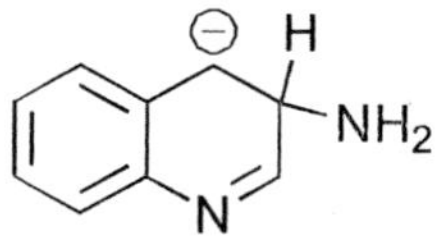

D)

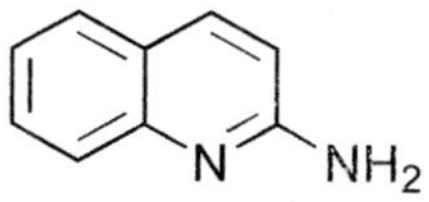

E)

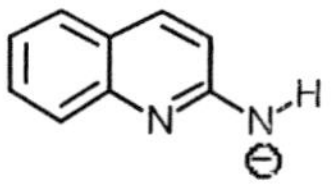

Ans: C

17. Indole is stabilized by several charge-separated resonance contributors. Which of the following is **not** a contributing charge-separated resonance structure?

Indole

A)

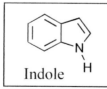

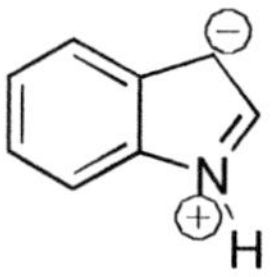

B)

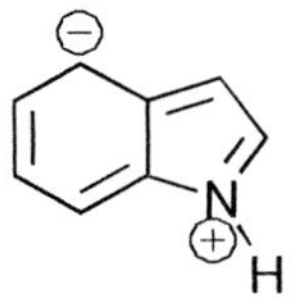

C)

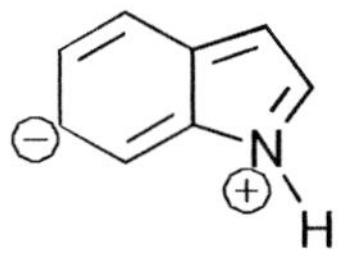

D)

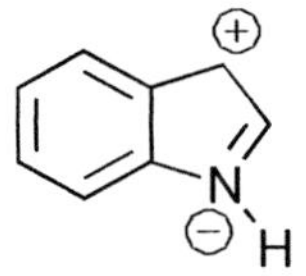

E)

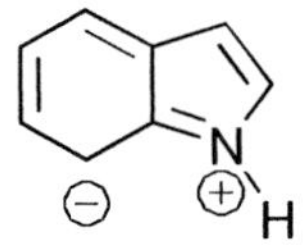

Ans: D

18. Predict the **major** product of the following reaction.

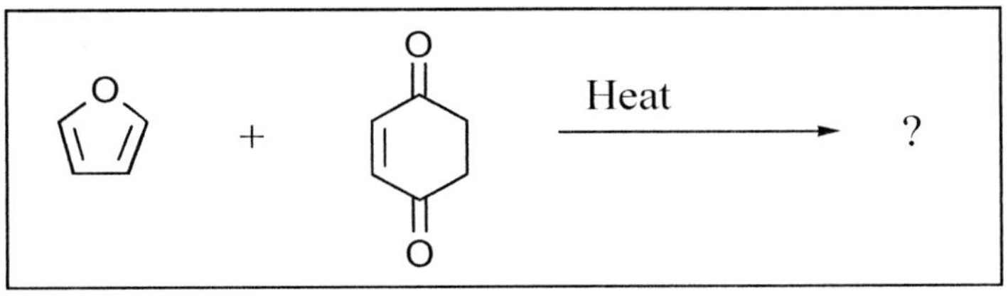

A)

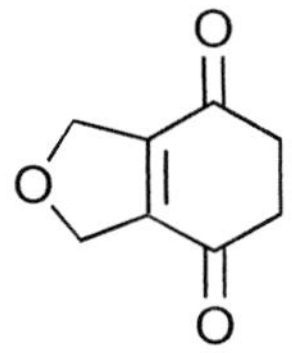

B)

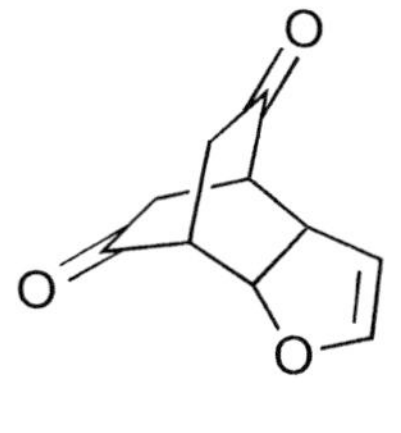

C)

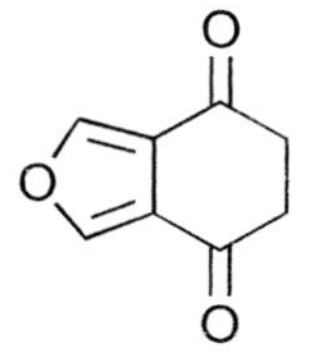

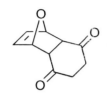

D)

E)

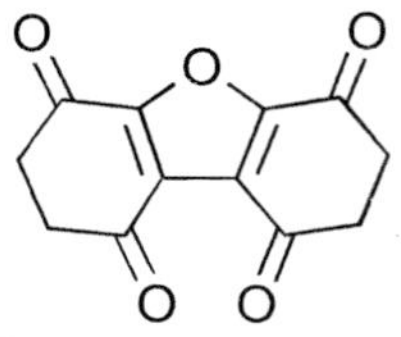

Ans: D

19. Predict the **major** product of the following reaction.

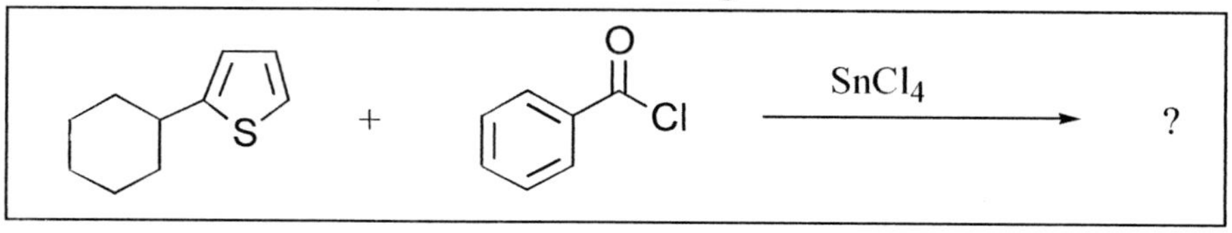

$$\text{cyclohexyl-thiophene} + \text{benzoyl chloride} \xrightarrow{\text{SnCl}_4} ?$$

A)

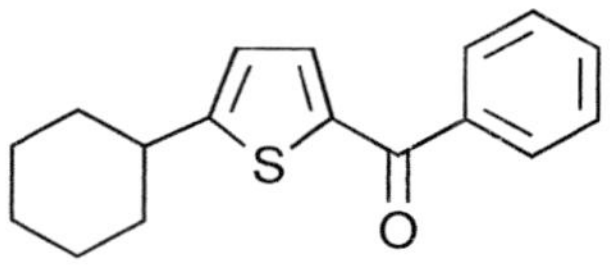

B)

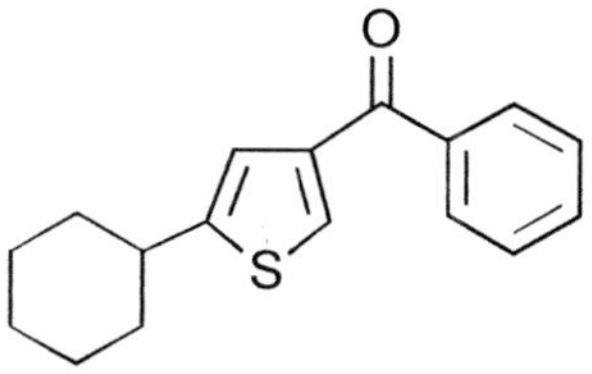

C)

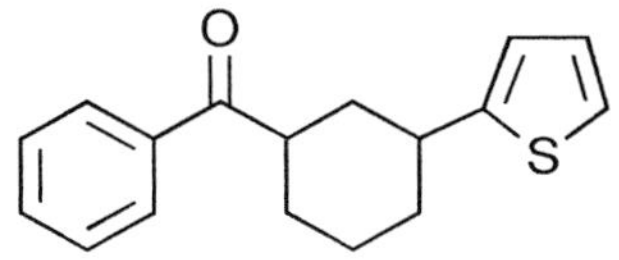

D)

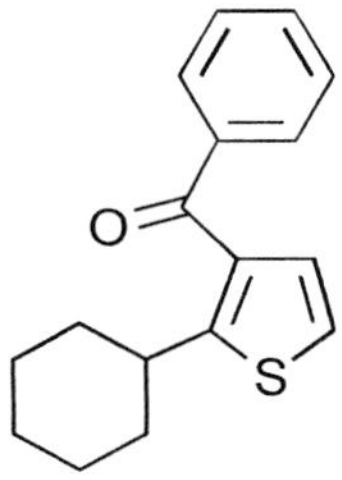

E)

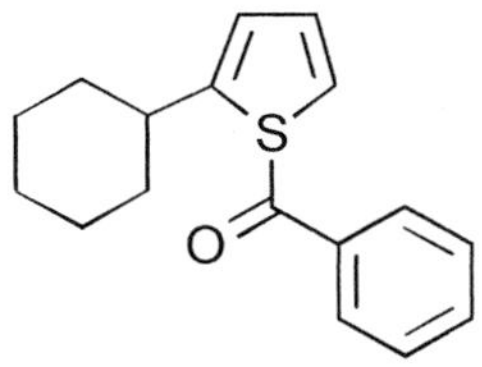

Ans: A

20. Which of the following is one of the oldest known treatment agents for malaria?
    A) Strychnine B) Quinine C) Taxol D) Morphine E) Brucine
    Ans: B

21. 2,5-hexanedione can be dehydrated to give which of the molecules below?

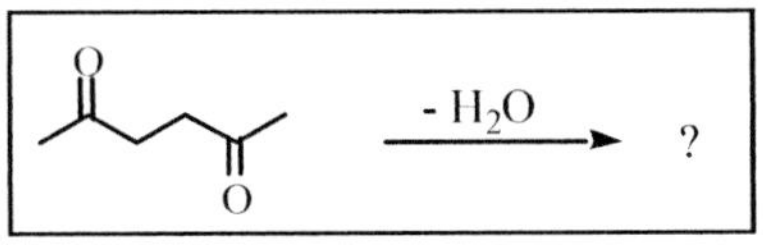

A) 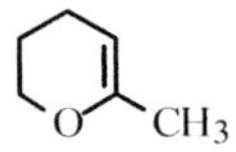 B) 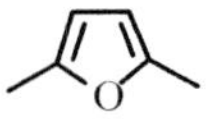 C) 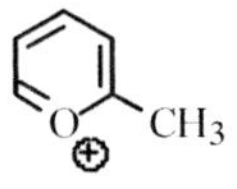 D) 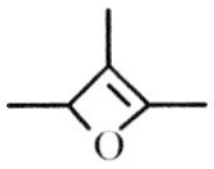 E) 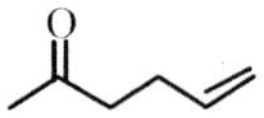
    Ans: B

22. Which reagent might convert 2,5-hexanedione to 2,5-dimethylfuran?

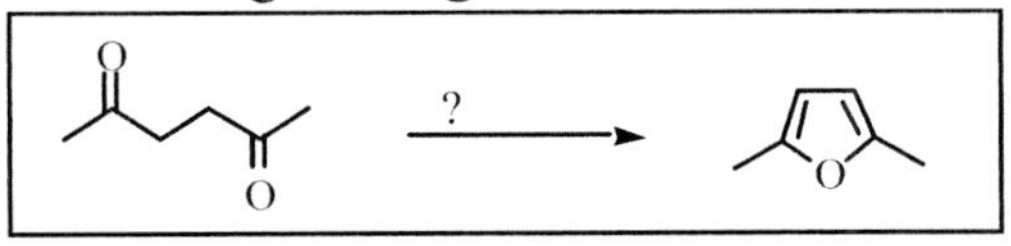

    A) $NaBH_4$, CH_3OH B) H_2, Pt   C) NaOH, heat   D) P_2O_5 E) Na, EtOH
    Ans: D

23. You would expect a very strong nucleophile (e.g., H₂N⁻) to attack 2-methylpyridine where?

A) Position a B) Position b C) Position c D) Position d E) Position e
Ans: A

24. You would expect a powerful electrophile (e.g., Br⁺) to attack 2-methylpyridine mostly at which carbon?

A) Position a B) Position b C) Position c D) Position d E) Position e
Ans: C

25. Which of the following is **not** aromatic?

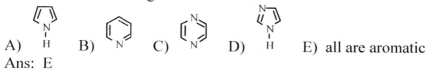

A) B) C) D) E) all are aromatic
Ans: E

26. Which of the following compounds is **not** a heterocycle?
A)

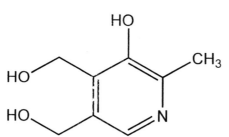

B)

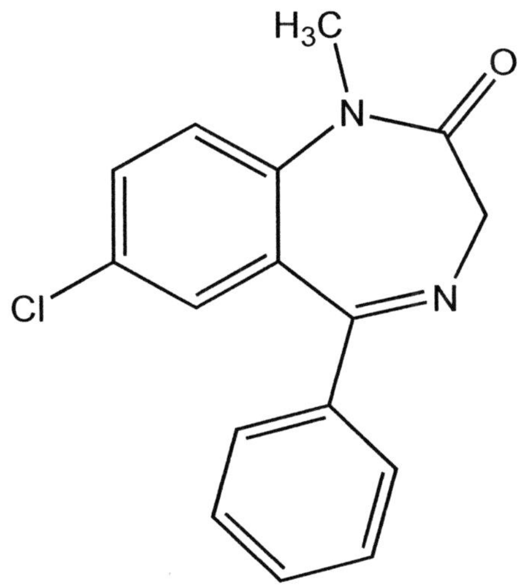

C)

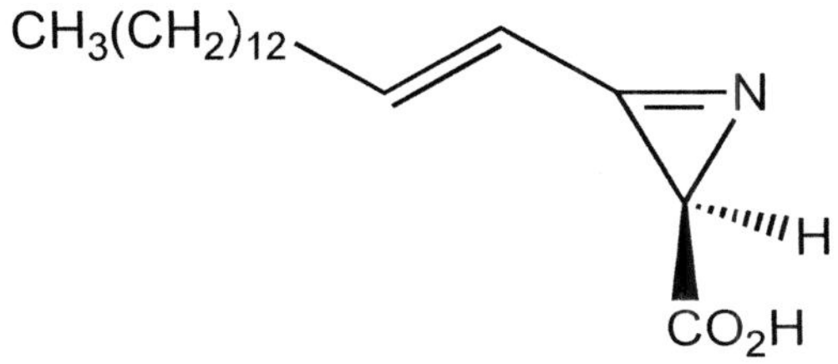

D)

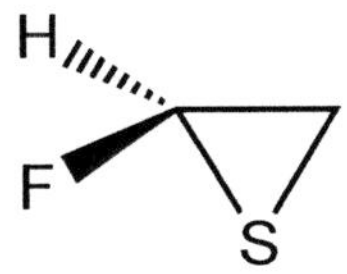

E)

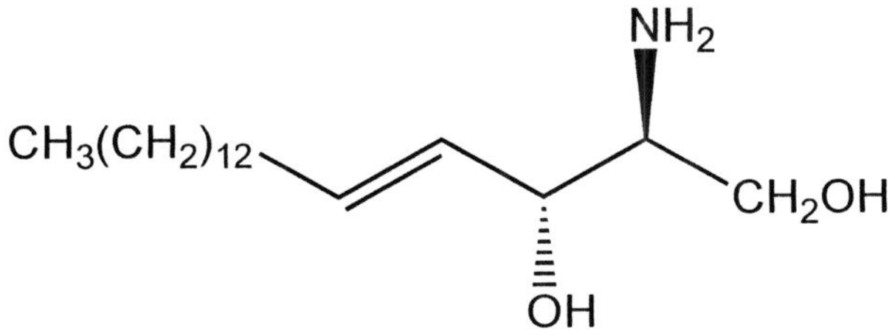

Ans: E

27. What is the product of the following reaction?

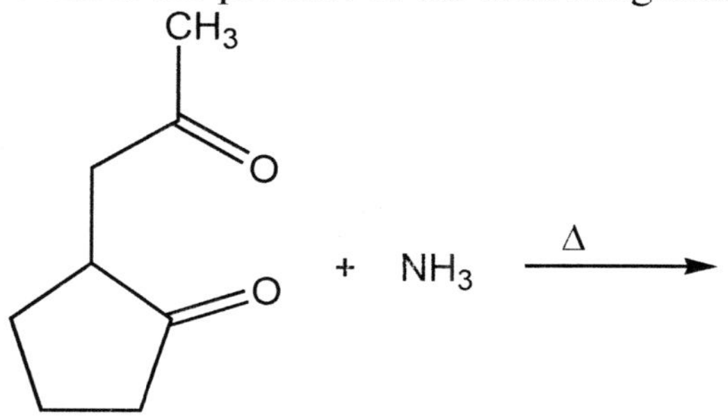

+ NH$_3$ $\xrightarrow{\Delta}$

A)

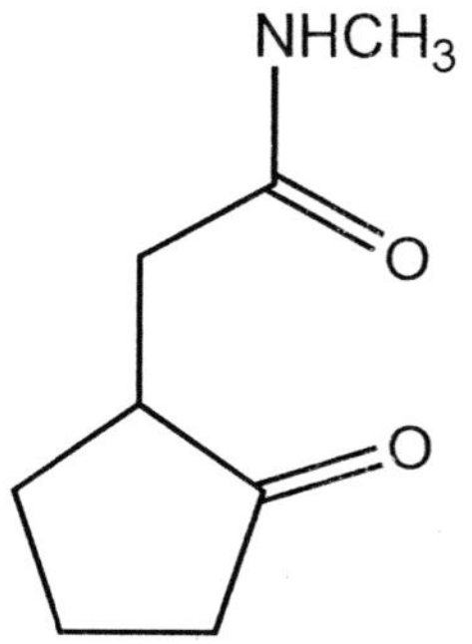

B)

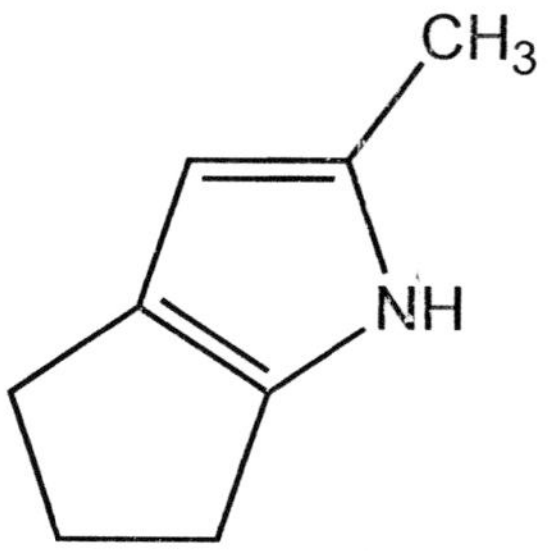

C)

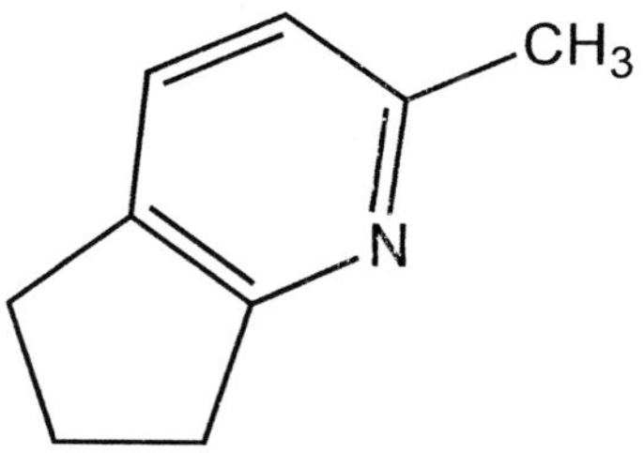

D)

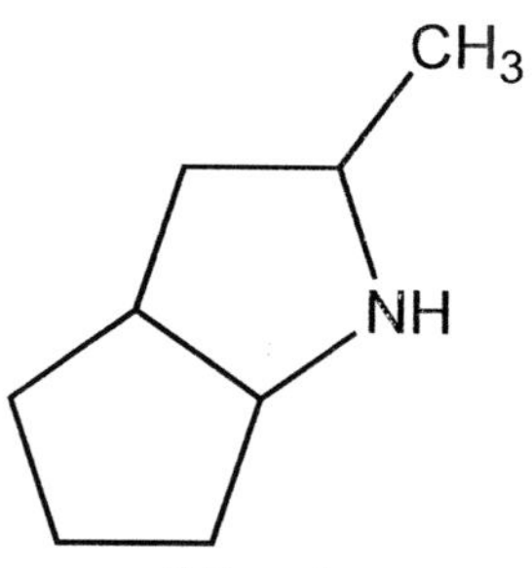

E)   none of the above

Ans: B

28. Which of the following compounds is **not** an alkaloid?

A)

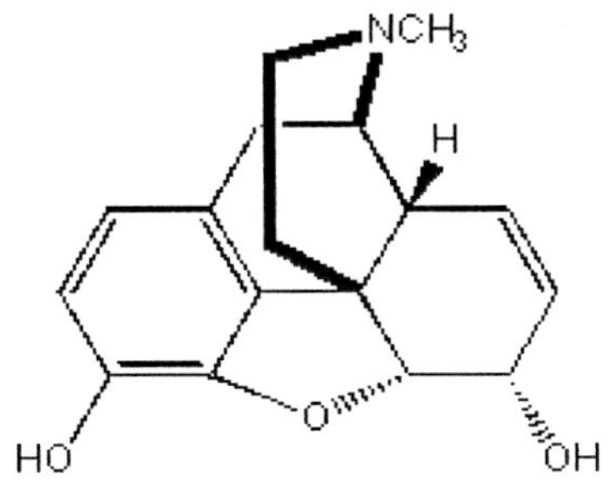

B)

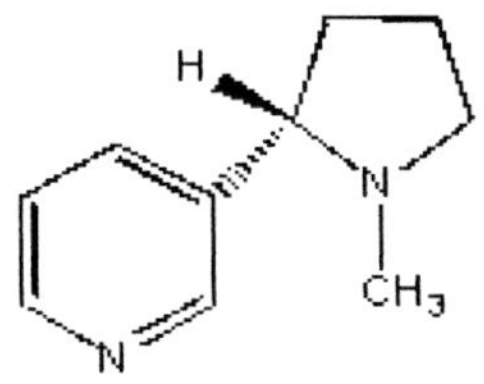

C)

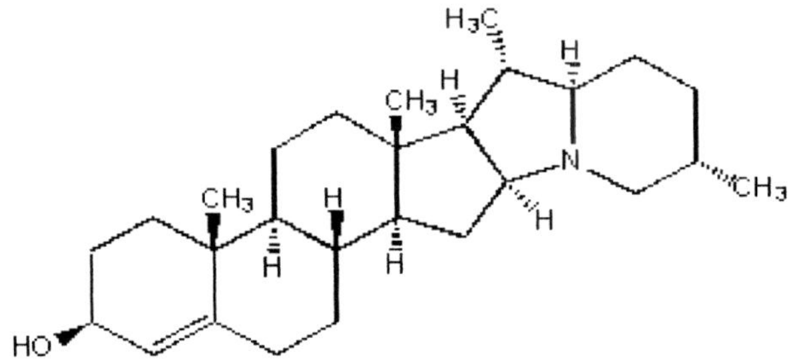

D)

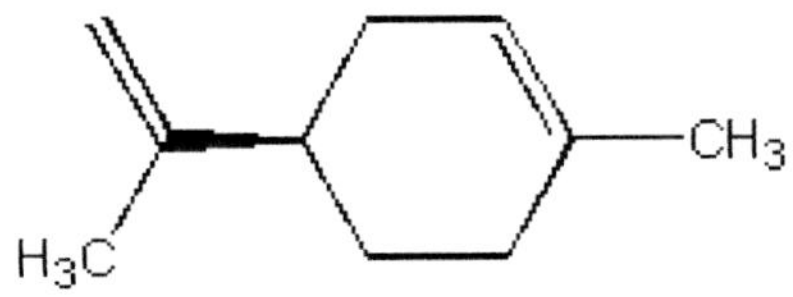

E)   All of the above are alkaloids.

Ans: D

Chapter 26: Amino Acids, Peptides, Proteins, and Nucleic Acids: Nitrogen-Containing Polymers in Nature

1. Of the following, what is the most likely reason that cooking with Nutrasweet (Aspartame) destroys the sweetness?

$$HO-\overset{\overset{\displaystyle O}{\|}}{C}-CH_2-\underset{\underset{\displaystyle NH_2}{|}}{CH}-\overset{\overset{\displaystyle O}{\|}}{C}-\underset{\underset{\displaystyle H}{|}}{N}-\underset{\underset{\displaystyle CH_2-C_6H_5}{|}}{CH}-\overset{\overset{\displaystyle O}{\|}}{C}-OCH_3$$

Aspartame

   A)   It undergoes decarboxylation
   B)   It undergoes an intramolecular cyclization
   C)   It undergoes amide hydrolysis
   D)   It undergoes evaporation
   E)   It undergoes loss of N_2
   Ans: B

2. What is dicyclohexylcarbodiimide (DCC) used for in peptide synthesis?
   A)   DCC protects the amino group of the intended N-terminal amino acid.
   B)   DCC activates the carboxyl group toward nucleophillic attack.
   C)   DCC cleaves the blocking groups from the final peptide.
   D)   DCC is the resin (solid support) used to anchor the growing polypeptide.
   E)   DCC removes the peptide from the resin at the conclusion of the synthesis.
   Ans: B

3. Which of the following amino acids is theoretically capable of existing in two diastereomeric forms?
   A) Cysteine   B) Threonine   C) Leucine   D) Serine   E) Tryptophan
   Ans: B

4. A heptapeptide containing 2 alanine residues and one each of glutamine, phenylalanine, proline, tyrosine and valine was analyzed as follows:

   1. Treatment with 2,4-dinitrofluorobenzene followed by complete hydrolysis yielded 2,4-dinitrophenylalanine.

   2. Partial hydrolysis with aqueous acid yielded the following fragments: ala-glu, pro-tyr, ala-val, tyr-ala, and val-phe-pro.

   What is the structure of the peptide?
   A)   ala-phe-pro-tyr-ala-glu-val   D)   ala-val-phe-tyr-pro-ala-glu
   B)   ala-val-phe-pro-tyr-glu-ala   E)   val-ala-phe-tyr-pro-ala-glu
   C)   ala-val-phe-pro-tyr-ala-glu
   Ans: C

5. Why is the following **not** a good two step route for the preparation of pure L-alanine?

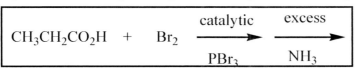

   A) The bromination is not selective (the CH_3 and CH_2 groups are both brominated).
   B) Ammonia is not sufficiently nucleophillic to react with a secondary bromide.
   C) Only the CH_3 group is brominated.
   D) The product will be racemic.
   E) Propanamide would be the major product.
   Ans: D

6. Disulfide bonds in proteins
   A) result from oxidation of thiols (RSH).
   B) function to help maintain the shape of proteins.
   C) can be broken by reduction reactions.
   D) link two cysteine amino acid residues.
   E) All of these are true.
   Ans: E

7. Which amino acid **does not** form a characteristic blue color with ninhydrin?
   A) Cysteine   B) Lysine   C) Proline   D) Valine   E) Tryptophan
   Ans: C

8. What material can be used repetitively (on a given sample) to sequence a polypeptide from the N-terminal end?
   A) Chymotrypsin   D) Edman reagent
   B) Sanger reagent   E) Carboxypeptidase
   C) Trypsin
   Ans: D

9. How many tripeptides containing one residue each of L-alanine, L-valine, and glycine are possible?
   A) 2   B) 3   C) 4   D) 6   E) 9
   Ans: D

10. Which of the following is **least** likely to be found in nature?

A)

D)

$(CH_3)_2CH$ — $\overset{H}{\underset{NH_2}{\overset{|}{C}}}$ — CO_2H

B) $(R)\text{-HSCH}_2-\overset{|}{\underset{NH_2}{CH}}-CO_2H$

E) $(R)\text{-CH}_3-\overset{|}{\underset{NH_2}{CH}}-CO_2H$

C) $(S)\text{-HOCH}_2-\overset{|}{\underset{NH_2}{CH}}-CO_2H$

Ans: E

11. Which amino acid does not have an enantiomer?
A) Alanine   B) Glutamine   C) Histidine   D) Aspartic acid   E) Glycine
Ans: E

12. How many amino acid residues are present in the following polypeptide?

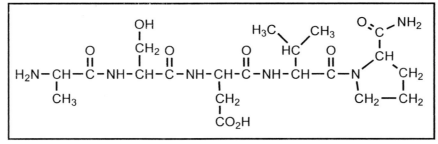

A) 4   B) 5   C) 6   D) 7   E) 8
Ans: B

13. What would be the abbreviated name of the following polypeptide?

A)   val-thr-glu-ala-gln
B)   ala-thr-glu-val-gln
C)   met-ser-asp-leu-pro-NH$_2$
D)   ala-ser-asp-val-gln
E)   ala-ser-asp-val-pro-NH$_2$
Ans: E

14. It was not until 1974 that γ-carboxyglutamic acid (shown below) was discovered (by researchers at the University of Colorado) in polypeptides. Based on your knowledge of organic chemistry, what is the most likely reason that this particular amino acid escaped identification so long?

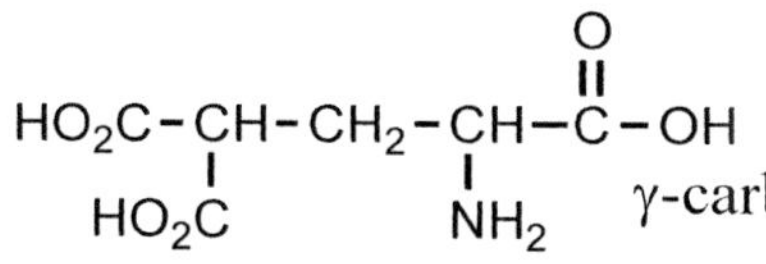

γ-carboxyglutamic acid

A) it tended to spontaneously form a cyclic anhydride:

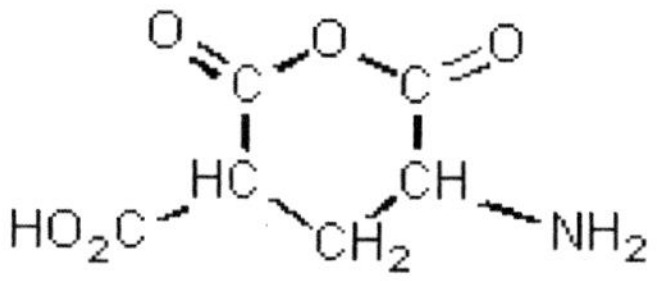

B) it tended to spontaneously lose carbon dioxide:

$$\longrightarrow \quad glutamic\ acid\ +\ CO_2$$

C) it easily underwent a reverse-Knovenagle reaction:

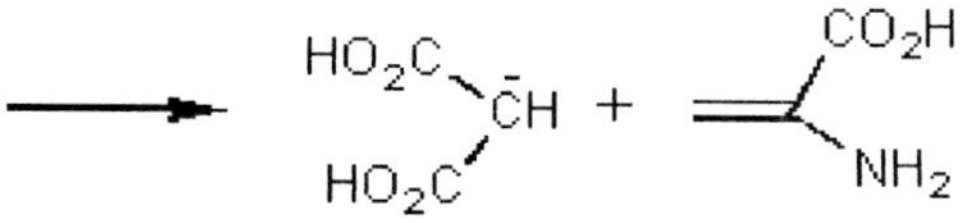

D) it tended to spontaneously form a cyclic amide (lactam):

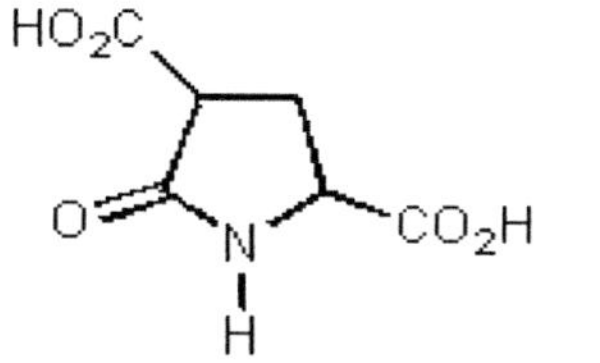

E) it was simply too polar to extract into non-polar organic solvents

Ans: B

15. The artificial sweetener aspartame is a derivative of the dipeptide asp-phe. If aspartame (asp-phe) was prepared from *racemic* amino acids, how many stereoisomers (diastereomers + enantiomers) could be formed?

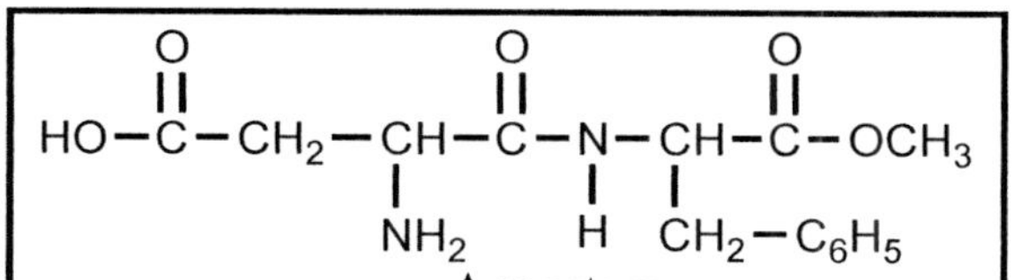

Aspartame

A) 2   B) 3   C) 4   D) 6   E) 8

Ans: C

16. Chymotrypsin catalyzes hydrolysis of peptide bonds where?

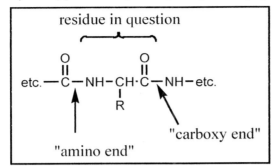

A) At the carboxy end of residues with basic side chains
B) At the amino end of residues containing aliphatic residues
C) At the carboxy end of residues with aromatic side chains
D) At the amino end of residues with aromatic side chains
E) At the carboxy end of methionine residues
Ans: C

17. The primary structure of a protein refers to the
A) sequence of amino acids.
B) overall 3-dimensional shape.
C) localized shape of the backbone.
D) degree of aggregation with other proteins.
E) structure of the active site.
Ans: A

18. Which of the following amino acids would have the **highest** isoelectric point?
A) Lysine   B) Glutamine   C) Aspartic acid   D) Alanine   E) Tryptophan
Ans: A

19. Nearly all amino acids immediately release N_2 gas upon diazotization (treatment with aqueous HCl and sodium nitrite). Which amino acid would not?
A) Lysine   B) Histidine   C) Tyrosine   D) Cysteine   E) Proline
Ans: E

20. Why is the additional (ring) nitrogen in tryptophan not very basic?

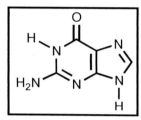

A)   Cyclic amines are not basic.
B)   It is too far from the carboxyl group to be effected.
C)   Aromatic amines are weakly basic because of resonance.
D)   The additional amine group is offset by an additional carboxylic acid group.
E)   It is sp^2 hybridized as therefore not as basic.
Ans: C

21. What is the name of the DNA base shown?

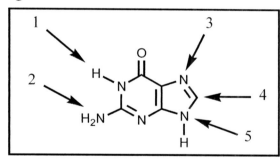

A) Guanine   B) Cytosine   C) Adenine   D) Uracil   E) Thymine
Ans: A

22. In a DNA molecule, at which point would the base shown be attached to a deoxyribose fragment?

A) 1   B) 2   C) 3   D) 4   E) 5
Ans: E

23. The difference(s) between DNA and RNA is (are):
    A)   DNA incorporates 2-deoxyribose sugars rather than ribose.
    B)   RNA is smaller than DNA.
    C)   DNA uses thymine, RNA uses uracil.
    D)   Two of the above are true.
    E)   All of the above are true.
    Ans: E

24. Although traces of racemic amino acids have been found in meteorites, nearly all
    naturally occurring amino acids on Earth have the stereochemistry shown. What is true
    of this stereochemistry? (Assume R = alkyl)

    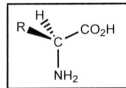

    A)   Amino acids are of the (R) configuration.
    B)   Amino acids are of the (S) configuration.
    C)   Amino acids are not chiral.
    D)   Amino acids are meso compounds.
    E)   Amino acids easily change configuration.
    Ans: B

25. Which attractive force is responsible for maintaining the tertiary structure of proteins?
    A)   Disulfide linkages   D)   Hydrophobic interactions
    B)   Hydrogen bonds   E)   All of these
    C)   Salt bridges
    Ans: E

26. Which amino acid is responsible for the condition known as phenylketonuria (PKU)
    which occurs in a small fraction of the population?
    A) Tryptophan   B) Histidine   C) Phenylalanine   D) Proline   E) Valine
    Ans: C

27. Which of the following statements is **not** true of amino acids?
    A)   They are less acidic than carboxylic acids.
    B)   In acid solution (pH ~ 2) they would show an IR absorption near 1720 cm^{-1}.
    C)   They are soluble in water but not in non-polar organic solvents.
    D)   They are more basic than amines.
    E)   In basic solution (pH ~ 12) they would show an IR absorption near 3300 cm^{-1}.
    Ans: D

28. The organic portion of which of the following biological materials *does not* consist mainly of polypeptides and/or proteins?
    A) Enzymes   B) Hair   C) Hemoglobin   D) Membranes   E) Insulin
    Ans: D

29. What would result from the following reactions?

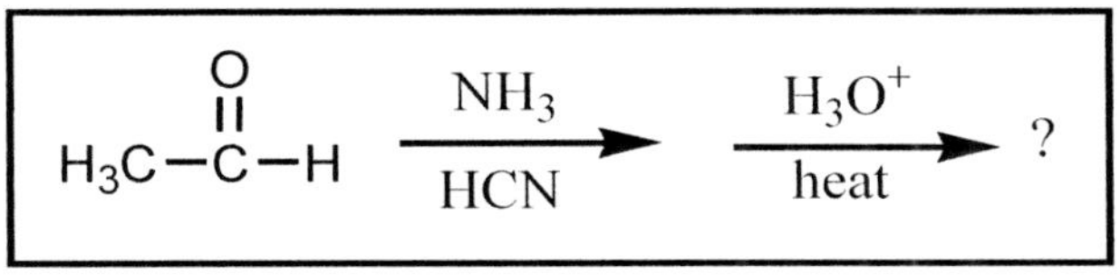

A)

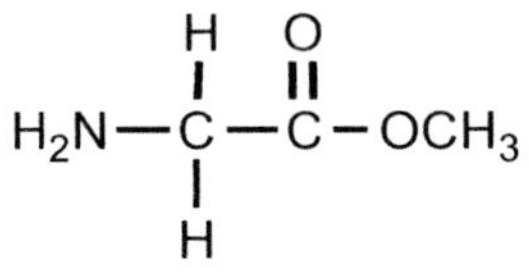

B)

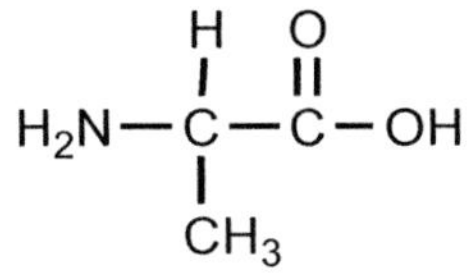

C)

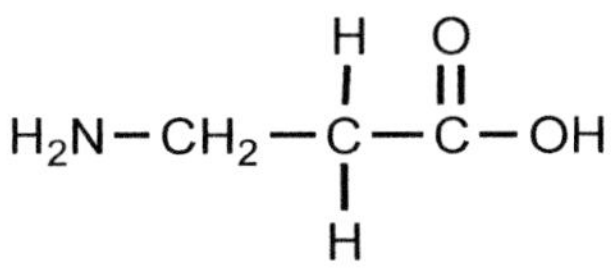

D)

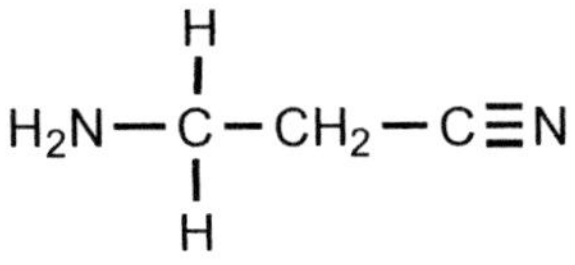

E)

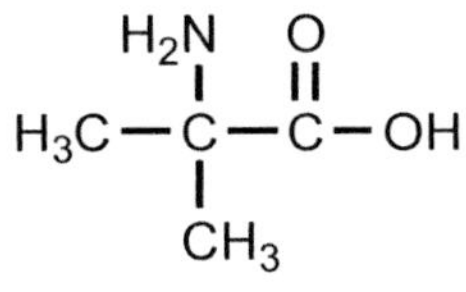

Ans: B

30. Which nitrogen in the imidazole ring of histidine is the more basic?

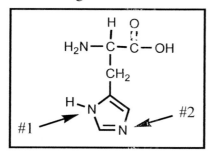

A)   #1
B)   #2
C)   both have same basicity
Ans: B

D)   neither is basic
E)   the histidine N-H is actually acidic

31. Which of the following represents how a typical amino acid would mainly exist in **basic** solution (pH > 7)?

A)

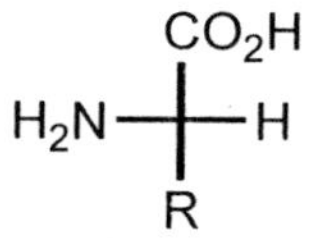

CO_2H
H_2N—|—H
R

B)

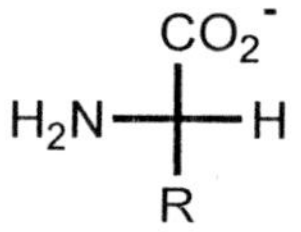

CO_2^-
H_2N—|—H
R

C)

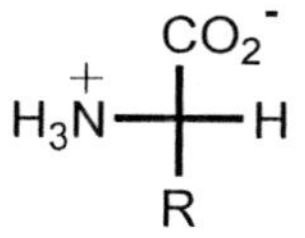

CO_2^-
$H_3\overset{+}{N}$—|—H
R

D)

CO_2H
$H_3\overset{+}{N}$—|—H
R

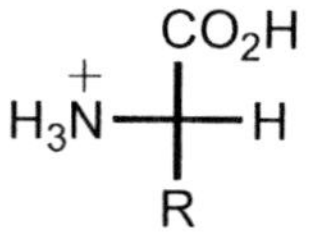

E)   none of the above
Ans: B

32. Which amino acid is shown?

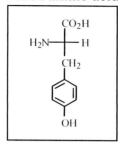

A) Alanine   B) Glycine   C) Tyrosine   D) Lysine   E) Arginine
Ans: C

33. Which of the following amino acids contains an aromatic ring?
A) Alanine   B) Serine   C) Tyrosine   D) Asparagine   E) Glycine
Ans: C

34. Given that the pK_a of the acidic form of proline is 2.0, and the pK_a of the basic form of proline is 10.6, what is the isoelectric point?
A) 2.0   B) 6.3   C) 4.4   D) 10.6   E) 7.0
Ans: B

35. Amino acids are covalently bonded to each other through_____.
A) hydrogen bonding   D) α and β folds
B) disulfide bridges   E) none of the above
C) peptide bonds
Ans: C

36. How many polypeptides would be present if the following was treated with trypsin?

CysGlyGluArgGlyPhePheTyrThrProLysAlaLeuTyr

A) 1   B) 2   C) 3   D) 4   E) 5
Ans: C

37. Folding of polypeptides influenced by distant residues is an example of what protein structure?
A) Primary   B) Secondary   C) Tertiary   D) Quaternary   E) none of the above
Ans: C

38. The secondary structure of proteins is held together by hydrogen bonds between which protein sub-structures?
    A)   The C=O and N-H on amino acid side chains
    B)   The C=O on the protein backbone and the N-H on the amino acid side chains
    C)   The C=O on the amino acid side chains and the N-H on the protein backbone
    D)   The C=O and the N-H on the protein backbone
    E)   There are no hydrogen bonds involved with secondary structure.
    Ans: D

39. At the isoelectric point, the amino acid alanine will exist as what structure?
    A)   A positive ion   D)   A zwitterion
    B)   A negative ion   E)   A carbocation
    C)   An uncharged molecule
    Ans: D

40. What process would one use to make multiple copies of a fragment of DNA?
    A)   Polymerase chain reaction   D)   Translation
    B)   Electrophoresis   E)   Merrifield solid-phase synthesis
    C)   Transcription
    Ans: A

41. Which of the following DNA base pairs can participate in Watson and Crick type hydrogen bonding?
    A) A-T   B) G-T   C) G-C   D) Both A and B   E) Both A and C
    Ans: E